In Situ Aeration: Air Sparging, Bioventing, and Related Remediation Processes

BIOREMEDIATION

The *Bioremediation* series contains collections of articles derived from many of the presentations made at the First, Second, and Third International In Situ and On-Site Bioreclamation Symposia, which were held in 1991, 1993, and 1995 in San Diego, California.

First International In Situ and On-Site Bioreclamation Symposium

Second International In Situ and On-Site Bioreclamation Symposium

Third International In Situ and On-Site Bioreclamation Symposium

Bioremediation Series Cumulative Indices: 1991-1995

For information about ordering books in the Bioremediation series, contact Battelle Press. Telephone: 800-451-3543 or 614-424-6393. Fax: 614-424-3819. Internet: sheldric@battelle.org.

In Situ Aeration: Air Sparging, Bioventing, and Related Remediation Processes

Edited by

Robert E. Hinchee
Battelle Memorial Institute

Ross N. Miller
U.S. Air Force Center for Environmental Excellence

Paul C. Johnson
Arizona State University

BATTELLE PRESS
Columbus • Richland

Library of Congress Cataloging-in-Publication Data

Hinchee, Robert E.
    In situ aeration: air sparging, bioventing, and related remediation
    processes / edited by Robert E. Hinchee, Ross N. Miller, Paul C.
    Johnson.
        p.   cm.
    Includes bibliographical references and index.
    ISBN 1-57477-003-9 (hc : acid-free paper)
    1. In situ remediation—Congresses. 2. Groundwater—Air sparging—
    Congresses. 3. Soil vapor extraction—Congresses. I. Hinchee, Robert E.
    II. Miller, Ross N. III. Johnson, Paul C.
    TD192.8.I57 1995
    628.1′683—dc20   95-32297
                                                                    CIP

Printed in the United States of America

Additional copies may be ordered through:
Battelle Press
505 King Avenue
Columbus, Ohio 43201, USA
1-614-424-6393 or 1-800-451-3543
Fax: 1-614-424-3819
Internet: sheldric@battelle.org

CONTENTS

FOREWORD

This book and its companion volumes (see overleaf) comprise a collection of papers derived from the Third International In Situ and On-Site Bioreclamation Symposium, held in San Diego, California, in April 1995. The 375 papers that appear in these volumes are those that were accepted after peer review. The editors believe that this collection is the most comprehensive and up-to-date work available in the field of bioremediation.

Significant advances have been made in bioremediation since the First and Second Symposia were held in 1991 and 1993. Bioremediation as a whole remains a rapidly advancing field, and new technologies continue to emerge. As the industry matures, the emphasis for some technologies shifts to application and refinement of proven methods, whereas the emphasis for emerging technologies moves from the laboratory to the field. For example, many technologies that can be applied to sites contaminated with petroleum hydrocarbons are now commercially available and have been applied to thousands of sites. In contrast, there are as yet no commercial technologies commonly used to remediate most recalcitrant compounds. The articles in these volumes report on field and laboratory research conducted both to develop promising new technologies and to improve existing technologies for remediation of a wide spectrum of compounds.

The articles in this book discuss the use of air sparging, bioventing, and other aeration processes to remediate hydrocarbon-contaminated soils and groundwater. It is now well understood that the primary limiting factor associated with in situ hydrocarbon remediation is the availability of an adequate electron acceptor to stimulate aerobic degradation. Oxygen is the most commonly used electron acceptor and, when introduced successfully, generally is the most effective. Early bioremediation efforts were primarily water-based, involving the introduction of oxygen or hydrogen peroxide dissolved in water. Water-based technologies appear to have found a niche, but solubility and hydrogen peroxide stability problems frequently have limited their application. Bioventing and air sparging make possible the introduction of gaseous oxygen (usually as air) in situ to deliver substantially more oxygen than is possible with water-based processes.

Bioventing has become a relatively mature technology for in situ remediation of hydrocarbons in the vadose zone, and applications for more recalcitrant organics are beginning to emerge. In situ air sparging, although inherently more difficult to control because of the multiphase flow problem, is a technology that is beginning to mature and is receiving widespread commercial application. The in situ aeration technologies reported in this volume cover the spectrum from those in practice to those just beginning to emerge.

The editors would like to recognize the substantial contribution of the peer reviewers who read and provided written comments to the authors of the draft articles that were considered for this volume. Thoughtful, insightful review is crucial for the production of a high-quality technical publication. The peer reviewers for this volume were:

David Ahlfeld, *University of Connecticut*
Bruce M. Applegate, *University of Tennessee*
Ralph S. Baker, *ENSR Consulting & Engineering*
Gary Barker, *Amoco Production Co.*
Gerhard Battermann, *TGU-GmbH* (Germany)
Danielle Beaumier, *National Research Council Canada*
Frank Beck, *U.S. Environmental Protection Agency*
David M. Belcher, *ABB Environmental Services, Inc.*
Alvin K. Benson, *Brigham Young University*
James Berg, *Aquateam A/S* (Norway)
William R. Berti, *DuPont Co.*
Alan D. Bettermann, *BioRenewal Technologies, Inc.*
Gale Billings, *Billings & Associates, Inc.*
Jeffery Billings, *Billings & Associates, Inc.*
Paul Boersma, *CH2M Hill, Inc.*
Edward J. Bouwer, *Johns Hopkins University*
Gijs D. Breedveld, *Norwegian Geotechnical Institute*
Tormod Briseid, *SINTEF Oslo*
Anthony Brown, *H₂O Science*
Richard A. Brown, *Groundwater Technology, Inc.*
Clifford J. Bruell, *University of Massachusetts*
Mark Brusseau, *University of Arizona*
Bob Buchanan, *University of California at Berkeley*
Ronald J. Buchanan, *DuPont Co.*
William A. Butler, *DuPont Co.*
Sean R. Carter, *Matrix Environmental Technologies*
Philip Caunt, *Biotal Ltd.* (UK)
Evan Cox, *Beak Consultants Ltd.* (Canada)
Paul Currier, *Army Corps of Engineers*
Mohamed Dahab, *University of Nebraska Lincoln*
M. Amine Dahmani, *University of Connecticut*
Brunilda Davila, *U.S. Environmental Protection Agency*
John W. Davis, *Dow Chemical Co.*
Eric W.E. Denman, *Groundwater Technology Canada*
Ludo Diels, *S.C.K.-C.E.N./V.I.T.O.* (Belgium)
Allen J. Dines, *BioRenewal Technologies, Inc.*
Douglas C. Downey, *Parsons Engineering Science, Inc.*
R. Ryan Dupont, *Utah State University*
Richard U. Edgehill, *University of Queensland*
Robert Edwards, *Booz Allen & Hamilton, Inc.*
Richard Esposito, *Southern Co. Services*
Marty Faile, *U.S. Air Force*
Jim A. Field, *Wageningen Agricultural University* (The Netherlands)
Stephanie Fiorenza, *Rice University*
Dean Foor, *Battelle Columbus*

Eric A. Foote, *Battelle Columbus*
Giancarlo Gabetto, *Castalia* (Italy)
Florian Gleisner, *Karlsrühe University* (Germany)
James Gonzales, *U.S. Air Force*
James M. Gossett, *Cornell University*
Charles W. Greer, *National Research Council of Canada*
Peter Guest, *Parsons Engineering Science, Inc.*
Patrick Haas, *U.S. Air Force*
Paul Hadley, *California Environmental Protection Agency*
John Haines, *U.S. Environmental Protection Agency*
Jerry Hansen, *U.S. Air Force*
Joop Harmsen, *DLO Winand Staring Centre* (The Netherlands)
M. Lynn Haugh, *BioRenewal Technologies, Inc.*
Barbara Hemmingsen, *San Diego State University*
Kim Henke, *Booz Allen & Hamilton, Inc.*
Stephen E. Herbes, *Oak Ridge National Laboratory*
Pat Hicks, *Groundwater Technology, Inc.*
Desma Hogg, *Woodward-Clyde Ltd.* (New Zealand)
Michael L. Holroyd, *Biotal Ltd.* (UK)
Brian Hooker, *Battelle Pacific Northwest*
Michael H. Huesemann, *Battelle Pacific Northwest*
Scott G. Huling, *U.S. Environmental Protection Agency*
W. Ji, *University of Connecticut*
Jay Johnson, *ABB Environmental Services, Inc.*
Richard L. Johnson, *Oregon Graduate Institute*
Eric Klingel, *IEG Technologies Corporation*
William G. Langley, *IEG Technologies Corporation*
Michael D. Lee, *DuPont Co.*
Brian Looney, *Westinghouse Savannah River Co.*
William R. Mahaffey, *ECOVA Corporation*
Michael C. Marley, *Envirogen, Inc.*
Timothy R. Marshall, *Woodward-Clyde Consultants*
James Mercer, *GeoTrans, Inc.*
Jeffrey Dean Meyers, *Conoco*
Ali Mohagheghi, *National Renewable Energy Lab*
James G. Mueller, *SBP Technologies Inc.*
Brent J. Moore, *Komex International Ltd.* (Canada)
Thomas G. Naymik, *Battelle Columbus*
Christopher H. Nelson, *Groundwater Technology, Inc.*
John T. Novak, *Virginia Polytechnic Institute & State University*
Bradley M. Patterson, *CSIRO* (Australia)
Michael Piotrowski, *Matrix Remedial Technologies, Inc.*
Albert Pollack, *Battelle Columbus*
Petra M. Radehaus, *Colorado School of Mines*
Svein Ramstad, *SINTEF* (Norway)

Kenneth F. Reardon, *Colorado State University*
Mark E. Reeves, *Oak Ridge National Laboratory*
Laura E. Rice, *Institute of Gas Technology*
Mark S. Romich, *BioRenewal Technologies, Inc.*
Rejean Samson, *École Polytechnique de Montréal*
Richard Scholze, *U.S. Army Corps of Engineers*
Thomas J. Simpkin, *CH2M Hill, Inc.*
Rodney S. Skeen, *Battelle Pacific Northwest*
Gerald E. Speitel, *University of Texas at Austin*
Lee Scott Stevenson, *Groundwater Technology, Inc.*
John Sutherland, *U.S. Food and Drug Administration*
Robert D. Taylor, *Booz Allen & Hamilton, Inc.*
Alison Thomas, *U.S. Air Force*
Michael F. Tschantz, *University of Tennessee*
Leon G. C. M. Urlings, *TAUW Infra Consult b.v. Environment*
    (The Netherlands)
Jack van Eyk, *Delft Geotechnics*
F. Michael von Fahnestock, *Battelle Columbus*
Dan W. Waddill, *Virginia Polytechnic Institute & State University*
Herb Ward, *Rice University*
Darsh Wasan, *IIT*
Candida C. West, *U.S. Environmental Protection Agency*
Mark A. Widdowson, *Virginia Polytechnic Institute & State*
    University
Alec T. Winters, *EA Engineering Science & Engineering, Inc.*
Johannes C.M. de Wit, *TAUW Milieu b.v.* (The Netherlands)
Martin Wittmaier, *University of Karlsrühe* (Germany)
Roger Woeller, *Water & Earth Science Assoc., Ltd.* (Canada)
Arthur Wong, *Chester Environmental*
Hilke Würdemann, *Karlsrühe University* (Germany)
Andreas Zeddel, *Umweltbundesamt* (Germany)
Tom Zwick, *Battelle Columbus*

The figure that appears on the cover of this volume was adapted from the article by Acomb et al. (see page 57).

Finally, I want to recognize the key members of the production staff, who put forth significant effort in assembling this book and its companion volumes. Carol Young, the Symposium Administrator, was responsible for the administrative effort necessary to produce the ten volumes. She was assisted by Gina Melaragno, who tracked draft manuscripts through the review process and generated much of the correspondence with the authors, co-editors, and peer reviewers. Lynn Copley-Graves oversaw text editing and directed the layout of the book, compilation of the keyword indices, and production of the camera-ready copy. She was assisted by technical editors Bea Weaver and Ann Elliot. Loretta Bahn was responsible for text processing and worked many long hours incorporating editors' revisions, laying out the camera-ready pages and figures, and maintaining the keyword list. She was assisted by Sherry Galford and Cleta Richey; additional support was provided by Susan Vianna and her staff at Fishergate, Inc. Darlene Whyte and Mike Steve proofread the final copy. Judy Ward, Gina Melaragno, Bonnie Snodgrass, and Carol Young carried out final production tasks. Karl Nehring, who served as Symposium Administrator in 1991 and 1993, provided valuable insight and advice.

The symposium was sponsored by Battelle Memorial Institute with support from many organizations. The following organizations cosponsored or otherwise supported the Third Symposium.

Ajou University–College of Engineering (Korea)
American Petroleum Institute
Asian Institute of Technology (Thailand)
Biotreatment News
Castalia
ENEA (Italy)
Environment Canada
Environmental Protection
Gas Research Institute
Groundwater Technology, Inc.
Institut Français du Pétrole
Mitsubishi Corporation
OHM Remediation Services Corporation
Parsons Engineering Science, Inc.
RIVM–National Institute of Public Health and the Environment
   (The Netherlands)
The Japan Research Institute, Limited
Umweltbundesamt (Germany)
U.S. Air Force Armstrong Laboratory–Environics Directorate
U.S. Air Force Center for Environmental Excellence
U.S. Department of Energy Office of Technology Development
   (OTD)
U.S. Environmental Protection Agency
U.S. Naval Facilities Engineering Services Center
Western Region Hazardous Substance Research Center–
   Stanford and Oregon State Universities

Neither Battelle nor the cosponsoring or supporting organizations reviewed this book, and their support for the Symposium should not be construed as an endorsement of the book's content. I conducted the final review and selection of all papers published in this volume, making use of the essential input provided by the peer reviewers and other editors. I take responsibility for any errors or omissions in the final publication.

Rob Hinchee
June 1995

Do Conventional Monitoring Practices Indicate In Situ Air Sparging Performance?

Paul C. Johnson, Richard L. Johnson, Chris Neaville,
Erik E. Hansen, Steve M. Stearns, and Ira J. Dortch

ABSTRACT

Short-term pilot tests play a key role in the selection and design of in situ air sparging systems. Most pilot tests are less than 24 h in duration and consist of monitoring changes in dissolved oxygen, water levels in wells, soil gas pressures, and soil gas contaminant concentrations while air is injected into the aquifer. These parameters are assumed to be indicators of air sparging feasibility and performance, and are also used in the design of full-scale systems. In this work we assess the validity of this critical assumption. Data are presented from a study site where a typical pilot-scale short-term test was conducted, followed by continued operation of a full-scale system for 110 days. Conventional sampling practices were augmented with more discrete and detailed assessment methods. In addition, a tracer gas was used to better understand air distributions, vapor flow paths, and vapor recovery efficiency. The data illustrate that conclusions regarding the performance and applicability of air sparging at the study site vary significantly depending on the monitoring approach used. There was no clear correlation between short-term pilot-test data and extended system performance when using data collected only from conventional groundwater monitoring wells.

INTRODUCTION

In situ air sparging (IAS) involves the injection of air into contaminated aquifers to (1) treat contaminant source areas trapped within water-saturated and capillary zones, (2) remediate dissolved contaminant plumes, or (3) provide barriers to dissolved contaminant plume migration (Ardito & Billings 1990, Bohler et al. 1990, Griffin et al. 1990, Middleton & Hiller 1990, Marley et al. 1990, Wehrle 1990, Brown & Fraxedas 1991, Brown et al. 1991, Kabeck et al. 1991, Marley et al. 1991, Ahlfeld et al. 1992, U.S. EPA 1992, Beausoleil et al. 1993, Johnson et al. 1993, Pankow et al. 1993, U.S. EPA 1993, Boersma et al. 1994). It is generally accepted that the injected air provides a source of oxygen to facilitate aerobic biodegradation, as well as providing a means to strip volatile chemicals from the saturated zone.

Short-term pilot tests play a key role in the selection and design of in situ air sparging systems (Brown et al. 1991, U.S. EPA 1992, Boersma et al. 1994). Most tests are less than 24 h in duration and make use of existing monitoring wells at a site. Dissolved oxygen, water elevations, soil gas pressures, and extracted soil gas contaminant concentrations are typically measured while air is being injected into the aquifer (Johnson et al. 1993, Lundegard 1994). Increases in dissolved oxygen and decreases in dissolved contaminant levels are assumed to be favorable indicators of feasibility, whereas changes in groundwater levels measured in monitoring wells and vadose zone air pressures are assumed to be indicators of the area of treatment.

In this work we assess the validity of these critical assumptions. Data are presented from a study site where a typical pilot-scale short-term test was conducted, followed by continued operation of a full-scale system for 110 days. Conventional sampling practices were augmented with more discrete and detailed assessment methods. In addition, a tracer gas was used to better understand air distributions, vapor flow paths, and vapor recovery efficiency.

The goal of this work was not to assess if air sparging "works" at this site; instead the emphasis was placed on comparing (1) sampling results from conventional monitoring wells with data from discrete interval implants and (2) short-term pilot-test data with similar measurements over a longer period of continued operation.

SITE DESCRIPTION AND HISTORY

The air sparging pilot study was conducted at a site that had been operated as a service station for approximately 20 years. Storage tanks, lines, and pumps were removed prior to this study.

Figure 1 presents a geologic cross section interpolated from the results of both conventional drilling activities and soil cores obtained with direct-push (Geoprobe®) soil samplers. As will be seen, the site geology had a significant impact on the air sparging study results presented below.

Superimposed on this geologic cross section are field-screening and laboratory soil analysis results. The highest concentrations of petroleum hydrocarbons indicated in Figure 1 are located in the vicinity of the underground storage tanks at depths of 15 to 20 ft (4.6 to 6.1 m) below ground surface (BGS). Total petroleum hydrocarbon concentrations in soil, as measured by modified EPA method 8015, were greatest in samples taken from 20 to 25 ft (6.1 to 7.6 m) BGS. Concentrations were as high as 12,000 mg/kg, but most source zone values ranged from 1,000 to 2,000 mg/kg.

The site is located on a river island, and consequently groundwater levels are tidally and seasonally influenced. On a daily basis, fluctuations of between 0.1 and 0.5 ft (0.03 and 0.15 m) are observed across the site. Large seasonal fluctuations are also possible, and records indicate that water table elevations have

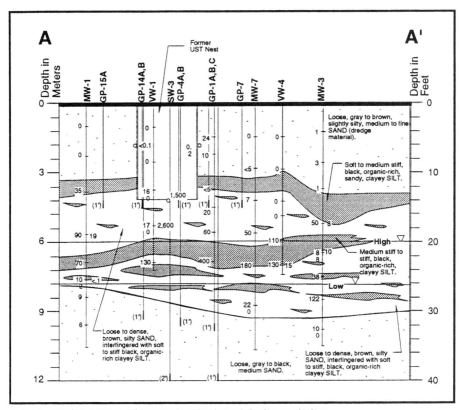

Note: Contact lines between soil types are based on interpolation between borings

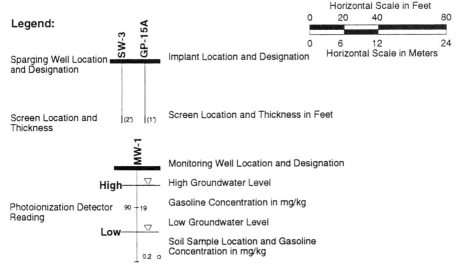

FIGURE 1. Interpolated geologic cross section for the study site.

fluctuated between 17 and 27 ft (5.2 and 8.2 m) BGS. During the period of this study, groundwater was consistently encountered at approximately 25 ft (7.6 m) BGS, which is close in depth to the recorded low for recent years.

The sum of dissolved concentrations of benzene, toluene, ethylbenzene, and xylenes (BTEX) in groundwater exceeded 20 mg/L in many on-site monitoring wells prior to the remedial activities. At the time of this study, mobile free-phase petroleum liquid was not observed at any groundwater monitoring locations. Based on the observed contaminant distribution, groundwater monitoring data, and the water table fluctuation data it can be inferred that a petroleum hydrocarbon smear zone exists between 17 to 27 ft (5.2 and 8.2 m) BGS.

HISTORY OF REMEDIAL ACTIVITIES

A groundwater pump-and-treat system was installed approximately 2 years prior to this study. At that time the system consisted of a single recovery well (RW-1) capable of a pumping rate of 20 gal/min (75 L/min). Due to high dissolved iron concentrations, however, the water treatment system operation was erratic. Consequently, long-term average pumping rates were 2 to 10 gal/min (7.5 to 38 L/min). A second groundwater extraction well (RW-2) was added to the system a few months prior to this study, with an average pumping rate of approximately 10 gal/min (38 L/min).

A soil vapor extraction system was also installed with the pump-and-treat system. Various combinations of six vapor extraction wells were used during the period leading up to the air sparging study. Total vapor flowrate for the combined system of vapor extraction wells ranged from 60 to 100 ft^3/min (1.7 to 28 m^3/min) at applied gauge vacuums of 40 to 80 in H$_2$O (75 to 150 mm Hg), respectively. Total hydrocarbon vapor concentrations declined from 70,000 mg/m^3 to approximately 1000 mg/m^3 over the 18-month period preceding the in situ air sparging study.

Figure 2 presents total dissolved BTEX concentrations detected in the groundwater recovery wells over the initial 18 months of operation of the combined groundwater pump-and-treat/soil vapor extraction systems. Concentration "spikes" shown in Figure 2 are indicative of the discontinuous system operation.

Based on this information, it was decided to evaluate alternative processes that might accelerate remediation at the study site. Of the limited alternatives available, in situ air sparging was selected because it could easily be integrated with the existing groundwater pump-and-treat/soil vapor extraction system.

IN SITU AIR SPARGING STUDY

In preparation for the pilot-test study, three 2-in. (5.1-cm)-diameter polyvinyl chloride (PVC) air injection wells were installed (SW-1, SW-2, and SW-3). These wells were constructed by standard drilling and installation practices: short 2-ft (0.6-m) well screens were placed 38 to 40 ft (12 to 13 m) BGS, and the well

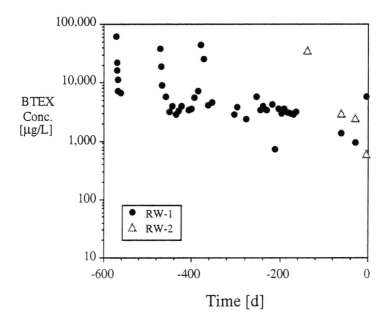

FIGURE 2. Total dissolved BTEX concentrations [µg/L] in groundwater samples from the groundwater recovery system during operation of the vapor extraction/groundwater recovery system (pre-air sparging study).

annulus above this zone was sealed to ground surface with a bentonite grout. A fourth smaller-diameter air injection well (SW-4), constructed from steel, with a 1-ft (0.3-m) screened interval was pushed to a depth of 30 ft (10 m), but was not used during this study. In addition, numerous 6-in. (0.15-m)-long, 0.5-in. (1.2-cm)-diameter, metal screen implants were installed using a Geoprobe® drive-point system. These were installed at depths of approximately 15, 30, and 40 ft (4.5, 9, and 12 m) BGS, and connected to ground surface via lengths of flexible polypropylene tubing. The discrete implants placed at 15 ft (4.5 m) BGS were used for vadose zone pressure monitoring and soil gas sampling, while those placed at 30 and 40 ft (9 and 12 m) BGS were used for obtaining groundwater samples. Locations of the vapor extraction wells, groundwater recovery wells, groundwater monitoring wells, air injection wells, and discrete implants are shown on the site plan view given in Figure 3.

SAMPLING AND ANALYSES PROTOCOLS

Groundwater and vapor samples were collected for analyses prior to, during, and after air injection. The sampling and analyses procedures are briefly explained below.

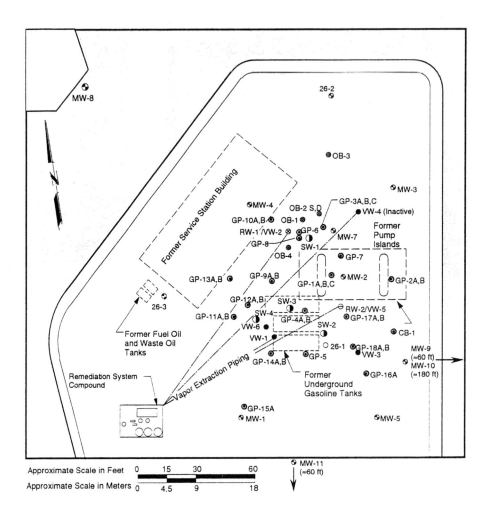

Legend:

RW-1/VW-2	⊗	Active Recovery/Vapor Extraction Well			
MW-1	☉	Monitoring Well	SW-1	◖	Air-Sparge Well
VW-1	●	Vapor Extraction Well	GP-1	⊙	Geoprobe Exploration Point
OB-4	◉	Vapor Observation Point	26-1	○	Former Monitoring Well

FIGURE 3. Study site plan view showing locations of injection wells, extraction wells, and monitoring locations.

Dissolved Oxygen Measurements in Groundwater

Dissolved oxygen (DO) levels in groundwater were measured with a continuous flow-through cell and electronic dissolved oxygen meter as pictured in Figure 4a. For each sampling event and each location, a peristaltic pump was

(a)

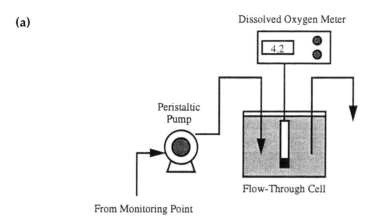

(b)

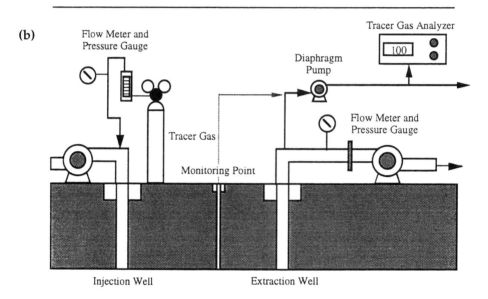

FIGURE 4. Pilot study monitoring: (a) dissolved oxygen measurements and (b) tracer gas measurements and helium recovery test.

used to continuously supply groundwater to a small jar in which an electronic DO sensor (Leeds and Northrup Model 7931) was placed. When the sensor reading had stabilized (usually within a few minutes) the value displayed on the meter was recorded. The DO meter was calibrated before and several times during each sampling event.

Dissolved Hydrocarbon Concentrations in Groundwater

After recording the stabilized dissolved oxygen concentrations, zero headspace groundwater samples were collected in 40-mL volatile organic analysis

(VOA) vials. The samples were placed in an ice chest and shipped to an analytical laboratory for BTEX analysis. The peristaltic pump head tubing was replaced with new tubing between successive sampling locations.

Hydrocarbon Concentrations in Vapor Samples

Vapor samples were collected from vapor extraction well flow lines and vadose zone monitoring points in pre-evacuated stainless-steel canisters and shipped to an analytical laboratory for analysis of BTEX compounds and TPH.

Tracer Gas Analyses

Soil gas samples were collected from 15 ft (4.5 m) BGS vadose zone implants, vapor extraction wells, groundwater monitoring wells, and process flow lines with a diaphragm pump. The diaphragm pump outlet vapor stream was passed before the intake to a portable helium detector (Mark Model 9820) as illustrated in Figure 4b.

PROCESS MONITORING

Flowrates and pressures were recorded for each air injection and vapor extraction well during the test. Prior to, and during the pilot study, flowmeters were calibrated by the following procedures: (1) flowmeters on the tracer gas delivery system (He and SF_6) were first calibrated with a dry test meter and stopwatch, (2) then vapor extraction and air injection well flowmeters were calibrated relative to the tracer gas flowmeters. This second calibration was accomplished by injecting tracer gas into the injection/extraction piping and monitoring the resulting tracer gas concentration downstream (at a distance sufficient to ensure adequate mixing). Flowrates of the process streams could then be calculated from a mass balance on the tracer gas, utilizing the known tracer gas delivery rates and resulting dilution of tracer gas downstream of the tracer gas introduction point. It was necessary to use this approach because a sufficiently large dry test meter was not available to calibrate the higher flowrate process flowmeters. In this approach all system flowmeters are calibrated relative to each other to simplify interpretation of recovery efficiency data.

PILOT TEST ACTIVITIES

The sequence of the two-phase pilot test study operation is outlined in Table 1. In the first phase, a single air injection well/single vapor extraction well test was conducted for 3 days. This was followed immediately by the second phase, which consisted of an extended, 110-d, full-scale (three air injection wells, three vapor extraction wells) pilot study and subsequent postoperation monitoring. Observations and results from these studies are discussed below.

TABLE 1. Sequence of pilot test study activities.

Exp. Time [d]	Description of Activities
0⁻ *pretest*	• collect groundwater samples from all monitoring wells • collect groundwater samples from all discrete implants • measure dissolved oxygen at all groundwater sampling locations • connect vapor extraction system to well VW-5 ($\approx$50 SCFM at $\approx$40 in H_2O gauge vacuum) • collect vapor sample from VW-5 • measure vadose zone vacuums • calibrate VW-5 process flowmeter • turn off groundwater recovery system
0⁺ to 3 *single injection well/single extraction well test*	• initiate air injection into sparge well SW-2 (8.5 psig, 10 SCFM) • collect vapor samples from VW-5 • measure vadose zone pressures • measure dissolved oxygen at all groundwater sampling locations • collect groundwater samples from all monitoring wells • collect groundwater samples from all discrete implants • begin He injection • calibrate air injection flowmeter
3 *full-scale extended pilot test*	• begin air injection to SW-1 and SW-3 ($\approx$7 and 12 psig, respectively, 10 SCFM into each well) • continue air injection at SW-2 • connect vapor extraction system to wells VW-2, VW-5, VW-6 • measure vadose zone vacuums • measure dissolved oxygen at all groundwater sampling locations • collect groundwater samples from all monitoring wells • collect groundwater samples from all discrete implants
17	• turn on groundwater recovery system (RW-1, RW-2)
110 *system shutdown*	• turn off air injection system • measure dissolved oxygen at all groundwater sampling locations • collect groundwater samples from all monitoring wells • collect groundwater samples from selected discrete implants
125, 142 *post-test monitoring*	• measure dissolved oxygen at all groundwater sampling locations • collect groundwater samples from all monitoring wells • collect groundwater samples from all discrete implants

RESULTS AND DISCUSSION:
SHORT-TERM PILOT TEST (0 to 3 DAYS)

Operating Conditions

During the short-term pilot study, air was injected into a single air sparging well (SW-2) and vapors were recovered with a single vapor extraction well (VW-5). Initially, the air injection flowrate was 10 ft^3/min (28 m^3/min) at a gauge pressure of 8.5 psig (440 mm Hg); however, over 3 days the injection pressure gradually decreased to ≈6.5 psig (340 mm Hg), and the injection flowrate increased slightly to 12 to 14 ft^3/min (0.35 to 0.40 m^3/min). The VW-5 vapor extraction flowrate was maintained at ≈50 ft^3/min (1.4 m^3/min), with an applied gauge vacuum of ≈40 in H$_2$O (76 mm Hg).

Dissolved Oxygen and Helium Concentrations

Figure 5a presents dissolved oxygen (DO) levels measured in groundwater monitoring wells. These levels increased over the duration of the study in most monitoring wells, and in many cases approached oxygen saturation (≈8 mg/L). Those wells that showed little increase were > 60 ft (18 m) from the air injection well.

Helium concentrations measured in the vapor space of these wells are displayed in Figure 5b. These concentrations increased to levels close to that in the injected air stream (≈0.4%) in most of the wells. As might be expected, a strong correlation can be seen between the dissolved oxygen level and helium vapor concentration increases.

Figure 5b also presents helium vapor concentrations for a number of saturated zone implants that, during the short-term test, became dry (would only yield vapor). A positive gauge pressure of ≈115 in H$_2$O (215 mm Hg) was measured at implant GP-5B (32 ft [9.8 m] BGS), and GP-17B (40 ft [12 m] BGS) would freely yield an air/water mixture without pumping for several days following startup. Note that most of these dry implants are located at ≈30 ft BGS.

For comparison, Figure 6a presents DO levels measured in groundwater samples collected from the discrete saturated zone implants (≈30 and 39 ft [9 and 12 m] BGS). With the exception of implant GP-17B, which went artesian at startup (as discussed above), no significant increases in dissolved oxygen were detected during the short-term pilot test at the implants.

Figure 6b presents the concentration of helium measured in the vadose zone (15 ft [5 m] BGS) discrete implants. Helium was detected at only two of the vadose zone monitoring implants, and the helium concentration approached the injection concentration at only one of those points.

In comparing Figures 5 and 6, one can see significant differences between the data resulting from each of the two monitoring approaches. Conventional monitoring well data alone suggest a broad and fairly uniform saturated zone air distribution profile, with evidence of injected air having traveled distances up to 60 ft (18 m) from the air injection point. By conventional practices, these

(a)

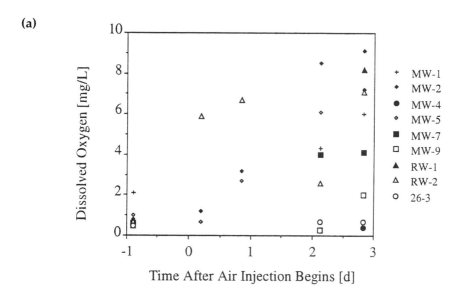

(b)

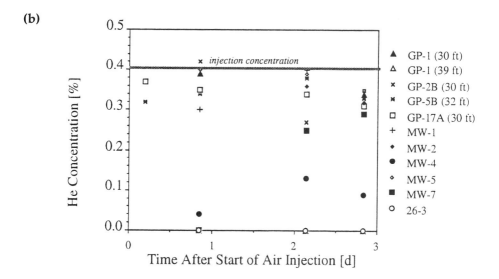

FIGURE 5. Monitoring data from 3-day single injection well/single extraction well pilot test: (a) dissolved oxygen levels in conventional monitoring wells and (b) helium concentrations in conventional monitoring wells and saturated zone implants that became dry during the test.

significant increases in DO levels would be interpreted to suggest that air sparging is a feasible alternative for this site.

On the other hand, it is difficult to formulate such optimistic conclusions from the discrete implant data. The DO data could be interpreted to suggest

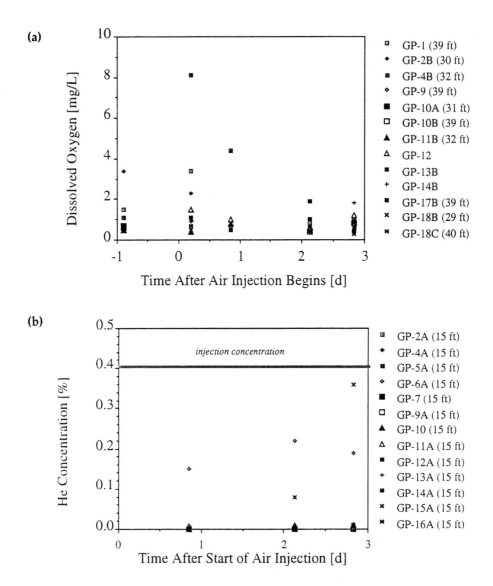

FIGURE 6. Monitoring data from 3-day single injection well/single extraction well pilot test: (a) dissolved oxygen levels from saturated zone implants, and (b) helium concentrations in vadose zone implants.

limited oxygen transfer effectiveness, whereas the vadose zone implant He data suggest a very asymmetric air distribution. These data alone might suggest limited usefulness of air sparging at this site.

If one interprets the data presented in Figures 5 and 6 collectively, instead of independently, another quite different, but more realistic picture of the saturated zone air distribution emerges. At this study site it is likely that, as injected air migrated upward and away from the air sparging well, its vertical migration was impeded. Consequently, an air "bubble" formed and began to spread laterally across the site. Wherever this bubble was intersected by a monitoring well, the well would act as a preferential conduit for vertical air migration to the vadose zone. This conceptual picture is supported by the data presented in Figures 5 and 6, the geologic cross section presented in Figure 1, and the observations that some of the 30-ft (9-m) BGS saturated zone implants went dry after air injection was initiated.

The data also suggest that site geology was also a key factor controlling the vadose zone airflow distribution. Helium was not detected in most 15 ft (4.5 m) BGS vadose zone implants. Thus, the injected air, upon reaching the vadose zone, might have been restricted to moving laterally beneath the silty layer located at ≈20 ft (6 m) BGS (see Figure 1).

This data set illustrates how one's perception of injected air distributions and air sparging feasibility at any site can be significantly influenced by the monitoring approach selected. At this study site, the conventional monitoring well data by itself clearly paints an optimistic picture of airflow and potential effectiveness. On the other hand, the discrete implant data indicate quite the opposite, as the data yield little that can be taken as a positive effect of the 3 days of air sparging. For reference, it should be noted that most current air sparging feasibility evaluations are based on short-term pilot test monitoring well data.

Although the short-term pilot test data presented are unique to this particular study site, it should be noted that this site is not atypical of many proposed air sparging sites. The following observations are offered to those planning future pilot test studies: (1) dissolved oxygen data collected from conventional monitoring wells can be used to quickly assess the lateral extent of air distribution in the saturated zone, but little can be inferred about vertical air distribution or oxygen transfer efficiency, and (2) discrete implant data provide an indication of changes on a more local scale, but given the unpredictable nature of air distributions in the saturated zone, significant changes in short time periods will likely be observed at only a few implants.

One should also take care not to interpret that one monitoring approach is "better" than another. Clearly, at the study site, it is the combination of both data sets that provides the most realistic picture of the resulting air distribution.

Helium Recovery Test

A helium recovery test, as illustrated in Figure 4b, was conducted during the short-term pilot test. In brief, helium was injected at a constant rate, and its recovery by the vapor extraction system was monitored. Figure 7 summarizes the results of this test, where the helium recovery is expressed as a percentage of its injection rate. Even with a vapor extraction rate that was greater than the air injection rate by a factor of 5, only about 40% of the injected helium was recovered by the vapor extraction system at steady state during the first 2 days of air injection. On the second day of the short-term pilot test, a 40-ft (12-m) soil core (denoted CB-1 on Figure 1) was obtained from a location roughly 30 ft

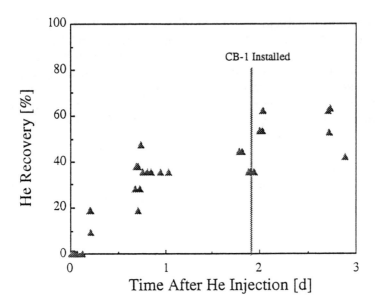

FIGURE 7.   Helium recovery test results from single injection well/single extraction well test.

(9.1 m) from injection well SW-2. The opening of this new airflow pathway is reflected in the increase in helium recovery to ≈50%. This observed increase in efficiency is again consistent with the conceptual picture (suggested above) of a large air bubble spread laterally across the site beneath a geologic air confining unit located at some depth between the air injection point and the groundwater table.

It should be noted that, during this short-term pilot test, pressures at the vadose zone monitoring implants were consistently less than atmospheric. Despite this, a significant fraction of the helium injected at the air sparging well escaped capture. Thus, the data from this study site suggest that at some sites, negative vadose zone pressure measurements and extraction/injection flowrate ratios greater than unity may not be sufficient to ensure complete contaminant vapor capture. In cases where vapor capture is important, users should consider including tracer gas recovery studies in their pilot-test and full-scale system operating protocols.

RESULTS AND DISCUSSION:
EXTENDED FULL-SCALE PILOT TEST

During the short-term pilot test, the emphasis was placed on collecting and comparing the monitoring data from monitoring wells and more discrete direct-push implants. Some conclusions from this work have already been discussed above. One important question remains, however: Are short-term data any indication of long-term air sparging system performance? Given our limited ability to predict air sparging system performance at any given site, we often rely on key indicators to gauge feasibility. An example for air sparging systems is the reliance on dissolved oxygen measurements from conventional monitoring wells. To better assess if any relationships exist between typical air sparging pilot test monitoring data and long-term system performance, an extended full-scale air sparging pilot test was initiated following completion of the short-term pilot-scale test. Details and results from the extended full-scale test are discussed below.

Operating Conditions

At the conclusion of the 3-day pilot test, air injection into two additional wells (SW-1 and SW-3) was initiated at flowrates of ≈ 10 ft^3/min (0.3 m^3/min) per well. Air injection was continuous (not pulsed) for the duration of the study. In addition, extraction wells VW-2 and VW-6 were connected to the vapor extraction system. This "extended" pilot test was conducted until day 107, at which time air injection ceased. For 1 month following system shutdown, groundwater samples were collected at 2-week intervals for laboratory BTEX analyses and field DO measurements.

Groundwater Monitoring Data

Figures 8 through 10 present a subset of the data collected during the extended pilot test. Figures 8a and 8b present BTEX and DO concentrations, respectively, in groundwater samples obtained from monitoring wells located within 40 ft (12 m) of any air sparging well. All three wells exhibit similar behavior. Dissolved hydrocarbon concentrations rapidly decreased as DO levels rose at the start of air injection. During air injection, the dissolved BTEX levels remained relatively low and constant. DO levels, however, steadily declined during the duration of the study. No clear explanation can be given for this behavior, although this general trend was observed in all the DO data. Possibilities include declining instrument sensitivity, decreasing oxygen transfer efficiency, and increasing oxygen uptake rates. Once air injection ceased, dissolved BTEX levels rebounded to roughly their pretest levels, and dissolved oxygen levels declined to their pretest conditions. These data suggest that groundwater samples obtained from these monitoring wells were not very representative of conditions within the aquifer during air injection.

In comparison, Figures 9a and 9b present BTEX and DO concentrations, respectively, in groundwater samples obtained from saturated zone discrete implants located within 15 ft (4.5 m) of any air sparging well. The dissolved BTEX data appear to be less significantly affected by the air injection, and little change is observed during or after air injection. DO levels did increase in most implants following full-scale system startup, in contrast to the data collected during the 3-day single injection well test (Figure 7a). However, like the monitoring well

(a)

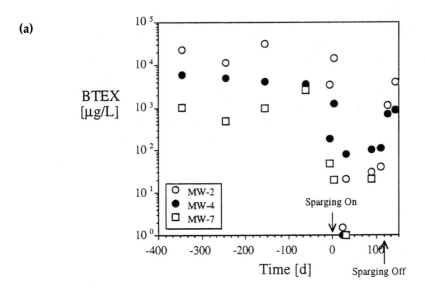

(b)

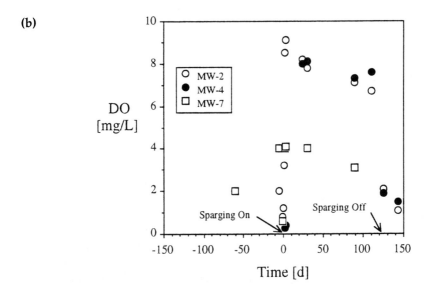

FIGURE 8. Monitoring data from extended full-scale pilot test: (a) dissolved BTEX concentrations and (b) dissolved oxygen levels in groundwater from monitoring wells <40 ft (12 m) from an air sparging well.

data, DO levels declined over the course of the study, and dropped to their original low levels once air injection ceased.

In comparing the data from the two monitoring approaches, it may be concluded that, during air injection, discrete implant samples are more representative of aquifer conditions than monitoring well groundwater samples. The data also

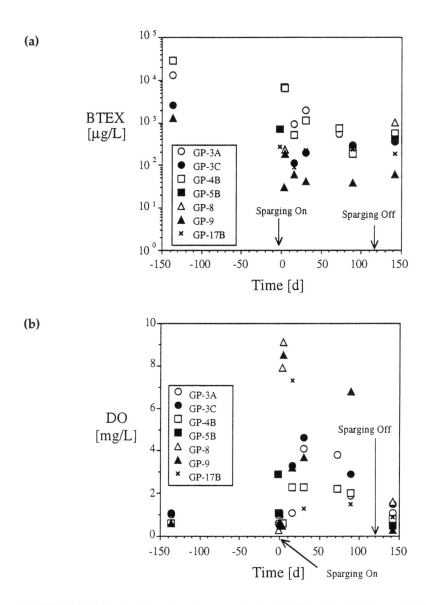

FIGURE 9. Monitoring data from extended full-scale pilot test: (a) dissolved BTEX concentrations and (b) dissolved oxygen levels in groundwater from implants located <15 ft (4.5 m) from an air sparging well.

suggest that a waiting period of greater than 1 month may be required following system shutdown before representative samples can be obtained from monitoring wells directly impacted by the injected airflow. As shown in Figure 8a, the monitoring well dissolved BTEX concentrations at the study site exhibited an

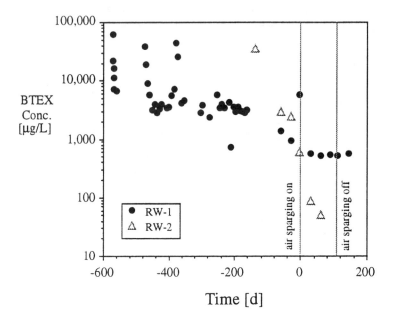

Time [d]

FIGURE 10. Dissolved BTEX concentrations in groundwater samples from the groundwater recovery system during the extended full-scale air sparging test.

increasing trend for the 1-month monitoring period following cessation of air injection.

Groundwater Recovery System Data

Figure 10 presents dissolved BTEX concentrations in groundwater samples obtained from the groundwater recovery system, which was in operation during the extended full-scale pilot test. Little change can be observed in the data, if one considers the trends established prior to initiation of air injection. In fact, it could be suggested that the pre-air sparging declining trend in RW-1 was retarded by the air injection process. These data may also indicate that the air injection stimulated aquifer mixing.

SUMMARY AND CONCLUSIONS

Data from the short-term pilot test and extended full-scale system study illustrate the following:

1. Significant differences existed between the data collected for the two monitoring approaches studied.

2. Short-term pilot-test data collected from conventional monitoring wells yielded the most optimistic picture of long-term system performance.
3. Short-term pilot-test discrete implant monitoring results were less promising as they showed little effect of in situ air sparging during the 3-day pilot test.
4. The combined data set suggested that the vertical migration of the injected air was restricted, and consequently a large horizontal air bubble was formed.
5. When the full-scale system was shut down after 110 d of operation, dissolved BTEX levels in monitoring well groundwater samples increased significantly during the month-long period of postoperation monitoring.
6. In comparison, groundwater samples obtained from the discrete implants and the groundwater recovery system did not rebound when the system was turned off.
7. In both monitoring wells and discrete implants, dissolved oxygen increased rapidly when injection was initiated, but then slowly declined during the period of continued operation.
8. No clear correlation existed between the groundwater monitoring data collected during the short-term pilot test and the results of the 110-d full-scale system study.
9. Discrete implant pilot-test and extended full-scale system performance data were more consistent in that no significant changes in groundwater parameters were observed throughout the study.

The reader should note that, as stated earlier, the goal of this study was not to assess if air sparging "works" at this site. Data collected in this study may be unique to this site, and the apparent ineffectiveness of the air sparging system may be attributed to many factors, including the short duration of the study, the specific system design, and the chosen operating conditions.

ACKNOWLEDGMENTS

The authors would like to thank Frank Fossati and Shell Oil Company for sponsoring this research.

REFERENCES

Ahlfeld, D. P., M. A. Dahmani, W. Ji, and M. Farrell. 1992. *Field Study of Behavior of Air Sparging.* Technical Report 92-10, Environmental Research Institute, The University of Connecticut at Storrs.

Ardito, C. P., and J. F. Billings. 1990. "Alternative Remediation Strategies: The Subsurface Volatilization and Ventilation System." *Petroleum Hydrocarbons and Organic Chemicals in Ground Water: Prevention, Detection and Restoration,* Houston, TX.

Beausoleil, Y. J., J. S. Huber, and G. W. Barker. 1993. "The Use of Air Sparging in the Remediation of a Production Gas Facility." *Society of Petroleum Engineers Paper No. 26000,* SPE/EPA Exploration and Production Environmental Conference, San Antonio, TX.

Boersma, P., P. Newman, and K. Piontek. 1994. "The Role of Groundwater Sparging in Hydro-carbon Remediation." Presented at the *American Petroleum Institute Pipeline Conference*, Houston, TX.

Bohler, U., J. Brauns, H. Hotzel, and M. Nahold. 1990. "Air Injection and Soil Aeration as a Combined Method for Cleaning Contaminated Sites — Observations from Test Sites in Sedimented Solid Rocks." In: F. Arendt, M. Hinsenveld, and W. J. van den Brink (Eds.), *Contaminated Soil '90*. Kluwer Academic Publishers. pp. 1039-1044.

Brown, R. A., and R. Fraxedas. 1991. "Air Sparging — Extending Volatilization to Contami-nated Aquifers." *USEPA Symposium on Soil Venting Proceedings*, Houston, TX.

Brown, R. A., C. Herman, and E. Henry. 1991. "The Use of Aeration in Environmental Cleanups." *Haztech International Pittsburgh Waste Conference Proceedings*. Pittsburgh, PA.

Griffin, C. J., J. M. Armstrong, and R. H. Douglass. 1990. "Engineering Design Aspects of an In Situ Soil Vapor Remediation System (Sparging)." *In Situ Bioreclamation 1990*.

Ji, W., A. Dahmani, D. Ahlfeld, J. D. Lin, and E. Hill. 1993. "Laboratory Study of Air Sparging: Air Flow Visualization." *Ground Water Monitoring and Remediation*, Fall 1993.

Johnson, R. L., P. C. Johnson, D. B. McWhorter, R. Hinchee, and I. Goodman. 1993. "An Over-view of In Situ Air Sparging." *Ground Water Monitoring and Remediation*, Fall 1993.

Kaback, D. S., B. B. Looney, C. A. Eddy, and T. C. Hazen. 1991. "Innovative Ground Water and Soil Remediation: In Situ Air Stripping Using Horizontal Wells." *Fifth National Outdoor Action Conference on Aquifer Restoration, Ground Water Monitoring, and Geophysical Methods Proceedings*, Las Vegas, NV.

Lundegard, P. 1994. "Actual Versus Apparent Radius of Influence — An Air Sparging Pilot Test in A Sandy Aquifer." *API/NGWA Conference — Petroleum Hydrocarbons and Organic Chemicals in Ground Water: Prevention, Detection and Restoration Proceedings*, Houston, TX.

Marley, M. C. 1991. "Air Sparging in Conjunction with Vapor Extraction for Source Removal at VOC Spill Sites." *Fifth National Outdoor Action Conference on Aquifer Restoration, Ground Water Monitoring, and Geophysical Methods Proceedings*, Las Vegas, NV.

Marley, M. C., M. T. Walsh, and P. E. Nangeroni. 1990. "A Case Study on the Application of Air Sparging as a Complimentary Technology to Vapor Extraction at a Gasoline Spill Site in Rhode Island." Presented at the *Hydrocarbon Contaminated Soils and Groundwater Conference*, University of Massachusetts, Amherst, MA.

Middleton, A. C., and D. H. Hiller. 1990. "In Situ Aeration of Groundwater: A Technology Overview." *1990 Environment Canada Montreal Conference Proceedings*.

Pankow, J. F., R. L. Johnson, and J. A. Cherry. 1993. "Air Sparging in Gate Wells in Cutoff Walls and Trenches for Control of Plumes of Volatile Organic Compounds (VOCs)." *Ground Water*, 31(4): 654-663.

U.S. EPA. 1992. *A Technology Assessment of Soil Vapor Extraction and Air Sparging*. EPA/600/R-192/173. U.S. Environmental Protection Agency. September.

U.S. EPA. 1993. *Groundwater Remediation for UST Site*. EPA-510-F-93-017. U.S. Environmental Protection Agency. October.

Wehrle, K. 1990. "In Situ Cleaning of CHC Contaminated Sites: Model-Scale Experiments Using the Air Injection (In Situ Stripping) Method in Granular Soils." In: F. Arendt, M. Hinsenveld, and W. J. van den Brink (Eds.), *Contaminated Soil '90*. Kluwer Academic Publishers. pp. 1061-1062.

Air Sparging: Much Ado About Mounding

Paul D. Lundegard

ABSTRACT

Groundwater mounding is the upward movement of the water table that can occur in association with air injection into the saturated zone. Multiphase flow simulations are here used to define general mounding behavior and dynamics under simplified subsurface conditions. Field observations at three sites are then used to describe a range of expected groundwater mounding responses for subsurface conditions, ranging from relatively homogeneous to highly heterogeneous. Results show that mounding (1) is a transient response that is usually negligible at steady state, (2) dissipates by radial wavelike spreading, and (3) occurs well beyond the saturated zone region of airflow.

INTRODUCTION

When air is injected into the saturated zone, groundwater must necessarily be displaced. Where the displacement of groundwater has a vertical component, there will be a local rise in the water table. This is sometimes called water table mounding. Physical mounding of the water table should be distinguished from a mounding of the piezometric surface without displacement of the water table that can occur during transient system behavior, especially under confined conditions. Mounding has been used by some as an indicator of the "radius-of-influence" of the sparge well (Brown & Jasiulewicz 1992; Marley et al. 1992). Mounding is also considered to be a design concern because it represents a driving force for lateral movement of groundwater and dissolved contaminants and can therefore lead to spreading of the plume. The magnitude of mounding depends on site conditions and the location of the observation well relative to the sparge well. Mounding can vary from negligible to several feet in magnitude (Brown et al. 1993; Boersma et al. 1993; Lundegard & LaBrecque in press). This paper discusses the results and implications of multiphase flow simulations of air sparging, as well as several field tests.

SIMULATIONS

Simulations of the flow of air and water around an air sparging well were performed with a multiphase, multicomponent simulator (TETRAD) originally developed for the study of problems encountered during exploitation of petroleum and geothermal resources (Vinsome & Shook 1993). It has been used previously to investigate the impact of various geologic and engineering factors on air sparging flow behavior (Lundegard & Andersen 1993).

Simulations defined two primary stages of transient behavior that lead to a steady-state flow pattern (Figure 1). The first stage is characterized by an expansion in the region of airflow. During this stage, the rate of air injection into the saturated zone exceeds the rate of airflow out of the saturated zone into the vadose zone. This situation is analogous to the inflation of a "balloon" of air in the saturated zone. It is during this transient expansion stage that groundwater mounding first develops. It extends from near the injection well to beyond the region of airflow in the saturated zone. When injected air breaks through to the vadose zone, the region of airflow in the saturated zone begins to collapse or shrink (Figure 1). During this second transient stage of behavior, the establishment of preferred pathways of higher air permeability from the point of injection to the vadose zone functions like a leak in the "balloon" of air. The "balloon" shrinks until the rate of air leakage to the vadose zone equals the rate of air injection. During the transient collapse stage, mounding near the sparge well dissipates. This behavioral pattern has also been observed in the field (Brown et al. 1993; Boersma et al. 1993; Lundegard & LaBrecque in press).

Additional aspects of the groundwater mounding response to air injection were revealed by closer examination of the spatial and temporal changes in the amount of mounding. At a position outside the steady-state region of airflow and just below the presparging water table, head increases sharply to a maximum and then declines and levels off (Figure 2). This behavior reflects the buildup and decay of the groundwater mound at this location. Examination of the changing fluid saturation pattern across a horizontal clipping plane just above the presparging water table demonstrates the dynamics of mound buildup and decay (Figure 3). During the transient expansion stage, mounding reaches its greatest magnitude; and its maxima is at the location of the sparge well under homogeneous conditions (Figure 3a). With continued sparging, the mound begins to collapse at the location of the sparge well and spreads radially in a wavelike fashion (Figure 3b). As the mound wave moves away from the sparge well it decreases in amplitude. When steady-state conditions are achieved, little or no mounding exists. These relationships are shown schematically in Figure 4.

FIELD OBSERVATIONS

Site 1

The mounding response under natural field conditions was monitored as part of a detailed pilot test in a dune sand aquifer (Lundegard & LaBrecque in press).

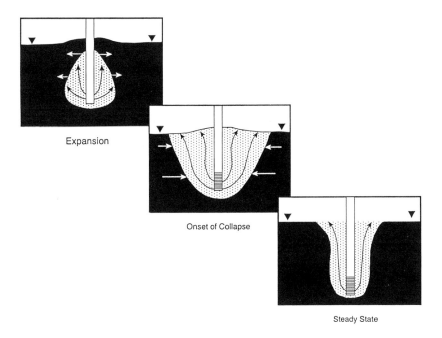

FIGURE 1. Schematic representation of the behavioral stages occurring during continuous air sparging. Mounding first develops during the transient expansion stage, dissipates during the collapse stage, and is generally negligible at steady state.

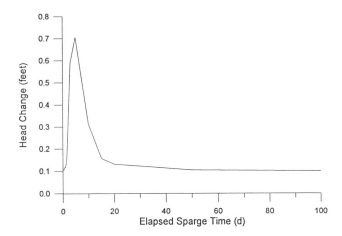

FIGURE 2. Mounding response during numerical simulation of air sparging. Observation point is just below the presparging water table and outside the steady-state region of airflow.

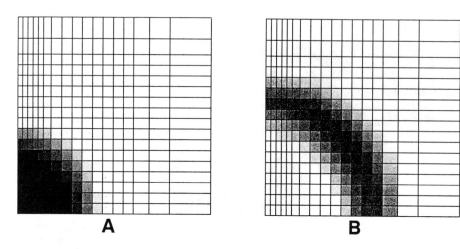

FIGURE 3. Horizontal view of simulated mounding behavior. Water saturation across a clipping plane just above the presparging water table (black =
high water saturation; white = low water saturation). Grid represents a
one-quarter symmetry element of the model domain. Sparge well located
in the lower left corner of the grid. (A) Dome-like mounding around the
sparge well during the early transient expansion stage. (B) Mounding
during late transient expansion stage. Note wavelike spreading and dissi-
pation of the mound.

This test provides a useful basis for comparison with the numerical simulations
and other field tests because the subsurface conditions are very homogeneous and
isotropic relative to most sites. Air was injected approximately 13 ft (4 m) below
the water table at a steady-state pressure of 6 psig (41.4 kPa) and rate of 18 scfm
(0.52 m^3/minute). Groundwater mounding was logged digitally in observations
wells at distances of 5 to 63 ft (1.5 to 19 m) from the sparge well.

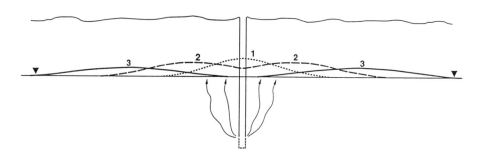

FIGURE 4. Schematic cross section representing progressive mounding
behavior at three times ($t_1 < t_2 < t_3$).

Transient mounding of the water table was observed in all of the wells that were monitored (Figure 5). With the air compressor running constantly at its maximum capacity, mounding reached a peak and then dissipated, consistent with the simulation results discussed above and observations at other sites (e.g., Boersma et al. 1993; Brown et al. 1993). Within 3 to 4 h of continuous air injection, the mounding virtually disappeared at all observation locations.

While a rapid mounding response was observed at all locations, the time required to reach maximum mounding varied. It took longer for mounding to peak at the more distant observation locations (Figure 6). Additionally, the magnitude of the mound diminished with distance from the sparge well (Figure 7). This behavior is expected for relatively homogeneous conditions and is entirely consistent with the simulation results.

An electrical resistance tomography survey at Site 1 defined a principal region of airflow in the saturated zone that is only 8 ft (2.4 m) in maximum width (Schima et al. 1994; Lundegard & LaBrecque in press). Mounding, however, occurred well beyond the actual region of airflow, and plots of maximum mounding versus distance did not clearly define the region of airflow (Figure 7).

Site 2

In contrast to Site 1, this field test was conducted at a site consisting of heterogeneous, interstratified gravel, sand, and silt. Air was injected approximately 9 ft (2.7 m) below the water table at a steady-state pressure of 6.2 psig

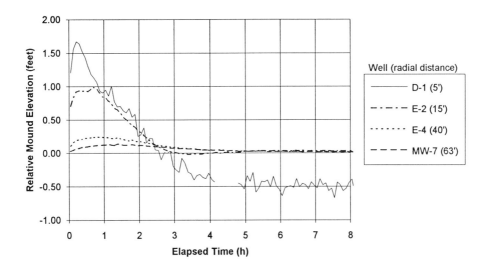

FIGURE 5. Plot of mounding versus elapsed sparge time at Site 1. The rapid rise to a peak followed by a gradual decrease towards presparging levels is the typical transient response observed at most sites. Legend shows radial distance from sparge well to observation well. D-1 transducer removed from well between 4.2 and 4.7 h.

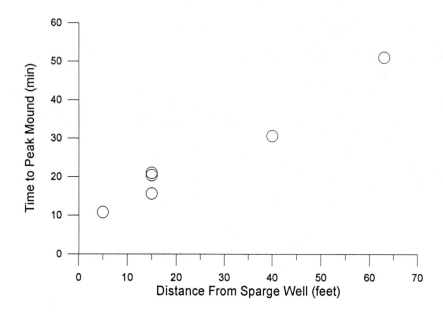

FIGURE 6. Plot of elapsed time to peak mounding versus distance from sparge well at Site 1. Note later arrival of mound peak at more distant locations.

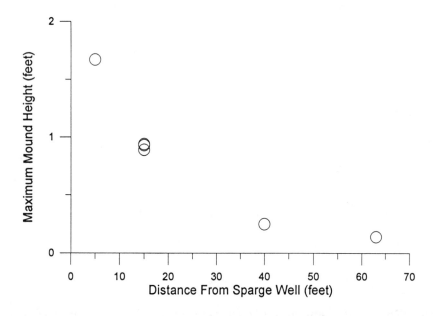

FIGURE 7. Plot of maximum observed mounding versus distance from the sparge well at Site 1. Note decline in magnitude of mounding with increased distance. The steady-state region of airflow in the saturated zone is 8 ft (2.4 m) in radius at this site.

(42.8 kPa) and 20 scfm (0.57 m³/minute). Groundwater mounding was logged digitally in four observation wells at distances of 6, 22, 33, and 108 ft (1.8, 6.7, 10, and 33 m) from the sparge well.

Groundwater mounding showed the typical transient increase to a peak followed by a gradual decrease in all four wells (Figure 8). Water levels underwent about 85% recovery back towards their pre-sparging levels after 5.3 h of continuous sparging. Recovery was somewhat slower than observed at Site 1. The maximum amount of mounding, 1.3 ft (0.4 m), was observed in well U-6, the closest well to the sparge well. However, unlike Site 1, where the amount of mounding decreased with increased distance from the sparge well, greater mounding was observed at well S-4, 33 ft (10 m) from the sparge well, than at well MW-2, 22 ft (6.7 m) from the sparge well. This response reflects the type of non uniform airflow behavior that might be expected under the highly heterogeneous conditions present at Site 2. When the system was shutoff after 5.3 h, water levels fell sharply in each well and then gradually rose again towards pre-sparging levels. This shutoff response reflects the flow of groundwater back into the region of airflow in the saturated zone.

Site 3

This field test was conducted at another site characterized by heterogeneous interstratification of gravel, sand, and silt. Air was injected approximately 9 ft below the water table at a steady-state pressure of 5.5 psig (37.9 kPa) and 5 scfm

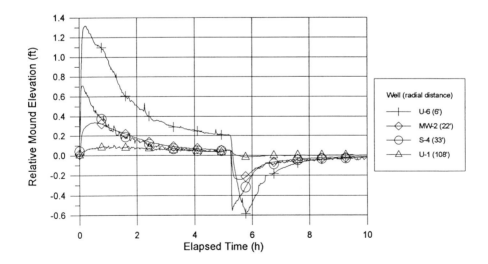

FIGURE 8. Plot of mounding versus elapsed sparge time at Site 2. Note the magnitude of mounding is greater 33 ft (10 m) from the sparge well than it is at 22 ft (6.7 m) from the sparge well. This anomaly suggests heterogeneity in the saturated zone.

(0.14 m³/minute). Groundwater mounding was measured in 12 observation wells at distances of 11 (3.3 m) to 98 ft (30 m) from the sparge well.

As illustrated by the simulations and the test at Site 1, the magnitude of mounding decreases regularly with increased distance from the sparge well when subsurface conditions are relatively homogeneous (Figure 7). However, at Site 3 no simple relationship exists between the maximum extent of mounding and distance (Figure 9). Substantial water level changes occurred in monitoring wells a considerable distance from the sparge well. It is likely that water level changes in some of the distant wells reflect a piezometric response only, rather than a physical rise in the water table at those locations. The highly irregular relationship between extent of mounding and distance from the sparge well indicates extreme lateral diversion of injected air, which is consistent with other site data on pressure increases in saturated zone piezometers, bubbling occurrences in wells, and increases in dissolved oxygen.

DISCUSSION

The simulation and field results described in this paper provide additional insight into the behavior of groundwater mounding caused by air sparging. Local

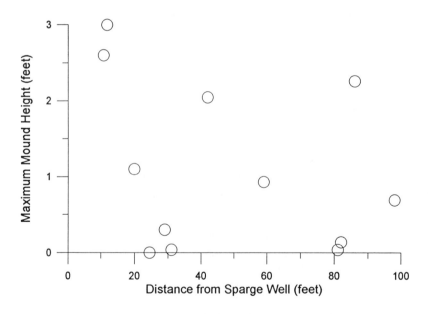

FIGURE 9. Plot of maximum observed mounding versus distance from the sparge well at Site 3. The highly irregular relationship indicates extreme lateral diversion of injected air, reflective of the heterogeneous site conditions. In this situation the piezometric mounding observed in wells will likely overestimate the actual displacement of the water table.

maxima in the amount of mounding will occur in areas that are likely associated with air emergence to the vadose zone. These maxima will be centered on the sparge well under homogeneous conditions. Mounding is a transient response to sparging, and mounding dissipates by radial, wavelike spreading and attenuation.

The transience of groundwater mounding at most sites has important implications for the risk of lateral movement of the contaminant plume. Because the water table returns close to its presparging position during continuous air injection, the driving force for lateral movement of groundwater caused by air injection becomes very small. Lateral groundwater movement in response to the natural groundwater gradient will occur and will be modified by the region of lower effective permeability to water within the region of airflow. This effect can potentially cause a persistent rise in groundwater elevation on the upgradient side of the sparge well(s), leading to lateral diversion of groundwater flow. Where cross-gradient arrays of sparge wells are used, this phenomenon may be more pronounced.

An important aspect of groundwater mounding is that it is not a direct indicator of the physical presence of air in the saturated zone. Water table mounding at a given place and time may or may not be associated with mobile air in the saturated zone at the same location. Some mounding will occur beyond the region of airflow in the saturated zone. Additionally, a transient pressure increase without water table mounding commonly occurs beyond the limits of air flow, especially where air flow is partially confined. Because of its transient nature and the fact that the water table is displaced ahead of injected air, water table mounding can be a misleading and overly optimistic indicator of the distribution of airflow within the saturated zone. Where the maximum extent of mounding does not decrease regularly with increased distance from the sparge well, lateral diversion of airflow due to subsurface heterogeneity is very likely, especially if there is little mounding in the immediate vicinity of the sparge well.

REFERENCES

Boersma, P., F. S. Petersen, P. Newman, and R. Huddleston. 1993. "Use of ground water sparging to effect hydrocarbon biodegradation." National Ground Water Association, Dublin, Ohio, *Proceedings Petroleum Hydrocarbon and Organic Chemicals in Ground Water: Prevention, Detection, and Restoration*, pp. 557-559.10.

Brown, A. B., R. E. Payne, and P. F. Perlwitz. 1993. "Air sparge pilot testing at a site contaminated with gasoline." *National Ground Water Association, Dublin, Ohio, Proceedings Petroleum Hydrocarbon and Organic Chemicals in Ground Water: Prevention, Detection, and Restoration*, pp. 429-444.

Brown, R. A. and F. Jasiulewicz. 1992. "Air sparging: a new model for remediation." *Pollution Engineering*, July 1, 52-55.

Lundegard, P. D. and G. Andersen. 1993. "Numerical simulation of air sparging performance." *National Ground Water Association, Dublin, Ohio, Proceedings Petroleum Hydrocarbon and Organic Chemicals in Ground Water: Prevention, Detection, and Restoration*, pp. 461-476.

Lundegard, P. D. and D. LaBrecque. In press. "Air sparging in a sandy aquifer (Florence, Oregon): Actual and apparent radius of influence." *Journal of Contaminant Hydrology*, 19(1).

Marley, M. C., D. J. Hazebrouck, and M. T. Walsh. 1992. "The application of in situ air sparging as an innovative soils and ground water remediation technology." *Ground Water Monitoring Review, Spring*:137-145.

Schima, S., D. J. LaBrecque, and P. D. Lundegard. 1994. "Using resistivity tomography to monitor air sparging." *Proc. of the Symposium on the Applic. of Geophy. to Engin. and Envir. Problems, Envir. and Engin. Geophy. Soc.*, pp. 757-774.

Vinsome, P.D.W. and G. M. Shook. 1993. "Multi-purpose simulation." *Journal of Petroleum Science and Engineering* 9:29-38.

Air Sparging Technology:
A Practice Update

Michael C. Marley, Clifford J. Bruell, and Harley H. Hopkins

ABSTRACT ━━━━━━━━━━━━━━━━━━━━━━━━━━━━━━━━━━━

An evaluation of data describing in situ air sparging (IAS) systems at 59 sites has been assembled into a database by the American Petroleum Institute (API-IAS Database). The IAS radius of influence (ROI) is defined in the field based on measurements in a number of physical, chemical, or biological monitoring parameters. Measurement of ground-water dissolved oxygen levels was the technique used most often to evaluate the ROI. Other parameters such as pressure changes in the vadose and saturated zones, groundwater mounding, air bubbling in wells, and tracer gases were used to aid in the evaluation of IAS ROI. A review of 37 pilot studies revealed that IAS ROI is generally between 3 m and 8 m (10 to 26 ft). Analysis of design and operation data at 40 IAS sites revealed that a typical IAS well is 5.08 cm (2 in.) in diameter, with a 0.61 m (2 ft) screen, positioned 1.52 to 3.05 m (5 to 10 ft) beneath the water table. The wells typically were operated at an over-pressure of less than 34.45 kPa (5 psi) with a flowrate of less than 8.5 m^3/h (5 cfm).

INTRODUCTION

In situ air sparging is a remediation technology primarily applied to the removal of volatile organic contaminants (VOCs) or biodegradable organic compounds from groundwater aquifers (Gudemann & Hiller 1988; Ardito & Billings 1990; Loden & Fan 1991; Marley 1991; Marley et al. 1992). Conceptually, IAS is simple: clean air is injected into the aquifer beneath the water table to induce mass transfer of contaminants to the vapor phase and mass transfer of oxygen to the aqueous phase. IAS usually is used in conjunction with soil vapor extraction (SVE) to control the migration of sparged contaminants in the vadose zone (Brown & Jasiulewicz 1992; Marley et al. 1992).

An evaluation of data provided by API members and consultants detailing IAS systems at 59 sites has been assembled into the API-IAS Database (Marley & Bruell 1995). This document was developed to provide guidance to API site managers concerning IAS system design, operation, and evaluation. A total of

53 sites with pilot-scale data and 19 sites with full-scale data were input to the database. Only 12 sites had long-term water quality data available. However, significant reductions of dissolved volatile organic compounds (VOCs) resulting from IAS were observed at these sites. While a few sites achieved closure, IAS was still in progress at the remaining sites. Long-term water quality data following IAS system shut-down was very limited.

API-IAS DATABASE FINDINGS

Radius of Influence

A field pilot-scale evaluation is usually conducted to evaluate the feasibility of applying IAS technology. Pilot tests of IAS technology reported in the API-IAS Database were usually less than 1 day in duration. In that time period, significant improvements in groundwater quality were not observed. The predominant outcome of pilot-scale evaluations was the estimation of an IAS well radius of influence (ROI).

ROI can be defined as the distance from an IAS sparging well where airflow can be detected or where the effects of air contact, groundwater mixing, or groundwater oxygenation are detectable. This distance is usually estimated by one or more measurements. It should be noted that although the term "radius of influence" is used, the current understanding of the movement of air in the saturated zone suggests that radially symmetric airflow is unlikely in IAS system operation.

Parameters Used to Estimate Radius of Influence. Generally, numerous variables are monitored in the course of a pilot test. From an analysis of the engineering reports used to assemble the API-IAS Database, only selected monitoring parameters were cited by report authors as the definitive factors that were used to determine the IAS ROI. Figure 1, developed from the database, indicates the frequency of use of various monitoring parameters for determining the IAS radius of influence. It should be noted that multiple factors were often cited as determining the ROI at a given site. Descriptions of several of the widely used monitoring parameters are presented below.

The use of helium or sulfur hexafluoride (SF_6) as a tracer gas appears to be an effective method to determine IAS ROI. The tracer test consists of injecting helium or SF_6 in air into the pressurized line going to the sparging well. The tracer gas content is then measured at vadose zone monitoring points surrounding the IAS well. It should be noted that this method has not been widely used.

Electrical resistivity tomography (ERT) is an experimental technique that uses cross-borehole resistivity surveys to yield a multidimensional image of air distribution on a macroscale (Schima et al. 1994; Lundegard 1994).

Measurements of positive pressure distributions in the saturated or the unsaturated zone have been used as indicators of ROI. Another technique to determine ROI involves comparing vadose zone pressures in a combination IAS/SVE

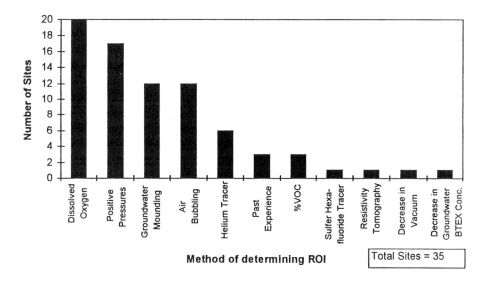

FIGURE 1. Method used to determine in situ air sparging radius of influence (ROI) vs. number of sites.

system while cycling the IAS system on and off. IAS influence is revealed by comparing of plots of measured vadose zone pressures vs. distance from the sparging well before and after IAS system activation. However, due to the nature of pressure propagation from an air source, the use of saturated or unsaturated zone pressures may result in overestimating the ROI.

Air bubbling observed in monitoring wells in a pilot test is a key indicator of air movement in the saturated zone. Bubbling is a direct sign of the presence of air channels. However, in some cases the presence of an open monitoring well may serve as a preferential pathway for air movement. Movement of air in preferential channeling pathways may result in overestimation of the ROI.

Groundwater mounding (also known as upwelling) often is used to determine IAS-ROI because it is easily measured. Mounding is indicative of bulk water displacement; however, the response is transient, and care must be taken in data interpretation.

Groundwater dissolved oxygen (DO) content may be depleted in the vicinity of hydrocarbon spills due to the proliferation of aerobic hydrocarbon using bacteria. Following several hours or more of sparging, groundwater DO levels have been observed to increase significantly at one or a number of monitoring points. Regardless of the transport mechanism, an increase in groundwater DO is the most popular method for estimating the ROI of an IAS system.

Experimentally Determined ROI Results. A distribution of ROI values obtained from both pilot-scale and full-scale system operations, reported from 37 sites, was developed from the API-IAS Database. The results are presented in Figure 2. At a limited number of sites, ROI values greater than 12 m (40 ft)

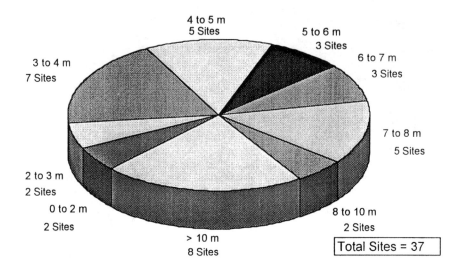

FIGURE 2. Reported in situ air sparging radius of influence (meters) vs. number of sites.

were reported; however, tne testing procedures and analyses of data collected at these sites were considered to be of questionable reliability. The IAS-ROI has been determined at the majority of sites reported to be between 3 and 8 m (10 and 26 ft).

Influence of IAS Configuration and Site Characteristics on ROI

A number of parameters reported in the database, including the depth of the IAS well screen below grade, depth of the IAS well screen below the water table, soil hydraulic conductivity, IAS flowrate, IAS well pressure, and IAS well overpressure, were graphically analyzed to determine their relationship with the measured ROI. Overpressure is defined as the pressure in excess of that required to overcome the hydrostatic head. A graphical analysis of the data revealed no apparent distinguishable relationships between ROI and the afore-mentioned parameters. At several sites, when IAS system pressures and flows were doubled, only slight increases in ROI resulted. Observations at a flooded site revealed that increased system pressures and flows did not significantly increase the ROI; however, a denser distribution of air-filled channels occurred within previously established ROI.

Influence of Soil Type on IAS System Operation

IAS technology is generally being applied within sandy soils. The application of IAS technology was deemed infeasible at seven sites where soils contained high levels of silts or clays. Figure 3 shows the relationship between overpressure

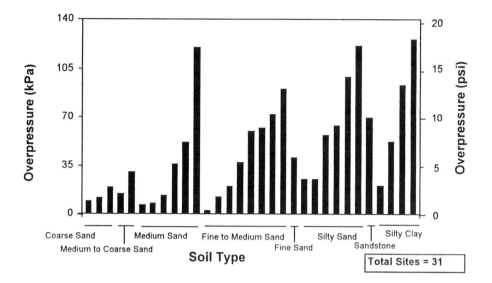

FIGURE 3. Soil type vs. overpressure.

applied and soil type. Silty or clay soils generally require higher overpressures to achieve flow. In the field, operating overpressure must be selected with great care. Excessive overpressures may result in destruction of the soil formation and may promote soil fracturing. The unusually low overpressure observed in tight soils at some sites may be a result of soil fracturing and short-circuiting. A graphical analysis of overpressure vs. air injection flowrate data revealed no correlations.

Design of Air Sparging Systems

Typical IAS design parameters have been published previously (Johnson et al. 1993; Loden & Fan 1992). Typical design and operating parameters from the API-IAS Database are presented in Table 1. Data from pilot-scale and full-scale sites were included within the analysis.

DISCUSSION

Numerous parameters have been measured in the field to determine the IAS ROI. Each method has potential shortcomings. The most reliable methodologies to estimate ROI appear to be the appropriate use of tracer gases or the measurement of DO. The influence of system configuration or soil type on ROI is not well defined. Because of soil heterogeneities, ROI appears to be site specific. Further refinement of field pilot-scale measurements is recommended to evaluate IAS ROI.

TABLE 1. Typical design and operating parameters for in situ air sparging wells.

Parameter and Range	Most Often Used Value (No. of Sites)	Second-Most Often Used Value (No. of Sites)	Third-Most Often Used Value (No. of Sites)	Total Number of Sites
Screen length 0.15 - 3.05 m (0.5 - 10 ft)	0.61 m (2 ft) 16 sites	0.91 m (3 ft) 8 sites	1.52 m (5 ft) 7 sites	40
Well diameter 2.54 - 10.16 cm (1 - 4 in.)	5.08 cm (2 in.) 17 sites	10.16 cm (4 in.) 7 sites	2.54 cm (1 in.) 5 sites	37
Overpressure 2.41 - 125.67 kPa (0.35 - 18.2 psi)	2.41 - 34.45 kPa (0.35 - 5 psi) 14 sites	34.45 - 68.90 kPa (5 - 10 psi) 9 sites	68.90 - 103.35 kPa (10 - 15 psi) 5 sites	31
Well screen depth below water table 0.61 - 8.08 m (2 - 26.5 ft)	1.52 - 3.05 m (5 - 10 ft) 10 sites	3.05 - 4.57 m (10 - 15 ft) 8 sites	0.61 - 1.52 m (2 - 5 ft) 6 sites	31
In situ sparging flowrate 2.21 - 67.96 m^3/hr (1.3 - 40 cfm)	2.21 - 8.50 m^3/hr (1.3 - 5 cfm) 16 sites	8.50 - 16.99 m^3/hr (5-10 cfm) 9 sites	25.48 - 33.98 m^3/hr (15 - 20 cfm) 5 sites	39
In situ sparging pressure 24.11 -172.25 kPa (3.5 - 25 psi)	34.45 - 68.90 kPa (5 - 10 psi) 17 sites	68.90 - 103.35 kPa (10 - 15 psi) 8 sites	137.80 - 172.25 kPa (20 - 25 psi) 6 sites	40
(SVE ROI)/(IAS ROI) ratio 0.16 - 7.42	1 - 2 12 sites	0.16 - 1 6 sites	3 - 4 3 sites	26

ACKNOWLEDGMENTS

This work was funded in part by the API, Washington, DC. The authors wish to acknowledge the efforts of Mr. Krishna S. Mummareddi of the University of Massachusetts at Lowell.

REFERENCES

Ardito, C. P., and J. J. Billings. 1990. "Alternative remediation strategies: The subsurface volatilization and ventilation system." In *Proceedings of the Conference on Petroleum Hydrocarbons and Organic Chemicals in Ground Water: Prevention, Detection, and Restoration.* Houston, TX, NWWA/API. pp. 281-296.

Brown, R. A., and F. Jasiulewicz. 1992. "The use of aeration in environmental clean-ups." Presented at Haztech International, Pittsburgh Waste Conference, Pittsburgh, PA. May 14-16.

Gudemann, H., and D. Hiller. 1988. "In situ remediation of VOC contaminated soil and ground water by vapor extraction and ground water aeration." In *Proceedings of Petroleum Hydrocarbons and Organic Chemicals in Ground Water: Prevention, Detection and Restoration.* Houston, TX. NWWA/API, pp. 147-164.

Johnson, R. L., P. C. Johnson, D. B. McWhorter, R. E. Hinchee, and I. Goodman. 1993. "An overview of in situ air sparging." *Ground Water Monitoring and Remediation* 13(4): 127-135.

Loden, M. E., and C.-Y. Fan. 1992. "Air sparging technology evaluation." In *Proceedings of the National Conference on the Control of Hazardous Materials."* San Francisco, CA, Hazardous Material Control Research Institute. pp. 328-334.

Lundegard, P. D. 1994. "Actual versus apparent radius of influence-air sparging in a sandy aquifer." In *Proceedings of Petroleum Hydrocarbons and Organic Chemicals in Ground Water: Prevention, Detection and Restoration.* Houston, TX. NGWA/API, pp. 191-206.

Marley, M. C. 1991. "Air sparging in conjunction with soil vapor extraction for source removal at VOC spill sites." Presented at the Fifth National Outdoor Action Conference, NWWA, Las Vegas, NV.

Marley, M. C., and C. J. Bruell. 1995. *In Situ Air Sparging: Evaluation of Petroleum Industry Sites and Considerations for Applicability, Design and Operation.* API Publication 4609, American Petroleum Institute, Washington, DC. (In Press).

Marley, M. C., D. J. Hazebrouck, and M. T. Walsh. 1992. "The application of in situ air sparging as an innovative soils and ground water remediation technology." *Ground Water Monitoring Review, Spring:* 137-145.

Schima, S., D. J. LaBrecque, and P. Lundegard. 1994. "Using Resistivity Tomography to Monitor Air Sparging." In *Proceedings of the Symposium on Applications of Geophysics to Engineering and Environmental Problems.* Environmental Engineering and Geophysics Society, Englewood, CO. pp. 757-774.

Sparging Effectiveness for Groundwater Restoration

Paul M. Boersma, Keith R. Piontek, and Pixie A.B. Newman

ABSTRACT

Sparging is becoming a widely applied groundwater remediation technology, even though there are few published case studies with post-sparging groundwater monitoring data to document cleanup. The best way to monitor the effectiveness of sparging systems and predict achievable postsparging contaminant concentrations is still uncertain. Most monitoring data from sparging systems are indirect measurements of system performance [dissolved oxygen, groundwater levels, soil vapor pressures, soil vapor oxygen/volatile organic compound (VOC) concentrations] rather than direct analysis of dissolved-phase contaminants. Furthermore, few distinctions have been made regarding achievable cleanup levels and required treatment durations in (1) dissolved-phase plumes and (2) source areas with residual nonaqueous-phase liquid (NAPL). This paper discusses changes in dissolved-phase chlorinated volatile organic compound (CVOC) concentrations at two sites where sparging was undertaken. Both sites are favorable for sparging, having relatively uniform, clean, fine- to medium-grained sandy soil. One site had a known presence of NAPL, while the other was a dissolved-phase plume without NAPL. The case studies indicate (1) significant variations in treatment effectiveness over small distances, (2) the importance of understanding the effects of soil anisotropy in monitoring sparging systems, and (3) differences in postsparging monitoring results between areas of dissolved-phase plumes and residual NAPL.

BACKGROUND

Airflow Through Saturated Media

Airflow through saturated media has been described by Ji et al. (1993), Ahlfeld et al. (1994), and others. For pore diameters typical of sands, silts, and clays, the air flows in discrete channels, with the density and distribution of the air channels determined by the soil pore-size distribution. Air flows through channels of least air entry pressure (channels with the largest diameter connected pore spaces). A consequence of this is that when sparging systems are cycled on and off, the air channel distributions likely reestablish themselves in the same pattern.

The potential for low-permeable strata to deflect airflow pathways also has been reported in laboratory studies (Ahlfeld et al. 1994) and in the field (Marley et al. 1992). Less often reported in field studies is the effect of natural anisotropy in homogeneous soil on sparging effectiveness. A soil exhibits anisotropy if its properties vary with direction (e.g., if the vertical hydraulic conductivity [K_z] is not equivalent to the horizontal conductivity [K_x and/or K_y]). The greater the difference between K_z and K_x or K_y, the greater is the preference for horizontal airflow over vertical flow. Soil heterogeneity can reduce treatment effectiveness and possibly preclude any chance of reasonable treatment. Anisotropy also can cause less, but still significant, changes in the uniformity of groundwater treatment.

Mass Removal in Sparging Systems

Sparging systems remove saturated zone contaminants through a combination of volatilization and biodegradation (if the contaminants are biodegradable). It is our experience on petroleum hydrocarbon sites that, in the short term (weeks/months), volatilization accounts for much more removal of hydrocarbons than does biodegradation (Boersma et al. 1993). Biodegradation only becomes more significant for mass removal with long-term system operations.

Initially, rates of contaminant volatilization may be very high as dissolved-phase contaminants partition into the air channels or the air channels directly contact residual NAPL. However, with time, the rate of contaminant volatilization decreases and likely becomes diffusion-limited as contaminants must diffuse into the air channels from greater distances. For dissolved-phase plumes, the diffusion limitations may be partially overcome by cycling the sparging system on and off. Cycling temporarily changes the groundwater flow and redistributes dissolved-phase contaminants relative to the air channels (Newman et al. 1994). However, cycling the sparging system has some, but generally much less effect, on the residual NAPL distribution. Because the air channel and residual NAPL distribution remain the same, dissolution of the NAPL between the air channels is still diffusion-limited. This raises questions about the ability of sparging systems to effectively treat residual NAPL through volatilization. The exception is the area a few to several feet around a sparging well where, in sandy soil, sparging systems may achieve 20 to 40% air saturation of previously water saturated soil (Acomb et al. 1995). In such areas, there may be sufficient air contact with the NAPL to effectively volatilize it.

With long-term sparging operations, biological processes may contribute significantly to further removal of residual, degradable NAPL. However, contaminant biodegradation resulting from air sparging is generally limited by the rate of oxygen transfer from the gaseous to the aqueous phase, and diffusion within the aqueous phase. Thus, sparging-induced contaminant biodegradation is subject to the same basic limitations as sparging-induced contaminant volatilization.

CASE STUDIES

This section presents observations at two sparging case studies, which form the basis for the discussion. While similar results have been observed at other sparging sites, these two were selected as representative. In case study No. 1, a release of perchloroethylene (PCE) through floor drains underneath the building resulted in vadose zone contamination and development of a dissolved-phase plume. During the site investigation, the soil was logged by a geologist on 2-ft (0.6-m) intervals and classified as a clean, fine- to medium-grained sand with depth to water at about 35 ft (10.6 m) below ground surface (bgs). A sieve analysis on selected samples confirmed field description. Based on pump tests, the soil hydraulic conductivity is 1×10^{-2} cm/s. During the site investigation, there was no indication of field-scale heterogeneity. Soil vapor extraction (SVE) was implemented for several months to remove PCE from the vadose zone soil underneath the building and to prevent further contaminant loading to the groundwater. A 30-day groundwater sparging pilot test was then conducted. One groundwater sparging well was installed through the building floor and screened from 25 to 27 ft (7.6 to 8.2 m) below the water table. Two monitoring piezometer nests were installed at horizontal distances of 10 and 20 ft (3 to 6 m) from the sparging well. Within each nest, one piezometer was screened from 8 to 10 ft (2.4 to 3 m) below the water table, and the other from 18 to 20 ft (5.5 to 6 m) below the water table. For most of the sparging pilot test, the system was operated for 4 hours per day at a 10-scfm (0.28-m^3/min) flowrate. Groundwater samples collected from each piezometer about every 5 days were analyzed for PCE. The piezometers were also monitored for pressure buildup or bubbling, either of which might have suggested that injected air was short-circuiting through the piezometers. Pressure buildup or bubbling was not detected. Figure 1 shows the system layout. The changes in dissolved-phase PCE concentrations during and after the pilot test are shown in Figure 2.

In case study No. 2, a large release of petroleum solvents resulted in both vadose zone and groundwater contamination. Groundwater is about 15 ft (4.6 m) bgs. After 150 gal (555 L) of floating NAPL were recovered, contamination in the source area still included NAPL at residual saturation 1 m above and below the groundwater table. An analysis of the NAPL showed it occupied about 20% of the saturated zone pore space in the affected area and consisted of mostly non-priority pollutants such as hexane and mineral spirits. PCE, trichloroethylene (TCE), and other chlorinated solvents made up 1 to 2% of the NAPL. The NAPL was a continual source of VOC contamination in the groundwater. The soil at the site was logged at numerous borings on 2-ft (0.6-m) intervals by a geologist and classified as a uniform, clean, fine- to medium-grained sand. The field analysis was confirmed by sieve analysis of selected samples. Based on slug test results, a 1×10^{-2} cm/s hydraulic conductivity was estimated.

A groundwater extraction and SVE system were installed at the site. After 700 operating days, average VOC concentrations in the soil were less than 14 µg/kg (based on more than 100 soil samples collected vertically and horizontally

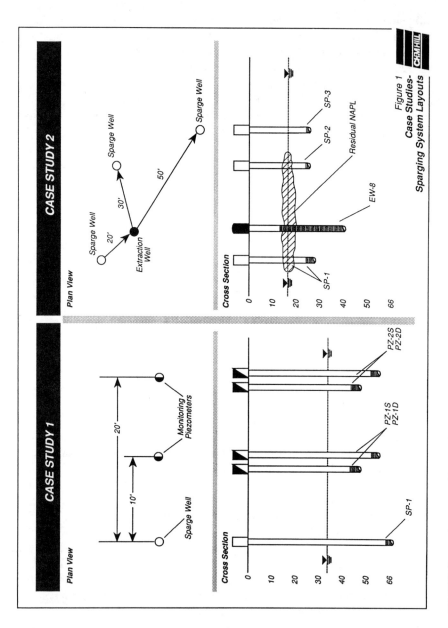

FIGURE 1. Case studies—sparging system layouts.

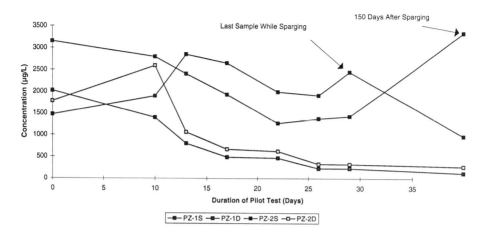

FIGURE 2. Change in dissolved-phase PCE during/after sparging.

throughout the target zone). After 4 years of operation, the groundwater extraction system had reached an asymptote of about 1,500 µg/L of total dissolved-phase VOCs in the groundwater discharge. Continual release of VOCs from the residual NAPL to the groundwater prevented further reduction in dissolved-phase concentrations. A sparging system was then employed to directly contact the residual NAPL with a gas to better volatilize the VOCs. Three sparging wells were installed in the source area around an operating groundwater extraction well. The sparging system was continuously operated for 5 months, during which time groundwater samples from the extraction well were analyzed monthly. Samples from the well were also analyzed bimonthly for several months before and after the sparging pilot test. The sparging system layout is shown in Figure 1, and the changes in the dissolved-phase VOC concentrations in water from the extraction well are shown in Figure 3.

DISCUSSION

Monitoring Well Network Design and Reliability

Sparging-induced changes in dissolved-phase contaminants can be monitored with monitoring wells screened over 10 to 20 ft (3 to 6 m) of the aquifer, discrete piezometers screened over 1 to 2 ft (0.3 to 0.6 m) of the aquifer, and/or multilevel monitoring points installed with a geoprobe and each screened over a few inches. The data from case study No. 1 (presented in Figure 2) suggest that the interpretation of sparging effectiveness may vary significantly, depending on the type of monitoring system employed. The data from this site suggest removal efficiencies of 85% in the lower 15 to 25 ft (4.6 to 7.6 m) of the sparging zone and 15% in the upper 15 ft (4.6 m) of the sparging zone after 30 days of sparging.

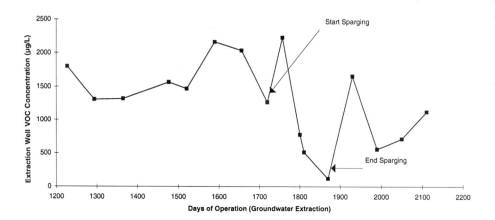

FIGURE 3. Change in dissolved-phase VOCs during/after sparging.

We believe that the building previously discussed (which prevents infiltration through the soil) and the degree of treatment achieved with the SVE system immediately above the sparging system prevented continued contamination of the shallow groundwater. The lower treatment efficiency in the shallow groundwater is not attributed to new contamination in the shallow zone, but appears to be due to anisotropy, and possibly pore-scale heterogeneity, which altered airflow pathways through this zone. Field-scale soil heterogeneity was not detected during continuous logging of the soil. Analysis based solely on monitoring wells screened over the upper 15 ft (4.6 m) of the aquifer would have resulted in an incomplete and inaccurate assessment of the sparging effectiveness at the site. Likewise, still more vertically and horizontally spaced monitoring points might have resulted in a still more complex and varied picture of treatment effectiveness. In summary, vertical variations in treatment effectiveness were observed even though no changes in soil type or grain size distribution were observed.

The term "radius of influence" is often applied to groundwater sparging systems. However, even in apparently uniform sands, directional differences in soil permeability will result in spatially varied levels of treatment effectiveness. In case study No. 1, better treatment was effected in the lower target area than the upper target area. Given the variation in treatment effectiveness within a region generally influenced by sparging, the term "radius of influence" may be misleading. The term "zone of sparging influence," defined as "an irregularly shaped zone within which varying degrees of treatment will result," represents a better conceptual understanding of sparging systems.

Some data from monitoring wells and piezometers are suspect because of the potential for the wells or piezometers to become preferred-flow pathways for the sparged air (Johnson et al. 1993). The authors have observed this at some sites when injected air bubbles up through a monitoring point. In such cases, one would expect fairly rapid decline of dissolved-phase VOC concentrations since the VOCs in the wells would be quickly stripped. In such cases, a pressure of 1 to several centimeters of water can also be measured in the wells. The gradual decline of dissolved-phase VOC concentrations presented in Figure 2, and the lack of detectable pressure in the wellhead, suggest that airflow is not short-circuiting through the piezometers at this site. Thus, these wells probably serve as good indicators of what is happening in the aquifer in their immediate vicinity.

Sparging in Residual NAPL Versus Dissolved-Phase Plumes

A main difference between case study No. 1 and case study No. 2 is that, at the former site, sparging was implemented in a dissolved-phase plume whereas at the later, sparging was implemented in an area of nonmobile, residual NAPL. Theoretical considerations and the postsparging monitoring results at the two sites suggest that there may be significant differences in treatment potential and required duration for residual NAPL sites compared to those for dissolved-phase plume sites.

Within the dissolved-phase plume at site No. 1, a 50% overall reduction of dissolved-phase PCE was observed after 30 days of sparging. In the area of residual NAPL at site No. 2, there was a 50% reduction after 60 days of sparging and a 90% reduction in dissolved-phase VOCs after 150 days (as measured in samples collected from an operating groundwater extraction well within the sparging zone). In the site No. 1 dissolved-phase plume, postsparging monitoring data indicated that dissolved-phase PCE concentrations were similar to those at the end of the sparging period (Figure 2). In the area of residual NAPL at site No. 2, post-sparging monitoring data indicated that dissolved-phase VOC concentrations increased to nearly the same level as before the test (Figure 3). After 5 months of sparging, the NAPL still provided further VOC loadings to the dissolved-phase plume.

The data suggest that sparging at residual NAPL sites may exhibit limitations similar to those observed with groundwater extraction at residual NAPL sites (e.g., preferential fluid flow channels and contaminants needing to diffuse to those preferential flow channels). When air directly contacts a NAPL, the partitioning of VOCs into the air is relatively fast (as in the soil immediately adjacent to a sparging well). The rate-limiting step is likely VOC diffusion within the NAPL. However, with sparging, some or much of the NAPL more than 5 to 7 feet (1.5 to 2.1 m) from the sparge well may not directly contact the air. Thus, the VOCs still must diffuse into and through the water to an air channel. While a sparging system may be effective at treating the NAPL in the area where much of the water-filled porosity is converted to air-filled porosity, in areas further from the sparge well where air channel density is lower, it will take much longer to treat residual NAPL.

The above discussion focuses primarily on contaminant volatilization. With time, it may be possible to biodegrade the residual NAPL as a result of oxygen transfer from the vapor phase into the dissolved-phase. However, some of the same diffusion limitations for VOC mass transfer apply for oxygen mass transfer. There have been no conclusive estimates of oxygen transfer efficiency in sparging systems, but estimates have ranged from 0.05 to 0.5% (Boersma et al. 1993). In a conceptual cylinder 30 ft (9 m) in diameter, 15 ft (4.6 m) in length, with an average total petroleum hydrocarbon contamination of 2,000 mg/kg, and a sparging flowrate of 20 scfm (0.6 m³/min), it would take 5 to 50 years to provide the stoichiometric requirements of oxygen for hydrocarbon biodegradation.

RECOMMENDATIONS

Based on the discussion presented, the following recommendations are made for implementing sparging systems. First, given typical anisotropy of even apparently uniform soil, vertically discrete groundwater monitoring points should be used with data from traditional monitoring wells to assess the performance of groundwater sparging systems. Anisotropy and pore-scale heterogeneities will cause vertical variation in treatment effectiveness. Second, spatial variations in treatment effectiveness around a groundwater sparging well suggest that the term "radius of influence" is misleading. A term such as "zone of sparging influence" is more accurate, and its use is recommended. Third, at most NAPL sites, a sparging system will probably have to operate for several years to volatilize and/or biodegrade the NAPL that is beyond the zone where 20 to 40% air saturation is achieved.

REFERENCES

Acomb, L. D. McKay, P. Currier, S. Berglund, T. Sherhart, and C. Benediktson. 1995. "Neutron Probe Measurements of Air Saturation Near an Air Sparging Well." In R. E. Hinchee, R. M. Miller, and P.C. Johnson (Eds.), *In Situ Aeration: Air Sparging, Bioventing, and Related Remediation Processes.* Battelle Press, Columbus, OH. pp. 47-61.

Ahlfeld, D., A. Dahmani, and W. Ji. 1994. "A Conceptual Model of Field Behavior of Air Sparging and its Implications for Application." *Groundwater Monitoring Review and Remediation*, Fall.

Boersma, P., F. S. Petersen, P. Newman, and R. Huddleston. 1993. "Use of Groundwater Sparging to Effect Hydrocarbon Biodegradation," in *Proceedings of the 1993 Petroleum Hydrocarbons and Organic Chemicals in Groundwater: Prevention, Detection, and Restoration Conference* (Houston, TX).

Ji, W., A. Dahmani, D. Ahlfeld, J. Lin, and E. Hill. 1993. "Laboratory Study of Air Sparging: Air Flow Visualization." *Groundwater Monitoring Review and Remediation*, Fall 1993.

Johnson, R., P. Johnson, D. McWhorter, R. Hinchee, and I. Goodman. 1993. "An Overview of In Situ Air Sparging." *Groundwater Monitoring Review and Remediation*, Fall 1993.

Marley, M., D. Hazebrouck, and M. Walsh. 1992. "The Application of In Situ Air Sparging as an Innovative Soils and Groundwater Remediation Technology." *Groundwater Monitoring and Review*, Spring 1992.

Newman, P., R. Huddleston, P. Boersma, and F. S. Petersen. 1994. "The Effect of Sparging on Groundwater Hydraulics and Water Quality," *Air and Waste Management Association Annual Convention* (Cincinnati, OH).

Neutron Probe Measurements of Air Saturation Near an Air Sparging Well

Lawrence J. Acomb, Daniel McKay, Paul Currier,
Scott T. Berglund, Thomas V. Sherhart,
and Catharine V. Benediktsson

ABSTRACT

A neutron probe was used to measure changes in percent air saturation during air sparging in a uniform, aeolian sand. Air was injected about 15 ft (4.6 m) below the water table at air flowrates of 4 to 16 ft^3/min (cfm) (0.11 to 0.45 m^3/min). The neutron probe data show that during air sparging the distribution of injected air changed through time, initially expanding outward from the sparge well screen, then consolidating around the air sparging well, until a steady-state condition was reached. The maximum radius of influence, measured at an air flowrate of 16 cfm, was about 15 ft (4.6 m) during steady-state flow. At all air flowrates the percent air saturation was highest near the air sparging well and decreased radially away from the sparging well. Near the sparging well, the percent air saturation ranged from about 30% to >50% at air injection rates of 4 to 16 cfm (0.11 to 0.45 m^3/min). Where the percent air saturation is similar to that in the vadose zone, volatilization and biodegradation may occur at rates similar to those in the vadose zone. Selected air saturation results are presented, and dissolved oxygen and saturated zone pressure data are summarized.

INTRODUCTION

In situ air sparging is being used to remediate diesel-fuel-contaminated soils in the zone of water table fluctuation at a remote Alaskan Federal Aviation Administration (FAA) air navigation aid site. In situ air sparging was selected because it appeared capable of meeting the remedial objectives within a suitable time frame, had the least impact on the operation of the facility, and had the lowest estimated cost.

The sparging system injected air 15 ft (4.6 m) below the water table at flowrates of 4, 8, 12, and 16 cfm (0.11, 0.23, 0.34, and 0.45 m^3/min). The process was monitored to assess both the radius of influence of the air sparging well and the effectiveness of the remedial processes. The monitoring efforts centered on using a neutron probe to measure changes in saturation below the water table during air sparging. Simultaneous dissolved oxygen and saturated zone pressure data were collected using a data logger. The monitoring methods and results may be applicable to the design, operation, and monitoring of air sparging systems at many sites.

SITE CONDITIONS

The FAA site, known as Strawberry Point, is on Hinchinbrook Island approximately 15 mi (24 km) southwest of Cordova, Alaska. The site soils consist of a uniform, fine, aeolian sand (approximately 94% passing the number 60 sieve and 3% passing the number 200 sieve) with a porosity of about 40% to 44%. The water table fluctuates from about 6 to 14 ft (1.8 to 4.3 m) below grade. Residual saturation concentrations of diesel fuel (5,000 to 30,000 mg/kg) are smeared through the zone of water table fluctuation over a portion of the site that includes the air sparging injection well and monitoring wells. The saturated hydraulic conductivity is estimated to be about 1×10^{-2} to 3×10^{-2} cm/s (Johnson et al. 1988; Baehr & Hult 1991) and the horizontal conductivity is estimated to be 3 to 6 times greater than the vertical conductivity (Baehr & Hult 1991).

MONITORING METHODS

A neutron probe was used to measure the changes in saturation caused by air sparging. Neutron probes contain a radioactive fast neutron source (typically americium 241-beryllium) and a slow or thermal neutron detector. The cloud of fast neutrons released by the source collide with nuclei of similar mass (principally hydrogen), slowing or thermalizing the neutrons, which are then counted by the thermal neutron detector. The thermal neutron count rate is converted to a water content using calibration curves. The neutron source and detector are housed in a cylindrical probe, which is suspended on a cable in an access pipe while a reading is taken.

In this study, the neutron probe access pipes (labeled NP 1, NP 2, NP 3, and NP 4 on Figure 1) consisted of 2-in. (5.1-cm), schedule 40, black iron pipes capped on the bottom and located at distances of 4, 7, 11, and 15 ft (1.2, 2.1, 3.3, and 4.6 m) from the air sparging injection well. The access pipes were installed with the use of a hollow-stem auger and are surrounded by formation soils washed or collapsed into place. The porosity of the soil surrounding the neutron probe access pipes ranges from about 40% to 50%, which is similar to, or slightly greater than, the porosity measured in brass liner samples. Neutron probe measurements were taken at 2-ft (0.61-m) intervals, from the water table to about 16 ft (4.9 m) below the water table. Individual neutron probe counts lasted 32 s,

Well Legend and Type of Monitoring		% Saturation	Dissolved Oxygen	Pressure
SW 7 Air Sparging Injection Well	⊕			✓
NP 1 through NP 4 Neutron Probe Access Tubes	O	✓		
MW 5, MW 6, and MW 10 Conventional Monitoring Wells	◑		✓	✓
MC 1 through MC 4, and MC 13 Nested Monitoring Wells	●		✓	✓

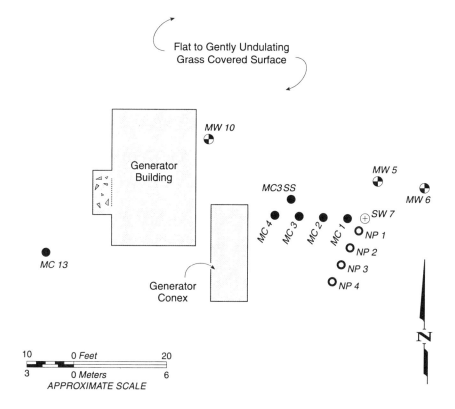

FIGURE 1. Site plan showing air sparging injection well and monitoring wells used in the study.

and a profile of the four access pipes could be completed in about 15 to 30 min. Each neutron probe count measured the moisture in a 3- to 6-in. (7.5- to 15-cm) radius around the probe.

Baseline neutron probe measurements taken below the water table before air sparging were assumed to represent 100% fluid saturated conditions (percent saturation = volume fluid/volume voids × 100%). Measurements taken during and after air sparging were divided by the baseline measurements to calculate the percent fluid saturation during and after air sparging. The fluid saturation values were then converted to air saturation values (volume air/volume voids × 100%). The neutron probe counting error has a normal distribution, resulting in air saturation values with a standard deviation of about 1.5%. The conversion to air saturation values was made to avoid potential confusion between water and fuel saturations. The neutron probe detects both hydrogen in petroleum hydrocarbons and hydrogen in water, so in contaminated soil, the neutron probe "water" saturation value is actually the sum of the water and hydrocarbon values. The diesel-range organic (DRO) concentrations indicate that fuel saturation (volume fuel/volume voids × 100%) in the zone of water table fluctuation may range from about 5% to 22%.

Dissolved oxygen was measured using galvanic probes connected to a data logger. The dissolved oxygen probes were installed in nested monitoring wells with short screen sections, and in standard monitoring wells located at radial distances up to 20 ft (6.1 m) from the air sparging injection well (Figure 1). Each dissolved oxygen monitoring well had a compression fitting seal at the top of the well to minimize the extent to which the monitoring well created a preferential airflow path. A hose was extended through the compression fitting and below the water table so that the monitoring well could be pumped during the tests.

Pressure transducers connected to data loggers were used to monitor changes in saturated zone pressure during air sparging. The pressure transducers were installed in nested monitoring wells and conventional monitoring wells at distances of 4 to 69 ft (1.2 to 21 m) from the air sparging injection well.

AIR SATURATION MONITORING RESULTS

The neutron probe data show that during air sparging the distribution of injected air changed through time. Airflow through myriad channels generated an area of reduced percent water saturation and increased percent air saturation, which initially expanded upward and outward from the sparge well screen to the water table. Within about 1 hour, air paths with lower resistance began to capture air from higher resistance paths and the air channels consolidated around the air sparging well. During this consolidation, the radius of influence decreased and the air saturation near the sparging well increased. After several hours, the air saturation appeared to approach a steady state condition. These changes in the distribution of injected air have been computer modeled and measured in the field (Lundegard & Anderson 1993; Lundegard 1994).

The changes in saturation at the Strawberry Point site are illustrated in Figures 2 and 3. Figure 2 shows a cross section through the sparging well and four neutron probe access pipes at various times during and following air injection at a flowrate of 8 cfm. In each cross section, the percent air saturation data

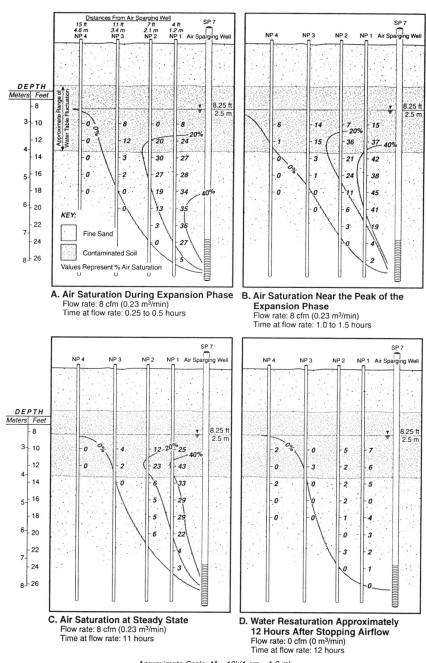

A. **Air Saturation During Expansion Phase**
Flow rate: 8 cfm (0.23 m³/min)
Time at flow rate: 0.25 to 0.5 hours

B. **Air Saturation Near the Peak of the Expansion Phase**
Flow rate: 8 cfm (0.23 m³/min)
Time at flow rate: 1.0 to 1.5 hours

C. **Air Saturation at Steady State**
Flow rate: 8 cfm (0.23 m³/min)
Time at flow rate: 11 hours

D. **Water Resaturation Approximately 12 Hours After Stopping Airflow**
Flow rate: 0 cfm (0 m³/min)
Time at flow rate: 12 hours

Approximate Scale: 1" = 10' (1 cm = 1.2 m)
Air saturation contour locations are approximate only and are based on visual interpretation by the author

FIGURE 2. Cross section through the air sparging well and neutron probe pipes showing changes in air saturation through time.

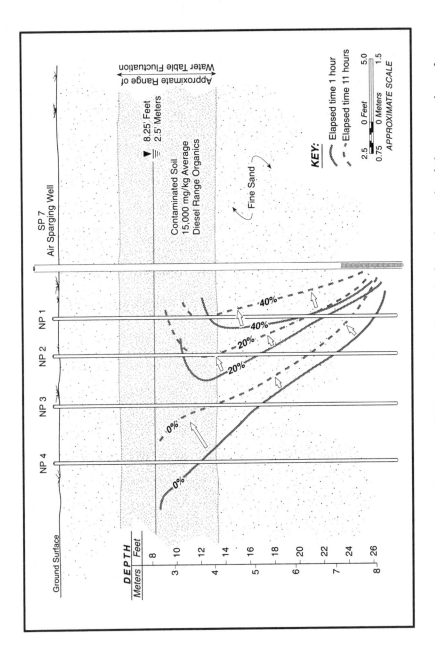

FIGURE 3. Example of the consolidation of air channels from the peak of the expansion phase to the steady-state phase.

is shown to the right of access pipes NP 1 through NP 4. The approximate locations of the 0%, 20%, and 40% air saturation contours, as visually interpreted by the authors, are shown on the figures. Figures 2A, 2B, and 2C show the air saturation during the expansion phase, near the peak of the expansion phase, and as the airflow approaches a steady-state condition, respectively. The transition from the expansion phase to the consolidation phase did not occur at the same time throughout the sparge-affected area. Figure 2D shows the air saturation 12 hours after air injection was stopped. The air saturation at all of the monitored locations was less than 10%; however, the soil had not completely resaturated with water. At each of the monitored air injection rates (4, 8, 12, and 16 cfm [0.11, 0.23, 0.34, and 0.45 m³/min]), similar phases of airflow were observed and the peak of the expansion phase was reached in about 1 h. Very similar air saturation values were obtained after stopping air injection at each of these air injection rates.

Figure 3 illustrates the consolidation of air channels from near the peak of the expansion phase to near a steady-state condition by showing the change in position of the 0%, 20%, and 40% air saturation contours.

Figure 4 shows the distribution of air below the water table approaching steady-state conditions at air injection rates of 4, 8, 12, and 16 cfm (0.11, 0.23, 0.34, and 0.45 m³/min). At these air injection rates, the distribution of air appears similar, with the injected air occupying an irregular cone expanding from the sparge well screen upward toward the water table. At all air injection rates, the air saturation was highest near the sparging well and decreased radially away from the sparging well. In addition, the air saturation at most measured points increased with increasing air injection rates. As the air injection rate was increased, the 40% air saturation contour appears to have expanded outward more than the 20% or 0% air saturation contours. This trend may indicate that much of the additional air at each increased injection rate flowed in channels closer to the sparging well and not through more distant channels, suggesting diminishing returns for higher air injection rates. For example, if 20% air saturation does not limit remedial processes, then increasing the air injection rate and increasing the percent air saturation within the original 20% air saturation radius without significantly expanding the 20% air saturation radius is probably not cost effective. Figure 4 also shows that the 20% and 40% air saturation contours appear to close back toward the air sparging well near the water table. If the diameter of the individual air channels and air velocity in the channels is uniform throughout the channel length, some decrease in air saturation higher in the sparge cone may be expected as air channels fan out and become more widely spaced. Some decrease in air saturation near the water table may also be related to the residual diesel fuel saturation (estimated at 5% to 22%) which is not as readily forced from the soil void spaces as water.

An increase in air saturation in the contaminant smear zone, below the static water table, was used to define the radius of influence. In the uniform sands at the Strawberry Point site, a relatively high degree of radial symmetry probably exists. However, at most sites, soil heterogeneity will likely distort the injected air distribution such that radial symmetry may not be assumed (Ji et al. 1993).

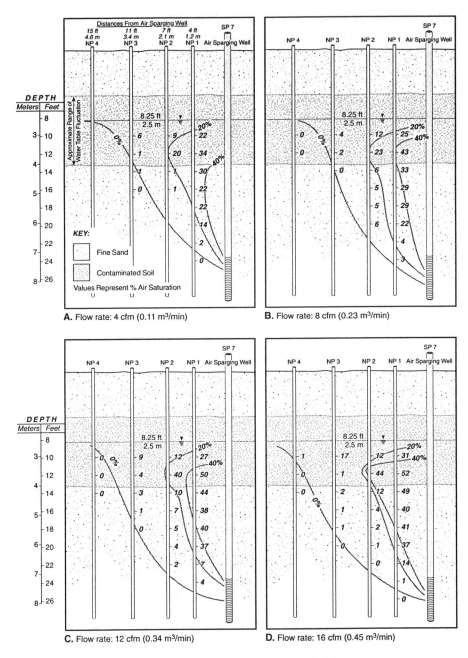

Approximate Scale: 1" = 10' (1 cm = 1.2 m)

Air saturation contour locations are approximate only and are based on visual interpretation by the author

FIGURE 4. Air saturation approaching steady-state flow at selected air injection rates.

Also, Lundegard and Anderson (1993) indicate that the air sparging radius of influence is related to the horizontal-to-vertical permeability ratio. In the uniform sandy soils of the project site, higher air injection rates appeared to produce a larger maximum radius of influence both at the peak of the expansion phase, and during steady-state conditions, as interpreted in Figure 5. The maximum radius of influence, measured at an air injection rate of 16 cfm (0.45 m^3/min), appeared to be more than 15 ft (4.6 m) at the peak of the expansion phase and to decrease to about 15 ft (4.6 m) during steady-state flow. The significance of the maximum radius of influence is thought to be low because the rates of remedial processes associated with 1% air saturation are likely limited by diffusion (Johnson 1994). (In addition, the neutron probe counting error limits confidence in the locations of the 0% air saturation contour.) The most significant aspect of these radius of influence measurements may be that the radius is relatively

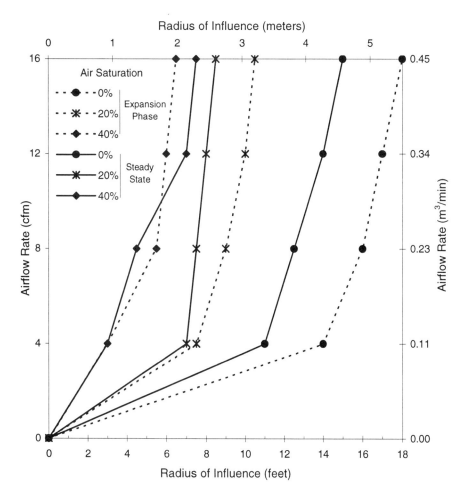

FIGURE 5. Approximate radius of influence versus flowrate.

small (less than 15 ft [4.6 m]) compared to many radius of influence measurements and sparge well spacings referenced in the literature (Johnson et al. 1993; Lundegard 1994). Greater remedial significance may be attached to the 20% or 40% air saturation radii. As shown in Figure 5, these radii also appear to correlate with the air injection rates, but are estimated to reach a maximum of only about 8.5 and 7.5 ft (2.6 and 2.3 m), respectively, at the Strawberry Point site.

AIR SATURATION
MONITORING IMPLICATIONS

The air saturation data collected at Strawberry Point suggest that air sparging remediation of residual petroleum hydrocarbon contaminants may occur at different rates in concentric areas around the sparge well, due to varying air saturation values (Figure 6). Near the sparge well, where the air saturation is similar to that in the vadose zone (for example, greater than about 20%), volatilization and biodegradation of residual petroleum hydrocarbon contaminants may occur at rates similar to those in the vadose zone. Farther from the sparge well, where the air saturation is lower (for example, less than about 20%), volatilization and biodegradation are likely limited by diffusion (Johnson 1994). Where there is no measurable dewatering (0% air saturation), it is likely that little or no remediation occurs. (The only process available is the advection of dissolved oxygen from areas with some air saturation.)

The relatively small radius of influence of the Strawberry Point sparging wells suggests that air sparging systems should be designed with numerous closely spaced injection wells. To offset the cost of installing numerous air sparging wells, future designs may emphasize inexpensive, quickly installed sparge wells such as small-diameter driven well points.

The air saturation data also suggest that air sparging to treat migrating dissolved-phase contaminants in a sparge curtain may have limited effectiveness because the presence of the injected air decreases the hydraulic conductivity within the sparging cone. The reduced conductivity tends to reduce groundwater flow through the treatment zone (the cone with greater than 0% air saturation), and it tends to increase groundwater flow in areas between the sparge wells or around the ends of the treatment zone, where the air saturation is 0%.

The air sparging expansion phase appears to have a greater radius of influence than occurs during steady-state flow, suggesting that the cost effectiveness and efficiency of air sparging systems may be improved by pulsing airflow to the injection well. The benefits of pulsed operation could also include a potential reduction in diffusion rate limitations by groundwater movement as the airflow to a sparging well is turned on and off. The duration of pulse cycles may be based on the duration of the expansion phase and on the rate of decrease in dissolved oxygen during the off cycle. As pointed out by Lundegard (1994), the presence of an expansion phase also indicates that short-term air sparging pilot tests may overestimate the steady-state radius of influence.

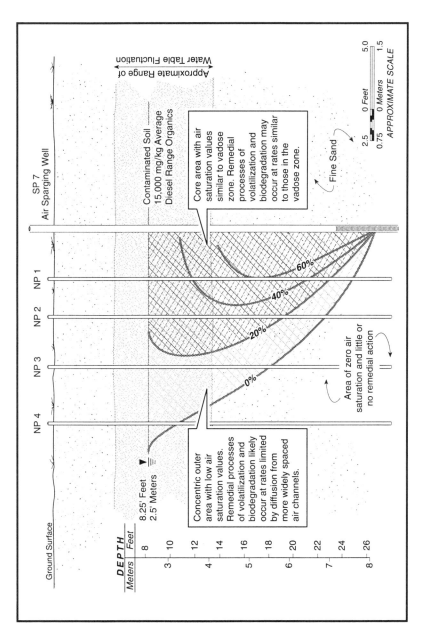

FIGURE 6. Remedial processes may occur at different rates in concentric areas around the air sparging well.

DISSOLVED OXYGEN MONITORING RESULTS

Dissolved oxygen concentrations were measured in nested and conventional monitoring wells located 4 to 20 feet (1.2 to 9.2 m) from the air sparging well. The dissolved oxygen monitoring results are summarized below:

- The dissolved oxygen concentration before initiating air sparging was less than 0.1 mg/L at each monitoring location.
- In monitoring well MC 1, the nested well screens at the 10- to 11.5-ft (3- to 3.5-m) and the 15- to 16.5-ft (4.6- to 5.0-m) depths may have been dewatered at the 4 cfm (0.11 m³/min) injection rate and were positively dewatered at the 8, 12, and 16 cfm (0.23, 0.34 and 0.45 m³/min) injection rates. The dewatering was identified when water could not be pumped from the wells; instead, air flowed from the hose which penetrated the well cap compression fitting and terminated below the static water table.
- Similarly, in MC 2, located 8 ft (2.4 m) from the sparge well, the nested screen at the 10- to 11.5-ft (4.6- to 5.0-m) depth was dewatered during air injection at 16 cfm (0.45 m³/min).
- Increased dissolved oxygen concentrations were recorded up to 14 ft (4.3 m) from the sparging well in MW 6, where dissolved oxygen increased from near zero mg/L to about 5 mg/L during air injection at 8, 12, and 16 cfm (0.23, 0.34, and 0.45 m³/min). No increase in dissolved oxygen was recorded in MC 3 SS, located 20 ft (6.1 m) from the air sparging well.

PRESSURE MONITORING

Pressure changes in the saturated zone, particularly a water table mound, have been used as indicators of the radius of influence of air sparging systems (Johnson et al. 1993; Lundegard 1994). At Strawberry Point, pressure transducers and a data logger recorded changes in the saturated zone pressure before, during, and after air injection. Observations drawn from these pressure data follow.

An increase in saturated zone pressure and water table elevation was measured across the study site almost immediately after air injection began. The pressure increase reached a peak within about 20 to 40 minutes at all monitoring locations and air injection rates. The maximum water pressure increase graphed against distance from the air injection well (Figure 7) shows that:

- Higher air injection rates produced larger pressure increases.
- The pressure increase and water table mound decrease exponentially away from the air injection well.
- Most importantly, a pressure increase or water table mound can be readily measured 69 ft (21 m) from the injection, which is far beyond

the radius of remedial influence as measured by an increase in air saturation or increase in dissolved oxygen. As pointed out by Lundegard (1994), saturated zone pressure increases appear to be an unreliable indicator of the radius of remedial influence of air sparging systems.

After reaching a peak, the saturated zone pressures decreased over several hours and for a brief time fell below the presparging pressures, before stabilizing at the presparging pressure. The decrease in saturated zone pressure below the presparging pressure is caused by the consolidation of air channels and has been computer modeled and measured in the field by Lundegard (1994), and Lundegard and Anderson (1993).

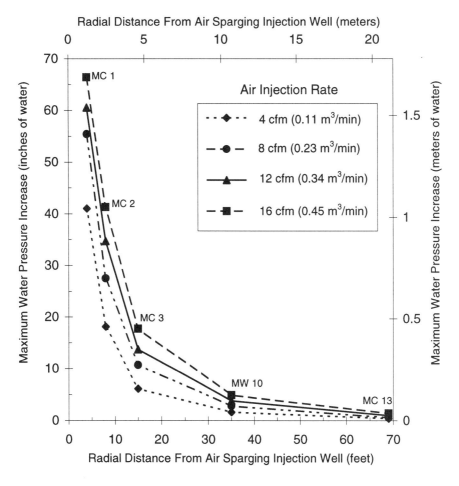

FIGURE 7. Maximum water pressure increase versus distance from the air sparging well at various air injection rates.

CONCLUSIONS

The Strawberry Point monitoring indicates the following:

- The distribution of injected air changes through time, initially expanding outward and upward from the sparging well screen to the water table through myriad channels, then consolidating around the injection wells as channels with lower resistance capture air from higher resistance channels, before finally reaching a steady-state flow condition.
- Air sparging appears well suited to the remediation of residual petroleum hydrocarbon contamination below and in the zone of water table fluctuation.
- In homogeneous sands, the remedial radius of influence of air sparging wells, as indicated by increases in air saturation and dissolved oxygen, may be on the order of 10 to 15 ft (3 to 4.6 m).
- Pulsed air injection may yield a larger remedial radius of influence and reduce diffusion limitations.
- Air saturation values near the injection well may be similar to vadose zone air saturation values, suggesting that volatilization and biodegradation may occur at rates similar to those in the vadose zone.
- Farther from the air sparging well, where lower air saturation conditions exist, volatilization and biodegradation rates may be limited by diffusion.
- The neutron probe is a valuable tool for assessing the distribution of injected air during sparging.
- The change in saturated zone pressures (water table mound) is an unreliable indicator of and may greatly overestimate the air sparging remedial radius of influence.

ACKNOWLEDGMENTS

The Strawberry Point air sparging research demonstration is being conducted under a research contract (#DACA39-93-C-0148) with the U.S. Army Corps of Engineers Cold Regions Research and Engineering Laboratory (CRREL). Funding, logistical support, and equipment have generously been supplied by the Federal Aviation Administration and CRREL.

REFERENCES

Baehr, A. L., and M. F. Hult. 1991. "Evaluation of Unsaturated Zone Air Permeability Through Pneumatic Tests." *Water Resources Research* 27: 2605-2617.

Ji, W. A., Dahmani, D. P. Altfeld, J. Ding Lin, and E. Hill, III. 1993. "Laboratory Study of Air Sparging & Air Flow Visualization." *Ground Water Monitoring & Remediation* 13(4): 115-125.

Johnson, P. C., M. W. Kemblowski, and J. D. Colthart. 1988. "Practical Screening Models for Soil Venting Applications." *Proceedings of the 1988 Petroleum Hydrocarbon and Organic Chemicals in Groundwater: Prevention, Detection, and Restoration Conference*, p. 521. Houston, TX.

Johnson, R. L. 1994. "Enhancing Biodegradation With In Situ Air Sparging: A Conceptual Model." In R. E. Hinchee (Ed.), *Air Sparging for Site Remediation*, pp. 14-22. CRC Press, Inc., Boca Raton, FL.

Johnson, R. L., P. C. Johnson, D. B. McWhorter, R. E. Hinchee, and I. Goodman. 1993. "An Overview of In Situ Air Sparging." *Ground Water Monitoring & Remediation* 13(4): 127-137.

Lundegard, P. 1994. "Actual Versus Apparent Radius of Influence: An Air Sparging Pilot Test in a Sandy Aquifer." *Proceedings of the 1994 Petroleum Hydrocarbon and Organic Chemicals in Groundwater: Prevention, Detection, and Restoration Conference*, pp. 191-206. Houston, TX.

Lundegard, P. D., and G. Anderson. 1993. "Numerical Simulation of Air Sparging Performance." In *Proceedings of the 1993 Petroleum Hydrocarbon and Organic Chemicals in Groundwater: Prevention, Detection, and Restoration Conference*, pp. 461-476. Houston, TX.

Evidence of Preferential Vapor Flow During In Situ Air Sparging

Ralph S. Baker, Michael E. Hayes, and Seth H. Frisbie

ABSTRACT

A pilot study was recently conducted at a Superfund site in New England to assess the ability of soil vapor extraction/in situ air sparging (SVE/IAS) to remediate volatile organic contamination found in dense, sandy soils. A water table was present at 1.5 to 2.1 m below ground surface (bgs) with an associated capillary fringe thickness of approximately 1 m. An average of 0.11 standard m^3/min of air was injected at a pressure head of 775 cm H_2O into a sparge well screened from 3.6 to 4.0 m bgs for the 4-day SVE/IAS portion of the pilot study. Over this period, the highest air pressure head measured at any of the 17 piezometers that had been installed at depths ranging from 0.1 to 2.1 m bgs in the vicinity of the sparge well was 27 cm H_2O at a point 9.4 m from the sparge well and 0.4 m bgs. A monitoring well adjacent to that point was the only monitoring well to exhibit a significant increase in dissolved oxygen (DO), despite the fact that two closer monitoring wells lying 4.3 and 4.6 m from the sparge well showed no change in DO during the test. A piezometer 13.4 m from the sparge well at 1.3 m bgs detected pressure heads as high as 17 cm H_2O, whereas other piezometers closer to the sparge well exhibited less or no change in pressure during the test. The highly nonuniform distribution of air pressures and DO is evidence of preferential flow of the injected air. These results are consistent with other site data indicative of heterogeneous and anisotropic soil conditions.

INTRODUCTION

In situ air sparging (IAS) is increasingly used in conjunction with soil vapor extraction (SVE) and bioventing as a means of removing contaminants from water and soils in both the saturated and unsaturated zones (Loden 1992; Marley et al. 1992; Hinchee 1994). Upon injection below the water table, air displaces water as it makes its way toward the surface, stripping volatile organic compounds (VOCs) from portions of the porous medium. The vapor phase VOCs are transferred to the vadose zone, where they can be collected by SVE. By increasing the oxygen content in the saturated as well as the unsaturated zones, air sparging can provide the additional benefit of enhancing aerobic biodegradation of constituents that may not have volatilized (Boersma et al. 1993; Johnson et al. 1993; Brown et al. 1994).

Preferential water flow has been widely recognized as an important multiphase flow phenomenon during infiltration into unsaturated soil (Baker and Hillel 1991). Evidence has also been presented of preferential vapor flow during SVE in moist unsaturated soils (Baker and Wiseman 1992). With respect to IAS, early conceptualizations frequently depicted a uniform and conical distribution of air bubbles emanating from an air sparging point. Recognition is increasingly being given, however, to the prevalence of channeling and other nonuniformly distributed patterns of vapor flow during air sparging in porous media of sandy textures or finer (Ji et al. 1993; Ahlfeld et al., 1994). Consequently concerns have been expressed (Johnson 1994) as to the effectiveness of air sparging in treating the entire contaminated zone, notwithstanding some indications that elevated dissolved oxygen (DO) levels may be more widely distributed around a given sparge point than are the discrete air-filled channels (Pijls et al. 1994; Brown et al. 1994).

A pilot study was recently carried out at a New England Superfund site to assess the ability of SVE/IAS technology to remediate the VOC contamination found in subsurface soils. Due to time constraints, the IAS portion of the study was limited to one week; therefore, the focus was on the physical response of the site to SVE/IAS, rather than on aspects of long-term contaminant removal.

MATERIALS AND METHODS

The site of the SVE/IAS pilot study contains VOCs (both chlorinated and nonchlorinated solvents) that were released into surface soils and groundwater over the course of several decades. The site currently has a surface covering of concrete and/or asphalt, with some minor cracks evident. Soil at the test location is characterized as a fine sandy loam to gravelly sandy loam/fill to a depth of approximately 2.4 m below ground surface (bgs), overlying a gravelly fine sandy loam to gravelly coarse sand extending to approximately 5 m bgs. Underlying the sand is 1 to 2 m of compact till, over fractured bedrock. Because the water table was anticipated to be at 1.8 to 2.4 m bgs, with an associated capillary fringe thickness of approximately 1 m, and to minimize the generation of investigation-derived waste, two horizontal SVE wells (H-1 and H-2), 10.2 cm ID with 0.05-cm slots, were placed in 0.25-m-deep parallel trenches as shown in Figure 1. No granular or gravelly sub-base was observed beneath the asphalt or concrete pavement that might allow air drawn into the SVE wells to bypass the deeper soil. Had such a layer been present, shallow placement of the SVE wells would not have been justified. The gravel pack around the wells was covered with concrete, asphalt-treated with sealant and a polyethylene surface seal, but adjacent paved areas remained unsealed.

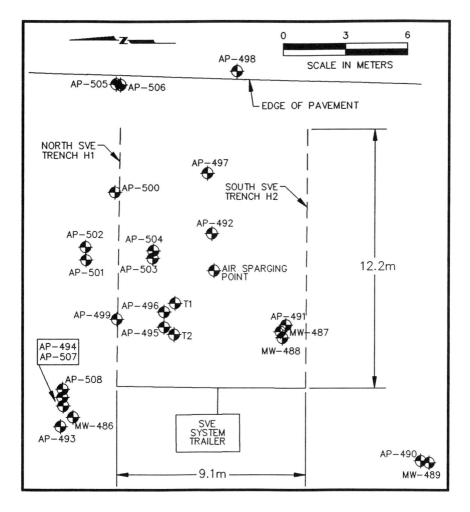

FIGURE 1. Plan view of SVE/IAS pilot test site. AP = piezometer; MW = monitoring well; and T = tensiometer.

Nineteen 1-cm-ID air piezometers (AP490-AP508) were installed to the depths indicated in Figure 2, throughout the immediate vicinity of the SVE/IAS system. The bottom of each tube was centered within a 0.3-m sand pack. In addition, four 5-cm-ID groundwater monitoring wells were installed with screened intervals of 1.8 to 3.4 m bgs (MW486, MW487, and MW489) and 3.1 to 4.6 m bgs (MW488), at locations shown in Figure 1. The air sparging well (5 cm ID) was installed with its screen extending from 3.7 to 4.0 m bgs.

Prior to the SVE/IAS test, the SVE system was operated without IAS for 5 days (designated as Phases 1 and 2). Phase 3 comprised the combined SVE and IAS pilot test and is the subject of this article. Pressures at piezometers were read with a portable pressure transducer. DO in groundwater was monitored

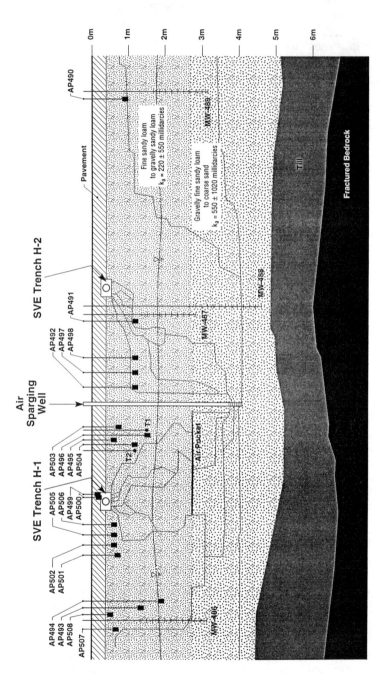

FIGURE 2. SVE/IAS pilot test representative cross-section (looking from west to east), showing approximate stratigraphy, relative positions and depths of monitoring points, and hypothetical airflow pathways. Predominant soil textures (USDA classification) and mean air permeabilities are: 0 to 2.4 m bgs — fine sandy loam to gravelly sandy loam, $k_a = 220 \pm 550$ millidarcies; and 2.4 to 3.0 m bgs — gravelly fine sandy loam to gravelly coarse sand, $k_a = 550 \pm 1,020$ millidarcies. Features are not all actually in same plane.

by in situ colorimetric measurements using CHEMets™ ampoules. The reagent-filled vacuum ampoules are packaged in two kits with separate sets of nine comparative colorimetric standards each, the first of which encompasses the 0- to 1.0-mg/L range, and the second the 1- to 12-mg/L range. The measurement process consists of first slowly purging the well so as to avoid aeration, carefully lowering the sampling unit containing an ampoule into the well, tugging on a control line to break the ampoule open allowing water to be drawn into the ampoule, and withdrawing the unit for immediate colorimetric measurement. Groundwater elevations were continuously monitored with Teflon™-coated pressure transducers.

During the final day of Phase 3, separate injections into the IAS well of tracer gases (1% (vol/vol) CH_4 in air; 50% (vol/vol) SF_6 in air) were conducted to furnish additional data regarding airflow paths and apparent air velocities. The arrival of CH_4 at AP491, AP492, and AP494 was monitored with a Geotechnical Instruments Model GA90 Infra-Red Gas Analyzer after passing the sample through coconut charcoal to remove interfering compounds from the sample matrix. The arrival of SF_6 at selected piezometers was observed qualitatively at AP492 and AP498 only, using a TIF model 5550 halogen detector. The signal of the detector was attenuated to obtain a stable baseline to mitigate the presence of interfering compounds in the sample stream.

RESULTS AND DISCUSSION

During the 4 days of combined SVE/IAS, air was injected into the sparge well at a mean flow (±1 standard deviation) of 0.11 ± 0.03 standard m^3/min (SCMM), and at a mean gauge pressure head of 775 ± 67 cm H_2O. While quasi-steady state extraction and injection conditions were maintained, the northerly SVE trench, H-1, consistently extracted over three times as much air as the southerly trench, H-2, (2.7 ± 0.4 vs. 0.8 ± 0.1 SCMM) at the same applied vacuum head (95 ± 16 cm H_2O), suggesting higher air permeabilities in the vicinity of H-1. The water table during the test was shallower than expected (1.5 to 2.1 m bgs), with an associated capillary fringe thickness of approximately 1 m, based on tensiometer observations. These findings justified the shallow placement of the SVE trenches for the purposes of the pilot test.

Air Pressure

During each of the 4 days of the IAS pilot test, the piezometers were read three times, generally early morning, mid-day, and late afternoon. Air pressures monitored at the piezometers varied considerably with space and time. Figure 3 presents the mean of the twelve pressure head readings for each piezometer as a function of its distance from the sparge well. If airflow were well distributed within a homogeneous porous medium, one would expect to observe an exponential decline in pressure with distance from the pressure source; but this relationship is clearly not evident. The highest air pressure head measured at any of

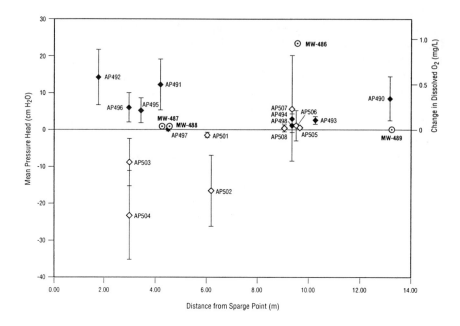

FIGURE 3. Pressure during IAS and change in dissolved oxygen (end of SVE only vs. end of SVE/IAS) at monitoring points as a function of distance from the sparge point. Error bars show ± 1 standard deviation about mean pressure. Data are symbolized as follows: piezometers positioned between 0.1 and 0.5 m bgs — open diamonds; those between 1.2 an d 2.1 m bgs — solid diamonds; monitoring wells — open circles.

the piezometers during the test was 27 cm H$_2$O at AP507, a point 9.4 m from the sparge well and only 0.4 m bgs. A slightly deeper monitoring point, AP490, located 13.4 m from the sparge well in a different direction detected a peak pressure head of 17 cm H$_2$O; whereas several of the piezometers closer to the sparge well exhibited considerably smaller pressures. In contrast to many of the deeper units, several of the shallower piezometers (AP502, AP503, and AP504) exhibited a vacuum, revealing that they were more strongly influenced by the SVE wells than by the sparge well. Many more of the piezometers, both shallow and deep, had registered vacuums during the earlier, pre-IAS phase. Even then, however, the distribution of vacuum was spatially heterogeneous.

The heterogeneous distribution of pressures during IAS suggests that airflow occurred in the form of spatially separated air-filled channels (as depicted hypothetically in Figure 3). This mode of airflow can be expected to occur in a heterogeneous porous medium because air (as with other nonwetting fluids) cannot displace water from the medium until the air entry pressure (capillary resistance) is exceeded, at which time it will first displace water from the largest interconnected pores in the medium. Since these pore networks exist within the most permeable regions of the soil, such as sandy or gravelly lenses, air will invade such features preferentially, at the lowest entry pressures, following the path(s) of least resistance. If the influx of injected air still cannot be accommodated, successively smaller pore networks will also become conductive to air, each at successively higher entry pressures. A piezometer will display relatively higher pressures when it directly intersects a major airflow path, and lower pressures when it lies a distance from such flow paths. It should be acknowledged that vadose zone measurements (using air piezometers) are an indirect means of monitoring air channels in the saturated zone. Thus the evidence provided by soil physical analyses, monitoring wells, and tracer gas tests needs to be considered in combination.

The air permeabilities of 24 undisturbed cores collected from various locations within 50 m of the pilot test site and tested at ambient (as received) moisture content ranged over four orders of magnitude, from <0.3 to 2,800 millidarcies. Mean (±SD) air permeabilities were 220 ± 550 millidarcies and 550 ± 1,020 millidarcies for samples collected from depths of 0 to 2.4 m (n = 17), and 2.4 to 3 m (n = 7), respectively. Sparged air may have migrated upward until it encountered lower permeability soils at a depth of approximately 2.4 m bgs, then laterally until the resistance of the upper zone was overcome. Nonetheless, the heterogeneous pattern of airflow that was observed may not have been entirely a reflection of heterogeneous and anisotropic conditions in the subsurface. The injection of air at a pressure head of 775 cm H_2O was not required to initiate airflow, and may have represented an "overpressure," since the sum of the pressure heads required to introduce air into the formation is estimated to be approximately 370 cm H_2O (216 cm H_2O to displace water from the 216-cm-deep portion of the sparge tube below the water table, 50 cm H_2O for friction losses, and perhaps 100 cm H_2O to overcome the entry pressure). Although lateral migration of vapors has been attributed to overpressurization during IAS (Brown and Fraxedas 1991; Loden 1992), the extent to which a moderate overpressure may induce or exacerbate preferential flow is not known.

Dissolved Oxygen

The effect of IAS on groundwater aeration was evaluated by the change in DO in each monitoring well between the beginning and end of the test (Figure 3). The only monitoring well to exhibit a significant increase in DO (from <0.05 to 1.2 mg/L) was MW486, 9.8 m from the sparge well. Meanwhile, two closer monitoring wells, MW487 and MW488 (4.3 and 4.6 m from the sparge well, respectively) showed no detectable change in DO (the detection limit being 0.05 mg/L). It is noteworthy that MW487 is clustered with AP507 (the only shallow piezometer that showed such an elevated pressure response, as discussed above), AP494 (a monitoring point that increased in soil gas O_2 concentrations during Phase 3 from 10.7% to 14.6%), and AP493 (that declined in soil gas O_2 concentrations over the same period from 20.0% to 5.5%). Increases in DO levels in monitoring wells do not necessarily reflect DO levels in the aquifer, because of in-well aeration effects (Johnson et al. 1993; Hinchee 1994); however, they do indicate preferential airflow in the aquifer when they occur in some monitoring wells and not others. The fact that, of four monitoring wells, only one (MW486) exhibited increases in DO suggests that, although the sand pack of MW486 may have short-circuited air to the shallower zone, the monitoring wells did not in general function in this manner.

Water-Table Response

Changes in groundwater elevations prior to and during the SVE/IAS test are presented in Figure 4. A pronounced but transient water table rise is evident upon the onset of IAS, as is a corresponding collapse upon its cessation. Similar

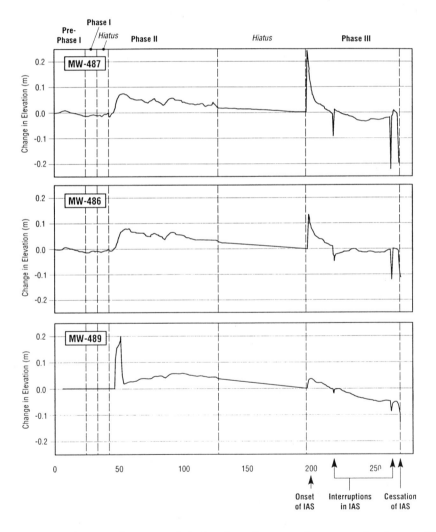

FIGURE 4. Changes in groundwater elevations at three monitoring wells during Phases I and II (SVE) and III (SVE/IAS).

observations have been reported previously (Boersma et al. 1993). The effect is greatest at MW487, nearest the sparge well, and least at MW489, farthest from the sparge well. The zone of water table response to IAS is apparently quite widespread, but it does not necessarily imply that air-filled pathways extend into the vicinity of MW489, and the DO concentration indicated they did not intercept the well. Comparison of the DO and water-table data suggests further that monitoring the water table response to IAS is not an accurate predictor of the zone of effective groundwater aeration.

Tracer Gas Tests

None of the three CH_4 injections made at the sparge well were detectable above background (0.1%) concentrations at the monitoring points. The decision, based on safety considerations, not to inject CH_4 at concentrations above 1% in air may have precluded subsequent detection of CH_4.

Separate SF_6 injections made at the sparge well were detected at AP492 and AP498, arriving at apparent air velocities of 1.6 and 1.1 cm s^{-1}, respectively. Although these values are similar, and thus not indicative of preferential flow per se, continued observations revealed episodic detections of tracer gas that support the hypothesis that preferential flow was observed. After the first 2.0-min-long injection of SF_6 into the sparge well, the following was recorded at AP492: 200 s without detection (ND); 17 s of detection (D); 188 s ND; 18 s D; 249 s ND; 11 s D; 415 s ND; and 20 s D. A similar episodic appearance of SF_6 at AP498 after the second 2.0-min-long injection occurred as follows: 854 s ND; 12 s D; 760 s ND; 16 s D; 1858 s ND; and 18 s D. A possible explanation is the accumulation of injected gas in an "air pocket" beneath a lower permeability layer (Marley et al. 1992; Johnson et al. 1993). With continued influx of gas into the pocket, pressure builds until the entry pressure of the overlying layer is attained. The gas then displaces water from its preferred pathways as it travels toward the detection point, but as it does so the pressure in the remaining air pocket dissipates, allowing water to reenter the pathways. Thereupon air pressure must again build before reinvasion, breakthrough, and detection can recur. Such a picture would need to be confirmed with appropriate air pressure measurements; however, it is consistent with recent work describing the effect on IAS of higher permeability zones lying beneath lower permeability strata (Ji et al. 1993). It may be noted that the longer interval between detections that occurred toward the conclusion of each test may have resulted as tracer concentrations approached the detection limit and a periodic breakthrough episode passed undetected.

CONCLUSIONS

Several lines of evidence have been presented in support of preferential vapor flow during the SVE/IAS pilot test. While the subject site is heterogeneous and may therefore exhibit more pronounced evidence of preferential flow than less heterogeneous sites, the remediation community should acknowledge that subsurface heterogeneity, at many scales, is more common in the field than homogeneity. It is probably the limited nature of many data sets that lends the impression that conditions are not heterogeneous. Collectively the site data indicate that the site is heterogeneous and not well suited to IAS. They also demonstrate that when preferential flow is prominent, the area of influence of IAS cannot reliably be estimated from DO measurements, water table response, or pressure measurements. The role that overpressurization may have played in exacerbating preferential flow during the test is undetermined.

More generally, where IAS is dominated by preferential vapor flow, the area of effective treatment is likely to be a small fraction of the area intended for treatment, and the potential risks of lateral mobilization and off-site migration of VOCs are increased. To better predict when and to what extent preferential flow during IAS will be a concern, well-controlled field experiments will need to be initiated and comprehensively monitored in a variety of settings. IAS constitutes an inherently complex and dynamic type of multiphase flow that will require considerable attention if greater understanding is to be gained. The potential benefits to be gained demand such an effort.

REFERENCES

Ahlfeld, D. P., A. Dahmani, and W. Ji. 1994. "A Conceptual Model of Field Behavior of Air Sparging and Its Implications for Application." *Ground Water Monitoring Review*, (Fall): 132-139.

Baker, R. S., and D. Hillel. 1991. "Observations of Fingering Behavior during Infiltration into Layered Soils." In T. J. Gish and A. Shirmohammadi (Eds.), *Proc. National Symp. on Preferential Flow*, pp. 87-99. Amer. Soc. Agri. Eng., St. Joseph, MI.

Baker, R. S., and J. T. Wiseman. 1992. "Importance of Vadose Zone Monitoring during Soil Vapor Extraction Pilot Studies." *Proc. 1992 USEPA/A&WMA Int. Symp.: In Situ Treatment of Contaminated Soil and Water*, pp. 26-35. Air & Waste Management Assoc., Pittsburgh, PA.

Boersma, P., F. S. Petersen, P. Newman, and R. Huddleston. 1993. "Use of Groundwater Sparging to Effect Hydrocarbon Biodegradation." *Proc. 1993 Petroleum Hydrocarbons and Organic Chemicals in Ground Water: Prevention, Detection, and Restoration*, pp. 557-559.10. API and NGWA, Washington, DC.

Brown, R. A., and R. Fraxedas. 1991. "Air Sparging — Extending Volatilization to Contaminated Aquifers." *Proc: Symposium on Soil Venting*. EPA/600/R-92/174, R.S. Kerr Environmental Research Laboratory, Ada, OK.

Brown, R. A., R. J. Hicks, and P. M. Hicks. 1994. "Use of Air Sparging for In Situ Bioremediation." In R. E. Hinchee (Ed.), *Air Sparging for Site Remediation*, pp. 38-55. Lewis Publishers, Boca Raton, FL.

Hinchee, R. E. 1994. "Air Sparging State of the Art." In R. E. Hinchee (Ed.), *Air Sparging for Site Remediation*, pp. 1-13. Lewis Publishers, Boca Raton, FL.

Ji, W., A. Dahmani, D. P. Ahlfeld, J. D. Lin, and E. Hill. 1993. "Laboratory Study of Air Sparging: Air Flow Visualization." *Ground Water Monitoring Review*, (Fall):115-126.

Johnson, R. L. 1994. "Enhancing Biodegradation with In Situ Air Sparging: A Conceptual Model." In R. E. Hinchee (Ed.), *Air Sparging for Site Remediation*, pp. 14-22. Lewis Publishers, Boca Raton, FL.

Johnson, R. L., P. C. Johnson, D. B. McWhorter, R. E. Hinchee, and I. Goodman. 1993. "An Overview of In Situ Air Sparging." *Ground Water Monitoring Review*, (Fall):127-135.

Loden, M. E. 1992. *A Technology Assessment of Soil Vapor Extraction and Air Sparging.* U.S. Environmental Protection Agency Technical Report EPA/600/R-92/173, Risk Reduction Engineering Laboratory, Cincinnati, OH.

Marley, M. C., D. J. Hazebrouck, and M. T. Walsh. 1992. "Air Sparging in Conjunction with Vapor Extraction for Source Removal at VOC Spill Sites." In P. T. Kostecki, E. J. Calabrese, and M. Bonazountas (Eds.), *Hydrocarbon Contaminated Soils, Vol. II*, pp. 579-589. Lewis Publishers, Boca Raton, FL.

Pijls, C.G.J.M., L.G.C.M. Urlings, H.B.R.J. van Vree, and F. Spuij. 1994. "Applications of In Situ Soil Vapor Extraction and Air Injection." In R. E. Hinchee (Ed.), *Air Sparging for Site Remediation*, pp. 128-136. Lewis Publishers, Boca Raton, FL.

Air Sparging and Bioremediation: The Case for In Situ Mixing

Wilson S. Clayton, Richard A. Brown, and David H. Bass

ABSTRACT

Air sparging has sparked considerable controversy in the remediation industry. Some feel air sparging is a significant advance in remedial technology, whereas others feel that air sparging is a very limited technology. A central question in this debate is the presence (or lack thereof) of groundwater mixing during air sparging. Groundwater mixing is important to overcome the diffusion limitations of sparging caused by air channeling and effectively deliver oxygen for in situ bioremediation. Possible mechanisms of groundwater mixing include physical displacement, capillary interactions of air and water, frictional drag, makeup of evaporative loss, thermal convection, and movement of fines. Physical groundwater displacement and groundwater movement resulting from capillary pressure gradients are the two most likely and most commonly effective mechanisms. An important question is the relative degree of groundwater mixing during nonsteady-state and steady-state sparging. Evidence indicates that mixing occurs primarily during nonsteady-state air sparging. Because groundwater mixing is important to overcome the diffusion limitations of air sparging, it is important to operate sparging systems to maximize mixing. Field data show that pulsed sparging, which emphasizes the nonsteady-state aspects of air sparging, greatly enhances groundwater mixing.

INTRODUCTION

Air sparging is a diffusion-limited process, because injected air does not penetrate the entire soil matrix (Ahlfeld et al. 1994, Clayton and Nelson 1995). During air sparging for in situ bioremediation, the diffusion path lengths for transport of oxygen through groundwater are defined by the distances between air channels. Where channel spacing is large, diffusion alone is not sufficient to transport adequate oxygen into all areas of the aquifer for enhanced aerobic bioremediation. Mixing of groundwater during air sparging is an important mechanism to overcome this diffusion limitation and provide adequate oxygen transport into the aquifer.

Groundwater mixing has commonly been considered in the context of site-scale bulk groundwater flow. However, mixing over shorter distances may significantly reduce the diffusion limitation of sparging, without generating bulk groundwater flow in an organized pattern. This may be significant where nonsteady-state mixing mechanisms serve to induce groundwater flow in opposite directions at different times, preventing development of a discernible site-scale flow pattern.

This paper considers the mechanisms which might be important for groundwater mixing during sparging, and presents some field evidence which supports the concept that groundwater mixing does occur during sparging, especially during nonsteady-state sparging conditions. Also, it is shown that pulsed sparging serves to enhance groundwater mixing and is therefore an effective means to improve the effectiveness of sparging.

Possible Mechanisms for Groundwater Mixing During Air Sparging

Physical Displacement by Invading Air. Groundwater is physically displaced as air invades the soil during sparging. Also, bidirectional mixing can occur as a result of subsequent water imbibition. These processes occur during nonsteady-state airflow conditions, where the air saturation (percentage of void space which is air filled) changes with time. The effectiveness of physical displacement to mix groundwater is related to the amount of water displaced, and the duration of nonsteady-state flow conditions. The rate of water displacement is permeability limited, and therefore the duration of these effects is generally greater in low-permeability soils. The process acts over both short-range distances (centimeters) and site-scale distances.

Capillary Interaction of Air and Water. While physical displacement of water by air involves changes in fluid saturation, capillary fluid interactions during sparging can cause groundwater movement without a change in air saturation. During air sparging, a capillary pressure exists which is equal to the pore air pressure minus the pore water pressure. The pore water pressure at a point is therefore equal to the pore air pressure minus the capillary pressure. The air pressure and capillary pressure vary spatially and temporally during sparging. Also, operating conditions may result in an air pressure which is elevated more than the value of capillary pressure, resulting in an increased pore water pressure. The spatial variation of this induced pore water pressure leads to induced hydraulic gradients which may act over short or long distances.

The above process can be expected to be more pronounced during nonsteady-state conditions, when higher air injection pressures can be maintained. In fact, theoretical considerations imply that a condition of zero hydraulic gradient resulting from capillary interactions is a criterion for steady-state airflow conditions during sparging (McWhorter 1994, Corey 1994). Pulsed sparging may enhance this mixing mechanism by increasing the time in which the site is in a nonsteady state.

Frictional Drag by Flowing Air. Frictional drag on groundwater can be induced by transfer of shear stresses from flowing air to pore water during non-darcy airflow conditions (Civan and Evans 1993). In this case, shear stresses induced in the groundwater at the pore scale will act parallel to the direction of airflow, and will be equal and opposite to the shear stress in the flowing air. This phenomenon may not contribute to groundwater movement during darcy flow conditions, where frictional drag within the flowing air phase is considered insignificant. For fluid flow in a porous medium, a critical value of Reynolds number (Re) for non-darcy flow is 1 (Corey 1994), which corresponds to an air velocity of 0.015 to 0.15 m/s for fine sands to coarse sands.

Water Flow in Response to Evaporative Loss. Evaporative loss of water to the injected airstream can result in water inflow to the sparged zone to maintain volume balance. This volume balance approach must consider changing air satur-ations and is very sensitive to the degree of air saturation and its effect on the rate of evaporation. This is also a thermodynamic process, where heat lost to evapora-tion cools the groundwater, leading to downward density-driven flow. This flow would be opposite to that induced by frictional drag (for upward airflow).

Thermal Convection. Thermal convection can occur through density driven flow of cooled groundwater as indicated above, or through heating of ground-water by injecting heated gases. As above, this process is sensitive to the air saturation developed by its effect on heat transfer. The heat capacity of air is much less than that of water, potentially limiting the warming of groundwater.

Migration of Fines. Fines migration has been shown to significantly reduce the permeability of petroleum reservoirs by "sealing" pore throats (Sarkar and Sharma 1990). Fines migration also has been observed during sparging in both laboratory sand tank studies (Hoag 1992) and in field studies. Airflow paths may be destabilized by changes in air permeability caused by fines migration, and the resulting redirection of airflow may cause groundwater mixing as the water is displaced by or displaces air.

Relative Importance of Possible Groundwater Mixing Mechanisms

Based on the above discussion, physical displacement of water and capillary interactions would seem to be relevant primarily during nonsteady-state condi-tions. Frictional drag, evaporative loss, thermal convection, and fines migration may also cause groundwater mixing after steady-state conditions are reached, but the magnitude of mixing resulting from these processes may be less than that which occurs during the nonsteady state.

EVIDENCE FOR GROUNDWATER MIXING

Field Measurements of
Nonsteady-State Groundwater Mixing

Water displacement has been measured in situ during air sparging using time domain reflectometry (TDR). TDR is a well established and accurate means to measure the moisture content of soils (Topp et al. 1994). Because the moisture content decreases as air invades the soil during air sparging, the TDR data accurately reflect the displacement of water which contributes to groundwater mixing during sparging. In this application, TDR measures soil moisture content over a volume of approximately 500 cm^3.

Figure 1 depicts time series TDR data from a relatively homogeneous site consisting of poorly sorted (well graded) fine to coarse sand soil during continuous injection air sparging at a distance of 3 m from the injection point and at an elevation 5 m above the injection point. The initial moisture content of approximately 36.5% is equal to the soil porosity. The moisture content decreased during the first 20 minutes by up to 1.5%, indicating that air had displaced water from 4% of the soil pore volume. Subsequently, water flowed back into the area; and the moisture content increased before reaching a relatively constant value after 70 minutes of air injection. These data show the bidirectional nature of nonsteady-state groundwater mixing by physical displacement.

TDR data was collected at a second site (Figures 2a and 2b) consisting of extremely well sorted (poorly graded) very fine sand (hydraulic fill) during 2 days of sparging pilot tests. On the first day of testing, air was injected continuously at

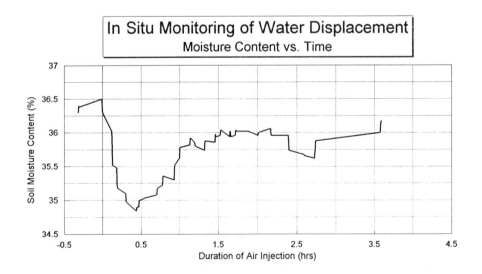

FIGURE 1. In situ monitoring of soil moisture content shows bidirectional nonsteady-state physical displacement of pore water by air sparging.

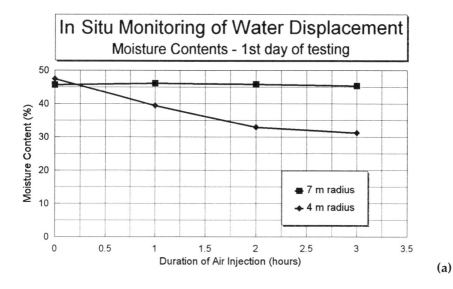

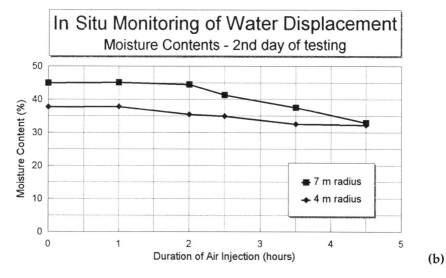

FIGURE 2. (a) Air injection at a 5.3-m depth in hydraulic fill results in a 14%
decrease in moisture content at a radius of 4 m during sparging. Air penetration does not occur at the 7-m radius. (b) A second day of air injection
at the site at a more shallow (3-m) depth results in displacement of groundwater by air at both 4 m and 7 m radii.

a depth of 5.3 m for 1 h at each of three flow rates; 5, 10, and 15 scfm. The initial
moisture content of 45% represents the porosity of the very loose hydraulic fill.
The moisture content decreased to 31% at the 4-m radius, but no air saturation
was detected at the 7-m radius. On the following day, after 18 hours without air

injection, further testing showed that the soil moisture content at the 4-m radius increased to 38%. This indicates that groundwater had reentered the zone, yet a significant amount of trapped air was still present.

On day 2 of testing, air was injected at a more shallow depth of 3 m below water at a rate of 5 scfm for 1 h, 10 scfm for 1½ h, and 15 scfm for 2 h. Air injection at this more shallow depth resulted in decreased moisture content at both the 4- and 7-m radii, which shows that multilevel sparging can be used to enhance groundwater mixing by displacing water from different airflow paths at different times. The data also show that the presence of trapped air in the aquifer prior to sparging resulted in a slower rate of water displacement at the 4-m radius than on the first day of testing.

The differences between air saturations measured at the two sites described above show how a different degree of mixing will occur at each sparging site. Soil at the second site had a much more uniform pore size distribution, which can be expected to result in higher air saturations during air invasion (McWhorter and Sunada 1990). Obviously, because a greater volume of water was displaced at this site, the degree of groundwater mixing was much greater than at the first site. The data from the second site also indirectly indicate that the degree of site-scale airflow channeling was probably minimal. If airflow were highly channelized, then the two locations where discrete point measurements were collected would be unlikely to both intersect air channels. The data suggest that relatively uniform air saturations were developed within the zone influenced by sparging, which implies that the displacement of groundwater would also occur uniformly across the site.

Indirect Evidence of Groundwater Mixing

Some of the mechanisms that may be involved in groundwater mixing are not easily quantified. However, data from a number of field studies provide indirect evidence that mixing probably does occur during sparging, regardless of the mechanism. These data include measurements of DO (dissolved oxygen) distribution and mass removal, which reflect the overall effectiveness of mass transfer during sparging as indirect evidence of groundwater mixing.

DO Distribution. Dissolved oxygen measurements taken just after sparging is initiated in a pulsed sparge system provide strong indirect evidence of groundwater movement. Field studies in several such cases have indicated that DO measured in monitoring wells can increase in response to the re-initiation of sparging, long before the sparge air reaches the monitoring wells. Two examples are discussed below.

At one site, an operating sparge system was turned off overnight, and monitoring wells 3 m away showed negligible DO by morning. When the sparge system was restarted, DO in these monitoring wells rose to 6 to 8 mg/L within 5 minutes, even though tracer tests had shown a travel time of 45 minutes for sparge air to reach these wells.

At another site, sparging was conducted at a depth of about 15 m below top of water, resulting in elevated DO in monitoring wells screened at similar depths. A week after shutdown of this sparge well, sparging was initiated about 10 m below the top of groundwater (at an injection pressure too low to have driven sparge air 5 m further down into the groundwater). DO in the deep monitoring wells, which had returned to near zero, increased to measurable levels shortly after shallower sparging began.

In each of these cases, residual air saturations were likely present within the saturated zone as a result of the previous sparging. Dissolution of oxygen from the trapped air into the groundwater was slow under nonsparging conditions, as reflected by the low DO in the monitoring wells. Immediately upon initiation of sparging, however, the rate of oxygen dissolution into groundwater increased dramatically, indicating a more intimate contact between the trapped air and groundwater. The source of the increased air/groundwater contact may have been principally air movement (the probable explanation in the first example) or groundwater movement (as was certainly the case in the second example), but the net result was increased mixing.

Changes in DO distribution during a sparging pilot test at a pipeline spill site also show the results of mixing. Depth to water was ~8 m and the sparging well was screened ~10 m below water. Three nested monitoring points were installed at 3 (OWN-1), 10 (OWN-2), and 16 m (OWN-3) distances from the sparging well. Each monitoring point had four 5-ft screened intervals, set at the water table surface (A), 4 m below (B), 7 m below (C), and 10 m (D) below water. The sparging well was operated continuously for 54 h, and DO readings were routinely monitored. The data are summarized in Table 1.

We have considered that a change in DO was statistically significant if:

1. the increase in DO was greater than 2 mg/L (the background variability in DO readings without sparging was 0.5 mg/L), or
2. the minimum or maximum DO reading was greater than 2 standard deviations of the average reading.

The initial DO readings were highly stratified, ranging, for example, in OWN-2 from 0.2 to 8.2 mg/L. If mixing occurs, then the DO level in this case might fluctuate as low-DO and high-DO strata are mixed. This is especially true because DO levels would be expected to significantly increase in the vicinity of a static air channel leading to further stratification of DO.

As can be seen from Table 1, only point OWN-3D, the deepest and farthest monitoring point, did not meet either statistical criterion. OWN-1A through D, OWN-2D, and OWN-3B had net DO increases greater than 2 mg/L. All the remaining points had a minimum or maximum reading greater than 2 standard deviations from the mean. These data indicate that significant groundwater mixing had to occur in order for the groundwater to be effectively oxygenated.

Mass Removal. The final piece of evidence is the rate of mass removal that is often observed during sparging. Without groundwater mixing, one would expect

TABLE 1. Changes in DO measured during sparging provide indirect evidence for groundwater mixing through the effective oxygenation of an initially stratified DO distribution.

Well I.D.	Dissolved Oxygen Concentration (mg/L)						
	Initial	Mean	SD	Mean + 2SD	Mean – 2 SD[a]	Maximum	Minimum
OWN-1A	2.2	9.1	1.7	12.4	5.8	10.6[b]	2.2
OWN-1B	1.0	9.1	1.8	12.7	5.4	10.6[b]	1.0
OWN-1C	0.2	6.6	3.8	14.2	–1.1	10.2[b]	0.2
OWN-1D	1.2	8.7	2.4	13.4	4.0	10.6[b]	1.2
OWN-2A	3.6	3.4	1.1	5.5	1.3	5.4	1.0
OWN-2B	0.2	0.9	0.5	1.9	0.0	2.4	0.2
OWN-2C	8.2	8.3	0.5	9.2	7.4	9.4	7.4
OWN-2D	0.8	2.0	1.0	3.9	0.1	4.6[b]	0.8
OWN-3A	0.8	0.7	0.3	1.3	0.1	1.6	0.4
OWN-3B	1.4	2.5	1.6	5.7	–0.58	5.6[b]	0.8
OWN-3C	1.6	1.5	0.4	2.2	0.9	2.4	1.0
OWN-3D	5.6	4.8	0.6	6.0	3.6	5.8	3.8

(a) SD = standard deviation.
(b) Greater than 2 mg/L increase from initial value.

a significant and rapid drop in the level of mass removal. Table 2 shows measured mass removal rates that are significantly higher than those calculated for a static, nonmixed system. The nonmixed calculations are based on a 1% contact between air and groundwater and an extraction rate of 10% of vapor saturation for the groundwater contacted.

TABLE 2. Mass removal data from two sparging sites show more effective remediation than for soil venting only or calculated mass removal rates for nonmixed sparging.

Mass Removal kg/day	Site A: Gasoline Spill 1,000 mg/kg BTEX av. initial	Site B: Solvent Spill 550 mg/kg TCE av. initial
Venting Only	7.4	10.5
Sparging – 1 Month	24	40.8
Sparging – 3 Month	14.7	24.4
Nonmixed – 10% Contact Maximum	3.9	5.3
Nonmixed – 30% Contact Maximum	14.2	19.6

PULSED AIR INJECTION TO ENHANCE GROUNDWATER MIXING

Because groundwater mixing enhances the effectiveness of sparging, it is productive to enhance the mechanisms that increase mixing. Physical displacement and capillary interactions provide powerful mechanisms for groundwater mixing, but primarily during nonsteady-state airflow conditions. These mechanisms are likely to contribute to the observed enhanced performance of pulsed sparging, which serves to maximize the nonsteady-state behaviors during sparging. The TDR data presented above (Figure 1) show that quasi-steady state airflow conditions can be reached within minutes to hours. Measurement of pressure gradients during sparging have indicated that an upward gradient can exist for 6 to 8 hours after the initiation of sparging (Boersma et al. 1994). These considerations all suggest that nonsteady-state groundwater mixing can be maximized by pulsed sparging cycles.

Field Data from Pulsed Sparging Sites

Mass Removal Data. The benefit of pulsing is demonstrated in Figure 3. As can be seen, there is a 3- to 5-fold increase in the mass removal rate going from continuous to pulsed sparging. This increased removal rate was sustained over a 16-week period. The pulsing duration was based on the drop in removal rate. When a sparge well showed low removal rates it was shut off and another well was activated. The pulsed frequency was on the order of 12 to 24 hours.

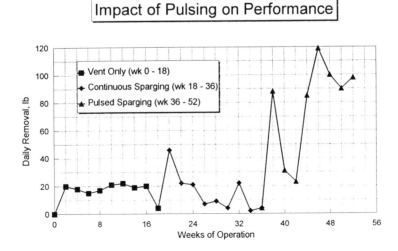

FIGURE 3. Mass removal rates were greatly improved by pulsed sparging after venting only and continuous sparging had been implemented.

Measurements of In Situ Water Displacement During Pulsing. TDR data (Figure 4) collected during pulsed air injection at a radius of 3 m and at the depth of air injection show the increased groundwater displacement that occurs during pulsing. The pulse sequence used is indicated on Figure 4. Moisture content values show a sharp, almost immediate response to each of a series of pulses. Each pulse displays the behavior of an initial decrease in moisture content at the initiation of the pulse, followed by stabilization of moisture content. When each pulse is discontinued, some water reenters the soil, but much of the air in soil pores remains trapped. The data also show that, in this case, each successive pulse resulted in a lower moisture content than the previous pulse, causing greater groundwater displacement.

CONCLUSION

Groundwater mixing is important during air sparging to effectively transport dissolved oxygen for in situ bioremediation. Groundwater mixing can be effective if it occurs at the pore scale as well as over site-scale distances, since either process can reduce the diffusion limitation of sparging. Theory and field measurements indicate that mixing does occur, is most pronounced during nonsteady-state conditions, and is enhanced by pulsed sparging. This mixing is commonly bidirectional, which may prevent development of a discernible site-scale flow pattern. Because sparging without groundwater mixing will be of limited effectiveness, the increased volatile organic compound removal and DO addition that occurs during sparging and is enhanced by pulsing provides strong indirect evidence that mixing does occur.

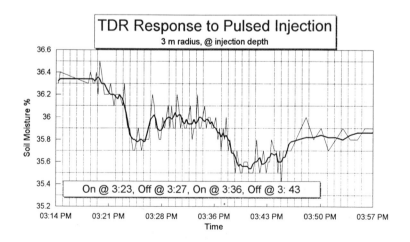

FIGURE 4. Time series moisture content data collected during pulsed sparging shows a distinct response to each air injection pulse, increasing the displacement of groundwater and improving mixing.

REFERENCES

Ahlfeld, D. P., A. Dahmani, and W. Ji. 1994. "A Conceptual Model of Field Behavior of Air Sparging and Its Implications for Application." *Ground Water Monitoring and Remediation* 14(4): 132-139.

Boersma, P. E., P. Newman, F. Petersen, R. Huddleston. 1994. "Effects of Sparging on Groundwater Hydraulics and Groundwater Quality." *Groundwater Monitoring* 1994.

Civan, R., and R. D. Evans. 1993. "Relative Permeability and Capillary Pressure Data from Non-Darcy Flow of Gas/Brine Systems in Laboratory Cores." Society of Petroleum Engineers, paper no. 26151, presented at the SPE Gas Technology Symposium, Calgary, Alberta, Canada, June.

Clayton, W. S., and C. H. Nelson. 1995 (in press). "In Situ Sparging: Chemical Transport and Mass Transfer." *Proceedings of 1995 Annual Meeting of the American Institute of Hydrology*, May, 1995, AIH, Minneapolis, Minnesota.

Corey, A. T. 1994. *Mechanics of Immiscible Fluids in Porous Media.* Water Resources Publications, Highlands Ranch, CO.

Hoag, G. E. 1992. Personal communication.

McWhorter, D. B. 1994. Personal communication.

McWhorter, D. B. and D. K. Sunada. 1990. "Exact Integral Solutions of Two-Phase Flow." *Water Resources Research*, 26(3): 399-413.

Sarkar, A. K. and M. M. Sharma. 1990. "Fines Migration in Two-Phase Flow." *JPT — Journal of Petroleum Technology*, May.

Topp, G. C., S. J. Zegelin, and I. White. 1994. "Monitoring Soil Water Content Using TDR: An Overview of Progress." *Proceedings of the Symposium on Time Domain Reflectometry in Environmental, Infrastructure, and Mining Applications*, September, 1994, sponsored by the United States Bureau of Mines and the Infrastructure Technology Institute at Northwestern University, Evanston, IL.

Water Displacement During Sparging Under Perched Water-Table Conditions

Dominic C. DiGiulio

ABSTRACT

The feasibility of using sparging to purposefully displace perched water in silt loam soils was evaluated at a field site in northwestern Oklahoma. During sparging, a transient response in water level measurements was observed in observation wells which is attributed to water displacement. Evidence of water displacement was manifested by water-table collapse upon the cessation of sparging.

INTRODUCTION

Sparging can be operationally defined as injecting air into saturated porous media at sufficient pressure to overcome frictional pipe, hydrostatic, and air-entry pressure loss. Sparging has been applied primarily to facilitate mass transfer of volatile organic compounds (VOCs) from groundwater to soil-air; although enhancement of aerobic biodegradation often is stated as a secondary goal. Despite its widespread use, the physics of air and water flow during sparging is not well understood making design difficult. Laboratory visualization studies conducted by Ji et al. (1993) suggest that sparging is largely a water displacement process. Removal of water allows advective airflow to occur in discrete soil regions having relatively lower air-entry and hydrostatic pressure.

This study was conducted to evaluate sparging as an enhancement to dual vapor extraction (DVE™) in displacing perched water. During pilot testing, little drawdown (0.3 m) had been observed in observation wells between two DVE™ wells spaced 6 m apart after 4 weeks of operation even though more than 113 m³ of water had been recovered. Both observation and DVE™ wells were screened only in the vadose zone. Most of the recovered water appeared to have originated through water-table upwelling from an underlying unconfined aquifer (DiGiulio 1995). Displacement of water in perched zones is necessary to ensure advective airflow and hence effective VOC mass transfer from these regions during venting.

METHODS AND MATERIALS

Sparging tests were conducted concurrently with DVE™ operation during July and August of 1994 at Site-8 on Vance AFB located in Enid, Oklahoma. Soils and groundwater are contaminated with petroleum hydrocarbons, trichloroethene (TCE), and vinyl chloride. Five underground storage tanks were removed at Site-8 in January 1989. Four of the tanks stored lubricating oil, diesel fuel, and kerosene. The remaining tank stored waste oils and solvents. Contaminated soils in the immediate vicinity of the tanks were excavated and replaced with fill consisting primarily of silt. After compaction of the fill, the site was completely paved with a 0.25-m (10-in.) concrete slab.

The spacing and screened interval of wells and probe clusters installed during this study are illustrated in Figures 1 and 2. Screened intervals illustrated in Figure 2 represent length of sandpack. SP-1, not shown in Figure 2, was screened (sandpack) 4.88 to 6.31 m (16 to 20.7 ft) below surface. Site topography is flat.

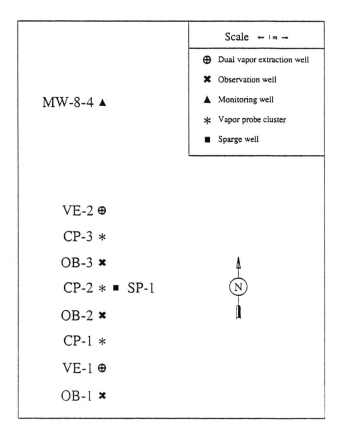

FIGURE 1. Location of wells and probe clusters used in study.

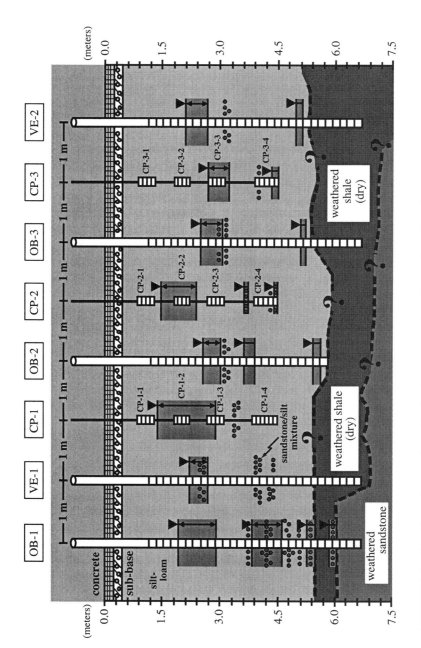

FIGURE 2. Stratigraphy and vertical placement of wells and probe clusters.

All boreholes were drilled to a diameter of 20.3 cm (8 in.) using hollow-stem augering techniques. Observation and DVE™ wells consisted of 10.2-cm (4-in.)-diameter, stainless-steel screen and risers. SP-1 consisted of 2.54-cm (1-in.)-diameter schedule 40 PVC. Deeper vapor probes were constructed from 0.64-cm (¼-in.)-O.D. copper tubing with brass Swagelok™ Quick Connects at the surface and stainless-steel, 0.64-cm (¼-in.)-O.D., 12.7-cm (5-in.)-long Geoprobe® well screens at the base. Shallow vapor probes (CP-1-1, CP-2-1, and CP-3-1) were constructed similarly except 0.32-cm (⅛-in.)-O.D. stainless-steel tubing was used. Cole-Parmer type K thermocouples were taped alongside each probe. Coarse sand was used to fill the annulus between the screened interval and borehole. A minimum of 30 cm (12 in.) of granular bentonite was used to seal off the well screens followed by the addition of cement to the surface. Vapor probes were separated with granular bentonite. Water level measurement was done manually with a Solinst water meter. Mini-permeability pneumatic permeability tests were conducted in each probe using the method of Joss et al. (1991).

In the first test, SP-1 was used as a monitoring well while injecting air 0.5 m away into CP-2-4. In the second test, SP-1 was used as a sparging well with water level monitoring in OB-2 and OB-3 both located 1.0 m from SP-1. Mass airflow was measured in SP-1 using a Dieterich standard annubar DNT-10™ in a 2.54-cm (1-in.)-diameter steel pipe with a Dwyer Capsehelic™ gauge to determine pressure differential. Mass flow was measured in CP-2-4 using a Gilmont 150-mm Accucal™ flowmeter. Static injection pressure was determined using a Dwyer Magnehelic™ gauge while temperature was measured using a Cole-Parmer digital thermometer.

Perched-water zones were identified by visual and manual examination of continuous split-spoon cores. A soil zone was assumed to be perched if soils appeared saturated. Soil texture was determined by particle size analysis on 4 soil samples collected while drilling OB-2. Textural analysis was conducted by the U.S. Army Corps of Engineers' Southwestern Division Laboratory in Dallas, Texas.

RESULTS AND DISCUSSION

Numerous saturated regions (perched zones), often associated with a sandstone-gravel/silt mixed soil, were identified while drilling (Figure 2). It is unclear whether sandstone-gravel/silt soils act as lower permeability lenses or higher permeability conduits for water flow. Consistently saturated medium indicative of a water table was not encountered at the maximum depth of drilling (6.7 m below surface). Water levels in observation wells prior to sparging, however, were consistently 2.4 m below surface indicating perched water flow to wellbores. Results of particle size tests outlined in Table 1 indicate that in the study area, residuum above weathered shale and sandstone consists of silt loam soils.

Soils in the immediate vicinity of CP-2-4 appeared saturated prior to sparging as evidenced by drilling logs and lack of vacuum during DVE™ testing. Vacuum

TABLE 1. Soil textural analysis from OB-2.

Depth (m)	Sand (%)	Silt (%)	Clay (%)	USDA Soil Textural Class	Moisture Content (% by mass)
0.0 - 0.61	6	65	29	silty clay loam to silt loam	28.9
1.52 - 3.05	2	77	21	silt loam	16.0
4.57 - 6.10	4	76	20	silt loam	20.8
4.57 - 6.10	4	73	23	silt loam	21.1

was detected in other probes within the cluster (CP-2-1 and CP-2-2 at 1.5 and 38.6 cm of water, respectively). Also a large pressure drop (from 5 to 1.58 atm) was observed within minutes of initiation of sparging at CP-2-4. Experience at this and other sites indicates that pressure buildup without airflow precedes air-entry, after which a rapid pressure drop is observed. The water level in SP-1 prior to sparging was well above its screened interval (2.44 m below surface) indicating conditions of local saturation.

Results of sparging tests are illustrated in Figures 3 and 4. Perched water zones appear hydraulically and pneumatically connected even though saturated soil regions observed in drilling cores appear erratic. In general, a rapid rise in water level was followed by a slow approach to baseline until the cessation of sparging, wherein a rapid decrease below baseline occurred followed again by a slow approach to baseline. Similar findings were reported by Ahlfeld et al. (1994).

The time required for return to baseline water levels after initiation of sparging increased with radial distance from sparging wells. Baseline water levels were observed in SP-1 within 200 minutes while sparging at CP-2-4 (0.5 m distance). When sparging at SP-1, baseline water levels were observed in OB-2 in excess of 400 minutes and were never reached at OB-3 prior to cessation of sparging (1,400 minutes). Both OB-2 and OB-3 were located 1.0 m from SP-1.

The magnitude of water-level rise was generally inversely related to distance from the point of sparging. A much greater water-level rise was observed in SP-1 when sparging at CP-2-4 compared to OB-2 and OB-3 when sparging at SP-1 even though air injection pressures were similar and the mass flowrate at SP-1 was 6.5 times that of CP-2-4. Water-level rise however was asymmetric.

Significant water-table collapse upon the cessation of sparging was only observed in wells where water levels had returned to near baseline conditions during sparging. This finding indicates that water-level rise alone does not indicate water displacement. The magnitude of water-level collapse was directly related the radial distance from a sparge well. Water-level collapse was over four times greater in SP-1 while sparging at CP-2-4 compared to OB-2 while sparging at SP-1.

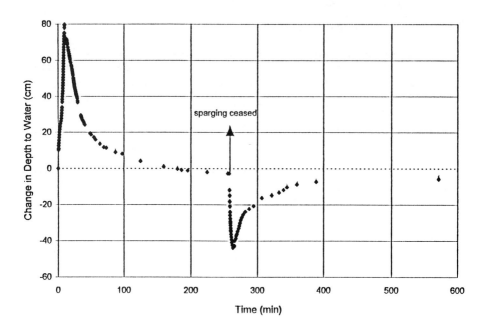

FIGURE 3. Change in depth to water at SP-1 from air injection at CP-2-4 (1.58 atm, 0.7 g/s) on 7/29/94.

Water displacement during sparging was evidenced by water-level collapse upon the cessation of sparging and by the similarity in pneumatic permeability at CP-2-4 in comparison with other vapor probes. Pneumatic permeability determined from vapor probes varied from 10^{-10} to 10^{-9} cm^2. Pneumatic permeability measured at CP-2-4 was 5.0×10^{-10} cm^2. Similarity in pneumatic permeability may indicate that soils in the immediate vicinity of CP-2-4 were dewatered to moisture levels comparable to background conditions.

The view of sparging as a water displacement process may be used to improve site design. Ji et al. (1993) observed that increased applied pressure caused increased air channel diameter and channel density. Enhanced channel formation indicates increased water displacement and volumetric air content in sparged soils which is manifested by water-level collapse at the cessation of sparging. Water displacement as a function of radial distance from a sparge well and applied pressure can be evaluated by determining the magnitude of water-level collapse at the cessation of sparging.

Increasing applied pressure above that required to overcome hydrostatic, capillary, and frictional head loss and decreasing spacing between sparge wells should increase water displacement and hence sparging efficiency. This would then enhance mass transport of VOCs and oxygen by increasing the surface area of contaminated soils receiving direct airflow and by decreasing the diffusion path length in soils which are likely saturated.

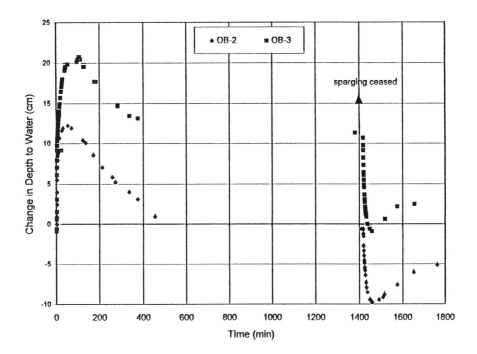

FIGURE 4. Water-level elevation change during sparging at SP-1 (1.47 atm, 4.58 g/s) on 8/9/94 - 8/10/94.

CONCLUSION

Water-level rise during sparging appears to be a transient response to pneumatic head addition. In this field study, increased water-level rise and subsequent collapse was observed with decreased distance from the point of sparging. The time required for return to baseline water levels increased with increased distance from the point of sparging. Significant water-level collapse occurred only where water levels had approached baseline conditions.

Water-level collapse upon the cessation of sparging is likely a manifestation of water displacement. Thus, sparging can be used as a stand-alone water displacement process or used with other water displacement/removal methods to achieve advective airflow in previously saturated media.

ACKNOWLEDGMENTS

The author is grateful to Mr. Bill Chatron of the U.S. Army Corps of Engineers for facilitating partial funding of this effort, Ms. Marilyn Wells of the U.S. Air Force for arranging site access base support, and Mr. Saba Tahmassebi of the Oklahoma Department of Environmental Quality for expeditious review of applicable permits. The author is also appreciative of Joseph Marsh, Robert Kuttes, Jeffrey Habey, and Arnold Harnes from Burns and McDonnell Engineering for assistance in collecting data.

DISCLAIMER

Although the research described in this paper has been funded wholly or in part by the U.S. Environmental Protection Agency (Robert S. Kerr Environmental Research Laboratory) and the U.S. Army Corps of Engineers (Tulsa District), it does not necessarily reflect the views of the Agency or the U.S. Army Corps of Engineers, and no official endorsement should be inferred.

REFERENCES

Ahlfeld, D. P., A. Dahmani, and W. Ji. 1994. "A Conceptual Model of Field Behavior of Air Sparging and Its Implications for Application." *Ground Water Monitoring and Remediation* (Fall): 132-139.
DiGiulio, D. C. 1995. "Use of a Combined Air Injection/Extraction (CIE) Well to Minimize Vacuum Enhanced Water Recovery." In: *Proceedings of the 9th National Outdoor Action Conference and Exposition*, National Ground Water Association, Dublin, OH.
Ji, W., A. Dahmani, D. P. Ahlfeld, J. D. Lin, and E. Hill. 1993. "Laboratory Study of Air Sparging: Air Flow Visualization." *Ground Water Monitoring and Remediation* 13(4): 115-126.
Joss, C. J., Baehr, A. L., and J. M. Fisher. 1991. "A Field Technique for Determining Unsaturated Zone Air-Permeability." In: *Proceedings of the Symposium on Soil Venting*. EPA/600/R-92/174. U.S. Environmental Protection Agency, Robert S. Kerr Environmental Research Laboratory, Ada, OK.

In Situ Reclamation of Fuel Oil from a Residence

Pamela E. Bell, Allison D. Williams,
Debra L. Petrak, Joe Hill, and Jeffrey A. Sitler

ABSTRACT

A multicomponent remediation system, relying largely on in situ bio-remediation, was implemented at a residential site contaminated with approximately 1,500 gal of #2 fuel oil from a leaking underground storage tank (UST). Contaminated materials included the basement block and underlying soils (total petroleum hydrocarbon [TPH] up to 7,400 mg/kg), excavated soils, surficial soils, subsurface soils (TPH up to 2,400 mg/kg), groundwater (TPH up to 642 mg/L), and a localized zone of free product. Components of the remediation system include product recovery, subslab ventilation, biosparging, and land treatment of contaminated soil. The subslab ventilation system is used to oxygen-ate and ventilate inaccessible, highly contaminated soil and gravel beneath the basement floor. The sparging system is used to oxygenate contaminated groundwater and subsurface soils. Contaminated surficial soil was treated using a one-time application of nutrients and solid chemical oxygen to stimulate native in situ bacteria to degrade the fuel oil. Stimulation of the native bacteria has been effective in reducing contaminant concentrations and increasing bacterial populations at the site. However, remediation effectiveness is being hindered by the presence of free product on a shallow water table, which redistributes fuel oil throughout the soil column during water table fluctuations.

INTRODUCTION

An estimated 1,500 gal of #2 fuel oil were released from a residential UST. During removal of the UST, petroleum-saturated soil was encountered and fuel was observed leaching through the basement walls, flowing across the ground surface, and discharging to a wetland 40 m downgradient of the house (Figure 1).

Contaminated materials consisted of approximately 40 m³ of soil generated during the emergency response actions and site investigations, 225 m³ of soil and gravel beneath the house, 2,000 m³ of soil downgradient of the former UST location, and groundwater over a 1,000 m² area. A zone of free product floating on the water table is located at the center of the site. Initial TPH concentrations measured in groundwater reached 643 mg/L, and soil TPH concentrations reached a maximum of 7,400 mg/kg. Soil saturated with fuel oil was also observed in many areas of the site.

Geologic materials at the site consist of clayey silt to a silty sand saprolitic soil overlying highly weathered quartz biotite gneiss. The saprolite has an average hydraulic conductivity of $2.5 \cdot 10^{-4}$ cm/s. The water table is shallow and fluctuates from 0 to 2 m below land surface. During wet periods, groundwater discharges to the land surface at the southern side of the site.

REMEDIATION PLAN

The remediation plan for the site was designed to address vapor migration, free product, contaminated soil, and contaminated groundwater. Soil and groundwater remediation is based on in situ biodegradation and relies on stimulation of native bacteria. The system consists of vapor extraction/subslab ventilation, landfarming, and biosparging. Free-product recovery has also been implemented at the site.

The subslab ventilation system was installed in November 1993 to eliminate vapor migration into the house and to aerate the soil and gravel beneath the basement slab, thus enhancing biodegradation of the fuel. The system consists of a blower connected to a manifold that pulls air from beneath the slab at four locations along the back wall of the house and exhausts the air to the outside. Fresh air is drawn beneath the slab at the front of the house via five subslab air intake points vented to the outside. This results in airflow beneath the slab that delivers oxygen to the soil by increasing the concentration gradient of oxygen in the gravel layer. Liquid nutrients were added to the soil via small holes drilled through the concrete slab.

On May 6, 1994, land treatment of the upper 0.4 m of undisturbed soil and the stockpiled soil was initiated. The surface soils were broken up with a backhoe and then a one-time application of a solid chemical oxygen source (Permeox, FMC) and slow-release nutrients were tilled into the soil. The nutrient and peroxygen quantities added were calculated based on measured fuel concentrations. The land treatment area was seeded with grass following the tilling operation.

Deeper soil and groundwater are being treated with a biosparging system consisting of two rotary vane blowers connected to five sparge wells (Figure 1). All of the wells inject air at a depth between 3 and 3.28 m below land surface. The well locations were selected to include the areas of highest contamination and perimeter locations to control the movement of free product and the contaminated groundwater plume.

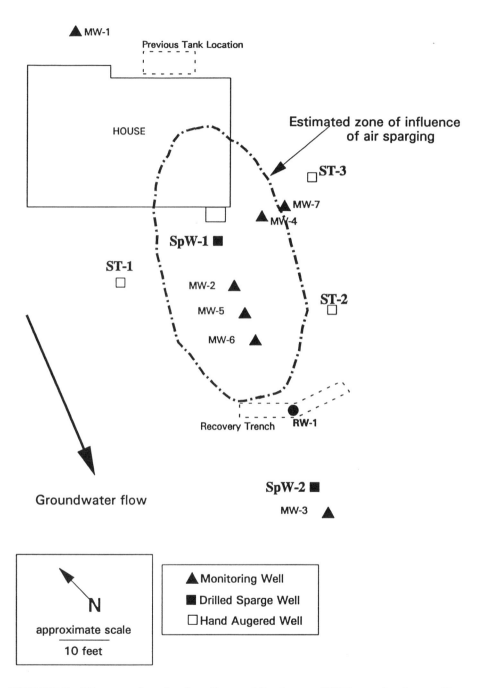

FIGURE 1. Site map showing locations of the former UST, monitoring wells, sparging wells, and the product recovery system. Groundwater flow is towards the southwest. The zone of influence isopleth was based on results of the zone of influence test.

RESULTS AND DISCUSSION

Subslab Bioremediation

The subslab ventilation system has operated continuously since its installation. Total organic vapors in the basement, measured using a Photovac Micro TIP, have decreased from a high of 750 ppm to below 0.1 ppm. TPH concentrations in soil samples collected from below the basement slab have decreased approximately 50%, from 7,400 to 1,500 mg/kg, between September 1993 and February 1995.

Soils

Following the addition of peroxygen and nutrients (May 7, 1994) to the surficial soil, the TPH concentrations in the landfarming area decreased to 54 mg/kg (Table 1). Soil samples collected 10 days after nutrient application had a fuel oil-degrading bacteria population of approximately 0.1 to 1.0% of the heterotrophic population. Soil samples collected 60 days (June 30, 1994) after nutrient application showed increased populations of fuel oil degraders and decreased nutrient and TPH levels, indicating an increase in bacterial activity and consumption of both petroleum and nutrients.

Heavy rainfall during July 1994 resulted in a sharp rise in water table elevation and a redistribution of petroleum throughout the soil column. This resulted in recontamination of previously remediated soil. Surface soil with TPH concentrations less than 100 mg/kg in June exhibited TPH concentrations of 418 and 506 mg/kg in August (Table 1). This process of recontamination was observed again in October when surface soil TPH concentrations increased to 1,800 and 1,300 mg/kg.

For the purpose of examining soil TPH concentrations, the site can be broken into sections that roughly correspond to a zone currently impacted by free product and a zone downgradient of the free product (south of the free-product recovery trench). In both zones, the average TPH concentration is higher in the 1- to 2-m depth interval than in either the 0- to 1-m-depth or the 2- to 3-m-depth interval (Table 1). The data are quite variable, which probably reflects both reintroduction of petroleum during the rise and fall of the water table and the heterogeneity of the soils and contaminant plume. At the 0- to 1-m-depth interval within the free product zone, there was an initial decrease in soil TPH concentration to below the detection limit. This was followed by 2 months of rain and a reintroduction of petroleum to the surface soils caused by the rising water table, which came to the surface during this time. There appears to be generally decreasing TPH concentrations in the 1- to 2-m-depth interval in the product zone. Identification of trends in the other depth intervals is more difficult. TPH is generally decreasing in the 2- to 3-m-depth interval in the product zone. The 1- to 2-m-depth interval downgradient of the product zone appears to be decreasing except for a spike of 3,900 mg/kg in January 1995.

TABLE 1. Soil TPH concentration data. Soil samples were hand-augered from areas within the contaminant plume and represent the zone containing free product and the zone downgradient of free product.

	Within Free-Product Zone		
Sample	Depth (m)	Date	TPH (mg/kg)
1	0-1	5/16/94	90
2	0-1	5/16/94	54
3	0-1	6/8/94	160
5	0-1	6/30/94	<33
7	0-1	8/4/94	418
8	0-1	8/4/94	506
9	0-1	9/27/94	250
11	0-1	10/19/94	1,800
12	0-1	10/19/94	1,300
13	0-1	11/14/94	600
16	0-1	12/12/94	1,400
17	0-1	1/27/95	370
5	1-2	6/3094	2,605
7	1-2	8/4/94	496
8	1-2	8/4/94	4,194
8	1-2	8/4/94	4,869
9	1-2	9/27/94	7,600
11	1-2	10/19/94	3,800
11	1-2	10/19/94	1,800
12	1-2	10/19/94	2,700
12	1-2	10/19/94	<20
13	1-2	11/14/94	170
13	1-2	11/14/94	700
16	1-2	12/12/94	290
16	1-2	12/12/94	290
17	1-2	1/27/95	24
17	1-2	1/27/95	270
11	2-3	10/19/94	3,000
12	2-3	10/19/94	320
13	2-3	11/14/94	26
16	2-3	12/12/94	860
17	2-3	1/27/95	250

TABLE 1. (continued).

Sample	Depth (m)	Date	TPH (mg/kg)
	Downgradient of Free-Product Zone		
4	0-1	6/8/94	180
6	0-1	6/30/94	58
10	0-1	9/27/94	820
15	0-1	12/12/94	730
18	0-1	1/27/95	150
10	1-2	9/27/94	4,000
10	1-2	9/27/94	1,700
15	1-2	12/12/94	1,900
15	1-2	12/12/94	620
18	1-2	1/27/95	250
18	1-2	1/27/95	3,900
15	2-3	12/12/94	1,800
18	2-3	1/27/95	870

Air Sparging

During zone of influence testing, water table displacement in all site wells was measured. Critical formation entry pressure was exceeded at 6 psi, which allowed an air injection rate of 1.7 to 3.1 m^3/h. Higher injection rates resulted in mounding of the water table to surface elevations and ejection of water from nearby monitoring wells. Water table mounding decreased linearly and anisotropically with distance and direction from the injection well. During testing of SpW-1, sidegradient observation wells MW-4 and MW-7 exhibited less pronounced water table mounding than downgradient wells MW-2 and MW-5 located at equivalent radial distances. Elongation of water table mounding would tend to suggest that preferential airflow pathways exist in the subsurface at the site resulting in elongated zones of influence (Figure 1). This orientation corresponds to and may be caused by the southwest-northeast trend of the relic bedding observed in the saprolite.

The groundwater dissolved oxygen (DO) concentration is monitored weekly in the monitoring wells. During the 6 months prior to installing the sparging system, wells in the contaminated zone had significantly lower DO concentrations (1.5 to 2.1 mg/L) than did uncontaminated, upgradient well MW-1 (5.1 mg/L). After 3 months of full-scale sparging, there was an increase in the average DO concentration in all wells (Figure 2). Greater increases in average DO concentrations were measured in many of the wells in the contaminate plume (monitoring wells 2, 3, 6, 7, and the recovery well) compared to MW-1, which is upgradient of the plume. During the month of January 1995 the sparge wells

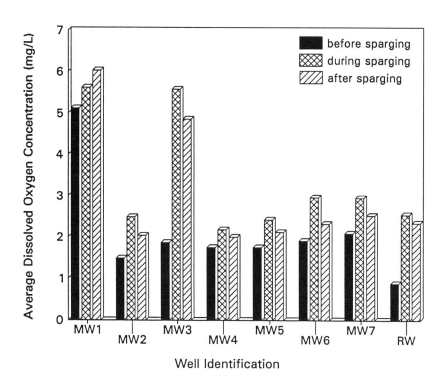

FIGURE 2. Average DO concentration in monitoring wells before sparging (6 months of data), during active sparging in all sparge wells (3 months of data), and during a 1 month shutdown of the sparging systems. Data from before sparging were collected from April to September 1994. Sparging data were collected from September 1994 to January 1995. Shutdown occurred during January-February 1995.

were turned off to see if there would be a corresponding decrease in the DO concentration due to microbial activity. All wells in the contaminant zone exhibited a decrease in the average DO concentration during shutdown, while MW-1 had an increase in the average DO concentration during the shutdown.

Free product is being hand-bailed from monitoring wells 2, 4, and 6 at weekly intervals. MW-6 consistently has the most free product with approximately 76 mL accumulation per week. Appearance of free product in monitoring wells 2 and 4 is sporadic.

CONCLUSIONS

In situ treatment of the shallow soil using a one-time application of peroxygen and nutrients was effective in rapidly stimulating the native bacteria and degrading the petroleum. Fluctuations in water table elevation continually redistribute contamination in the soils by smearing free product throughout the soil column. Because of the relatively large fluctuations in the water table elevation, it is evident that remediation of soils will be effective only after the free product is removed.

The movement of air injected by the biosparging system is strongly influenced by the orientation of the relic structure in the saprolite at the site resulting in an oblong zone of influence. Air sparging has been effective in elevating the average DO concentrations in monitoring wells within the contaminant zone. Decreased DO concentrations in wells within the contaminant zone and an increased DO concentration in the well upgradient of the contamination zone during a 1 month period of sparging shutdown indicates that there is an oxygen demand in the contaminant zone. This demand is likely due to the presence and activity of native in situ hydrocarbon-degrading bacteria.

Air Sparging: Effects of VOCs and Soil Properties on VOC Volatilization

Keh-Ping Chao and Say Kee Ong

ABSTRACT

The effect of the physical-chemical properties of volatile organic compounds (VOCs) and soil on the volatilization of VOCs during air sparging was investigated using a laboratory-scale air sparging system. The variables studied included two types of soils, three different VOCs, and various air flowrates. VOCs used were chloroform, trichloroethylene (TCE), and carbon tetrachloride. As expected, the percent removal efficiencies of VOCs over a 24-h period were proportional to the injected air flowrate and Henry's law constant. Experimental results also indicated that beyond a certain air flowrate, the mass of TCE removed was similar for the two porous media used in the experiments. The VOCs volatilized from the porous media appeared to be limited by the interfacial surface area of the water-air interface of the air channels. However, other physical processes, such as diffusion, may also be limiting.

INTRODUCTION

Air sparging, also called "in situ air stripping," is a remedial technology in which contaminant-free air is introduced into a contaminated aquifer to volatilize VOCs from the groundwater into the air phase. Several field-scale applications of the air sparging system have indicated that air sparging may be effective in remediating VOC-contaminated aquifers at a faster rate than a pump-and-treat system. Brown (1992) estimated that the time and cost for remediating VOC-contaminated soil may be reduced by as much as 50% using air sparging as compared to conventional pump-and-treat system.

Despite the preliminary success of this remedial technology at various contaminated sites, the design of an air sparging system is empirical and is generally based on the experience of the design engineer. This is due to the lack of understanding of the various processes that occur in the subsurface during air sparging. The objective of this study is to investigate the effect of various physical-chemical properties of the VOCs and soil on the removal of VOCs during air sparging using a laboratory-scale air sparging system. Experiments were conducted with two soil types, three different VOCs, and three injected air flowrates.

EXPERIMENTAL PROCEDURE AND MATERIALS

Materials and Methods

Experiments were conducted using a laboratory-scale air sparging system consisting of a 55-gal (208-L) polyethylene tank with a diameter of approximately 24 in. (61 cm) and a depth of 35 in. (89 cm) (see Figure 1). For each experimental run, the volume of soil used was approximately 48 gal (181 L). The depth of the soil in the tank was approximately 32 in. (81 cm). The free water surface was kept at 1 in. (2.5 cm) above the soil. This approach was to simulate a typical unconfined aquifer without an unsaturated zone. Air for sparging purposes was supplied by an oil-free air compressor. Injected air flowrates were controlled by a ball valve and measured by flow meters on the influent and effluent lines. The screen used was a porous stone diffuser with a diameter of 2 in. (5 cm) and a length of 4 in. (10 cm). The lower end of the screen was placed at approximately 2 in. (5 cm) above the bottom of the tank. Sampling points on the influent and effluent air flow lines were used to collect air samples for analysis.

Two different types of soil, fine sand with a D_{10} of 0.25 mm and a coarse sand with a D_{10} of 1.1 mm, were used for the experiments. VOCs used for the experiments were chloroform, trichloroethylene, and carbon tetrachloride. Physical-chemical properties of soils and VOCs used are presented in Table 1 and Table 2, respectively.

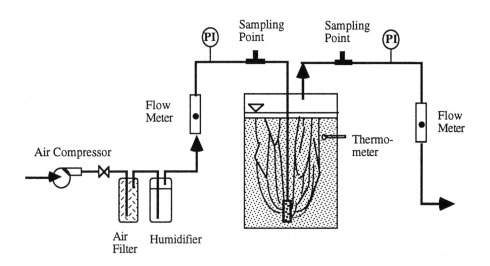

FIGURE 1. Sketch of laboratory-scale air sparging system.

TABLE 1. Physical properties of soils.

Soil Type	Fine Sand	Coarse Sand
Grain size, D_{10} (mm)	0.25	1.1
Uniformity coeff. (D_{60}/D_{10})	1.8	1.7
Particle density (g/cm^3)	2.6	2.8
Porosity	0.39	0.41
Hydraulic conductivity (cm/s)	0.012	0.057
Total carbon content (%)	0.251	0.225

Experimental Procedure

Each soil type was washed thoroughly with clean tap water and any free water was drained. Clean soil was thoroughly mixed with VOC-contaminated water, and the slurry was transferred to the tank layer by layer. Packing was completed within 20 min. The procedure ensured that the concentrations of VOCs throughout the packed column were fairly uniform. Efforts were taken to minimize volatilization of VOCs during packing as much as possible. The tank was immediately sealed, and the contaminated soil was allowed to equilibrate for at least 30 h before air was injected into the packed column. Three different air flowrates, 20, 35, and 50 L/min, were used for the experiments. Throughout the experiments, air samples from the effluent sampling port were analyzed every 15 min for the first 12 h, after which samples were taken hourly. The air sparging experiments were operated over a 24-h period and were terminated when the VOC concentration in the off-gas was low or remained relatively constant. VOC concentrations in the effluent off-gas were measured using a gas chromatograph (Shimazu GC-14A) equipped with a flame ionization

TABLE 2. Physical-chemical properties of VOCs.

Type of VOC	Chloroform	Trichloroethylene	Carbon Tetrachloride
Solubility (mg/L)	7,710	1,100	970
Henry's law constant (dimensionless)	0.15	0.40	1.24
Log K_{ow}	1.93	2.42	2.73
K_{oc} (mL/g)	31	126	110
Diffusion coeff. (10^{-5} cm^2/s)	1.12	1.03	0.99

detector. At the end of the experimental run, soil and water samples were collected from the tank and analyzed for residual VOC concentrations. The temperature of the air sparging system was maintained at 22 ± 3°C throughout each experimental run.

RESULTS AND DISCUSSION

Figure 2 presents data on typical changes in the normalized off-gas TCE concentrations with time for three air flowrates and two different types of soil. Normalized concentrations were obtained by dividing the off-gas TCE concentration at a given time to the initial off-gas TCE concentration in the headspace of the experimental apparatus. All curves showed an initial sharp drop in the off-gas concentration. This was followed by a fairly slower change in off-gas TCE concentration with time. This slow change in off-gas TCE concentration has been attributed to diffusion limitation by several researchers (Johnson et al. 1993; Ahlfeld et al. 1994), although this explanation has not been proven. For an air flowrate of 20 L/min, there appears to be a difference between the off-gas TCE concentration for the experimental run using coarse sand and the experimental run for fine sand. The higher concentrations in the off-gas of the coarse sand experiment indicate that a larger fraction of TCE was being volatilized from the coarse sand as compared to the fine sand. However, as the flowrate was increased to 50 L/min, the concentrations of TCE in the off-gas for both coarse and fine sand were found to be similar. Results as shown in Figure 2 would imply that air flowrate has reached a level value in which the masses of VOCs removed from both coarse and fine sand were similar. Conceptually, air flow through the soil column may be visualized as consisting of air channels with diameters in the range of several grain size diameters (Ji et al. 1993). Mass transfer from the liquid to vapor phase occurs across the water-air interface and is dependent on the interfacial surface area of liquid-vapor interface of the air channels. It is plausible that at a flowrate of 50 L/min, the effect of the soil type on mass transfer was minimal because the surface area available for mass transfer for both coarse and fine sand may be similar at this air flowrate. It must be emphasized that, although both soils have different D_{10} values, the uniformity coefficient and packed porosity for both soils were similar (see Table 1), which may have resulted in similar air flow patterns through the packed column beyond a certain air flowrate.

Figure 3 compares the change in the normalized off-gas TCE concentrations for TCE-contaminated water only ("water experiment") and TCE-contaminated fine sand at an air flowrate of 50 L/min. The "water experiment" was conducted with only the TCE-contaminated water present in the experimental apparatus. The off-gas TCE concentration for the TCE-contaminated sand experiment was at least one order of magnitude lower than the off-gas TCE concentration for the "water experiment." After an initial rapid decline in the off-gas TCE concentration, the rate of TCE removal from the "water experiment" continued to be

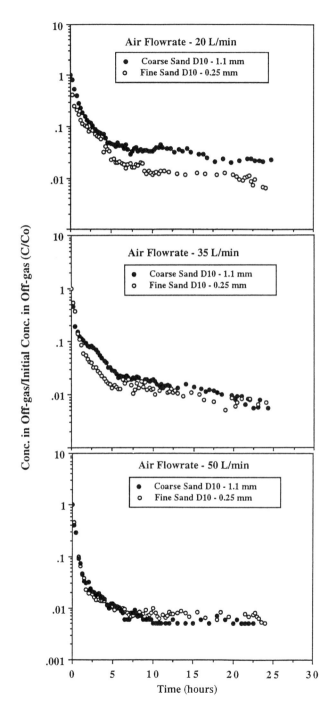

FIGURE 2. Change in normalized off-gas TCE concentrations for fine and coarse sand at three air flowrates.

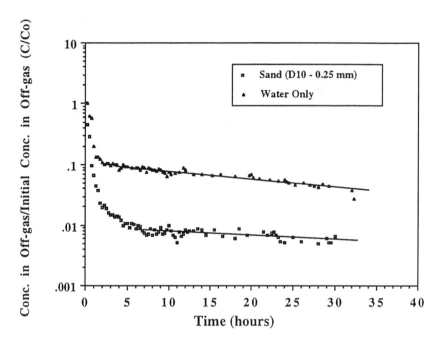

FIGURE 3. Comparison of TCE removal for TCE-contaminated water and TCE-
contaminated sand at an air flowrate of 50 L/min.

larger than that for the TCE-contaminated soil, as shown by the slope of the
change in TCE concentrations with time. Mixing plays an important role in the
"water experiment" (Matter-Muller et al. 1981), while mixing may be minimal
for the TCE-contaminated sand experiment, although micromixing has been
invoked as a possible factor affecting volatilization (Hein et al. 1994). Results
from this set of experiments would suggest that formation of air bubbles within
the porous media would be unlikely during air sparging as suggested by several
researchers (Sellers and Schreiber 1992; Brown and Fraxedas 1991).

   Percent removal efficiencies for chloroform, TCE, and carbon tetrachloride
over a 24-h period at three different air flowrates are presented in Figure 4.
As expected, the extent of VOC removal efficiencies was found to be proportional
to their Henry's law constant. According to the results in Figure 4, carbon tetrachloride (with the larger Henry's law constant of the three compounds) was
more easily volatilized than chloroform and TCE. The percent removal over
a 24-h period for carbon tetrachloride was almost twice that for chloroform for
the same air flowrate.

   The expectation that the removal efficiencies would be more than double
for an increase in air flowrate from 20 to 50 L/min was not evident, as shown
in Figure 4. This may be explained by the mass transfer of VOCs across the
interfacial area of the air-water interface of discrete air channels. Assume that
the air channels are cylindrical in shape and that the air velocity in the channel

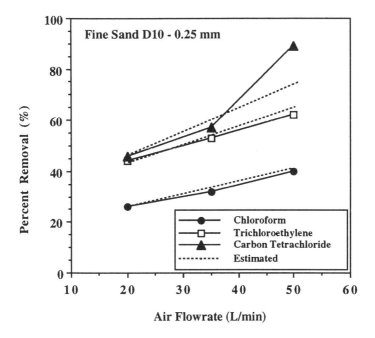

FIGURE 4. Removal efficiencies for three VOCs as a function of air flowrates.

remains the same even for a change in air flowrate. If the air flowrate was doubled, the interfacial surface area is expected to increase by only 41%, i.e., $(Q_{final}/Q_{initial})^{0.5} = (2)^{0.5}$. For the experiments presented in Figure 4, the interfacial surface area would increase by $(50/20)^{0.5}$ or 58%. This percent change is similar to the percent change in the removal efficiencies for TCE and chloroform for an increase in flowrate from 20 to 50 L/min. The above calculation implies that mass transfer may be limited by the available water-air interfacial area of discrete air channels formed during air sparging. In the case of carbon tetrachloride, the estimated percent removal was much less than the actual removal efficiencies. It is plausible that mass transfer of carbon tetrachloride at the air-water interface may be vapor-phase limited while for the other two VOCs, mass transfer may be aqueous-phase limited. Carbon tetrachloride has a higher Henry's law constant than the other two VOCs tested.

CONCLUSIONS

As expected, results presented indicate that Henry's law constant provided a qualitative assessment of the removal efficiencies of VOCs during air sparging. Depending on the soil types, it is plausible that beyond a certain air flowrate the removal rate for two different types of soil may be similar. Mixing plays an important role in the removal of VOCs from bulk solution. In the case of air sparging, mixing within the porous media would be limited to the size of the air channels within the porous media and, therefore, volatilization of VOCs would be limited and would be dependent the interfacial area available and on other slower mass transfer processes, such as aqueous diffusion. The incremental percent change in removal efficiency for a change in air flowrate appeared to indicate that the available interfacial surface area of air channels may play a role in VOC volatilization.

REFERENCES

Ahlfeld, D. P., A. Dahmani, and W. Ji. 1994. "A conceptual model of field behavior of air sparging and its implications for applications." *GWMR* (Fall): 132-139.

Brown, R. A. 1992. "Control technology news: VOC remediation costs, time frames reduced up to 50% with air sparging." *J. Air Waste Management Assoc.* 42(5):729.

Brown, R. A., and R. Fraxedas. 1991. "Air sparging-extending volatilization to contaminated aquifers." Prepublication draft presented at the Symposium on Soil Venting, April 29-May 1, Robert S. Kerr Environmental Research Laboratory, Houston, TX.

Hein, G. L., N. J. Hutzler, and J. S. Gierke. 1994. "Quantification of the mechanisms controlling the removal rate of volatile contaminants by air sparging." In J. N. Ryan and M. Edwards (Eds.), *Proc. of the 1994 National Conference on Environmental Engineering*, American Society of Civil Engineers, New York, NY.

Ji, W., A. Dahmani, D. P. Ahlfeld, J. D. Lin, and E. Hill. 1993. "Laboratory study of air sparging: Air flow visualization." *GWMR*, 13(4):115-126.

Johnson, R. L., P. C. Johnson, D. B. McWhorter, R. E. Hinchee, and I. Goodman. 1993. "An overview of in situ sparging." *GWMR*, 13(4):127-135.

Matter-Muller, C., W. Guer, and W. Giger. 1981. "Transfer of volatile substances from water to the atmosphere." *Water Res.*, 15:1271-1279.

Sellers, K., and R. Schreiber. 1992. "Air sparging model for predicting groundwater cleanup rate." *Proc. of the 1992 Conference on Petroleum Hydrocarbons and Organic Chemicals in Groundwater: Prevention, Detection and Restoration*, National Ground Water Association, Houston, TX, pp. 365-376.

Biosparging Results:
How Clean Is the Site?

Jeffery F. Billings, James E. Griswold, and Bradford G. Billings

ABSTRACT ————————————————————————

Biosparging, a technique similar to air sparging but with the design intent of plume discretization with low to moderate flows per sparge point and operational patience to allow for bioremediation, is producing remediation results distancing itself from air sparging in general. While some debate the efficacy of sparging, this paper discusses results at biosparging sites that are by design and operation significantly different than results from air sparging sites. The authors have participated in biosparging projects across the country for a number of years that have resulted in a range of applications with a large database of results. To provide insight into recent debate concerning the use of water quality results at sparging sites, data from permanent monitoring wells, located 50 to 200 feet beyond the direct influence of air movement, are provided. Water quality results from wells where systems have been off from weeks to more than a year also are provided, as well as confirmation borings of soil concentrations above, at, and below the water table. Additionally, results from new borings and monitoring wells are provided for systems after shutdown. Wells undergoing active sparging/ agitation can provide results indicating clean water. The question of how clean the site is remains. The authors provide data that should place the sampling debate in the proper forum, i.e., one of technique and interpretation, not one of the efficacy of biosparging.

INTRODUCTION

Biosparging is a variation of air sparging. A distinction can be made primarily based upon design and operation with the intent of maximizing the amount of in situ remediation due to biologic processes. The type, frequency, and use of monitoring data also separates the methodologies. There are differences with most other sparging operations as to the number and spacing of injection points, along with the rate at which air is supplied to any given point. Such distinctions merit consideration of biosparging as unique compared to air sparging, as has been the case with bioventing and sparging or venting of the vadose zone. Although similar to air sparging, the design, operation, and results of biosparging systems are different. Biosparging is more dependent upon the biodegradation component of remediation rather than the diffusion of volatiles into the injected airstream.

In applications implemented by these authors, biosparging systems are designed and installed to discretize the contaminant plume into small volumes into which airflow is readily controlled. The rate of air injection is lower than that usually associated with air sparging. As site remediation progresses, biodegradation becomes the prevalent remedial path. This is especially true for tightly sorbed and/or less volatile organic molecules. While biosparging is applied to stimulate biodegradation, it does not neglect the volatilization remediation path of air sparging or soil vapor extraction. The biosparging system utilized at all remediation sites discussed in this paper is the SVVS® technology, a United States patented and trademarked system. The authors operate the technology under a nonexclusive license.

Water quality results from some sparging efforts can lead to an erroneous conclusion that the entire site is clean. At times soil sampling confirmation is lacking. There may be programs wherein water quality results have been obtained from wells undergoing active aeration and extrapolated to the entire subsurface. Misapplications of sparging may have occurred at sites, including overpressurization and movement of the dissolved-phase or free-phase plume. Temporarily clean water can be obtained with overzealous sparging. Proper system design and operation, along with a measure of patience, will yield better remediation results.

RESULTS

This section presents examples of various protocols for evaluating whether a site is clean. All sites used the patented biosparging technology as the sole remedial action. Results of water samples with air injection off and with injection and extraction off for a range of time are presented. Soil samples above and below the water table with the system off, new boring and well locations with the system off, and an intensive sampling program conducted by the U.S. Environmental Protection Agency (EPA) to develop statistically significant results in a short period are presented.

Lomas

An unknown quantity of fuel was released at the Lomas site. Depth to groundwater is approximately 50 feet, with a flow direction southeast as depicted on Figure 1. Vadose zone lithology consists of silty sands to clay stringers, with very fine sand to boulders in the saturated zone. Monitoring wells are shown in the figure, with benzene, toluene, ethylbenzene, and total xylenes (BTEX) analytes. Of particular concern was the contamination in the downgradient portion of the site. Initial water quality results from these wells yielded benzene concentrations ranging from 4,000 to 12,000 parts per billion (ppb), and BTEX in a range of 5,000 to 60,000 ppb.

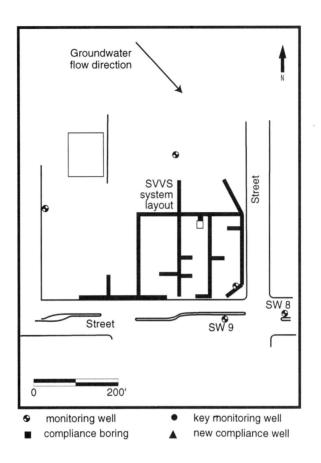

FIGURE 1. Lomas.

A biosparging system was installed in 1991 and water quality standards were reached in approximately 1 year. Another release site is located immediately downgradient with its upgradient wells not detecting encroachment of the Lomas plume. Wells SW-8 and SW-9 are located outside the influence of direct agitation. Air injection was terminated after 13 months and dissolved-phase contaminant levels have since remained below standards. Hydrocarbon levels from the vapor extraction system remained high (> 1,000 ppmv) despite the injection system being turned off. Extraction was terminated in 1994. The site remains in closure monitoring.

This site serves as an example wherein groundwater quality has been restored but the site cannot be described as totally clean. A significant amount of vadose zone contamination remains (based on the vapor emissions data) but appears to be no longer in contact with groundwater. The site illustrates that favorable water quality results can be sustained after air injection has ended, and that results acquired during injection are indicative of reclamation progress.

Montano

An unknown quantity of contamination was released at the Montano site. The initial extent of the dissolved-phase BTEX and naphthalene plume is shown on Figure 2. Depth to groundwater is about 40 ft (12 m), with flow direction to the southeast. All monitoring wells are located outside the influence of air agitation. A biosparging system was installed, and BTEX and naphthalene groundwater standards were achieved in less than 1 year. Levels of hydrocarbon vapor and carbon dioxide (an indicator of relative biologic activity) in the air extraction stream were observed to substantially decay. Injection was terminated, and three subsequent quarters of monitoring have yielded dissolved-phase concentrations which remain less than applicable standards to nondetectable. The site currently is under closure monitoring.

During remedial activities, a total of 20 soil borings were advanced in seven repeated areas on four occasions with soil headspace readings obtained every 5 ft (1.5 m) from surface to 10 ft (3 m) below the average water table. Figure 2

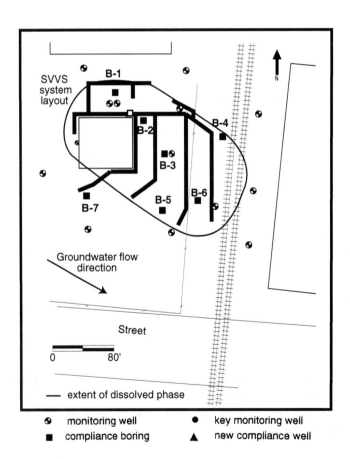

FIGURE 2. Montano.

identifies the approximate locations of these borings. Table 1 presents the headspace measurements. Review of the table indicates that adsorbed contamination was being remediated upwards from the depth at which air was injected.

The monitoring protocol at this site consisted of dissolved-phase monitoring, emissions monitoring of expelled hydrocarbon and carbon dioxide, along with direct verification of soil contaminant levels by redrilling. This combination gave sufficient information to the regulatory body and the potentially responsible party such that termination of active reclamation could be made with a reasonable expectation of minimal future impact.

Firehouse

A release of fuel from the fire department forced closure of a municipal supply well. Locations of pertinent features are shown on Figure 3. Depth to groundwater is approximately 20 ft (6 m), groundwater flow is to the southwest,

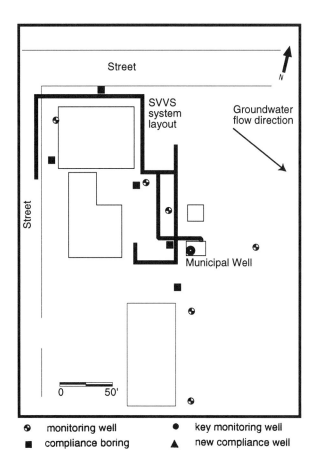

FIGURE 3. Firehouse.

TABLE 1. Soil headspace data for Montano site.[(a)(b)]

Depth (feet)	B-1				B-2				B-3				B-4	B-5				B-6	B-7	
	6/92	6/93	12/93	4/94	6/92	6/93	12/93	4/94	6/92	9/93	12/93	4/94	6/92	6/92	9/93	12/93	4/94	6/92	6/92	12/93
5	0				0				6											
10	0		0	0	0				2			0	0	0		0	0	0	8	0
15			0	0	3		0	0	1		0	0					0			0
20	6		0	0	2	7	0	0	1	1	0	0	0	0		0	0	0	24	0
25	20	319	224	8	322	0	0	0	1	1	0	0				0	0		59	0
30	137	117	135	42	289	246	41	13	2425	1626	199	189	0	64	348	120	13	0	99	5
35	740	898	249	328	1100	984	132	0	1036	202	11	12		665	508	105	129		85	61
40	117	20	21	4	209	11	0	2	217	9	5	0	11	672	258	35	94	6	603	0
45	193	8	9	0	87	4	0		192	2	0	0	21	96	13	5	3	48	328	0
50	136	1	0	0	114	0	0	0	45	0	0	0	18	35	0	0	5		30	0

(a) Refer to Figure 2 for boring locations. All headspace concentrations are expressed in parts per million by volume (ppmv), and 1 ft = 0.3 m.

(b) All data obtained using a photoionization detector incorporating a 10.2-eV lamp calibrated with a 1.0-benzene response factor to a 100-ppmv isobutylene-in-air standard. New Mexico regulatory soil action level is 100 ppmv.

and the geologic material consists of silty caliche layers intermixed with very fine sands.

A biosparging system was installed over the BTEX and methyl tertiary butyl ether (MTBE) plume. Groundwater standards were achieved within 3 years of operation. Initial levels of dissolved-BTEX were analyzed at 20,000 ppb. Hydrocarbon and carbon dioxide gathered by the associated vapor extraction system declined to low concentrations. Active reclamation was terminated and borings advanced at locations chosen by the regulatory entity as shown on the figure. Soil samples were obtained from the saturated and unsaturated zones, with soil analytes being BTEX, MTBE, and total recoverable petroleum hydro-carbons (TRPH). All results yielded contaminant concentrations less than their applicable standards to nondetectable. The site is in closure monitoring. Three quarters of water samples have been collected since shutdown, with all results remaining below standards to nondetectable.

The monitoring protocol leading to system shutdown at this site was the same as with the Montano project previously discussed (i.e., groundwater sampling, emissions monitoring, and a redrilling program). To enable the eventual reuse of the supply well, the ultimate remedial goal of this project is to cost-effectively reduce dissolved-phase contaminant levels beyond the regulatory limits to concentrations below the laboratory method detection limit.

Bloomfield

In the mid-1980s, free-phase product was noted in a municipal wastewater treatment unit. Location of product entrance was found and a sewer line was repaired. Remedial activities by another firm began at the Bloomfield site using pump-and-treat, groundwater depression, and free-product recovery, along with vacuum extraction. Significant funds were exhausted in those efforts and the extent of the plumes appeared to have increased. Groundwater depth at the site is 7 ft (2.1 m), and flow direction is to the south as shown on Figure 4. Geologic material consists of silty sands.

A biosparging system was installed in 1991, with contaminant conditions as depicted in the figure. Within 3 years of operation, free product was removed, vadose zone soil samples yielded headspace values below the regulatory action level, and BTEX standards were achieved for all parameters in the five key contract monitoring wells, except for benzene in MW-16. That well has been yielding benzene concentrations on the order of 30 ppb over the last four quarters of monitoring.

The authors shut down the system to conduct a remedial assessment. Four new locations, crossgradient from the key monitoring wells, were selected for installation of new wells. All wells were sampled two weeks later. Results from the new wells correspond with the existing wells, and concentrations at levels less than standards were obtained with one exception of 200 ppb benzene.

The assessment demonstrates that dissolved-phase contaminant levels obtained from the wells installed prior to the initiation of air injection provided representative indication of water quality in those areas. A mobile application

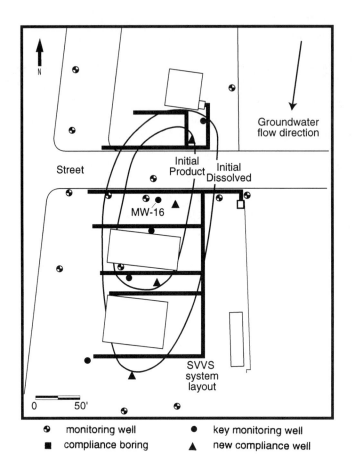

FIGURE 4. Bloomfield.

of the biosparging technology is now planned for the remaining contaminated area, with closure monitoring anticipated thereafter.

Buchanan

The authors were asked to place the patented technology into the EPA's Superfund Innovative Technology Evaluation (SITE) for a statistical evaluation of its ability to remediate pollutants such as BTEX, tetrachloroethene (PCE), trichloroethene (TCE), and 1,1-dichloroethene (DCE). The authors designed and aided in the installation of the system, and Brown & Root Environmental, Inc. functioned as the system operator. All sampling, analysis, and reporting was carried out independently for the EPA by Science Applications International Corporation. The Buchanan site is located at an operating manufacturing facility in the glacial tills of Michigan, with multiple subsurface units of silts, sands, and clays. The contaminants were released to a dry well during various die casting, plating, painting, and assembly operations at the facility.

The system was initiated in early 1993 with the demonstration planned for a 1 year evaluation. Prior to the demonstration, the authors were asked by the EPA to provide an estimate of the technology's ability to reclaim soils and groundwater. Our expectation was that at least a 30% reduction of all consti- tuents could be achieved in the immediate area during the evaluation period.

In 1994, the demonstration was terminated, and pre- and postoperation sampling results were compared. Emphasis of the project was on statistical evaluation of saturated and unsaturated zone soils. Over 120 locations and more than one million dollars were expended in the sampling and evaluation of numerous organic and inorganic parameters. Pertinent conclusions reached in the draft report of October, 1994 and EPA/540/MR-94/529 of January, 1995 are presented below. (Note: volatile organic compounds (VOC) concentrations are the sum of BTEX, PCE, TCE, and DCE.)

- "When evaluating system performance by comparing VOC concentra- tions in matched boreholes before and after one year of treatment, contaminant reductions ranged from 71% to 99%. This indicated that the system operated relatively uniformly over the entire vadose zone of the treatment plot, and no significant untreated areas were encountered, regardless of initial VOC concentration or lithology."
- "A comparison of VOC contamination before and after one year of treatment revealed a 99.3% reduction in the saturated zone."
- "A t-test was performed on log normal transformed total VOC data to determine if the reductions observed were significant. The results of the t-test indicate that the reductions observed were significant with a 90% confidence level."

These results were supplied to the EPA Enforcement Office for an anticipated reversal of the Record of Decision, which was to haul and burn soils, coupled with vacuum extraction and pump and treat. The cost effectiveness of the patented technology at this site is projected to be considerably better than the initial enforcement decision by the EPA. The protocols established by the EPA for evaluation of the technology were necessarily extreme, but the remedial approach was definitively observed by several independent bodies to exceed the stated cleanup expectations.

CONCLUSIONS

The patented biosparging technology was developed in the late 1980s and is now placing many sites at a closure position. However, care should be taken to prevent an early interpretation that a site is clean, or conversely that the technology doesn't work. Experience with the design and operations of the technology will clean a site, and its cleanliness can be verified. Operators can implement protocols to verify remediation success, including sampling wells outside direct air agitation, reboring and sampling soils, installing new wells, sampling when the system is off, and sampling over time. Results should indicate that the site can be cleaned, if the technology is properly applied.

If sufficient resources can be provided and the final goal is permanent project closure, monitoring methods and a decision-making sequence can be generally defined. Substantive water-quality measurements can be made from proper monitoring wells over the life of the project. This data is not only a history of dissolved-phase contamination in that area, but will indicate when the remediation rate is exceeding that of contaminant desorption or the vadose zone source has been detached from the capillary fringe. The need for interim wells is perhaps warranted in instances of excessive aeration, but it would be more cost-effective to simply terminate air injection temporarily for purposes of sampling.

Continuous observation of the emitted hydrocarbon concentrations of any associated vapor gathering system should be performed which would indicate the state of diffused and sparged contamination within the vicinity of air injection and extraction points. Similar monitoring of emitted carbon dioxide levels (even after the volatile hydrocarbon levels have diminished) can reveal when biologic activity attenuates due to the lack of degradable contaminants not otherwise remediated. These emissions measurements are a useful tool during operational phases to indicate which sections of a properly discretized site have responded favorably allowing redistribution of flows elsewhere.

As confirmation of remedial progress, successive borings can be advanced throughout a project's lifecycle. They would be most efficient when the other criteria mentioned above indicate the time is approaching for a possible end to active reclamation efforts. The larger subset of these borings should not be placed in close proximity to the sparge/vent points, but rather in areas where an overlapping of effect from adjacent sparge points is inferred.

In Situ Air Sparging for Bioremediation of Groundwater and Soils

Denis Lord, Jiyu Lei, Marie-Claude Chapdelaine,
Jean-Luc Sansregret, and Benoit Cyr

ABSTRACT

Activities at a former petroleum products depot resulted in the hydrocarbon contamination of soil and groundwater over a 30,000-m^2 area. Site remediation activities consisted of three phases: site-specific characterization and treatability study, pilot-scale testing, and full-scale bioremediation. During Phase I, a series of site/soil/waste characterizations was undertaken to ascertain the degree of site contamination and to determine soil physical/chemical and microbiological characteristics. Treatability studies were carried out to simulate an air sparging process in laboratory-scale columns. Results indicated 42% mineral oil and grease removal and 94% benzene, toluene, ethylbenzene, and xylenes (BTEX) removal over an 8-week period. The removal rate was higher in the unsaturated zone than in the saturated zone. Phase II involved pilot-scale testing over a 550-m^2 area. The radius of influence of the air sparge points was evaluated through measurements of dissolved oxygen concentrations in the groundwater and of groundwater mounding. A full-scale air sparging system (Phase III) was installed on site and has been operational since early 1994. Physical/chemical and microbiological parameters, and contaminants were analyzed to evaluate the system performance.

INTRODUCTION

In situ air sparging is a technology involving the injection of air, under pressure, into a contaminated zone below the water table. The elimination of contaminants from soil and groundwater can be achieved via two mechanisms, i.e., biodegradation and volatilization. The technology has been applied for remediation of a petroleum depot located in the Port of Québec. Activities over 30 years at the depot had led to the hydrocarbon contamination of soil and groundwater over a 30,000-m^2 area. Part of the contaminated soil was constantly water saturated. Site remediation works initiated in 1993 were carried out in three main phases: site characterization and treatability study, pilot-scale in situ testing, and design and operation of a full-scale treatment system. The sequential manner in which these phases were carried out is used to identify the best remediation technology and its optimum implementation.

PHASE I — SITE CHARACTERIZATION AND TREATABILITY STUDY

The first phase of the project included a characterization study to correctly define the contamination problem and to ascertain physical, chemical, and micro-biological characteristics of the site. The work allowed us to conclude that the site under study was contaminated by petroleum products (diesel fuel, furnace oil, and gasoline) over a 3-hectare surface area. Contamination was located at depths between 2 and 5 m, and part of the zone was constantly saturated. The soil consisted of fine sand with traces of silt. The pH of the soil was 8.5, and the available nitrogen (NH^+_4, NO^-_2, NO^-_3) and phosphorus were 13 mg/kg and 19 mg/kg respectively.

A laboratory treatability study was undertaken between January and April 1993 to evaluate the applicability of the technology to the site and to determine the appropriate treatment conditions. Samples of contaminated soil and water were taken from the site. The study was conducted in laboratory-scale columns of 20 L, packed with the contaminated soil. The columns were filled with the contaminated water to $2/3$ of height to create a water-saturated zone. The upper part of the soil column ($1/3$ of height) was unsaturated. For mass balance purposes, an activated carbon trap was connected to the outlet airflow of each column to adsorb volatile hydrocarbons escaping from the columns. Experiments were carried out for 8 weeks in a temperature control chamber where the temperature was maintained at about 15°C. Treatment conditions, such as addition of nutrients (NH_4NO_3, and K_2HPO_4) and air injection rate, were tested (Table 1). Analysis of the following parameters was done at 2-week intervals: total aerobic heterotrophic bacteria, hydrocarbon degrading bacteria, BTEX (U.S. EPA 1986) and mineral oil and grease (APHS, AWWA, WPCF 1985).

Results obtained from the column experiments are presented in Table 1. The initial density of both total aerobic heterotrophic and hydrocarbon-degrading bacteria was very low ($\leq 5.4 \times 10^2$ CFU/g). These microbial populations increased significantly with supply of air and addition of nutrients (columns 2 and 3). The samples taken from the column 1 also showed an increase in total aerobic hetero-trophic and hydrocarbon-degrading populations. One possible explanation is that during soil column preparation, the oxygenation of soil occurred due to involun-tary air penetration into the soil. In terms of BTEX and mineral oil and grease removal, the results (Table 1) showed that the percentage of removal was generally higher in the unsaturated zone than in the saturated zone, and that the highest contaminant removal was obtained in the column with a high airflow (column 3). BTEX removal percentages after 8 weeks of treatment could attain 94% in the unsaturated zone and 90% in the saturated zone from an initial concentration

TABLE 1. Analyses of microbiological parameters and contaminants for laboratory column experiments.[a]

Parameters	Zone	Initial Concentration	8 weeks of treatment		
			Column 1	Column 2	Column 3
Total aerobic heterotrophic bacteria (CFU/g)	Unsaturated	5.4×10^2	2.7×10^7	1.6×10^8	1.1×10^8
	Saturated	5.4×10^2	2.1×10^5	9.7×10^6	1.8×10^7
Hydrocarbon-degrading bacteria (CFU/g)	Unsaturated	$<1.0 \times 10^2$	1.3×10^4	5.5×10^5	3.4×10^5
	Saturated	$<1.0 \times 10^2$	$<1.0 \times 10^2$	6.3×10^4	6.0×10^4
BTEX (mg/kg)	Unsaturated	72.4	13.7	13.7	4.3
	Saturated	72.4	22.8	22.8	7.6
Mineral oil and grease (mg/kg)	Unsaturated	1,700	1,850	1,250	750
	Saturated	1,700	1,550	1,400	1,100

(a) Experimental conditions:
 Column 1: without air and nutrient injection.
 Column 2: injection of nutrients with a low flowrate of air.
 Column 3: injection of nutrients with a high flowrate of air.

of 72.4% mg/kg. The same treatment period achieved 56% elimination of mineral oil and grease in the unsaturated zone, and 35% in the saturated zone.

At the end of the 8-week experiment, the hydrocarbons adsorbed onto the activated carbon were analyzed. A mass balance study was made to estimate the contribution of biodegradation and volatilization to the elimination of hydrocarbons from the soil columns. The study showed a mass distribution as follows: 35.7% loss of hydrocarbons by biodegradation and 64.3% by volatilization.

PHASE II — IN SITU PILOT-SCALE TESTING

In view of the success obtained during the treatability study, the project then entered an in situ pilot-scale phase. The objective was to evaluate basic technological design parameters, which included the radius of influence, air injection pressure and airflow. The pilot-scale testing was conducted with 1 injection well and 4 observation wells. The injection well was equipped with a valve and a sample removal device. Airflow supplied by a compressor could be adjusted as required. The airflow was first adjusted to 42.5 m³/h, and groundwater levels were measured in the observation wells until stable conditions were observed. The oxygen levels were then measured. Testing was again repeated with an airflow of 21.25 m³/h in the injection well.

Figure 1 presents changes observed in groundwater mounding during the testing with 42.5 m³/h of airflow, at different time intervals and based on the

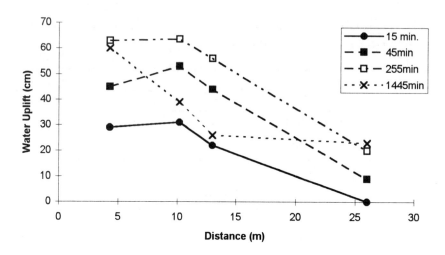

FIGURE 1. Groundwater mounding following air injection as a function of distance at different injection periods.

distance from the injection source. Groundwater reaction to air injection was swift, and only 15 minutes were required for groundwater mounding to be observed at 13 m. The mounding was continued for 3 h, followed by a slow descent. After a 24-h period, a stable profile was observed. Air injection influenced groundwater position up to 26 m from the point of injection. Dissolved oxygen measurements ranged from an average 0.5 mg/L prior to injection to near saturation levels of 11.0 mg/L following injection. These values were observed up to 26 m from the injection source. Ensuing testing with 21.25 m³/h of air injection indicated a radius of influence extended to 12.5 m.

PHASE III — FULL-SCALE TREATMENT SYSTEM

Table 2 presents the main hydrogeologic characteristics of the site and principal design parameters. The site was divided into four plots that functioned independently. A total of 119 injection wells were drilled on the whole area of the site. Air injection was done by using compressors located in an insulated enclosure to permit its operation during winter climatic conditions and to reduce noise levels. Air was channelled directly to the injection wells in polyvinyl chloride (PVC) piping, equipped with valves and sample recovery devices that allow for individual airflow adjustment. Because the contaminated area was widespread and relatively homogeneous, several well patterns were envisioned to optimize air injection efficiency. A triangular well installation was finally selected. Fertilizers (NH_4NO_3) were added by surface irrigation to stimulate bacterial activity. Hydrocarbon fumes released during the system's operation were treated prior to their release into the atmosphere by means of a natural biofilter. The biofilter consisted of a layer of uncontaminated surface soil averaging 2 m in depth. Air

TABLE 2. Site hydrogeologic characteristics and the air sparging design parameters.

Parameter	Description
Nature of the soil	Fine sand with traces of silt
Soil permeability	5×10^{-4} cm/s – 1×10^{-3} cm/s
Type of aquifer	Unconfined
Average groundwater depth	Between 1 and 4 m
Presence of floating particles	Fine layer in some areas
Injected airflow	25.5 m^3/hr well
Radius of influence	12.5 m

TABLE 3. Monitoring data from one plot of 7,000 m^2.

Parameter	Site characterization[a] November 1993	8 months of treatment[b] November 1994
Soil		
Mineral oil and grease (mg/kg)	20,000	9,100
Benzene (mg/kg)	810	n.d.[e]
Toluene (mg/kg)	95.3	n.d.
Ethylbenzene (mg/kg)	n.d.	n.d.
Xylenes (mg/kg)	n.d.	n.d.
TAHB[c] (CFU/g)	5.8×10^5	3.09×10^6
HDB[d] (CFU/g)	5.5×10^4	1.24×10^6
Groundwater		
Mineral oil and grease (µg/L)	60,000	1,180
Benzene (µg/L)	30	n.d.
Toluene (µg/L)	1,960	n.d.
Ethylbenzene (µg/L)	890	n.d.
Xylenes (µg/L)	300	n.d.
TAHB (CFU/mL)	5.03×10^5	2.73×10^5
HDB (CFU/mL)	1.17×10^2	1.96×10^3
O$_2$ (mg/L)	0.52	5.2
T (°C)	10.3	18.6

(a) Results are given as the mean of 13 samples.
(b) Results are given as the mean of 3 samples.
(c) Total aerobic heterotrophic bacteria.
(d) Hydrocarbon-degrading bacteria.
(e) Not detected.

sparging treatment was monitored using 24 observation wells located at equal distances over and around the site area. Soil and groundwater samples were collected from the site for analysis of the parameters indicated in Table 3.

The treatment system was implemented in the spring of 1994. Table 3 presents the results obtained from one plot, which received careful monitoring. The results showed an increase in the hydrocarbon-degrading bacterial population in both soil and groundwater samples collected after 8 months of air sparging operation. The treatment had also a significant effect on groundwater temperature and dissolved oxygen concentration. The groundwater temperature increased from 10.3°C to 18.6°C, and the dissolved oxygen, from 0.52 mg/L to 5.2 mg/L. After the same period of treatment, mineral oil and grease concentrations decreased from an average of 20,000 mg/kg to 9,100 mg/kg in the soil, and from 60,000 µg/L to 1,180 µg/L in the groundwater. Soil and groundwater BTEX concentrations averaged 905.3 mg/kg and 3,180 µg/L prior to system implementation. The treatment reduced BTEX concentrations to nondetectable levels.

CONCLUSION

After 8 months of in situ air sparging treatment, a significant amount of hydrocarbons (BTEX and mineral oil and grease) was eliminated from the site. The full-scale treatment is currently in progress in order to further decrease the level of contaminants at the site.

REFERENCES

APHS, AWWA, WPCF. 1985. *Standard Methods for the Examination of Water and Wastewater*, 16th ed. American Public Health Association and Water Pollution Control Federation.
U.S. EPA. 1986. *Test Methods for Evaluation Solid Waste — Physical/Chemical Methods*. 5W-846.

Biodegradation, Vapor Extraction, and Air Sparging in Low-Permeability Soils

C. Marjorie Aelion, Mark A. Widdowson,
Richard P. Ray, Howard W. Reeves, and J. Nikki Shaw

ABSTRACT

Soil vapor extraction and air sparging (SVE/AS) were implemented to remediate a gasoline-contaminated aquifer in the slightly permeable saprolitic soil of the Appalachian Piedmont of South Carolina. Samples from exhaust gases and multilevel soil probes were collected. CO_2 and O_2 were used as indicators of biodegradation. A portable combined hydrocarbon/O_2 meter and a CO_2 meter were used on site to monitor levels of volatile hydrocarbons (HC), CO_2, and O_2. Field data were verified in the laboratory by gas chromatography (GC). During the 8-h daily SVE operation, exhaust-gas HC mass extraction rates were greatest at daily startup and were reduced to $1/3$ of the initial rates after 1 h of operation and to $1/4$ of the initial rates after 8 h of operation. During the rest period after SVE operation, concentrations of BTEX remained stable and O_2 vapor concentrations in the vadose zone did not fall below 19%. Greater biodegradation appeared to occur as a result of SVE/AS. After SVE/AS, CO_2 ranged from approximately 1 to 4%, with greatest CO_2 and most depleted O_2 measured near the water table and coinciding with greatest BTEX concentrations.

INTRODUCTION

SVE/AS are being implemented to remediate groundwater and soil in Columbia, South Carolina, contaminated by leaking underground storage tanks at a former gasoline station. Appalachian Piedmont's saprolitic soils are characterized by zones of moderate to low-permeability soil. During initial site assessments, soil and groundwater were monitored for benzene, toluene, ethylbenzene, and xylenes (BTEX), and total petroleum hydrocarbons (TPH); a discrete zone of hydrocarbon (HC) contamination centered about the water table region was identified, including small amounts of free product.

In addition to the soil and groundwater sampling, exhaust gases were monitored during SVE and SVE/AS operation to estimate the physical removal of contaminants. Soil vapor was monitored in several nested soil vapor probes in the vadose zone during resting periods to estimate the biological contribution to contaminant removal. Measurements of volatile HC, CO_2, and O_2 were made over time using portable gas meters and were verified by GC in the laboratory to evaluate the impact of daily sampling times on HC concentrations and to investigate physical versus biological contaminant removal.

METHODS

The remediation system consisted of 12 SVE wells (two parallel lines of six wells each) connected to pipes below grade which led to a 5-hp vacuum pump (Figure 1). The SVE wells were approximately 6.9 m deep. SVE well screens were 10 cm in diameter, 1.5 m in length and located from 5.2 to 6.7 m below land surface (bls). Next, 6 AS wells, approximately 9.5-m deep, were connected in line to a compression pump. The AS well screens were 10 cm in diameter and 1.5 m in length, and they were located from 7.9 to 9.5 m bls. The vadose zone soil gas monitoring system consisted of five sample locations. Each soil probe contained four 0.6-cm nested sampling tubes located at discrete vertical intervals of 4.9, 5.8, 6.7, and 7.3 m bls. The water table fluctuated depending on seasonal rain patterns, but was approximately 7.4 m below land surface. Therefore, the deepest probes did not always draw air.

SVE was operated for 6 weeks, followed by a 3-week rest period. SVE/AS was then operated for 6 weeks, followed by a 6-week rest period. System flow rates measured at the exhaust were approximately 180 to 200 m^3/h. Flow from individual SVE wells ranged from 2 to 25 m^3/h, indicative of the heterogeneous nature of the low-permeability saprolite. During operating periods, the systems were on for an 8-h period, 3 days per week. Exhaust gases were collected three times each day of operation into 5-L Tedlar™ gas sample bags fitted with fill valves and syringe ports. Soil vapor was collected prior to system startup and during rest periods, in 5-L Tedlar™ bags using a small diaphragm pump. Samples were diluted by using a flow meter to transfer a known volume of sample and air to a clean Tedlar™ bag if concentrations were off-scale (Robbins et al. 1990).

Vapor samples were analyzed using portable gas meters and in the laboratory by GC. Volatile HC concentrations measured using the portable meters correlated highly with BTEX concentrations obtained using GC (r^2 value of 0.91). CO_2 measurements taken using the meter also correlated well to the GC CO_2 measurements, with an r^2 value of 0.96 (data not shown). BTEX levels were measured by GC using a temperature-programmed Varian 3700 equipped with a flame ionization detector and a megabore capillary column. The O_2 and CO_2 levels were measured using a temperature-programmed Varian 3400 GC equipped with a thermal conductivity detector and a stainless steel packed column. Both systems were equipped with Valco™ gas sampling loops to ensure accurate volumes for gas injections.

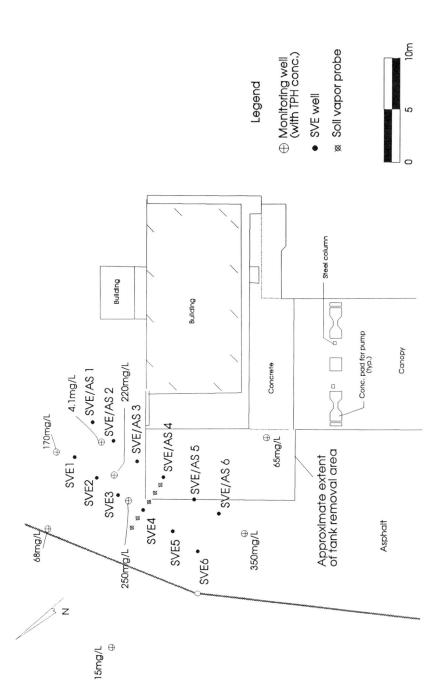

FIGURE 1. Site map including location of SVE and SVE/AS wells, soil vapor probes, and monitoring wells with total petroleum hydrocarbon (TPH) concentrations (mg/L).

Estimates of HC mass extraction rates were determined for each day of SVE and SVE/AS operation. HC concentrations (ppm) measured by the portable meter were converted to mass extraction rates (g/h) using the ideal gas law and an approximate molecular weight for aged gasoline of 100 g/mole (Johnson et al. 1990), and the exhaust gas flowrate (m^3/h). Total mass extracted (kg) was computed by integrating the mass extraction rates over time.

RESULTS

Exhaust Gas Concentrations

A preliminary testing of the exhaust gases was carried out over a 7-h sampling period (Figure 2A). Rates of mass extraction measured in exhaust gases based on HC concentrations derived from the portable meters followed the same patterns as those of BTEX measured by laboratory GC, suggesting that BTEX was a relatively constant proportion of the volatilized HCs. The initial sample taken at a flow rate of 204 m^3/h 15 min after system startup was approximately 3 times greater (23,500 g HC/h) than the sample taken 1 h after system startup (7,500 g HC/h). There was a slight decrease in HC mass extraction rates and BTEX concentrations during the remaining 5 hourly sampling periods; however, after the initial hour of sampling, HC mass extraction rates were fairly stable for the remainder of the sampling.

Based on these preliminary results, samples of exhaust gas were collected 3 times daily. As predicted by the preliminary monitoring, the first daily sample after the system had been shut down overnight was approximately 2 times greater (17,600 g HC/h) than that after 1.5 h of operation (8,200 g HC/h) (Figure 2B). This differential between initial sampling and subsequent daily sampling was reduced over the 3-week period of SVE operation. HC extraction rates during SVE operation were approximately 6,000 g/h.

Soil Vapor Concentrations
in the Vadose Zone

Soil vapor measurements in 1 of the 5 soil probes are shown in Figure 3 for BTEX, CO_2, and O_2 concentrations at three depths during system rest periods. BTEX concentrations remained relatively stable over the 3-week period following SVE (June 30 to July 18, 1994), and did not show significant changes compared to BTEX concentrations before the system was operational. However, distinct differences in concentrations were evident at different depths, for soil vapor probes P4-1 (7.3 m), P4-3 (5.8 m), and P4-4 (4.9 m). O_2 concentrations did not appear to be depleted at either P4-3 or P4-4. P4-1 had reduced O_2 levels and greater CO_2 and BTEX contamination than the shallower probes. P4-3 and P4-4, conversely, had lesser CO_2 and BTEX contamination and approximately atmospheric concentrations of O_2. Although CO_2 concentrations were greater than atmospheric, they were generally below 1% at all sampling times.

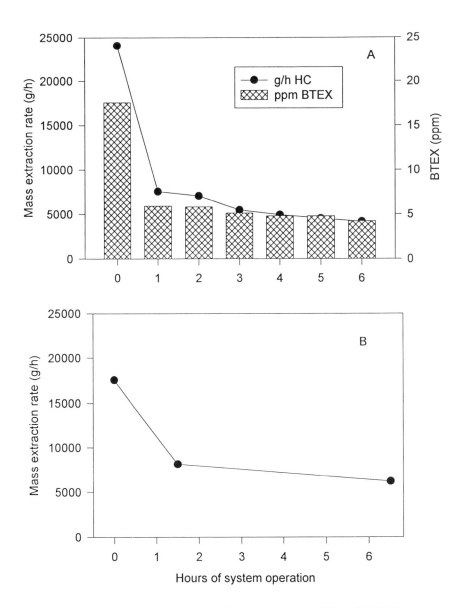

FIGURE 2. (A) Mass extraction rate of hydrocarbons (g/h) and BTEX concentrations (ppm) in exhaust gases over time in test SVE operation. (B) Mass extraction rate of hydrocarbons (g/h) during actual SVE operation.

After this 3-week rest period, the system was operated with SVE/AS combined for a 6-week period (days 70 to 106). A rest period was again established and soil vapor monitored. BTEX concentrations were reduced in the P4-1 sampler at 7.3 m due to physical removal of the combined SVE/AS system, although the BTEX concentrations in the shallower vapor probes were relatively

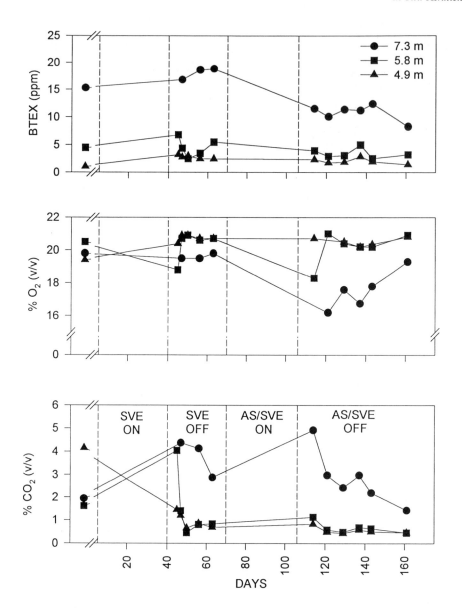

FIGURE 3. BTEX, CO$_2$, and O$_2$ concentrations in the vadose zone soil gases over time during rest periods after SVE operation, and after SVE/AS operation for one well nest at three depths (4.9, 5.8, and 7.3 m).

unchanged. A similar pattern of BTEX, CO$_2$, and O$_2$ concentrations was seen as in the previous soil vapor monitoring. Although O$_2$ was added to the subsurface during system operation, the deepest probe which was the most contaminated, contained the most depleted O$_2$ levels (16%), the greatest concentrations of CO$_2$, approximately 3 to 4%, and BTEX concentrations decreased over this 6-week period. In contrast, little biological activity appeared to occur in P4-3 and P4-4 and few changes in HC, CO_2 or O_2 concentrations were measured at 4.9 and 5.8 m.

DISCUSSION

The portable gas meter measurements of SVE exhaust gas and vadose zone soil gas were time- and cost-effective for on-site monitoring during remediation. Some drawbacks of using the meters and the sampling method described include the potential nonlinear response of the meters at high concentrations, and the need to dilute the samples. Also, O_2 values were not sensitive enough for use as a biological indicator for exhaust gases because of atmospheric dilution at the pump intake. In contrast, O_2 values were useful for vadose zone soil vapor sampling.

HC mass extraction rates varied over the daily SVE and SVE/AS operation with initial rates approximately 2 to 3 times those of subsequent samples. Preliminary exhaust gas sampling at various time intervals over a daily cycle may be necessary if these patterns are not known. In our case, approximately 2 hours were needed for equilibration and stabilization of mass extraction rates. Total mass extraction rates may be grossly miscalculated, if they are based on relatively few sampling points and extrapolated over large time periods.

The consumption of O_2 during rest periods has been shown to be an indicator of microbial processes over relatively short time periods of days to weeks. The heterogeneity of the saprolitic sediments made it difficult to know to what extent O_2 and CO_2 concentrations in the vadose zone were augmented or diminished, respectively, by the addition of either surrounding air from less contaminated areas (SVE) or atmospheric air (SVE/AS) during system operation. Hinchee and Ong (1992) found rapid depletion of oxygen in soil vapor derived from JP-4 degradation over a 40- to 100-h test period with concomitant CO_2 production. At the Columbia, South Carolina site, CO_2 production was present at elevated concentrations (1 to 5%) similar to those found by Hinchee and Ong (1992) and van Eyk (1994) and O_2 concentrations were depleted and therefore a good indicator of microbial metabolism. However, a 3-week resting period following SVE was insufficient for concentrations of CO_2 and O_2 in the vadose zone to change due to bacterial processes at the 4.9 and 5.8 m probes. At these depths it appeared that little or no biodegradation was occurring over that time interval.

Similarly, during the 6-week resting phase after SVE/AS, biodegradation did not appear to affect BTEX, O_2 and CO_2 concentrations in the probes at 4.9 and 5.8 m. The 6-week period did appear to be of sufficient duration to allow bacterial processes to impact concentrations at the deepest soil vapor probe (7.3 m) which was located near the water table surface and contained the greatest BTEX concentrations. Biological removal was suggested by the depleted O_2 concentrations at the lowest depth, even though the lowest depth may have received more of the sparged air because of its proximity to the AS wells. The greatest impact on contaminant concentrations occurred during SVE/AS as opposed to SVE alone, and may be attributable to physical and biological removal processes.

ACKNOWLEDGMENTS

This research was supported by a grant from the South Carolina Hazardous Waste Management Research Fund, the South Carolina Department of Health and Environmental Control, and a National Science Foundation Presidential Faculty Fellow Award in Engineering to C. M. Aelion. The authors would like to thank Mr. Peter Stone and Mr. Robert Faller from SCDHEC for their help.

REFERENCES

Hinchee, R. E., and S. K. Ong. 1992. "A rapid in situ respiration test for measuring aerobic biodegradation rates of hydrocarbons in soil." *J. Air Waste Manage. Assoc.* 42: 1305-1312.

Johnson, C. C. Stanley, M. W. Kemblowski, D. L. Byers, and J. D. Colhart. 1990. "A practical approach to the design, operation, and monitoring of in situ soil-venting systems." *Ground Water Monitoring Review* 10: 159-178.

Robbins, G. A., B. G. Deyo, M. R. Temple, J. D. Stuart, and M. J. Lacy. 1990. "Soil gas surveying for subsurface gasoline contamination using total organic vapor detection instruments, Part II. Field Experimentation." *Ground Water Monitoring Review* 10: 110-117.

van Eyk, J. 1994. "Venting and bioventing for in situ removal of petroleum from soil." In R. E. Hinchee, B. C. Alleman, R. E. Hoeppel, and R. N. Miller (Eds.), *Hydrocarbon Bioremediation*, pp. 243-251. Lewis Publishers, Boca Raton, FL.

In Situ Groundwater Aeration of Polycyclic Aromatic Hydrocarbons

Brian D. Symons, Ron Linkenheil, David Pritchard, Craig A. Shanke, and David Seep

ABSTRACT

At a former wood treating site in Minnesota, the feasibility of in situ groundwater aeration was investigated in a laboratory treatability setting, to evaluate biodegradability and optimal operation conditions of the site aquifer. After concluding that an aeration system would increase the dissolved oxygen concentrations in the groundwater enough to sustain microbial life, a field demonstration system was designed and installed. The system was operated for 1 year, during which groundwater quality at upgradient and downgradient wells was monitored to evaluate the system's effectiveness. The groundwater aeration system successfully reduced groundwater polycyclic aromatic hydrocarbon (PAH) concentrations, especially naphthalene. Naphthalene concentrations were reduced from 1,319 µg/L to below the laboratory detection limit of 0.5 µg/L. Cumulative concentrations of other PAH compounds were reduced from 98 µg/L to 23 µg/L during the 1-year test.

PILOT STUDY OBJECTIVES

A field-scale pilot groundwater aeration study was conducted at a former wood treating site for PAH-contaminated groundwater to answer the following questions: (1) Could groundwater be treated by the aquifer aeration system to remove naphthalene and avoid installation of a National Pollutant Discharge Elimination System (NPDES) groundwater pretreatment system? (2) Could the gradient control (GC) wells be shut down by meeting action levels with the groundwater aeration system? (3) Would operating the system adversely effect aquifer parameters? and (4) What are the optimal operating conditions for the groundwater aeration system?

AQUIFER AERATION SYSTEM DESIGN BASIS

A laboratory treatability study indicated that the average daily oxygen consumption within the aquifer was 2.4 mg O_2/L day, and the biodegradation half-life of naphthalene in the groundwater was estimated at 18 days, or a first-order rate constant of 0.0385/day. The oxygen consumption and biodegradation rates included adjustment for abiotic losses using a sterile control. The groundwater velocity and naphthalene half-life suggested that the groundwater containing naphthalene would need to travel 21.3 m (70 ft) before being biodegraded from 500 µg/L to 50 µg/L. Therefore, the air injection wells were located more than 21.3 m (70 ft) upgradient of Gradient Control Well 1 (GC-1) so that groundwater removed from this well would be reduced to less than 50 µg/L after exiting the aquifer aeration system.

Based on the treatability study results and a groundwater flow rate of 16.4 m^3 (578 ft^3) per day through the air injection system, the groundwater aeration system was designed to remove 0.0172 kg (0.038 lb) of naphthalene per day from the aquifer. The total air injection system was designed to deliver 0.76 m^3 (27 ft^3) per min of air to the aquifer to increase dissolved oxygen concentrations in the aquifer.

AQUIFER AERATION SYSTEM CONSTRUCTION

Construction of the groundwater aeration system was completed in September 1992. A 22-kW (30-hp) rotary-screw air compressor was selected to supply compressed air to each well. The compressor was housed in a 3.1-m (10-ft) by 3.7-m (12-ft) enclosure. An isolation ball valve, pressure regulator, pressure gauge, and flowmeter were installed in the enclosure to measure and control air flow to each air injection well. Polyvinyl chloride (PVC) piping (one pipe per well) was installed in a backfilled trench to transport air from the compressor to each well.

The aeration system design incorporated nine wells, 7.6 m (25 ft) apart from the center of each well (Figure 1). Each well included two casings, one to a depth of approximately 8 m (26 ft) below ground surface (bgs), and the other to a depth of approximately 12 m (38 ft) bgs in a uniform fine sand aquifer. The wells were designed to inject air approximately 3 m (10 ft) below the low water table elevation, which fluctuates between 6.7 m (22 ft) and 7.0 m (23 ft) bgs. The two casings were connected with a manifold near the ground surface, inside a utility box. A pressure gauge was connected to each casing to measure wellhead air pressure.

Two observation wells, OBS-1 and OBS-2, were installed downgradient of the air injection wells, in the same gradient direction with Well GC-1, as shown on Figure 1. One monitoring well, MW-21, was installed upgradient of the air injection wells in the same vertical plane as OBS-1, OBS-2, and GC-1.

AQUIFER AERATION SYSTEM STARTUP

System startup occurred on September 28, 1992. Only the deep injection point in each well was used during the startup of the pilot system. The GC

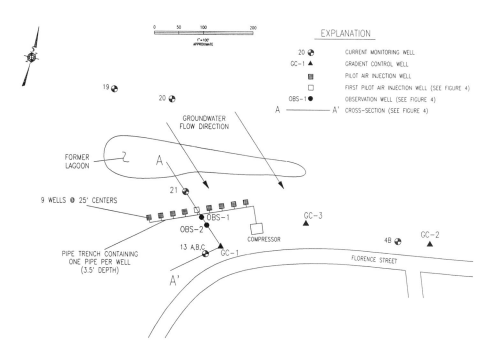

FIGURE 1. In situ aquifer aeration system pilot test site plan.

well pumping system (three wells, GC-1, GC-2, and GC-3, pumping at 50 gpm each) has operated continuously since 1986. Since startup both the GC well system and the groundwater aeration system have operated continuously. Extensive monitoring was conducted following startup for 2 days to assess the following parameters: air flowrate, air pressure, hydrocarbon vapor concentrations, aqueous-phase dissolved oxygen concentrations, and air-phase oxygen concentrations.

The groundwater aeration system radius of influence for each well was calculated using startup monitoring data. Five different methods of determining the radius of influence produced the following results: 4.0 m (13 ft) based on air-phase oxygen monitoring, 4.9 m (16 ft) based on air pressure monitoring, 6.7 m (22 ft) based on air-phase hydrocarbon monitoring, 9.1 m (30 ft) based on dissolved oxygen monitoring; and greater than 10.7 m (35 ft) based on groundwater elevation monitoring.

RESULTS

Naphthalene

Table 1 shows naphthalene concentrations for GC-1 during the pilot test. At the start of the test, the naphthalene concentration at GC-1 was 1,319 µg/L.

TABLE 1. Polycyclic aromatic hydrocarbon concentrations at gradient control well GC-1.

Polycyclic Aromatic Hydrocarbons	Prior[a] 05/04/92	Concentration (µg/L) After Groundwater Aeration System Startup												
		10/06/92	11/03/92	01/04/93	02/22/93	03/24/93	04/22/93	05/17/93	6/21/93	7/26/93	8/23/93	9/20/93	1/27/94	4/12/94
Naphthalene	1,319	770	56	430	<10	30	<10	<10	<9.6	<10	<10	<10	<10	<0.5
2-Methylnaphthalene	NA	25	13	17	3.8 J	NA	<10	<10	<9.6	<10	<10	<10	<10	<0.5
Acenaphthylene	6 J	4.7 J	2.7 J	2.5 J	1.1 J	1.9 J	<10	<10	<9.6	<10	<10	<10	<10	0.5 J
Acenaphthene	47	50	36	29	26	32	26	14	15	15	7.8 J	17	20	17
TOTAL 2-RING PAH	1,372	850	108	479	31	64	26	14	15	15	8	17	20	18
Fluorene	9	9.1 J	5.7 J	4.4 J	3.5 J	3.9 J	5.3 J	3.8	2.6 J	3.5 J	2.5 J	3.3 J	2.7 J	2.0
Phenanthrene	10	9.2 J	5.4 J	4.8 J	3.9 J	3.4 J	1.8 J	2.1	1.5 J	2.5 J	1.3 J	2.4 J	2.4 J	1.8
Anthracene	<9	<10	<10	<10	<10	<9.7	<10	<10	<9.6	<10	<10	<10	<10	<0.5
TOTAL 3-RING PAH	19	18	11	9	7	7	7	6	4	6	4	6	5	4
Fluoranthene	<9	<10	<10	<10	<10	<9.7	<10	<10	<9.6	<10	<10	<10	<10	<0.5
Pyrene	<9	<10	<10	<10	<10	<9.7	<10	<10	<9.6	<10	<10	<10	<10	<0.5
Benz(a)anthracene	<9	<10	<10	<10	<10	<9.7	<10	<10	<9.6	<10	<10	<10	<10	<0.5
Chrysene	<9	<10	<10	<10	<10	<9.7	<10	<10	<9.6	<10	<10	<10	<10	<0.5
TOTAL 4-RING PAH	0	0	0	0	0	0	0	0	0	0	0	0	0	0
Benzo(b)fluoranthene	<9	<10	<10	<10	<10	<9.7	<10	<10	<9.6	<10	<10	<10	<10	<0.5
Benzo(k)fluoranthene	<9	<10	<10	<10	<10	<9.7	<10	<10	<9.6	<10	<10	<10	<10	<0.5
Benzo(a)pyrene	<9	<10	<10	<10	<10	<9.7	<10	<10	<9.6	<10	<10	<10	<10	<0.5
Indeno(1,2,3-cd)pyrene	<9	<10	<10	<10	<10	<9.7	<10	<10	<9.6	<10	<10	<10	<10	<0.5
Dibenz(a,h)anthracene	<9	<10	<10	<10	<10	<9.7	<10	<10	<9.6	<10	<10	<10	<10	<0.5
Benzo(g,h,i)perylene	<9	<10	<10	<10	<10	<9.7	<10	<10	<9.6	<10	<10	<10	<10	<0.5
TOTAL 5-RING PAH	0	0	0	0	0	0	0	0	0	0	0	0	0	0
TOTAL PAH	1,391	868	119	488	38	71	33	20	19	21	12	23	25	21

(a) Prior to groundwater aeration system startup.   NA - Not analyzed.   J - Below quantitation limit (estimated value).

After startup, naphthalene concentrations decreased to a level below detection limits (< 10 µg/L) during the second quarter of 1993 and remained at that level, indicating that the groundwater aeration system was effective in removing naphthalene. Laboratory detection limits were lowered to 0.5 µg/L during the second quarter of 1994 to further define naphthalene and other PAH concentrations. Naphthalene remained undetected at this lower detection limit. Based on these data, 25 kg (55 lb) of naphthalene were removed each day.

Figure 2 shows that naphthalene concentrations at GC-3 varied throughout the test period from approximately 500 µg/L to over 900 µg/L. As expected, these results show that naphthalene concentrations at GC-3 were not affected by installing and operating the groundwater aeration system since GC-3 is outside the radius of influence of the aquifer aeration system. Groundwater contours showed that groundwater direction remained constant during the test period.

PAHs Other Than Naphthalene

Table 1 lists analytical results for specific PAHs as a function of time. Figure 3 shows GC-1 total PAH concentrations (excluding naphthalene) during the pilot test. Naphthalene was excluded because its concentration was much greater than other PAH compounds. Cumulative concentrations of the other PAH compounds decreased from 98 µg/L to 23 µg/L during the pilot test. Acenaphthene, fluorene, and phenanthrene accounted for the majority of detected PAH compounds in GC-1 after the second quarter of 1993. All 4- and 5-plus-ring PAH compounds were below detection limits throughout the test period.

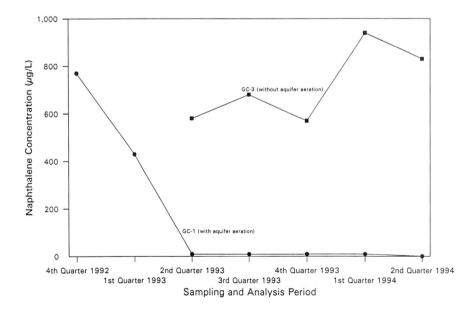

FIGURE 2. Naphthalene concentrations for GC-1 and GC-3.

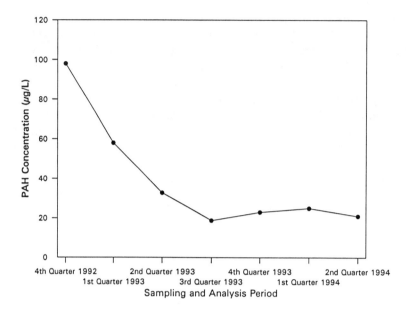

FIGURE 3. Total PAH without naphthalene for GC-1.

Aeration System Effects on Aquifer Characteristics

Previous investigations and laboratory treatability studies (RETEC 1992) indicated that oxygen levels should remain above 1 mg/L to provide optimum conditions for naphthalene degradation. Dissolved oxygen levels in upgradient wells prior to startup ranged from 0.2 to 0.8 mg/L. One month after system startup, dissolved oxygen concentrations in wells OBS-1, OBS-2, and MW-13C downgradient of the aeration system remained at levels near or above 10 mg/L, while dissolved oxygen concentrations remained above 1 mg/L at GC-1 which was also recovering groundwater from the deeper, nonaerated aquifer. Dissolved oxygen concentrations at MW-21, upgradient of the system but within the radius of influence of the groundwater aeration system, increased and generally remained at levels above 3 mg/L after 1 month of operation. Relative well depths are shown on Figure 4.

The optimum temperature range for microbial populations found in groundwater is between 10°C and 30°C (Clark et al. 1977). The majority of groundwater temperatures measured before and during the pilot test were relatively constant and slightly above 10°C, indicating that the aquifer provided a suitable microbial environment and that aquifer temperatures were not significantly affected by injection of air.

Groundwater elevations were monitored at MW-21, OBS-1, OBS-2, MW-3B, MW-19, MW-20, GC-1, GC-2, and GC-3. The location of these wells is shown on Figure 1. A seasonal variation was observed during the pilot test, with minimum elevations occurring during the second quarter of 1993 (spring) and maximum

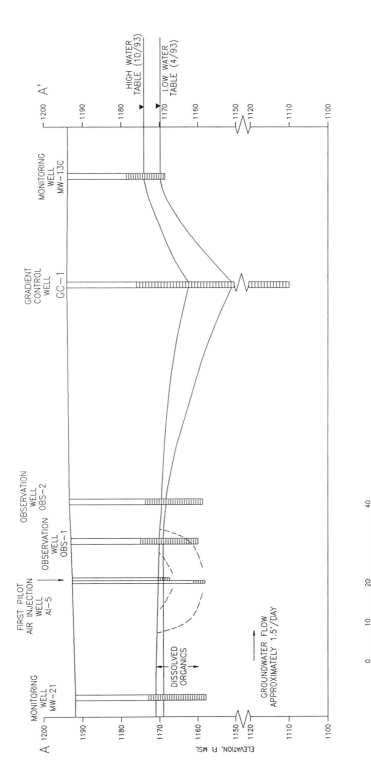

FIGURE 4. In situ aquifer aeration system pilot test cross section.

elevations occurring during the fourth quarters of 1992 and 1993 (fall) for most wells. Based on water level data, the water table elevation, reported as mean sea level (MSL), decreased toward the cone of depression caused by pumping at GC-1 (Figure 4). Air injection into the aquifer did not disrupt the long-term water table elevation or cone of depression caused by pumping at GC-1, although a short-term increase of 0.17 m (0.57 ft) to 0.26 m (0.86 ft) in the water table elevation at the monitoring wells was observed.

In Situ Respirometry Testing

From April 25 through May 2 1994, an in situ respirometry test was conducted to evaluate the aquifer aeration system efficiency. The compressor supplying air to the aquifer aeration system was turned off, and dissolved oxygen concentrations were measured at specific intervals. Dissolved oxygen measurements were taken with a dissolved oxygen meter at all air injection wells, and at wells MW-21, OBS-1, and OBS-2. The measurements were taken approximately 0, 0.08, 0.25, 0.75, 1.25, 2, 3, and 4.25 days after the compressor was turned off.

The oxygen uptake rate (mg O_2/L day) is the slope of the line on a graph of dissolved oxygen (mg/L) as function of time (days). The calculated oxygen uptake rates ranged from 2.7 mg O_2/L day to 10.6 mg O_2/L day. These field-determined oxygen uptake rates agreed well with the laboratory treatability results of 2.4 mg O_2/L day.

Based on the measured in situ oxygen uptake rates, the total amount of oxygen consumed each day was 8.31 kg (18.3 lb) O_2/day. The total amount of oxygen injected into the groundwater was calculated to be 430 kg (949 lb) O_2/day. The oxygen transfer efficiency (OTE) was calculated by dividing the amount of oxygen consumed by the amount of oxygen injected, resulting in an OTE of 1.93%. The calculated OTE was less than literature values of 4 to 15% (Metcalf and Eddy 1991) for coarse bubble diffusers. The lower OTE suggests that airflow rates to the groundwater may be reduced to increase the OTE and lower electrical operating costs of the groundwater aeration system.

SUMMARY

The groundwater aeration system was successful in reducing groundwater PAH concentrations, especially naphthalene, indicating that in situ aquifer aeration can be used to eliminate the need for a costly NPDES wastewater treatment system. As shown on Figure 2, by the second quarter of operation, naphthalene concentrations were reduced below the detection limit of 10 µg/L (from 98 to 23 µg/L). This is well below NPDES discharge requirements. Concentrations of other PAH compounds also were significantly reduced during aquifer aeration, as indicated on Figure 3.

During the second quarter of 1994, laboratory detection limits were reduced to further define PAH levels at low concentrations and to evaluate the feasibility of turning off the gradient control wells. Naphthalene remained undetected

(<0.5 µ/L) as did other PAH compounds, with the exception of acenaphthylene, acenaphthene, fluorene, and phenanthrene. Because these compounds were still above the low action levels established for this site, abandonment of the gradient control wells is not considered feasible at this time. This pilot study demonstrated that operation of the system did not adversely affect aquifer parameters. Results from this study were also very effective in optimizing operating conditions for the groundwater aeration system.

REFERENCES

Clark, J. W., W. Viessman, and M. J. Hammer. 1977. *Water Supply and Pollution Control.* Harper & Row, Publishers, New York, NY.

Metcalf and Eddy, Inc. 1991. *Wastewater Engineering Treatment Disposal and Reuse.* McGraw-Hill, Inc. New York, NY.

RETEC. 1992. *Work Plan for a Pilot-Scale Aquifer Aeration Biotreatment System Brainerd Tie Plant,* Brainerd, MN.

Design and Application of an Alternative Groundwater Sparging Technology

Todd W. Schrauf and Leslie H. Pennington

ABSTRACT

Density-driven convection, an alternative method of in situ groundwater sparging, is being used to remediate 27 underground storage tank releases involving a wide distillation range of petroleum hydrocarbons (gasoline to waste oil) in a variety of site soils (silty clay to sandy gravel). The described method overcomes many of the inherent disadvantages of air sparging methods currently in use (such as pressurized injection) without additional complexity in design, installation, or operation. The principles of operation and design for density-driven convection are discussed in detail and supported by field and laboratory studies. Primary factors affecting the hydraulic driving force, groundwater circulation patterns around the sparging well, and air stripping performance are identified and related to system design. The effectiveness of the system is demonstrated with results from full-scale system installations.

INTRODUCTION

Groundwater sparging is a term applied to the injection of air below the water table to induce contaminant removal by volatilization and enhancement of natural aerobic biodegradation. Two separate methods have been used to introduce air to the saturated subsurface: (1) pressurized injection of air into the pore space surrounding the sparge well; and (2) aeration of water within the sparge well by bubbling air through the wellbore water column. The latter method, which the authors have termed density-driven convection (Notice of Allowance for patent received), also is referred to as in-well aeration.

A diagram of a density-driven convection well is presented in Figure 1. Air is injected through a small-diameter line at the base of the well and allowed to bubble upward in the wellbore. The well is constructed with standard monitoring well construction materials, but includes upper and lower screen intervals separated by an annular seal. The upper screen straddles the water table surface

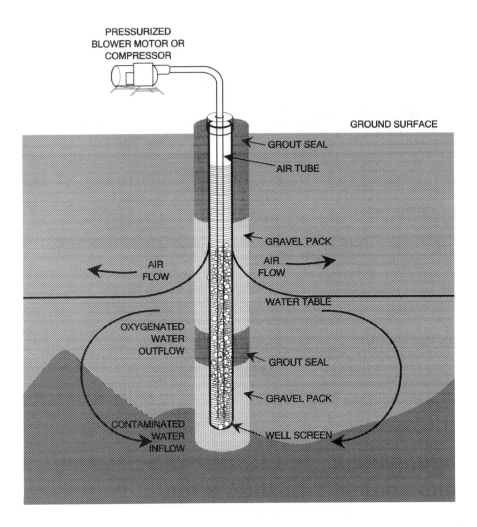

FIGURE 1. Schematic of density-driven convection system.

and exhaust air from the well is discharged to the vadose zone soils via the unwetted portion of the upper screen. Bubbling air within the well creates a hydrostatic head gradient along the wellbore which drives aerated water out of the upper well screen while simultaneously drawing resident groundwater in through the lower screen. Because only water circulates through the formation, the method is suitable for fine-grained soils and high air pressures are not required. The system may also be used to distribute alternative electron acceptors and biological nutrients.

The principles of wellbore hydraulics, groundwater hydraulics, and air-water mass transfer are presented. Evaluation of vadose zone aeration and vapor degradation, associated with exhausting of air through the upper well screen, follows the same principles used in the design of soil vapor extraction and bioventing systems and is not presented herein.

WELLBORE HYDRAULICS

Four distinct flow patterns, shown in Figure 2, have been observed in laboratory experiments (Govier et al. 1957) of the flow of gas-liquid mixtures in vertical pipes. The stable flow pattern observed is strongly dependent upon the superficial gas velocity (volumetric gas flowrate/cross-sectional area) and weakly dependent upon the superficial liquid velocity. The slug flow pattern has been observed in laboratory studies conducted by the authors using a 5 cm diameter clear plastic pipe at air flowrates of 0.3 to 2.3 m^3/h (0.2 to 1.3 cfm). Field measurements of wellbore fluid conductivity and pressure at a fixed measurement point over time also suggest a slug flow pattern in both 5-cm and 10-cm-diameter wells at air flowrates of 1.7 to 6.8 m^3/h (1 to 4 cfm). The identical slug flow pattern was observed using both open tube and air diffuser tips at the point of air injection. Slug flow is characterized by alternating bullet-shaped bubbles (termed Taylor bubbles), which are surrounded by a thin annulus of water, and water slugs containing small air bubbles.

The hydrostatic pressure gradient created along the wellbore during air injection is directly related to the density of the air-water mixture as illustrated in Figure 3. Prior to the introduction of air, the hydraulic head along the wellbore is equal to the static hydraulic head (H_i) in the surrounding formation (Figure 3a). Introduction of air into the wellbore (Figure 3b) results in a change in the average density of the wellbore fluid column and the creation of a vertical hydraulic head gradient (dH/dz) along the wellbore given by:

$$dH/dz = E_g/(1-2T_f/D)^2 - h_l \approx E_g \qquad (1)$$

where E_g is the volume of air per unit volume of mixture, T_f is the water film thickness around the Taylor bubble, D is the wellbore diameter, and h_l is the frictional head loss per unit length associated with water flow through the wellbore. Due to the high density contrast of air and water, the density of the air is ignored in Equation 1. T_f and h_l can be calculated using formulas presented by Govier and Aziz (1972), provided the air and water flowrates through the wellbore are known. For most cases of practical interest, the values of T_f and h_l are sufficiently small that dH/dz can be assumed to approximately equal E_g. Due to the compressibility of air, the value of E_g at a given air flowrate decreases with increasing depth below the water table.

As water flows out of the upper portion of the well into the formation, the height of the air-water column (i.e., the average hydraulic head) in the wellbore decreases so that the average hydraulic head in the wellbore matches that in the adjacent formation (Figure 3c). Because the density contrast of the wellbore fluid with the formation water creates the driving force for groundwater circulation, the term density-driven convection has been used to describe the process.

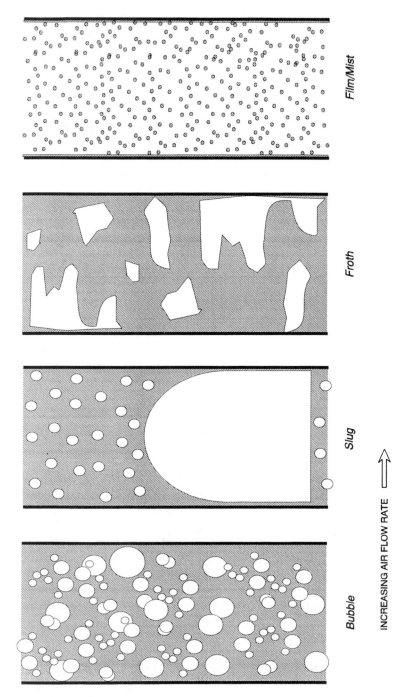

Film/Mist

Froth

Slug

INCREASING AIR FLOW RATE

Bubble

FIGURE 2. Observed flow patterns for air-water mixtures.

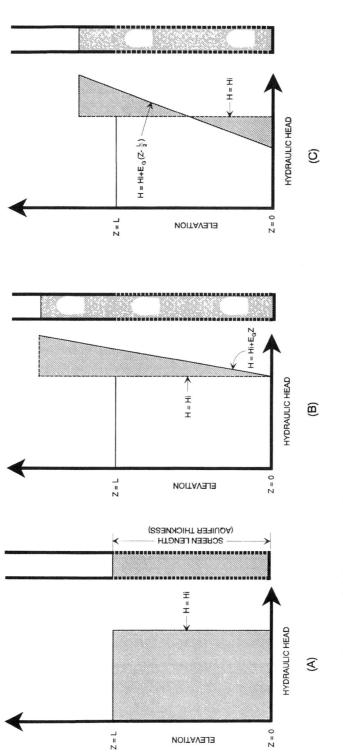

FIGURE 3. Evaluation of driving force for bubble/slug flow.

Laboratory experiments by Akagawa (1964) and Akagawa and Sakaguchi (1966) indicate the hydraulic gradient along the wellbore is strongly dependent upon the superficial air velocity and weakly dependent upon the superficial water velocity. Although the hydraulic gradient initially increases rapidly with increasing superficial air velocity, the hydraulic gradient asymptotically approaches a maximum of about 0.7 m/m at superficial air velocities of about 1.5 m/s. At a given superficial air velocity, the hydraulic gradient decreases slightly in direct proportion to the increase in superficial water velocity. Laboratory and field measurements of hydraulic gradient versus superficial air velocity conducted by the authors have agreed with these previously reported experimental results (Figure 4).

With the relationships presented in this section, the achievable hydraulic gradient and required air flowrate necessary to maintain that gradient can be determined. For shallow groundwater conditions the maximum achievable hydraulic gradient is limited by the depth to groundwater, unless the well casing can be extended above ground surface. Although the relationship between hydraulic gradient and air flowrate can be measured directly in the field, sufficiently accurate estimates for engineering design can normally be obtained from laboratory data.

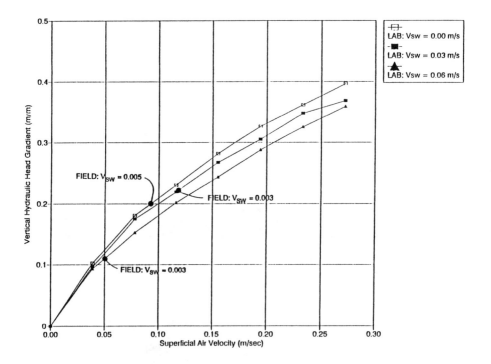

FIGURE 4. Measurements of hydraulic gradient versus superficial air velocity.

GROUNDWATER HYDRAULICS

The hydrostatic head gradient within the wellbore provides the driving force for groundwater circulation in the formation surrounding the sparge well. To evaluate the pattern of groundwater circulation around the sparge well, an analytical solution to Laplace's equation for steady-state groundwater flow in a two-dimensional (radial and vertical) flow field around a sparge well was obtained using separation of variables. The solution for the hydraulic head distribution, based on the flow geometry and boundary conditions presented in Figure 5, is given by:

$$h_D(r,z) = -4/\Pi^2 \sum_{n_{odd}} K_o(nk^*r)\cos(nkz)/K_o(nk^*r_w)n^2$$

$$k = \Pi/L; \quad k^* = k(K_z/K_r)^{0.5}$$

(2)

where: h_D = the dimensionless head change (head change divided by the total head differential at the sparge well)
K_o = the modified zero-order Bessel function of the second kind
L = the aquifer thickness
r = the radial coordinate (r=0 at centerline of well)
z = the vertical coordinate (z=0 at base of aquifer)
r_w = the well radius
K_r = the radial (horizontal) hydraulic conductivity
K_z = the vertical hydraulic conductivity

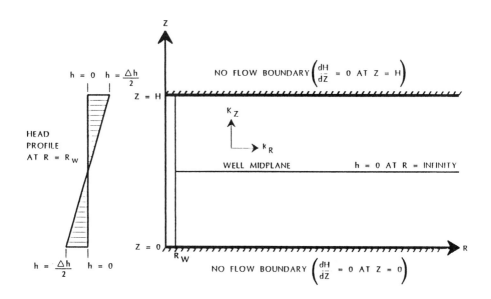

FIGURE 5. Boundary conditions for analytical solution.

Equation 2 is a function of three dimensionless spatial variables: $r_D = (r/L)$ $(K_z/K_r)^{0.5}$; $r_{wD} = (r_w/L)(K_z/K_r)^{0.5}$; and $z_D = (z/L)$. By virtue of the definition of these dimensionless variables, the effects of aquifer thickness and horizontal to vertical conductivity ratios are accounted for by scaling the problem to an equivalent dimensionless space. This is analogous to the use of type curve fitting techniques for pumping test analysis.

Of greater interest in defining the flow field around a sparge well is the pattern of groundwater flow, or streamlines around the well. Using Equation 2 to determine derivatives of hydraulic head with respect to r and z, a stream function may be defined as the cumulative flowrate Q_c over a line integral between $(r_w,0)$ and any arbitrary (r,z). This stream function is given by:

$$Q_c(r,z) = -8\Delta h(K_z K_r)^{0.5}r/\Pi \sum_{n_{odd}} \sin(nkz)K_1(nk^*r)/n^2K_o(nk^*r_w) \qquad (3)$$

where K_1 is the modified first-order Bessel function of the second kind. Equation 3 is also a function of the three dimensionless variables: r_D, r_{wD}, and z_D. For $r_{wD} < 0.03$, Equation 3 is a function of r_D and z_D only. The streamlines defined by Equation 3 are presented in Figure 6 for $r_{wD} = 0.01$, where each streamtube represents 10% of the total flow through the sparge well. As seen from Figure 6, outflow from the upper well screen is concentrated towards the top of the well, with 50% of the outflow occurring within the upper 15% of the total aquifer

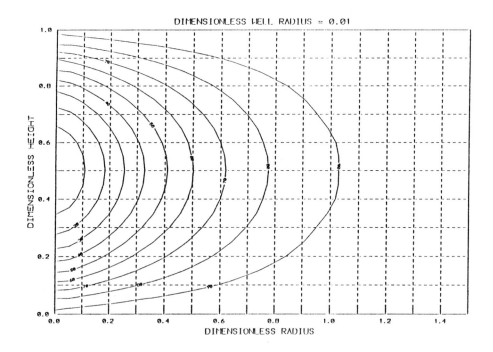

FIGURE 6. Sparge well streamlines as a percent of total flow.

thickness. As petroleum hydrocarbon contamination is normally concentrated near the top of the aquifer (or water table surface for unconfined aquifers), the system delivers most of the aerated water outflow to the most contaminated portion of the aquifer. The inflow to the well is similarly concentrated towards the base of the aquifer. As denser types of contamination, such as volatile chlorinated solvents, often accumulate near the base of the aquifer, the system may be particularly effective in removing such contamination. In comparison, pressurized injection systems treat a zone which cones outwards from the base of the aquifer and thus may not be effective in removing contamination concentrated at the aquifer base.

The radius of influence of a sparge well is theoretically infinite, but has been previously defined as the radial distance where the cumulative flow across the centerline $z_D = 0.5$ equals a certain percentage of the total groundwater circulation through the sparge well. For $r_{wD} < 0.03$, approximately 90% of the total flow occurs within a radius of $r_D = 1$. This effective radius of influence has been confirmed in laboratory bench-scale simulations of sparge well operation in a coarse sand using a rhodamine dye tracer. This radius of influence should be considered a maximum hydraulic radius of influence for system design, and spacing between sparge wells placed in a regular grid over the area of contamination should not exceed $r_D = 2$.

The total groundwater circulation rate (water flowrate) through the sparge well equals $Q_c(r_w, L/2)$. It is convenient to express the total circulation rate in dimensionless form as:

$$Q_D(r_{wD}) = Q_c(r_w, L/2)/\Delta hLK_r \qquad (4)$$

The dimensionless total flowrate is a function of r_{wD} only, as shown in Figure 7. Equation 4 is used to determine the achievable groundwater circulation rate, given measurements or estimates of the horizontal hydraulic conductivity.

In tight formations where groundwater circulation rates are reduced, a smaller well spacing may be desirable to reduce the operational life of the system. The simplest method of evaluating the relationship between well spacing and time to complete remediation is to use the estimated groundwater circulation rate (Equation 4) to determine the rate of hydrocarbon removal by biodegradation (assuming oxygen limited degradation) and volatilization. The estimated total mass of hydrocarbon to be removed within the aquifer volume Lr_D^2 is then divided by the removal rate.

Equation 4 was derived assuming that the well was fully screened across the aquifer. In actual field installations, the well is screened across only the upper and lower portions of the aquifer. Comparison of the analytical solution results to numerical (finite difference) model results, indicate that the effect of partial screening is relatively minor both in terms of the pattern of groundwater circulation and the total rate of circulation. Reducing the combined length of the upper and lower screen lengths to 40 and 20% of the total aquifer thickness reduced the total flow rate by 11 and 47%, respectively. In comparison, the total screen length is at least 60% of the total aquifer thickness in actual field installations.

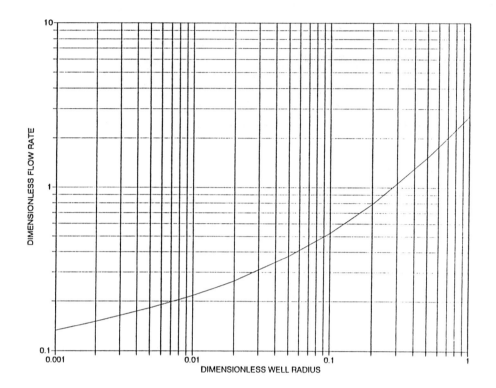

FIGURE 7. Dimensionless flowrate versus dimensionless well radius.

The analytical solution presented here assumes that the aquifer is confined, whereas many field applications are in unconfined aquifers. Hence, the solution may not be valid in unconfined aquifers where the water table rise at the well is large compared to the total aquifer thickness. Although the analytical solution was derived for a single well in an aquifer of infinite aerial extent, the effect of adjacent sparge wells can be accounted for using the principle of superposition.

CONTAMINANT REMOVAL MECHANISMS

Contaminant removal is effected during sparge well operation by two mechanisms: (1) supply of oxygen to promote aerobic biological degradation; and (2) removal (air stripping) of volatile organic compounds from the circulating groundwater. The rate of contaminant removal from the vadose zone by both mechanisms is dependent upon the rate of groundwater circulation through the sparge well and the rate of mass transfer between the air and water phases. The rate of groundwater circulation can be estimated using Equation 4.

The rate of mass transfer can be evaluated for volatile compounds (Henry's law constant >0.04) using a first-order approximation to Fick's law of diffusion.

Gvirtzman and Gorelick (1992) presented engineering estimates of mass transfer efficiency for TCE for slug flow and concluded the air bubbles in the sparge well would reach equilibrium partitioning between the air and water phases over a well length of 10 meters. The authors have conducted a more exact evaluation of mass transfer efficiency with similar results and found the percent decrease in groundwater solute concentration during one pass through the sparge well is strongly dependent upon the holdup ratio (ratio of average air velocity to average water velocity). The holdup ratio increases dramatically (up to a maximum of about 100) with increased air injection rates and can be controlled for a given water flow rate by selecting a suitable well diameter and air injection rate. Field measurements indicate that water exiting the sparge well is saturated with oxygen even over well lengths as small as 2 m. A single measurement of the removal efficiency of trichloroethylene over a well length of 6 meters indicated a removal efficiency of 98.5% (reduction from 250 to 3.7 μg/L), which compared favorably to a calculated removal efficiency of 96% assuming equilibrium portioning between the air and water phases.

Air stripping often results in the formation of calcium carbonate and iron oxide precipitates or scaling. Scaling tends to clog the well screen and reduce the rate of groundwater circulation. Scale has been readily removed from PVC well casing in field installations using a high-pressure water spray. Measurements of hydraulic conductivity in sparge wells, at the time of installation and following scale removal, showed no apparent reduction in well performance.

CASE HISTORY SUMMARY

The density-driven convection (DDC) system has been implemented at a total of 27 sites to date. Of these 27 sites, 8 cleanups have been completed and 11 systems have been operating for periods of greater than 6 months. These 19 sites are summarized in Table 1. A detailed case history for a single site has been previously presented by Schrauf et al. (1994). To evaluate the effectiveness of the DDC system, first-order decay constants were calculated from the change in maximum soil and/or groundwater concentrations over the operational life of the system. First-order decay is described by the equation $C/C_o = e^{-kt}$, where C/C_o is the ratio of the current to initial concentration, k is the decay constant, and t is elapsed time since start of remediation. Results of periodic monitoring at DDC sites generally indicate a first-order rate of decline in dissolved groundwater concentrations. Exceptions to this include sites where free product is present, because free product at the source area continues to dissolve into the groundwater until all residual free product is removed. For this reason, meaningful decay constants cannot be calculated at these sites based on maximum concentrations.

Comparison of the calculated decay constants for total petroleum hydrocarbons at sites remediated using DDC sparging with those undergoing natural attenuation (no active remediation) over periods of 26 to 41 months within the same geographical areas are presented in Figure 8. As calculated decay constants

TABLE 1. Case history summary (all concentrations in mg/L or mg/kg; S = soil; G = groundwater).

Release Type (FP = Free Product)	USCS Soil Type	Plume Area (m²)	Operating Period (mos)	Maximum Initial Concentration			Maximum Final Concentration		
				TPH	Benzene	Naphthalene	TPH	Benzene	Naphthalene
Completed Remediations									
Diesel	SW,GW	900	18	11,200 (S); 15 (G)		1.7 (S); 0.18 (G)	13 (S); 0.11 (G)	<0.1 (S); <0.002 (G)	<0.1 (S); <0.004 (G)
Waste Oil (FP)	SM,CL	1,000	12	190 (G)			3.7 (G)		
Gasoline	SW	50	6	67 (S); 15 (G)	0.1 (S); 0.78 (G)	0.5 (S); 0.09 (G)	<2.0 (S); <0.02 (G)	<0.1 (S); <0.002 (G)	<0.004 (G)
Gasoline, Diesel	SP,SM	200	12	18 (G)	0.19 (G)	0.14 (G)	0.13 (G)	0.021 (G)	<0.004 (G)
Gasoline, Diesel	SW,GW	3,000	18	1,600 (S); 190 (G)	4.7 (S); 7.8 (G)	0.63 (G)	19 (S); 1.3 (G)	<0.1 (S); <0.002 (G)	<0.1 (S); 0.01 (G)
Gasoline	SM,ML	240	12	0.65 (G)	0.34 (G)	0.01 (G)	0.06 (G)	0.008 (G)	<0.004 (G)
Gasoline	SM,ML	100	15	7,000 (S); 8.5 (G)	15 (S); 0.43 (G)	1.7 (S); 0.1 (G)	<2.0 (S); <0.02 (G)	<0.1 (S); <0.002 (G)	<0.1 (S); <0.004 (G)
Waste Oil	CL	100	5	1,300 (S); 66 (G)			<20 (S); <1 (G)	<0.1 (S); <0.002 (G)	
Ongoing Remediations									
Diesel	CL,SM	100	42	51,000 (S); 110 (G)	0.16 (S); 0.12 (G)	0.16 (G)	170 (S); <0.02 (G)	<0.1 (S); <0.002 (G)	0.7 (S); <0.004 (G)
Hydraulic Oil (FP)	CL	1,100	36	1,100 (G)			<1 (G)		
Gasoline (FP)	SC,SM	3,500	36	88 (G)	14 (G)	0.14 (G)	79 (G)	5.6 (G)	0.69 (G)
Gasoline (FP)	ML,SM	3,000	16	7.1 (G)	4.3 (G)	0.17 (G)	26 (G)	8.2 (G)	0.36 (G)
Gasoline (FP)	ML,SM	1,000	16	8.9 (G)	0.45 (G)	0.71 (G)	6.3 (G)	0.21 (G)	0.17 (G)
Diesel	CL	1,700	15	8,800 (S); 43 (G)	9.8 (S); 5.7 (G)	0.48 (G)	720 (S); 9.8 (G)	1.9 (S); 1.5 (G)	0.41 (G)
Gasoline	SP,SM	2,500	14	52 (G)	2.7 (G)	0.71 (G)	2.0 (G)	0.15 (G)	0.031 (G)
Gasoline	SP,ML	2,000	14	330 (G)	0.79 (G)	0.78 (G)	0.41 (G)	0.31 (G)	0.18 (G)
Gasoline	SM,ML	600	12	89 (G)	6.9 (G)	0.1 (G)	14 (G)	1.9 (G)	0.21 (G)
Gasoline	SP,ML	1,700	10	15 (G)	2.2 (G)		3.0 (G)	0.21 (G)	0.041 (G)
Gasoline (FP)	SM,ML	5,400	8	58 (G)	15 (G)	0.61 (G)	51 (G)	12 (G)	0.47 (G)

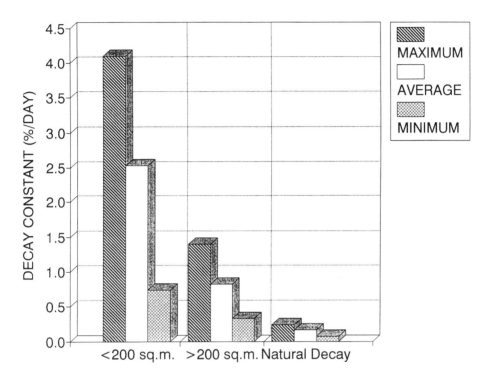

FIGURE 8. TPH decay constants for DDC sparging and natural attenuation.

for smaller sites (plume area <200 m²) are generally higher and more variable than larger sites, the calculated decay constants for these two groups are presented separately. For larger sites, these data indicate sparging accelerates the rate of contaminant removal by an average of five times that observed for natural attenuation. DDC sparging has been employed in conjunction with complementary technologies, including vapor extraction systems and groundwater recirculation systems. Groundwater recirculation involves extraction of contaminated groundwater at the downgradient edge of the plume and reinjection along the upgradient edge of the plume. The average decay constants for sites utilizing DDC sparging alone and those employing DDC sparging with either vapor extraction or groundwater recirculation are virtually identical. No significant difference was found when comparing average decay constants for sites with different soil types.

SUMMARY AND CONCLUSIONS

Slug flow is the characteristic flow pattern observed during in-well aeration. The driving force for groundwater circulation is the density difference of the air water mixture in the wellbore and the surrounding groundwater which creates a hydraulic head gradient along the well. The rate of groundwater circulation through the sparge well can be evaluated from the horizontal hydraulic conductivity and hydraulic head gradient along the well. Water circulation rates are necessary to determine the rate of contaminant removal by both biodegradation and volatilization. The effective radius of influence is a function of the saturated aquifer thickness and the ratio of horizontal to vertical hydraulic conductivity. Mass transfer of volatile substances between the air and water phases is relatively efficient, with oxygen saturation of the water phase occurring within a well length of 2 meters. Observed performance of systems operating for over 6 months indicates that the average rate of hydrocarbon degradation is increased 5 times over natural degradation rates.

REFERENCES

Akagawa, K. 1964. "Fluctuation of Void Ratio in Two-Phase Flow (1st Report, The Properties in a Vertical Upward Flow)." *Bulletin Japanese Society of Mechanical Engineers* 7(25): 122-128.

Akagawa, K., and T. Sakaguchi. 1966. "Fluctuation of Void Ratio in Two-Phase Flow (2nd Report, Analysis of Flow Configuration Considering the Existence of Small Bubbles in Liquid Slugs)." *Bulletin Japanese Society of Mechanical Engineers* 9(33): 104-110.

Govier, G. W., and K. Aziz. 1972. *The Flow of Complex Mixtures in Pipes*. Van Nostrand Co., New York, NY.

Govier, G. W., Radford, B. A., and J.S.C. Dunn. 1957. *Canadian Journal of Chemical Engineering*, 35: 58.

Gvirtzman, H., and S. M. Gorelick. 1992. "The Concept of In-Situ Vapor Stripping for Removing VOCs from Groundwater." *Transport in Porous Media 8*: 71-92.

Schrauf, T., P. J. Sheehan, and L. H. Pennington. 1993. "Alternative Method of Groundwater Sparging for Petroleum Hydrocarbon Remediation." *Remediation*, 4(1): 93-114.

A Laboratory Assessment
of Air Sparging Performance
on Oil-Contaminated Soil

Mark R. Harkness, John D. Ciampa, and Angelo A. Bracco

ABSTRACT

The efficacy of air sparging to remediate a subsurface plume of trans-former oil is evaluated in a comprehensive laboratory study. Shake flask assays containing contaminated soil indicated the oil was highly (>80%) biodegradable by indigenous bacteria when oxygen, nitrogen, and phosphorous were supplied. From 50 to 60% of the oil was removed from the soil in a 169-day biodegradation rate study performed in laboratory soil columns designed to mimic air sparged conditions. Maximal total petroleum hydrocarbon (TPH) biodegradation rates of ~70 mg/kg per day were observed in nutrient (N&P) amended columns at 23°C, based upon O_2 uptake and CO_2 production. The total TPH biodegraded in these columns was 3-fold higher than in an unamended control column.

INTRODUCTION

The release of hydrocarbon oils into the subsurface is problematic from several standpoints. Free-product oils float on groundwater surfaces and can move with groundwater flow. Other hydrophobic materials such as polychlori-nated biphenyls (PCBs), polycyclic aromatic hydrocarbons (PAHs), and chlori-nated solvents partition readily into the oil phase and may be mobilized as well (Sun & Boyd 1991). Pump-and-treat systems are commonly employed to contain such hydrocarbon spills, but are expensive to operate and do not represent long term solutions (Travis & Doty 1990). In situ bioremediation represents a promis-ing alternative. Air sparging has gained increasing acceptance as a means to treat lighter hydrocarbon (i.e. gasoline, diesel, jet fuel) spills (Bohler et al. 1990; Johnson et al. 1993). Air injected into the aquifer below the groundwater table strips the more volatile hydrocarbon compounds out of the saturated zone so that they can be biodegraded in the vadose zone or be collected by a soil vapor extraction (SVE) system. Oxygenation of the groundwater may stimulate bio-degradation in the saturated zone as well. To our knowledge, the efficacy of air sparging has not been demonstrated for heavier petroleum hydrocarbons, such as fuel or transformer oils. Results of the detailed laboratory study presented here indicate the approach has the potential to be effective at remediating these contaminants, particularly when the goal of the remediation is to eliminate the off-site movement of oil with the groundwater.

EXPERIMENTAL PROCEDURES AND MATERIALS

Oil-contaminated soil was obtained from an industrial site in Pittsfield, Massachusetts. The oil was lighter than water and contained transformer oil mixed with coal tar waste products and varying levels of PCBs (Aroclor 1260) and polychlorinated benzenes. The soil was obtained at water table depth, ~5 m below the ground surface, using a 12-cm-diameter continuous core sampler. This method produced a 75-cm-long consolidated soil core, which was characterized physically, chemically, and biologically.

To establish that favorable conditions for bioremediation existed in the Pittsfield soil and to test for limiting factors, a shake flask biotreatability study was performed using the soil and groundwater collected from the site. The biotreatability study was conducted in 250-mL flasks containing 50 mL of groundwater and 50 g of moist soil spiked to TPH concentrations of 10,000 or 24,000 mg/kg with free product oil. Multiple flasks were amended periodically with 40 mg of diammonium phosphate, while others received no nutrient amendments (unamended control) or were amended with mercuric chloride to halt any biological activity (killed control). Urethane foam stoppers were used to trap volatile emissions, while allowing air to pass into the flasks. The flasks were incubated at 175 rpm for 8 weeks at 20°C in a temperature-controlled shaker. Flasks were sacrificed at intervals and the oil extracted into methylene chloride using liquid-liquid extraction or soxhlet extraction for the water and soil phases, respectively. Changes in petroleum hydrocarbon concentrations were measured by infrared (IR) analysis using a modified EPA 418.1 procedure and by gas chromatography (GC) using a flame ionization detector (FID) (Fedorak & Westlake 1981).

Soil columns were fabricated to predict biodegradation rates that might be expected in the field and to screen for potential problems in implementing air sparging with nutrient addition. The design incorporated the ability to measure inlet and outlet O_2 and CO_2 concentrations to obtain instantaneous biodegradation rate data in the columns so that real-time responses to changes in process variables could be monitored (Figure 1). The columns were constructed out of beaded Kimax pipe (61 cm × 75 mm i.d. × 6 mm wall thickness). Five 10-mm-i.d. ports sealed with Teflon™ septa were placed onto the sides of the columns for soil and ground water sampling. Glass end caps for the columns were modified to include ports with glass stopcocks for gas and liquid sampling. A 63-mm-diameter fritted-glass sparge plate was inserted into the bottom cap so that air could be introduced. This section was packed with clean sand to bear the weight of the overlying soil. Smaller diameter glass side columns allowed the water

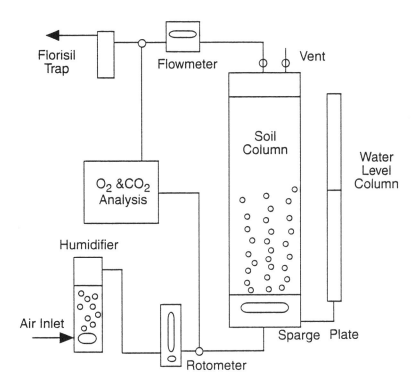

FIGURE 1. Schematic of the soil column configuration. Only one column is shown. Two additional columns and the multi-port valve system do not appear in this diagram.

height in the main columns to be monitored. Inlet air was filtered, humidified, and metered to each column through individual rotometers. Outlet gas flow was measured using an Omega (Stamford, Connecticut) FMA-5606 flowmeter. Oxygen and CO_2 concentrations were measured in the inlet and outlet gas streams using a YSI (Yellow Springs, Ohio) Model 59 (0 to 100%) O_2 meter and a Horiba (Irvine, California) Model APBA-250E CO_2 meter (0 to 1%), respectively. A multi-port valve system (Valco Instrument Co., Houston, Texas) allowed the inlet gas and column outlet gas streams to be sampled sequentially. Data acquisition was performed on a 286 IBM-compatible computer.

Three soil columns were packed with ~4.5 kg of soil spiked with recovered oil in a manner that approximated the in situ TPH concentration profile. Soil with a TPH concentration of 10,000 mg/kg was packed into the bottom and top 19 cm of each column, whereas soil with a TPH concentration of 24,000 mg/kg was packed into the center 10-cm section. Groundwater was then added until half the column was saturated. The experiment assessed the effect of nutrient addition, changes in groundwater level, and variation in air sparge rate on in situ biodegradation activity (see Table 1 for experimental design). Nutrients were added to two columns by slowly adding 1.2 L of a solution of trimetaphosphate

TABLE 1. Experimental design for column operation.

	Column 1	Column 2	Column 3
Nutrient addition[a]	No	Yes	Yes
Water level[b]	Static	Static	Cycled[c]
Air sparge rate (cc/min)[d]	25/50	25/50	25/50

(a) Nutrients were added from surface at 15-day intervals.
(b) Nominal groundwater level was half-column height.
(c) Water was cycled at ±7.5 cm from nominal height at 20-day intervals.
(d) Air sparging rate was alternated between 25 and 50 ccm on 5-day intervals.

and ammonia chloride (each 120 mg/L) in groundwater to the top of the columns and allowing the water to move through the columns under gravity. The third column was flooded with unamended groundwater. Temperature, air sparge rate, O_2 uptake, and CO_2 production were monitored in each column once every 3 h by the data acquisition system. The final TPH distribution within the column at the end of the study were measured by sectioning the column in 5-cm increments and analyzing the individual subsections. The columns were operated for 169 days at room temperature.

RESULTS AND DISCUSSION

The contaminated soil was a gray, gravelly glacial-outwash material, overlain by light brown, silty sand. The hydraulic conductivity of the contaminated zone was measured in the laboratory to be 1.0×10^{-2} cm/s, consistent with field conductivity measurements performed using pump tests. The conductivity was two orders of magnitude higher than that measured for the overburden soil, indicating the primary groundwater flow was through the outwash material. Maximal TPH concentrations of 16,000 to 22,000 mg/kg were observed in the outwash soil, where yellow droplets of oil were clearly visible in the soil pore structure. TPH concentrations fell off rapidly above and below the zone of highest contamination. Limited sampling indicated the PCB concentration in the soil was roughly proportional to the oil concentration (~1% by weight in the oil). Supplemental analyses indicated the outwash material contained ~10^3 cells/g oil-degrading bacteria, moderate levels of alkalinity (220 to 580 mg/kg) and of nitrogen (60 to 180 mg/kg, primarily in the form of total Kjeldahl nitrogen) and low levels of nonextractable total organic carbon (700 to 3,100 mg/kg) and orthophosphates (0 to 20 mg/kg).

The shake flask biotreatability study confirmed that an active indigenous oil-degrading bacterial population existed in the soil and that the bacteria were capable of biodegrading a substantial fraction of the oil present. This activity was enhanced by nutrient addition. The oil-degrading bacterial population increased

2 to 3 orders of magnitude to >10^6 cells/g after 2 weeks in nutrient-amended flasks, but no more than one order of magnitude in the unamended flasks. After 8 weeks, average TPH reductions in nutrient amended flasks were 80% and 59% in flasks where starting TPH concentrations were 10,000 and 24,000 mg/kg, respectively, as measured by GC/FID. Most of the reduction occurred in the aliphatic fraction of the oil. TPH concentrations in these flasks were still declining between weeks 6 and 8, suggesting that these percentages do not represent terminal biodegradation limits. TPH losses were 41% in the unamended flasks and 10% in the killed controls.

Biological activity in the soil columns was similar to that observed in the shake flasks. Oil-degrading bacterial populations in nutrient amended columns increased ~3 orders of magnitude to >10^6 cells/g in the first week of the study, then remained stable or slowly declined over time. Oil-degrading populations in the unamended column also increased with the onset of aeration, but were an order of magnitude lower than in the amended cases. The initial hydraulic conductivities measured in the columns ranged from 5.1 to 8.3 × 10^{-3} cm/sec, in reasonable agreement with values measured in the soil core and in the field. These values did not change substantially over time, indicating no plugging or biofouling occurred in the columns due to precipitation of nutrients or buildup of microorganisms. Channeling of air through the saturated soil zone was clearly visible throughout the study.

Oxygen utilization and CO_2 production were good indicators of biodegradation activity in the columns. The mass ratio of O_2 utilization to CO_2 production was ~1.0 in each column, close to the theoretical value of 1.1 for mineralization of hydrocarbons. Utilization and production numbers were substantially higher in the nutrient amended columns, with spikes in bioactivity corresponding to batch nutrient additions (shown for columns 1 and 2 in Figure 2). The maximal rate of O_2 uptake in column 2 was 45 mg/h and occurred 80 days into the study, yielding maximum TPH biodegradation rates of 70 mg/kg/day assuming complete mineralization of substrate (i.e. 3.5 mg of O_2 required for each mg of TPH degraded). Activity declined uniformly thereafter, perhaps due to a change in availability of easily degradable substrate. The air sparging rate did not have a statistically significant (based upon ANOVA analysis with a = 0.05) effect on bioactivity, although O_2 utilization was 10 to 15% higher when the sparge rate was 50 ccm. Bioactivity was similar in column 3, although the data were noisier due to the interaction of changes in water level on biodegradation (data not shown). The effect of water level was statistically significant (a = 0.05) and resulted in 30% higher O_2 utilization when the level was low as compared to when it was high.

Composite biodegradation TPH losses after 169 days were 50.8% and 57.9% for columns 2 and 3, respectively, based upon IR analysis of soil subsections. TPH losses in the unamended column were 17.2% using this method. Theoretical total TPH losses of 9.5%, 37.6%, and 34.4% were calculated for columns 1, 2, and 3, based upon total oxygen utilization assuming complete mineralization. However, all the hydrocarbons were not mineralized. Biomass was formed and a

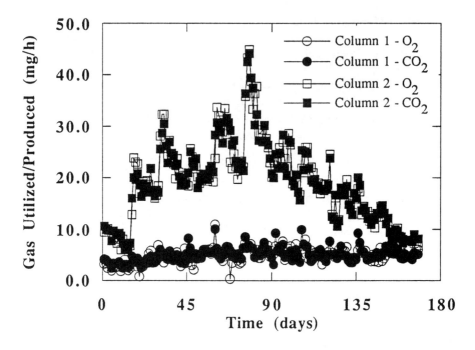

FIGURE 2. Daily averages of O_2 uptake and CO_2 production in soil columns 1 and 2. Spikes in gas utilization/production in column 2 correspond to batch nutrient additions.

rhamolipid-like biosurfactant (Zhang & Miller 1992) was observed in the leachate collected from the columns during nutrient addition, rendering the rate calculations based upon O_2 utilization highly conservative. With this in mind, actual maximum TPH biodegradation rates were probably closer to 100 mg/kg/day in columns 2 and 3.

The soil TPH analysis indicated that biodegradation was most pronounced in the unsaturated region of the nutrient-amended columns. TPH losses approached 80% in the upper 15 cm of these columns, consistent with shake flask results. TPH losses in the lower 15 cm were 40 to 60%. This suggests that oxygen transfer represents a primary limitation to biodegradation in the saturated zone, consistent with the observation of other researchers (Dibble and Bartha 1979). Some upward movement of oil from the high concentration zone was observed in columns 1 and 2, probably due to air movement. The effect was less pronounced in column 3. No biodegradation of PCBs in the columns was observed.

Actual rates in the field will not approach the rates observed in the laboratory because the average subsurface temperature in Pittsfield is 10°C to 12°C, significantly below the average temperature of the soil columns during the study (23.1°C). When supplemental column experiments were performed at 10, 15, and 20°C using smaller, water-jacketed columns, a 3 to 4-fold difference between bioactivity was observed between the columns at 10 and 20°C, based upon O_2

uptake and CO_2 production. This difference, in combination with more limited mass transfer normally encountered in the field, suggests that actual in situ biodegradation rates may be more than 5-fold lower than those observed in the laboratory. TPH biodegradation rates on the order of 2 to 20 mg/kg/day are commonly cited in air sparging field studies (Johnson et al. 1993). Predicted rates of oil biodegradation fall within that range, but should be established by field testing.

REFERENCES

Bohler, U. J., J. Brauns, H. Hotzel, and M. Nahold. 1990. "Air Injection and Soil Aeration as a Combined Method for Cleaning Contaminated Sites — Observations from Test Sites." In: F. Arendt, M. Hinsenveld, and W. J. Van Den Brink (Eds.), *Sedimented Solid Rocks in Contaminated Soils.* Kluwer Academic Publishers, Netherlands. pp. 1039-1044.

Dibble, J. T., and R. Bartha. 1979. "Effect of Environmental Parameters on the Biodegradation of Oil Sludge." *Appl. Environ. Microbiol.* 37:729-739.

Fedorak, P. M., and D.W.S. Westlake. 1981. "Microbial Degradation of Aromatics and Saturates in Prudhoe Bay Crude Oil as Determined by Glass Capillary Gas Chromatography." *Can. J. Microbiol.* 27:432-443.

Johnson, R. L., P. C. Johnson, D. B. McWhorter, R. E. Hinchee, and I. Goodman. 1993. "An Overview of In Situ Air Sparging." *Ground Water Monitoring Review* 13:127-135.

Sun, S., and S. A. Boyd. 1991. "Sorption of Polychlorinated (PCB) Congeners by Residual PCB-Oil Phases in Soils." *J. Environ. Qual.* 20:557-561.

Travis, C. C., and C. B. Doty. 1990. "Can Contaminated Aquifers at Superfund Sites be Remediated." *Environ. Sci. Technol.* 24:1464-1466.

Zhang, Y., and R. M. Miller. 1992. "Enhanced Octadecane Dispersion and Biodegradation by a Pseudomonas Rhamnolipid Surfactant (biosurfactant)." *Appl. Environ. Microbiol.,* 58:3276-3282.

Review of a Long-Term Air Sparging Pilot Test in a Shallow Aquifer

*David F. Weymann, Gregory D. Hoffman,
and Edward M. Kuhn*

ABSTRACT

A 5-month-long air sparging pilot study was conducted on a shallow surficial aquifer contaminated with gasoline. The pilot study documented the physical and biological response of the aquifer and evaluated sampling techniques. Results indicated that sparging increased biological activity, but the zone of influence was limited. A transition from methanogenic to aerobic conditions was indicated. Monitoring results were significantly affected by sampling techniques.

INTRODUCTION AND BACKGROUND

Air sparging is rapidly becoming a preferred technology for cleanup of hydrocarbon-contaminated sites (Hinchee 1994). While the physical and biological processes of contaminant attenuation associated with air sparging (i.e., volatilization and biodegradation) have been documented, reliable monitoring of system performance and quantification attenuating mechanisms at a particular site remain a challenge. A 5-month-long pilot study was conducted at an active remediation site in the coastal plain of North Carolina. Air sparging was proposed as a method of stimulating biodegradation in the groundwater. The specific objectives of the study were to (1) assess the viability of sparging at the site, (2) critically evaluate the sampling techniques used for collection of pilot test data, and (3) document evidence of bioremediation.

SITE CHARACTERISTICS

The site was a former gasoline service station at which both the soil and groundwater had been contaminated with gasoline. A biofeasibility analysis indicated a suitable microbial population and verified that the groundwater contained no materials that were inhibitory to microbial respiration. The site hydrogeology was characterized by an aquifer consisting of medium to coarse sands extending from approximately 1.5 m below land surface (bls) to approximately 4.0 m bls. The water table was typically 1.8 m bls. The aquifer was confined from above by clayey silt extending from the surface to approximately 1.5 m bls and from below by a continuous, tight, highly plastic clay at 4.0 m bls.

METHODS

Pilot Test Configuration

Air was injected below the groundwater through two injection wells. Four piezometers were installed for monitoring the aquifer response. An existing well was used to evaluate historical trends and to provide a control. The control well was located in an area of moderate contamination approximately 40 m from the sparging test area. The pilot test was configured as shown on Figure 1. A representative cross section transect showing well construction and site lithology is shown on Figure 2. Piezometers and monitor wells were used for collection of both groundwater and soil gas samples. The airflow rate was dictated by the air injection pressure. The injection pressure was selected to evacuate the well and to overcome the estimated air entry pressure without resulting in high airflow rates (Hoag 1993). During the test, the average injection pressures were 2.9 psi (20 kPa) and 2.8 psi (19.3 kPa) for sparge point 1 (SP-1) and sparge point 2 (SP-2), respectively. Airflow rates remained steady during operation with average rates of 1.7 cfm (0.048 m^3/min) and 1.4 cfm (0.040 m^3/min) for SP-1 and SP-2, respectively.

Sampling and Monitoring

Selected groundwater monitoring parameters included water level, dissolved oxygen, carbon dioxide, and contaminant concentrations. Dissolved oxygen was measured in wells with a field meter (Johnson et al. 1993) 1 m below the water table prior to purging. The aqueous carbon dioxide concentration was measured with colorimetric test kits. Benzene, toluene, ethylbenzene, and xylenes (BTEX) concentrations and microbial indicators were analyzed in a laboratory by U.S. Environmental Protection Agency (EPA)-approved methods. Microbiological indicators including pH, bacteria colony-forming units (CFUs), and nutrients also were evaluated.

Soil gas monitoring parameters included oxygen, methane, carbon dioxide, and volatile organic compounds (VOCs). The VOC concentrations in soil gas were measured with a photoionization detector. Percent levels of carbon dioxide, methane, and oxygen in soil gas were measured with a portable soil gas monitor. Components of soil gas were measured after purging wells for 2 min at approximately 0.6 cfm.

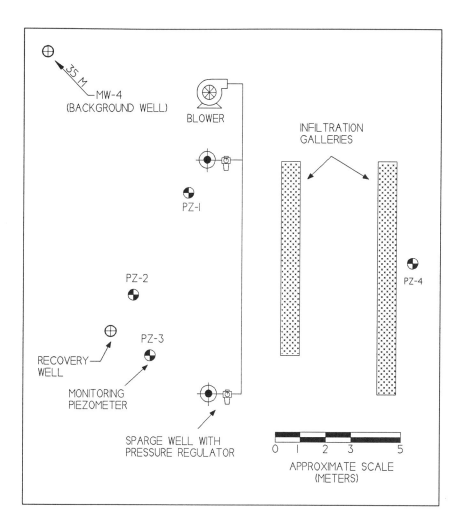

FIGURE 1. Air sparging system layout.

Respirometry Evaluation

Two methods were evaluated for utility in determining biological oxygen consumption rates in groundwater under oxygen excess conditions. In the first method, dissolved oxygen depletion was evaluated in PZ-3 by first aerating the water for approximately 10 seconds. Then, changes in oxygen concentration in the well were monitored over time using a dissolved oxygen probe and field meter. In the second method, groundwater samples were collected and oxygenated by gentle shaking in a glass jar. The samples were subsequently transferred to a biological oxygen demand (BOD) bottle, and changes in dissolved oxygen concentrations were observed over time. The bottle test was carried out in the field on samples from PZ-3 and repeated in the laboratory on water from RW-1.

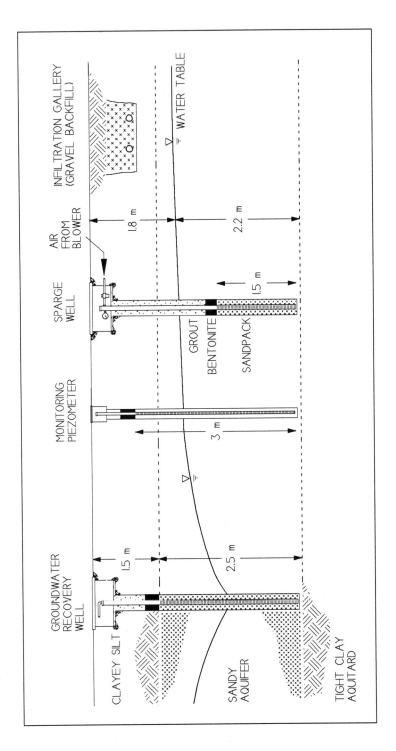

FIGURE 2. Representative cross section transect.

RESULTS AND DISCUSSION

Groundwater

The response of selected groundwater parameters to air sparging is shown in Figure 3. Overall, the only significant response occurred in PZ-1, suggesting a radius of influence of between 1.5 m and 3 m from the sparge point SP-1. The radius of influence may have been limited by the shallow saturated thickness of the aquifer or the placement of the screened interval.

The response to sparging in PZ-1 was characterized by a drop in contaminant concentrations, an increase in dissolved oxygen concentration, and significant increase in CFUs. Dissolved oxygen concentrations were initially near zero and were consistently elevated after initiating sparging. An increase in CFUs was observed in both PZ-1 and PZ-3. CFUs increased by a factor of 100 in PZ-1 and by a factor of 17 in PZ-3, providing evidence that microbial activity increased as a result of sparging. Observed changes in water levels and nitrogen and phosphate concentrations may also be consistent with sparging.

The sustained increase in dissolved oxygen in PZ-1 is evidence of the sparging response. However, the large initial increases may have been an artifact of the sampling procedure, which allowed short-circuiting of injected air to the well. During the first several sampling events, water levels and dissolved oxygen readings were taken in the wells after removing the well caps and allowing a short equilibration period. Dissolved oxygen concentrations in PZ-1 measured by this procedure typically were 8 mg/L. However, later inspection indicated that audible air bubbling developed within several minutes of removing the well cap. This observation suggested that the piezometer acted as a pressure sink causing short-circuiting of air through preferential pathways, resulting in artificially high oxygen concentrations. Short-circuiting of air was confirmed by taking dissolved oxygen readings immediately after removing the well cap and observing the subsequent increase in dissolved oxygen over time until the well water became saturated with oxygen. Similar short-circuiting indicators were not observed in other piezometers. Dissolved oxygen readings in PZ-1 were significantly lower and no bubbling was detected when measurements were taken immediately after uncapping the well. Short-circuiting of injected air to an observation well may impact monitoring parameters typically used to assess air sparging response.

Soil Gas

The soil gas response to air sparging is shown in Figure 4. Air injection resulted in significant trends in the soil gas composition and impacted a significantly greater area than that in the groundwater. Baseline soil gas monitoring in the source area indicated a methanogenic environment, as evidenced by high methane levels and low oxygen levels. The methane concentration in PZ-1 was originally 66% and increased to greater than 160% (the upper detection limit of the monitor) after initiation of sparging. While the manufacturer claims that the methane probe is not sensitive to VOCs such as BTEX, methane readings in

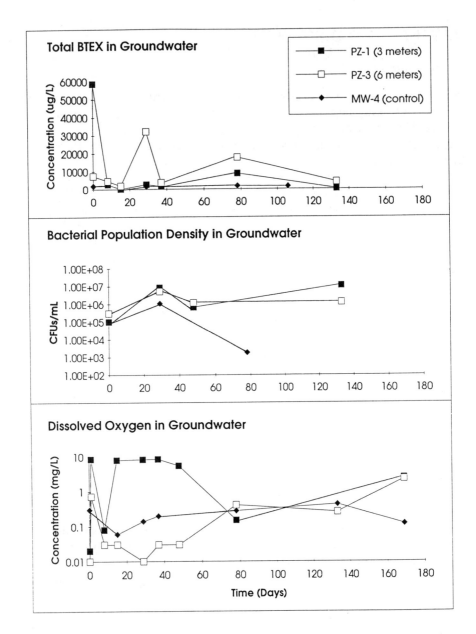

FIGURE 3. Response of selected groundwater parameters to air sparging.

excess of 100% suggest interference by other gas constituents. Methane detected in the soil gas may have been produced under anaerobic conditions in either the vadose zone or groundwater. Increased methane in PZ-1 after sparging suggests that methane existed in the groundwater and was transported into the vadose zone by sparging.

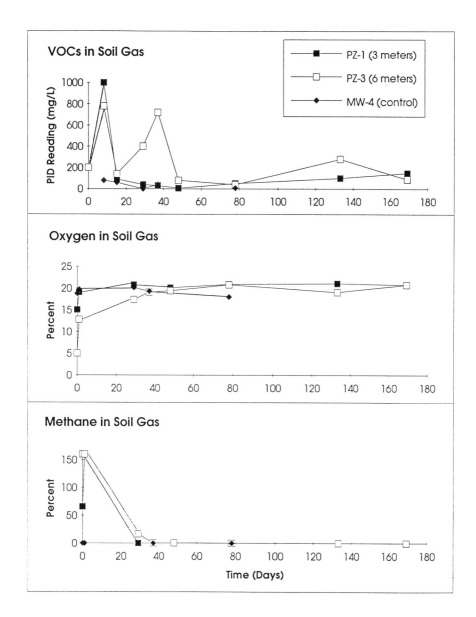

FIGURE 4. Response of selected soil gas parameters to air sparging.

Soil gas monitoring did not reveal consistent reductions in contaminant concentrations in the vadose zone and did not provide insight to attenuation mechanisms. Competing effects of air dilution by sparging and stripping of groundwater contaminants likely affected the results. The strong drop in methane concentration may indicate methane degassing or a cessation of methanogenic activity.

The soil gas purging time strongly influenced measurements during sampling. Measurements generally changed in a direction that would indicate atmospheric air was being brought to the well (e.g. oxygen and VOC levels). Some purging is required to draw a representative gas sample into the well. However, it was not clear how long the well should be purged to obtain a representative sample. These observations reinforce the need for a careful evaluation of sampling techniques.

Respirometry Evaluation

The results of the respirometry evaluations in PZ-3 and RW-1 are presented in Figure 5. Oxygen depletion in PZ-3 was much more rapid than the oxygen depletion in the BOD bottle. It was assumed that the method of aerating the water did not significantly strip contaminants from the sample, thus contaminant concentrations were not limiting to respiration. Further, it was assumed that oxygen depletion in the BOD bottle was due entirely to biological uptake by suspended microorganisms.

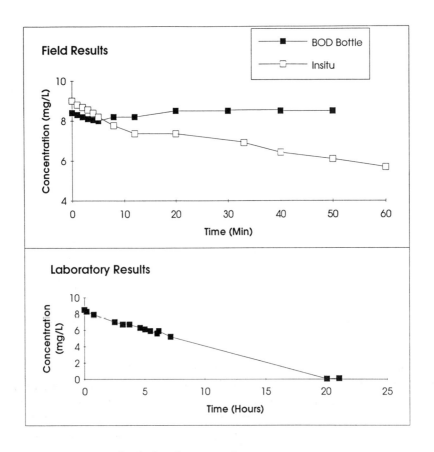

FIGURE 5. Oxygen depletion in groundwater.

Explanations for the rapid drop in dissolved oxygen in the well include diffusion, mechanical mixing, and uptake by microorganisms fixed to the well screen or sandpack. An analytical evaluation of radial diffusion from the well suggested that diffusion from the oxygenated well to the surrounding anoxic aquifer may contribute to oxygen depletion (Johnson et al. 1993). In addition, mechanical mixing caused by the required motion of the dissolved oxygen probe may have resulted in significant dilution of oxygenated water with water from outside the well casing. Another potential source of oxygen uptake is a microbial film on the well screen or sand pack that would not be represented by the BOD bottle sample. Both methods of respirometry may have limited utility since a potentially large portion of microorganisms contributing to contaminant degradation may be adhered to soil particles, as opposed to in suspension in groundwater.

CONCLUSIONS

Air sparging was evaluated as a potential remediation technology for a shallow surficial aquifer. The results of the long-term pilot test indicated a radius of influence of between 1.5 m and 3 m at the site. The shallow saturated thickness of the target aquifer may have limited the opportunity for lateral migration of air in the groundwater. The observed increase in bacterial count was evidence that biological activity was enhanced by increased dissolved oxygen. Soil gas monitoring indicated a methanogenic environment prior to sparging. The significant changes in soil gas composition with air sparging indicated a transition to aerobic conditions. However, any changes in gas composition indicating increased respiration were masked by dilution. The in-well respirometry method described is a commonly employed technique and is appealing in its simplicity; however, it may not accurately reflect the groundwater environment.

Monitoring parameters commonly cited as evidence of a sparging response may all be biased by preferential movement of injected air to the sampling point. If short-circuiting occurs, results will be biased to indicate a favorable response. Monitoring results are sensitive to sampling techniques and methods of analysis, suggesting that additional work is required to refine economical monitoring procedures that accurately reflect the aquifer response to air sparging.

REFERENCES

Hinchee, R. E. 1994. *Air Sparging for Bioremediation.* Lewis Publishers, Ann Arbor, MI.
Hoag, G. E. 1993. "Introduction to Air Sparging." In *Aeration Technologies for Soil and Groundwater Remediation*, pp. 8-12. Environmental Education Enterprises, Inc., Columbus, OH.
Johnson, R. L. 1994. "Enhancing Biodegradation with In-situ Air Sparging: A Conceptual Model." *Air Sparging for Bioremediation.* Lewis Publishers, Ann Arbor, MI.
Johnson, R. L., P. C. Johnson, D. B. McWhorter, R. E. Hinchee, and I. Goodman. 1993. "An Overview of In Situ Air Sparging." *Groundwater Monitoring Review* 13(4): 127-135.

Contamination Removal Rates in Pulsed and Steady-Flow Aquifer Sparging

Frederick C. Payne, Allan R. Blaske, and Gregory A. VanHouten

ABSTRACT

A field experiment was conducted to determine whether pulsed-injection aquifer sparging induced greater mass transfer of trichloroethylene (TCE) than steady-flow sparge air injection in the same location. Current literature indicates that, despite an increase in air-water interfacial surface area induced by sparge air injection, mass transfer of volatile contaminants from aqueous to gaseous phase is limited by aqueous-phase diffusion rates. It was hypothesized that pulsed sparge air injection would induce bulk water movement, minimizing the mass transfer rate limitation caused by aqueous-phase diffusion. This effect was expected to be observed through an increase in the rate of TCE concentration reductions as the experimental system shifted from steady to pulsed-flow operation. Experimental results showed highly variable groundwater TCE concentrations during steady-flow operations. Average TCE concentrations increased slightly during the steady-flow trials at both 1.5- and 3.0-m radial distances from the sparge well, but the increases were not significant. During the pulsed-flow trial, a significant decline in TCE concentrations was observed at the 1.5-m radius. At the 3.0-m radius, a slight decline was observed, which was not significant.

INTRODUCTION

Aquifer sparging has been identified as an alternative to pumping and above-ground treatment for recovery of organic contamination from groundwater. Practitioners claim that air injected into a contaminated aquifer drives mass transfer of volatile organic compounds from the aquifer into gaseous phase, from which it is transported out of the system. Several authors have recently addressed physical and chemical aspects of the technology in an effort to critically evaluate its potential to replace or enhance currently accepted remedial practices. Ji et al. (1993) conducted laboratory-scale experiments suggesting that air injected beneath an aquifer surface moves upward in channels which propagate through the porous medium. The air-water interfacial surface area created by the air channels increases the potential for mass transport from aqueous to gaseous phase. Pankow et al. (1993) linked the compound-specific efficiency of any aquifer sparge system to the compound's Henry's law constant. Therefore, contaminant removal rates would theoretically be directly proportional to the interfacial surface area induced by the sparge air injection. However, Johnson et al. (1993) introduced the concern that the limited interfacial surface area created by sparge air injection may be insufficient to drive meaningful mass transfer of volatiles from the aquifer. In this view, release of contaminants from the aquifer would be aqueous-phase diffusion-limited.

Johnson et al. (1993) suggested that pulsing sparge injection air may induce bulk mixing of the aquifer water mass and reduce the diffusion limitation on sparge-induced mass transfer. Boersma et al. (1993) and Newman et al. (1994) documented a short-lived mounding of the aquifer surface, due to displacement of water by injected air. The water mound drained away radially, and the site resumed its original piezometric surface while sparge air injection continued. Conversely, there was a collapse of the air channels upon cessation of sparge air injection, which caused a temporary depression of the aquifer surface. Given these observations, cyclical mounding and depression of the aquifer induced by pulsing the sparge air injection can be expected to provide the bulk water movement cited by Johnson et al. (1993).

A field experiment was conducted in a contaminated aquifer to test the hypothesis that pulsed sparge air injection can induce greater mass transfer than steady-flow sparge air injection. The experiment tracked aquifer concentrations of TCE in a network of monitor probes surrounding a sparge air injection well. Steady-flow sparge injection was run for 2 weeks, then the site was allowed to rest for 45 days. After the rest period, a water mounding test was run to determine the characteristic period of the water mound formation and collapse. The experiment was then continued with 2 weeks of pulsed-flow operation at the pulse period indicated by the mounding test.

METHODS

Site Description

Testing was conducted at a former manufacturing site in the suburban Detroit, Michigan area. Vadose zone soil at the site consists of fine- to medium-grained tan sand with some coarse sand and fine gravel. Soil deeper than 3.7 m below grade is a well sorted, fine sand with trace amounts of medium sand, and 12% silt. No clay size fraction was present. Groundwater is present at the site at approximately 3.7 m below grade and is contained in the fine sand. A layer of gray, dense clay was encountered at a depth of approximately 6.7 m below grade and prevented deeper investigation. The main contaminant at the site is TCE, which was released to the groundwater through a floor drain. The maximum concentration at the site was 1,400 ppb, and no nonaqueous-phase liquid was present. The study area was located approximately 75 feet down hydraulic gradient from the contaminant release point. Initial contaminant concentrations in the study area ranged from 2 ppb to 880 ppb, and were concentrated in the upper half of the saturated zone.

Sparge Well Construction and Operation

The sparge well was constructed using a 46-cm-long, 3-cm-diameter steel well point connected to a length of 2.5-cm-diameter polyvinyl chloride (PVC) piping. A well pack consisting of 1-cm-diameter washed pea gravel was installed around the well point. Native collapse filled the borehole annulus from a point above the well pack to the top of the water table surface. Airflow to the sparge well was driven by a positive-displacement blower at 2.5 L/s. During pulsed operation, the blower was operated on a timer, 14 min on and 14 min off.

Monitoring Probe Network Construction

Aquifer monitoring probes were installed into the saturated soil beneath the site using Geoprobe® sampling equipment. The probes consisted of 15-cm-long,

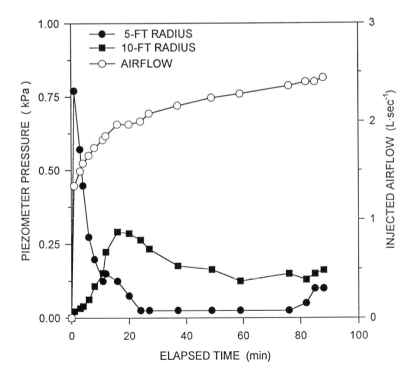

FIGURE 1. Water table mounding effects due to injection of sparge air into the aquifer over time.

1-cm-diameter stainless steel gauze screen implants connected to polyethylene tubing. The tubing was brought above grade and labeled. Then 38 probes were installed at 17 locations and three depths within the aquifer, along two vertical planes intersecting the sparge well. One plane was oriented roughly parallel to the groundwater flow direction, and the second was roughly perpendicular to groundwater flow. Monitoring probes were installed at distances ranging between 0.3 m and 19.8 m from the sparge point and at depths of 0.9, 1.8, and 2.7 m below the surface of the water table. Monitoring probes were concentrated in the area out to 6.1 m from the sparge point.

Groundwater Sampling and Analysis

A peristaltic pump was used to collect groundwater samples from the monitoring points. Water was allowed to fill the sample bottle and overflow a minimum of two bottle volumes before the bottle was sealed. Groundwater samples were placed into 40-mL vials with a Teflon™ septum lid and filled to zero headspace for analysis of TCE following U.S. Environmental Protection Agency (EPA) Method 8260.

During mounding tests, each probe was operated as a sealed piezometer. Prior to testing, the probe was opened to the atmosphere and allowed to equilibrate. A Magnehelic® pressure gauge was then attached to the probe line and remained sealed in place for the duration of each mounding test.

RESULTS

Groundwater Mounding Results

Boersma et al. (1993) describe groundwater mounding during sparge air injection. Tests were conducted at the site to determine the extent and stability of the mounding. Figure 1 is a diagram showing a plot of air injection rate (L/s) and groundwater mounding (measured as pressure in closed piezometers) versus time of operation at 1.5- and 3.0-m radii from the sparging point. Mounding of groundwater in the probe closest to the sparging well (1.5 m) was indicated by pressure changes of 0.75 kPa immediately upon initiation of air injection and decreased to less than 0.025 kPa after 42 min of operation. Mounding in the aquifer probe 3.0 m from the sparge well showed a maximum pressure change of 0.29 kPa after 15 min of injection and also decreased during operation. Sparge injection airflow increased with elapsed time, to a steady rate of 2.5 L/s after 90 min of operation. Based on the mounding test results, an air injection cycle of 14 min on, 14 min off was selected for the pulsed operation. This timing was chosen to induce maximum vertical displacement of the water mass.

TCE Concentration Data

TCE concentrations were measured in groundwater samples collected from the aquifer probes during constant and pulsed air injection. The test site was near the spill source, which led to large differences in initial concentrations among the probes. To allow for comparisons between points, the changes in TCE concentration were expressed as percentile increase or decrease relative to the initial value for each monitor probe in each trial. The data for each trial were plotted as percentage change versus time, with linear regression lines and 95% confidence intervals shown for each plot. The upper graphs in Figures 2 and 3 show slight

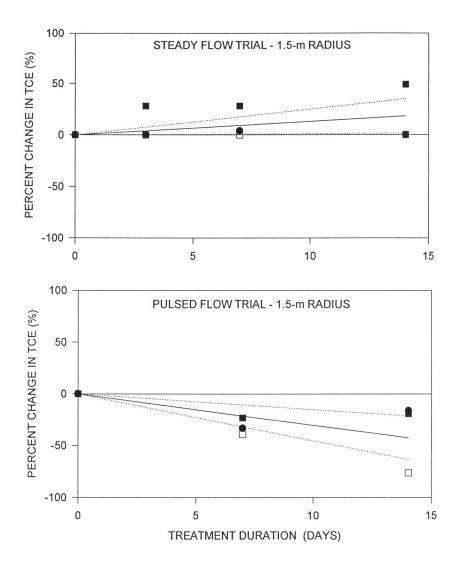

FIGURE 2. TCE concentrations in groundwater samples during steady-flow and pulsed sparge air injection: 1.5-m radius from injection well. Monitor probes depths were 0.9 m (●), 1.8 m (■) and 2.7 m (□) below the aquifer surface. Dotted lines indicate 95% confidence limits for the regression line.

increases in TCE concentrations during steady flow air injection, but the observed change at the 3.0-m radius was not significant. During pulsed air injection (14 min on, 14 min off), TCE concentrations at a distance of 1.5 m from the sparge well were observed to decrease over 40% from initial values. Concentrations at 3.0-m radius showed only a slight decrease, indicating that the influence of sparge air is less than 3.0 m.

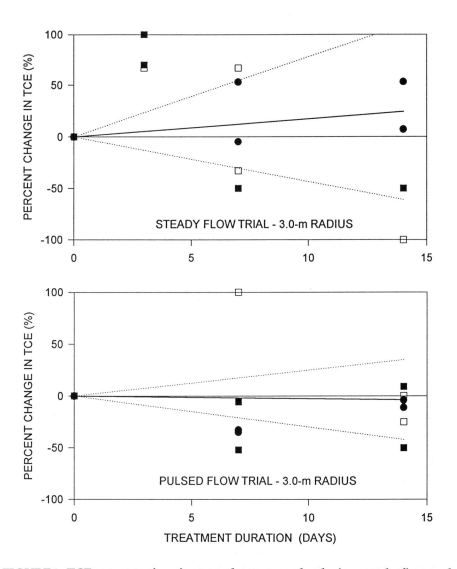

FIGURE 3. TCE concentrations in groundwater samples during steady-flow and pulsed sparge air injection: 3.0-m radius from injection well. Monitor probes depths were 0.9 m (●), 1.8 m (■) and 2.7 m (□) below the aquifer surface. Dotted lines indicate 95% confidence limits for the regression line.

DISCUSSION

TCE concentration decreases were observed during the pulsed trials, while TCE levels increased slightly during steady-flow trials. The effects of sparging were confounded by strong, pre-existing concentration gradients in the test aquifer. Future tests will be conducted at a greater distance from the source area to achieve relatively uniform pretest concentrations. Nonetheless, this initial comparison suggested that pulsed operation induced greater mass transfer than steady air injection. However, mass transfer rates could not be confirmed by off-gas capture, because gaseous-phase concentrations in the off-gas were below the laboratory detection limit of 50 µL TCE/L air. Longer-term test operation may have provided a clearer distinction between steady and pulsed-flow results.

REFERENCES

Boersma, P., F. S. Peterson, P. Newman, and R. Huddleston. 1993. "Use of Groundwater Sparging to Effect Hydrocarbon Biodegradation." *Proceedings of the 1993 Petroleum Hydrocarbons and Organic Chemicals in Groundwater: Prevention, Detection, and Restoration Conference,* Houston, TX, pp. 557-559.10.

Ji, W., A. Dahmani, D. P. Ahlfeld, J. D. Lin, and E. Hill III. 1993. "Laboratory Study of Air Sparging: Air Flow Visualization." *Ground Water Monitoring and Remediation,* pp. 115-126.

Johnson, R. L., P. C. Johnson, D. B. McWhorter, R. E. Hinchee, and I. Goodman. 1993. "An Overview of In Situ Air Sparging." *Ground Water Monitoring and Remediation,* pp. 127-135.

Newman, P., F. S. Peterson, P. E. Boersma, and R. E. Huddleston. 1994. "Effects of Sparging on Groundwater Hydraulics and Groundwater Quality." *Proceedings of the Air and Waste Management Association Annual Meeting,* Cincinnati, Ohio, June 19-24.

Pankow, J. F., R. A. Johnson, and J. A. Cherry. 1993. "Air Sparging in Gate Wells in Cutoff Walls and Trenches for Control of Plumes of Volatile Organic Compounds (VOCs)." *Groundwater* 31(4).

Air Sparging for In Situ Bioremediation of Toluene

Richard A. Brown, Wendy C. Leonard, and Maureen C. Leahy

ABSTRACT

Groundwater contamination was discovered at a manufacturing site in New York State. The contamination was due to the use of a burn pit to dispose of waste solvents, primarily toluene and a mixture of chlorinated ethenes. These solvents were partially absorbed into a sandy fill. Over a period of time, these adsorbed solvents leached into the groundwater and eventually impacted a local wetlands. Of longer term environmental concern was the existence of a municipal water well approximately 1,200 ft downgradient of the site. Air sparging was chosen as the remedial method to address the soil and groundwater contamination on site. Air sparging was chosen as a direct volatilization method and as an oxygen source for bioremediation. This case history illustrates the efficacy and limitations of air sparging for in situ bioremediation applications. The purpose of the paper is to discuss the selection, design, and operation of an air sparging/bioremediation system so that a remediation practitioner can adequately evaluate the use of air sparging for in situ bioremediation applications.

INTRODUCTION

Trichloroethylene (TCE) and other volatile organic compounds (VOCs) were detected in a municipal drinking water supply well. In sampling discharges into an adjacent river, the state regulatory agency detected similar, but not identical, VOCs in the cooling water discharges from a nearby plastic and rubber products manufacturing facility. The cooling water was derived from the facility's two 150-ft-deep bedrock wells, which were also found to be contaminated with VOCs including toluene. Although no direct link was established between the municipal well and the production wells, which are separated from the municipal well by a wetland and a stream, the company moved quickly to remediate its property.

SITE GEOLOGY

The site is situated within the 100-year floodplain of a broad valley with a slowly flowing river. The overburden sediments consist of a sandy fill material to a depth of approximately 5 ft. The fill is underlain by stratified alluvial sands. Bedrock underlies the overburden materials at approximately 20 ft below grade. The depth to groundwater is approximately 6 ft below grade.

EXTENT OF CONTAMINATION

A hydrogeologic investigation tentatively identified the source of the contamination as an area of the site where solvents had historically been burned in open trenches 20 to 30 years ago. A soil gas survey, soil borings, and chemical analyses of soil and groundwater samples were used to define the vertical and lateral extent of subsurface contamination. The concentrations of VOCs in the groundwater before treatment, as detected by EPA Method 624, ranged from a low of 10 parts per billion (ppb) at the outer edge of the plume to a maximum of 520,000 ppb in the central portion of the plume (Figure 1). Mass distribution based upon analysis of discrete soil and groundwater samples indicated that 95% of the total mass was absorbed to soil and the remaining 5% was in the dissolved phase. Over 70% of the total mass was absorbed to soils in the saturated zone. Toluene comprised 80% of the total VOCs.

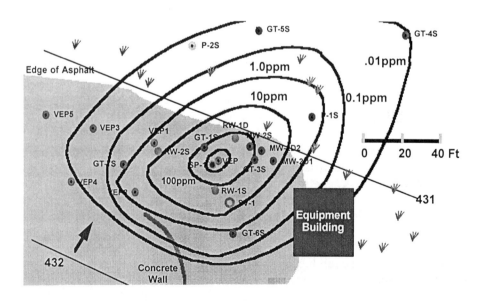

FIGURE 1. Total VOCs in groundwater.

BIOSPARGING

Based on a technology screening evaluation, a combined air sparging and soil vapor extraction (SVE) system was selected as the technology of choice based on the presence of the majority of the mass below the water table and the nature of contaminants. The system would act as a biosparge/biovent system to rapidly remove VOCs by biodegradation and as a sparge/vent to remove VOCs by volatilization. Toluene, which is very amenable to aerobic biodegradation and has a high Henry's constant (5.94×10^{-3} atm-m^3/mole), would be removed by both mechanisms, while the chlorinated solvents such as TCE, which also have high Henry's constants but are not readily treated by standard aerobic biodegradation, would be removed by volatilization alone. A groundwater extraction system consisting of two recovery wells also was selected to provide hydraulic control of the contaminated groundwater during treatment.

SYSTEM DESIGN

A biosparging system was installed consisting of 2 air sparge points and 7 SVE points as shown in Figure 2. The spacing of the air sparging and SVE points was determined from in situ pilot testing. The determined radii of influence were 16 ft for the air sparge points and 20 ft for the SVE points. The sparge

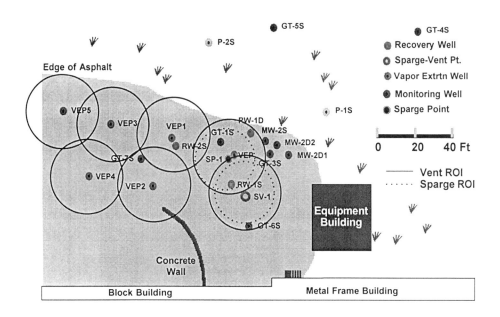

FIGURE 2. System design.

well was screened 8 to 10 ft below the water table. The injected airflow rate was 12 scfm/point and the extraction rate was 35 scfm/point.

RESULTS

The remediation system has been in operation for more than two years. During that time, the biodegradation of toluene has been measured by monitoring the concentration of carbon dioxide in the effluent from the vent system. Carbon dioxide concentrations have ranged from 0.1 to 1.0% (Table 1). Carbon dioxide production was converted to the pounds of toluene degraded assuming a 40% molar conversion of carbon from toluene into carbon dioxide. The carbon dioxide concentration was corrected for background by first subtracting 0.033% (the standard concentration of carbon dioxide in air) and then multiplying by 0.80 on the assumption that 20% of the CO_2 production was from the degradation of native organic matter. To date, approximately 5,230 lb (2,372 kg) of toluene have been biodegraded, as calculated from the carbon dioxide production.

In addition, approximately 200 lb (91 kg) VOCs have been removed by volatilization by the sparge/vent system and an additional 220 lb (100 kg) have been removed through the operation of the groundwater recovery system, for a total system removal of 5,650 lb (2,563 kg) (Figure 3).

Over this same time period, groundwater concentrations of total VOCs in monitoring wells have decreased between 95 and 99% (Figure 4). One well, which is outside the influence of the biosparging system (GT-7S), has not shown similar reductions. Due to a thin saturated thickness, air sparge wells were not installed in this area. A dual-phase extraction system is under consideration for this part of the site.

TABLE 1. Carbon dioxide percentages in SVE.

Week	SVE CO_2%[a]	Week	SVE CO_2%[a]	Week	SVE CO_2%[a]
1	0.20%	45	0.10%	98	0.50%
6	0.20%	47	0.12%	103	0.30%
8	0.30%	52	0.18%	105	0.30%
13	0.18%	56	0.15%	123	0.00%
21	0.10%	62	0.31%	127	0.65%
28	0.10%	81	1.00%	131	0.60%
32	0.17%	85	0.10%	136	0.20%
35	0.13%	89	0.45%	139	0.25%
39	0.18%	93	0.15%	140	0.30%

(a) Measured with Draeger tubes.

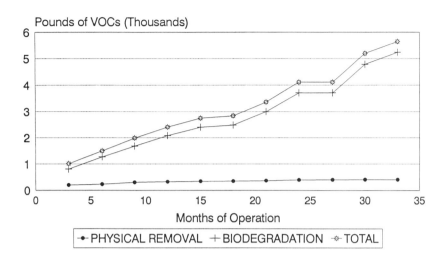

FIGURE 3. Estimated total VOC removal. (Physical removal includes SVE and groundwater recovery.)

CONCLUSIONS

Biosparging using the injection of air below the water table is an effective means of accelerating the bioremediation of compounds such as toluene trapped below the water table. These trapped solvents are not amenable to high mass

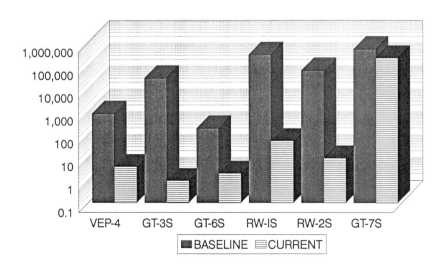

FIGURE 4. Groundwater cleanup effectiveness. (VOC reductions are > 99% except at GT-7S.)

removal processes such as soil vapor extraction, nor are they easily solubilized for groundwater extraction. Given the right subsurface geology, biosparging is more cost-effective than traditional in situ bioremediation using hydrogen peroxide as an oxygen source. Although capital costs for peroxide delivery and air sparge systems are comparable for the most sites, the overall present worth is significantly higher for peroxide systems. This difference is due to higher operating costs primarily because of the cost of peroxide supply and handling precautions. Operating costs for peroxide systems are typically 5- to 10-fold higher than for a sparge system treating a similar area. In addition, by combining biodegradation with volatilization, biosparging can be an effective treatment for mixtures of volatile contaminants in which not all compounds are amenable to biodegradation.

In Situ Biosparging at an Amoco Site: Subsurface Air Distribution and Biostimulation

Minoo Javanmardian, J. Scott Huber, Carl B. Olson,
Ward P. Schwartz, Carol A. Masin, and Victor J. Kremesec, Jr.

ABSTRACT

A pilot test was conducted at an Amoco Oil petroleum products storage terminal to investigate the effectiveness of in situ biosparging for soil and groundwater remediation. This process was designed to reduce hydrocarbon concentrations in both soil and groundwater by promoting in situ biodegradation through air injection at low flowrates below the water table. The radius of influence of injected air in soil and groundwater was between 4.5 to 6.0 m (15 to 20 ft) at air flowrates of 40 to 85 standard liters per minute (1.5 to 3.0 scfm), by oxygen, carbon dioxide, and dissolved oxygen measurements. A helium tracer test demonstrated relatively uniform air channel distribution within 4.5 m (15 ft) in the saturated zone. The oxygen uptake rate in soil was between 0.08% and 0.21% per hour, which corresponds to a theoretical soil hydrocarbon biodegradation rate between 1.5 to 3.9 mg/kg soil/day. A three-order-of-magnitude increase in bacterial population in the capillary fringe, the increase in groundwater bacterial population, and a reduction in groundwater benzene, toluene, ethylbenzene, and xylenes (BTEX) concentrations after one month of biosparging demonstrated the effectiveness of this technology in stimulating biological degradation in the groundwater.

INTRODUCTION

In the past few years, in situ air sparging has become a popular technology to remediate groundwater contaminated with volatile and semivolatile organic compounds (Johnson et al. 1993, Brown et al. 1994, Marley et al. 1992, Brown 1994). Two mechanisms are believed to be involved in removing contaminants from groundwater — volatilization and biodegradation.

Biosparging is essentially air sparging at low air flowrates (< 10 scfm) and is designed to stimulate the biodegradation mechanism by supplying oxygen to the groundwater while minimizing the volatilization mechanism. Air channels are believed to be the primary mechanism of oxygen distribution to the subsurface (Dahmani et al. 1993); however, their density, size, and spatial distribution are not clear. Some laboratory and field studies indicate that air channel distribution in the subsurface is asymmetric and heterogeneous (Dahmani et al. 1994). Asymmetric air distribution may limit the effectiveness of the sparging system to oxygenate the saturated and unsaturated zones. More studies are required to further determine the air distribution mechanism in the saturated zone under different site geologies.

A biosparging pilot test was conducted at an Amoco Oil petroleum products storage terminal in Michigan to investigate the effectiveness of this technology for oxygenating soil and groundwater. Direct and indirect measurements were performed during the pilot test to understand the homogeneity of air distribution in soil and groundwater, as well as biological activity as a result of air introduction to the subsurface.

SITE CHARACTERISTICS

The facility and surrounding areas are located on an outwash plain of glacial origin. The top layer of soil beneath the facility generally consists of 0.6 to 1 m (2 to 3 ft) of silty sand under which is predominantly a fine- or medium-grained sand that contains various percentages of gravel up to 6 m (20 ft) below grade. Silt is encountered below the sand layer and extends 12 m (40 ft) below surface level.

Table 1 summarizes the groundwater parameters obtained from the site assessment. The saturated hydraulic conductivity at the pilot area using slug test was 4.8×10^{-3} cm/s and the average groundwater velocity was estimated to be 45 m/year (150 ft/year).

Both soil and groundwater are impacted by refined products, mainly gasoline. The maximum BTEX level in soil and groundwater was estimated to be 150 mg/kg and 40 mg/L, respectively, with xylenes being the main contaminant in both media.

TABLE 1. Groundwater assessment parameters.

Parameter	Value
Depth to Water	4 to 4.25 m below surface level (13 to 14 ft)
Saturated Hydraulic Conductivity (slug test)	2.5×10^{-2} to 4.6×10^{-3} cm/s[a]
Hydraulic Gradient	1.6×10^{-3} – 2.5×10^{-3} m per horizontal m
Estimated Groundwater Velocity	7.5 to 88 m/y (25 to 250 ft/y)

(a) The saturated hydraulic conductivity in the test area was approximately 4.8×10^{-3} cm/s.

PILOT TEST PROCEDURES
AND MATERIALS

The in situ biosparging pilot test at this site consisted of oxygenating the saturated and unsaturated (vadose) zones by introducing air at flowrates between 40 to 200 slpm (1.5 to 7.0 scfm) and injection pressure between 3 to 5 psig below the water table. The air radius of influence in groundwater and soil were measured by dissolved oxygen concentrations in the saturated zone and oxygen, helium, and carbon dioxide concentrations, as well as pressure, in the unsaturated zone.

The biodegradation rates were measured by monitoring the depletion of oxygen after the system shut down in soil and groundwater. The bacterial population was measured before and after 1 month of biosparging in groundwater and the capillary fringe to document the effect of this technology on stimulating biological degradation. Figure 1 illustrates the pilot test area configuration.

Air Injection

Two sparge wells, one in the impacted area (F3) and one in the unimpacted area (A4), were selected for air injection. The sparge wells consist of 0.45 m (1.5 ft) 0.25-mm slot stainless steel well screen. The tip of each well screen was set at 6 m (20 ft) below the surface level, approximately 2 m (6 ft) below the water table. Injection well A4 served as a control point to account for natural variations in the unimpacted area. Air was injected at flowrates of 40, 85, and

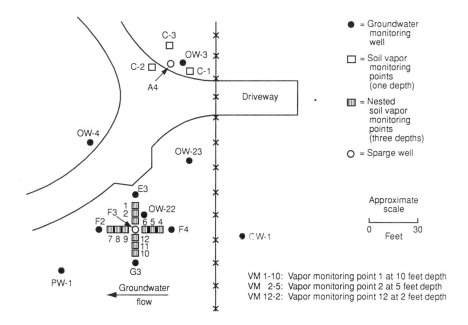

FIGURE 1. Pilot test area configuration.

200 slpm (1.5, 3.0, and 7.0 scfm) for 3 days, after which the system was shut down for rate measurements. The duration of the test for each flowrate was 25 h.

A helium tracer test was performed by injecting air containing 20% helium at 2.0 scfm for 7 h in F3, and monitoring pressure and helium concentrations in the vadose zone.

Soil Vapor Monitoring Points

Nested soil vapor monitoring points with 15 cm (6 in) stainless steel screens were installed at 13 locations around F3 (Figure 1). The nested points were installed 0.6, 1.5, and 3 m (2, 5, and 10 ft) below the surface level, at distances of 0, 1.5, 3.0, and 4.5 m (0, 5, 10, and 15 ft) from the sparge point F3. Vapor monitoring points were also installed around A4 (unimpacted area) at 1.5 m (5 ft) depth.

Groundwater Monitoring Points

Dissolved oxygen (DO) and BTEX concentrations were measured through 10 groundwater monitoring wells, four of which were 6 m (20 ft) from F3 and screened 1.2 to 1.8 m (4 to 6 ft) below the water table. Monitoring well OW-3 was used as the control to account for natural fluctuations.

RESULTS

Soil Vapor Monitoring

Oxygen, carbon dioxide, and total hydrocarbon concentrations were measured frequently during the air injection and shutdown periods. Figures 2a and 2b illustrate these results from a vapor monitoring point located 4.5 m (15 ft) from sparge point F3, at a 3-m (10-ft) depth (VM 1-10). Similar results were observed in VM 4-10, VM 7-10, and VM 10-10, which are located at the same distance and different direction from the sparge point. Figure 2a indicates that the total soil vapor hydrocarbon concentration increased during air injection for a short period of time, after which it started to decrease, and during shutdown it decreased below the initial concentration at time zero. Based on these results, volatilization occurred for a short period of time and is not likely to be a continuing removal mechanism for hydrocarbons. Oxygen and carbon dioxide concentrations reached their steady state levels of 21% and 1%, respectively, after 25 to 75 h of air injection, depending on the distance from injection point. The oxygen uptake and carbon dioxide production rates were significant in the impacted areas (Figure 2b), whereas these rates were negligible (approximately zero) in the unimpacted areas. (The figures for unimpacted areas are not shown.)

Helium Tracer Test

Figures 3a and 3b show helium concentrations and total pressure at two of the vapor monitoring points, 1.5 (VM 12-10) and 4.5 m (VM 10-10) from injection

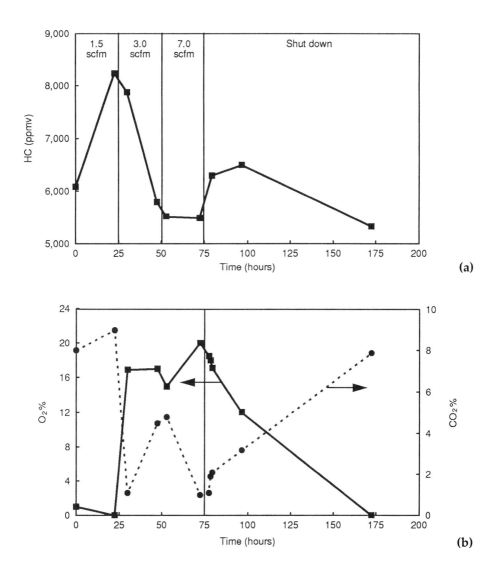

FIGURE 2. (a) Total hydrocarbon concentration at VM 1-10 during the pilot test. (b) Oxygen and carbon dioxide concentrations at VM 1-10 during the pilot test.

point F3, and at 3 m (10 ft) depth. The maximum gauge pressure measured at any vapor monitoring point was 2.5 mm (0.1 in.) of water, with the exception of the vapor monitoring point that was nested with the sparge point that showed 5 mm (0.2 in.) of water pressure. Helium was detected within 4 h of injection at all the vapor monitoring points, including the points shown in Figures 3a and 3b. A lag phase of 1 to 3 h was observed between pressure buildup and helium detection. Overall, during the 7-h injection period, helium was detected in all the 39 vapor monitoring points above 1% concentration, which indicated relatively homogeneous air distribution in the test area.

Groundwater Monitoring and BTEX Concentrations

Figure 4 shows the typical results of dissolved oxygen concentrations measured in unimpacted (OW-3) and impacted (OW-22) areas. Significant fluctuations were observed in DO levels, which made it difficult and unreliable to calculate the oxygen uptake rates. Although, the DO level increased during

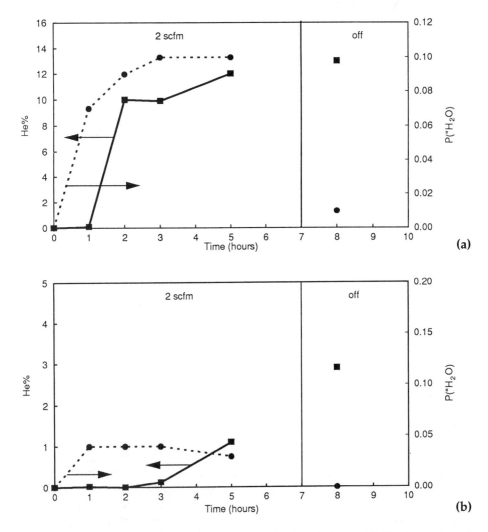

FIGURE 3. Helium tracer test results obtained from (a) VM 12-10 and (b) VM 10-10.

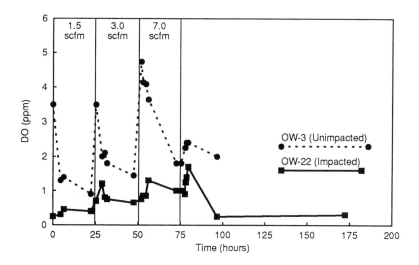

FIGURE 4. Typical dissolved oxygen concentrations in the pilot test area.

the sparging period, the maximum level did not exceed 3 ppm in the impacted areas. In general, no obvious correlation was observed between DO level and air flowrate. It should be noted that, during operation, no air bubbles were observed in any of the groundwater monitoring points, confirming that air was not short-circuiting to the monitoring wells.

The results of benzene and total BTEX concentrations in groundwater are illustrated in Figures 5a and 5b. The samples were obtained before and after 1 month of biosparging at 40 slpm (1.5 scfm) flowrate through 35 sparge points that were installed at 20-ft (6-m) centers in the test area. The results show a decrease in benzene and BTEX concentrations in all the wells in the impacted areas including OW-22 and PW-1. However, the measurements from OW-3, located in the unimpacted area, show no sign of BTEX detection after 1 month of air injection, indicating that biosparging at low air flowrate did not result in contaminant migration in groundwater.

Bacterial Population

The results of bacterial population counts in the groundwater and the capillary fringe from impacted and unimpacted areas are summarized in Figures 6a and 6b. Groundwater samples from monitoring wells and soil samples from the capillary fringe were analyzed for total number of heterotrophs (THT) as well as hydrocarbon degraders (HCD). The results are reported in colony-forming units (CFUs) per unit volume of water (mL), or unit mass of soil (g). A significant increase, as much as 3 orders of magnitude, was observed in THT and HCD, after 1 month of biosparging. It should be noted that, despite an increase in total number of heterotrophs, the population of HCD was not increased in OW-3 located in the unimpacted area.

DISCUSSION

Biodegradation Rates

The biodegradation rates in soil were measured by both oxygen uptake rates and vapor phase hydrocarbon losses during the shutdown period. The loss of oxygen in the impacted area was attributed to biodegradation, because the control (unimpacted) area did not show significant oxygen loss during the shutdown period. Table 2 shows the results of oxygen uptake rates, as well as theoretical

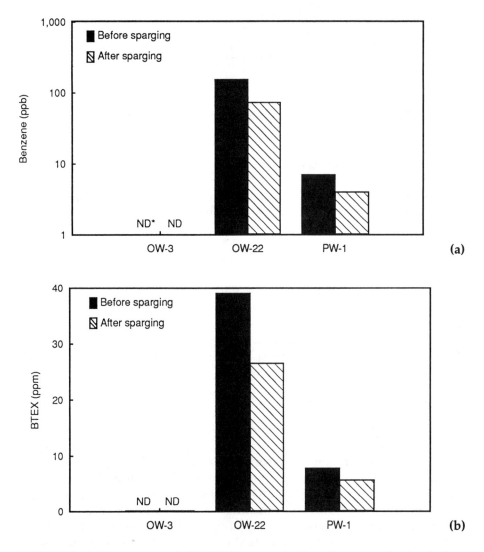

FIGURE 5. (a) Benzene and (b) BTEX concentrations in groundwater before and after biosparging (*ND = nondetect).

hydrocarbon degradation rates, in soil for 11 vapor monitoring points. The theoretical rate of hydrocarbon degradation (hexane equivalent), which is a function of temperature (25°C), porosity (0.3), pressure (1 atm), and soil density (1,440 kg/m³), was calculated based on in situ respiration procedures (Hinchee and Ong 1992). The variation of oxygen uptake rates of 0.08% to 0.21% per hour resulted in theoretical hydrocarbon biodegradation rates of 1.5 to 3.9 mg/kg/day. The actual hydrocarbon biodegradation rates measured in soil vapor monitoring

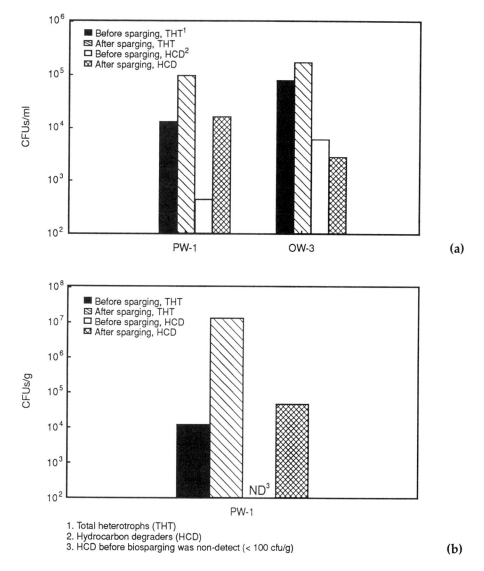

1. Total heterotrophs (THT)
2. Hydrocarbon degraders (HCD)
3. HCD before biosparging was non-detect (< 100 cfu/g)

(b)

FIGURE 6. Bacterial population (a) in groundwater and (b) in the capillary fringe before and after biosparging.

points were significantly less than the expected theoretical values (Table 2). Assuming equilibrium between soil and the vapor phase, the difference may be attributed to the biodegradation of residual hydrocarbons bound to the soil.

The oxygen uptake rates were not calculated for groundwater due to significant DO fluctuations in both impacted and unimpacted areas. However, the significant increase of bacterial population, particularly hydrocarbon degraders, in the capillary fringe and saturated zones of the impacted areas can serve as a good indicator of biodegradation stimulation in these areas.

Helium Tracer Test

Two possible mechanisms were identified for helium distribution in the subsurface:

1. **Helium distribution through air channels in groundwater.** This mechanism implies that the radius of influence of helium in groundwater and soil is comparable and transport through the groundwater is mainly responsible for helium distribution.
2. **Helium distribution through vapor transport in the vadose zone.** Under this scenario, it is assumed that helium rises in the vadose zone without significant distribution in groundwater and migrates in the soil horizontally, based on pressure gradient and/or diffusion.

The possibility of the second scenario was estimated by using the one-dimensional radial flow equation, which is utilized frequently for measuring air flowrates in venting systems (Johnson et al. 1990):

$$\frac{Q}{H} = \pi \frac{K}{\mu} P_a \frac{\left[1 - (P_b/P_a)^2\right]}{\ln \dfrac{R_a}{R_b}}$$

where Q/H = Flowrate per unit depth ($cm^3/cm/s$)
  K = Soil permeability to airflow (darcy)
  μ = Air viscosity: 0.018 cp
  P_a = Absolute pressure at point "a," atm
  P_b = Absolute pressure at point "b," atm
  R_a = Distance of point "a" from sparge point
  R_b = Distance of point "b" from sparge point.

By calculating the rate of radial airflow and knowing the total volume of air between points "a" and "b," it is possible to estimate the required time for air to travel between the two points. This simple calculation was carried out for VM 12-10 and VM 10-10 (Figures 3a and 3b). These two points are both screened 3 m (10 ft) below the surface level, and they are 1.5 m (5 ft) and 4.5 m (15 ft) from the sparge point, respectively.

TABLE 2. Oxygen uptake and hydrocarbon degradation rates in vadose zone.

Vapor Monitoring Point	Oxygen Uptake Rate (% O_2/h)	Theoretical Hydrocarbon Biodegradation Rate (mg/kg soil/day)	Measured Hydrocarbon Biodegradation Rate in Soil Vapor (mg/kg/day)
C-2 (control)	0	—	—
VM 1-10	0.21	3.89	0.18
VM 2-2	0.13	2.41	—
VM 2-5	0.22	4.07	0.48
VM 2-12	0.14	2.59	—
VM 4-10	0.13	2.4	0.39
VM 5-5	0.18	3.33	0.81
VM 8-10	0.12	2.22	0.2
VM 9-5	0.1	1.85	0.36
VM 10-5	0.08	1.48	0.46
VM 11-5	0.09	1.67	0.35

The radial flow equation was solved based on the following assumptions:

K = 5.58 darcys (saturated zone hydraulic conductivity of 4.8×10^{-3} cm/s)
μ = 0.018 cp
P_a = 1.000246 atm (gauge pressure: 0.1 in. of water)
P_b = 1.000098 atm (gauge pressure: 0.04 in. of water)
R_a = 1.5 m (5 ft)
R_b = 4.5 m (15 ft)

The radial flowrate per unit depth (Q/H) was calculated to be 0.25 cm³/cm/s. Assuming a porosity of 0.3, the total air volume between the two vapor monitoring points per unit depth was calculated to be:

$$\frac{V}{H} = \pi (R_b^2 - R_a^2) \times 0.3 = 1.75 \times 10^5 \text{ cm}^3/\text{cm}$$

and the minimum time for helium to reach from VM 12-10 to VM 10-10 will be:

$$\text{Time} = \frac{\dfrac{V}{H}}{\dfrac{Q}{H}} = \frac{1.75 \times 10^5}{0.25 \times 3,600} = 187 \text{ hours}$$

Because helium was detected in VM 10-10 after only 4 h of sparging, it is our belief that, at this site, the mechanism of helium distribution in the subsurface is via distribution of air channels in groundwater.

CONCLUSIONS

The pilot test demonstrated that biosparging will stimulate biodegradation of gasoline components in both soil and groundwater. Biological stimulation was demonstrated by a significant oxygen uptake rate in soil and a three-orders-of-magnitude increase in bacterial population in the capillary fringe and groundwater. Dissolved oxygen measurements were not consistent, and DO may not be an appropriate parameter to monitor the performance of biosparging based on this study. A helium tracer test demonstrated a fairly homogeneous distribution of air through groundwater and soil. Order-of-magnitude comparisons showed that the mechanism of air distribution in the vadose zone was through groundwater, and the air radius of influence in both groundwater and soil were comparable.

REFERENCES

Brown, R. A. 1994. "Treatment of Petroleum Hydrocarbons in Groundwater by Air Sparging." In Norris et al. (Eds.), *Handbook of Bioremediation*, pp. 61-85. Lewis Publishers, Boca Raton, FL.

Brown, R. A., R. J. Hicks, and P. M. Hicks. 1994. "Use of Air Sparging for In Situ Bioremediation." In R. E. Hinchee (Ed.), *Air Sparging for Site Remediation*, pp. 38-55. Lewis Publishers, Boca Raton, FL.

Dahmani, A., W. Ji, D. P. Ahlfeld, J. D. Lin, and E. Hill. 1993. "Laboratory Study of Air Sparging: Air Flow Visualization." *Groundwater Monitor and Remediation XIII* (4): 115-126.

Dahmani, A., D. Ahlfeld, G. Hoag, M. Farrell, and W. Ji. 1994. "Field Measurement of Air Sparging in a Connecticut Site: Results and Comments." In API *Proceedings of the 1994 Petroleum Hydrocarbons and Organic Chemicals In Groundwater: Prevention, Detection, and Remediation, Houston, Texas*, pp. 175-186.

Hinchee, R. E. and S. K. Ong. 1992. "A Rapid In Situ Respiration Test for Measuring Aerobic Biodegradation Rates of Hydrocarbons in Soil." *J. Air Waste Manage. Assoc.* 42(10): 1305-1312.

Johnson, R. L., P. C. Johnson, D. B. McWhorter, R. E. Hinchee, and I. Goodman. 1993. "An Overview of In Situ Air Sparging." *Groundwater Monitoring and Remediation XIII* (4):127-135.

Johnson, P. C., C. C. Stanley, M. W. Kemblowski, D. L. Byers, and J. D. Colthart. 1990. "A Practical Approach to the Design, Operation, and Monitoring of In Situ Soil-Venting Systems." *Groundwater Monitoring and Remediation Spring*: 159-178.

Marley, M. C., D. J. Hazebrouck, and M. T. Walsh. 1992. "The Application of In Situ Air Sparging as an Innovative Soils and Groundwater Remediation Technology." *Groundwater Monitoring Review* 12(2): 137-145.

Optimized Air Sparging Coupled with Soil Vapor Extraction to Remediate Groundwater

Michael Martinson, Joyce Linck,
Chris Manz, and Tim Petrofske

ABSTRACT

Air sparging coupled with soil vapor extraction (AS/SVE) has obvious benefits for groundwater contamination consisting of volatile organic compounds, particularly benzene, ethylbenzene, toluene, and xylenes (BTEX). Although AS/SVE is easily employed given suitable site conditions, optimized AS/SVE system operation and monitoring (O/M) are often overlooked once treatment is initiated. Site O/M typically is conducted with on-site field staff, or as an alternative, by remotely connecting to the site via modem and programmable logic controller (PLC). Two AS/SVE sites located in Wisconsin have used either traditional on-site O/M or the remote modem/PLC option to evaluate and optimize system operation. System on-time efficiency using remote telemetry was improved compared to traditional O/M and system operations.

INTRODUCTION

Available subsurface remedial technologies, particularly for petroleum hydrocarbons, have increased over the past two decades. Soil vapor extraction (SVE) was first demonstrated to be effective for subsurface removal of the volatile fractions of hydrocarbon contamination in the vadose zone. Within the past 10 years, air sparging (AS) applications have been added to potential technologies available for groundwater and vadose zone subsurface remediation.

Volatilization, or in situ air stripping, is the major process by which the volatile fraction of total petroleum hydrocarbon (TPH) removal is accomplished (Loden 1992). A secondary, but as important, remediation process for SVE is aerobic biodegradation that uses the increased oxygen provided during SVE operation (Dupont et al. 1991; Hinchee and Miller 1990; Loden 1992). Multiple air exchanges are induced by high SVE airflow rates in the unsaturated subsurface. Aerobic biodegradation for both nonvolatile and volatile TPH is enhanced by soil oxygen levels that can easily exceed 3 to 5% concentrations, and in lower airflow venting applications (i.e., bioventing), aerobic biodegradation can become the dominant remediation process (Hinchee 1993; Miller et al. 1991; Newman et al. 1993).

Likewise, volatilization can be the major process accomplishing volatile TPH removal from groundwater during AS (Loden 1992). Variations in AS operation can result in minimal air-stripping action of volatile TPH fractions from groundwater and greatly increased rates for in situ aerobic biodegradation of dissolved-phase contamination (Brown 1993).

Typically, either on-site visits by field staff or remote telemetry provides the means by which to evaluate and modify AS/SVE system operation. Site O/M methods can be accomplished by mobilizing field staff to the site or by remotely connecting to the site via modem/PLC. Functionally, a PLC examines the status of input interfaces, and, in response, controls various switches, valves, or monitoring equipment through output interfaces. During the remote scan of the PLC program, all inputs are examined, the control plan can be evaluated/altered, and output records are updated. Two sites (Figures 1 and 3) used AS/SVE remediation designs and offer comparisons of system operation for data evaluation/ system operation options. By continually evaluating the performance of combined AS/SVE treatment systems, and correspondingly, modifying the mode of system operation for the desired removal mechanisms, system efficiency is enhanced and regulatory closure can be achieved in the shortest possible time frame.

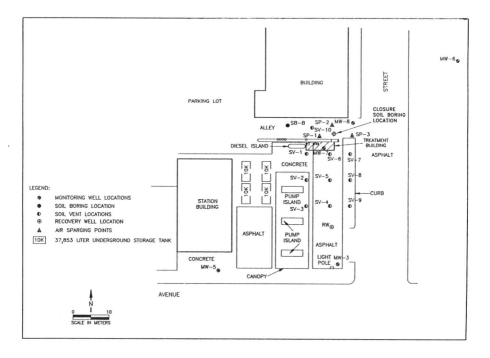

FIGURE 1. Site map: Site #1.

BACKGROUND SITE INFORMATION

Site #1

During a tank closure operation in 1988, residual impacted soil was noted surrounding a former tank basin (Figure 1). Subsurface soil consists of medium to fine sand with thin silt lenses (SP in Unified Classification System). Original remediation efforts at the site focused on a prior release from the former tank basin. In 1985, a pump-and-treat (P&T) system was installed, primarily for free-product recovery. The operation of the P&T system continued into 1987, and during that period approximately 1,230 L of free product were recovered.

From 1988 through 1991, SVE was employed seasonally to provide vadose zone remediation efforts and to achieve soil cleanup objectives in the area surrounding the former tank basin. While cleanup of unsaturated soils progressed

TABLE 1. Site #1: Groundwater analytical summary.

Date	Total BTEX Concentration (µg/L)			
	MW-3	MW-7	MW-8	SV-10
7/89	770	F[a]	NS[b]	NS
1/90	7	FP	NS	NS
7/90	34	FP	NS	NS
2/91	ND[c]	2,334	NS	NS
10/91	20	164	15,870	28
2/92	3	ND	1,009	62
4/92	AS/SVE Initiated -->			
5/92	28	1,664	2,730	ND
7/92	6	5,740	509	3
5/93	2	723	8	4
11/93	1	128	ND	ND
2/94	ND	9	ND	ND
5/94	7	ND	ND	ND
8/94	23	ND	12	ND
11/94	12	ND	4	ND

(a) FP - Free product.
(b) NS - Not sampled/installed.
(c) ND - Not detected at EPA Method 8020 detection limits.
Note: Wisconsin Administrative Code NR 140 limits (µg/L):

	Enforcement	Preventative Action
Benzene	5	0.5
Toluene	343	68.6
Ethylbenzene	700	140
Xylenes	620	124

during 1988 to 1991, changes in groundwater elevations periodically flushed additional TPH contamination into site groundwater as noted by increased dissolved-phase concentrations (Table 1). To accelerate remediation progress in 1992, particularly toward groundwater cleanup goals, AS was added to the system remediation design (Figure 2).

The primary goals for AS/SVE operation at this site were to flush remaining capillary fringe TPH and maximize volatilization/biodegradation processes for removal of contaminants. In particular, aerobic biodegradation environmental conditions were closely evaluated, and AS operation was continually modified to promote more efficient dissolved-phase remediation.

Site #2

The geology of Site #2 consists of 2.4 m of silty sand underlain by approximately 1.8 meters of clay which locally confines the underlying fine- to medium-grained sand. At this site (Figure 3) a P&T system, operating from October 1987 to the present, had recovered over 3,580 L of free product. During this period, only modest decreases were noted in dissolved-phase hydrocarbon concentrations (Table 2). A site bioassessment and laboratory bench-scale microcosm testing were completed in 1992 to provide design criteria for options to upgrade site remediation. Oxygen and nutrient additions to the site groundwater were found to be beneficial in optimizing aerobic biodegradation of TPH. A pilot test for

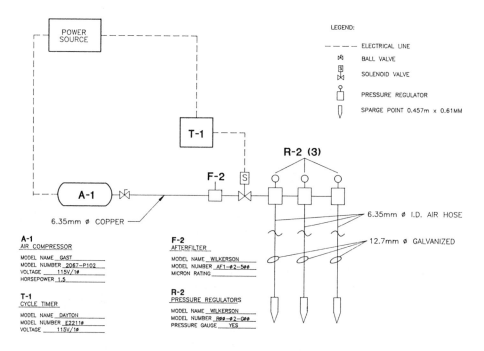

FIGURE 2. Site #1: Process and instrumentation diagram.

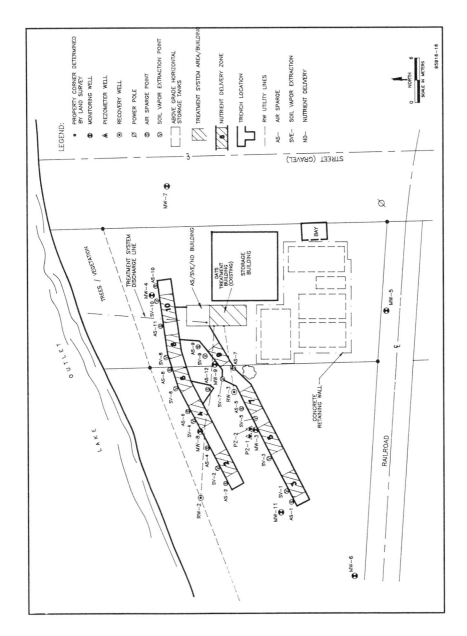

FIGURE 3. Site map: Site #2.

TABLE 2. Site #2: Groundwater analytical summary.

	Total BTEX Concentration (µg/L)				
Date	MW-3	MW-4	MW-8	MW-9	MW-15
1/89	108,500	43,440	NS[a]	NS	NS
10/90	64,700	NS	56,000	NS	NS
8/91	30,200	25,500	81,300	NS	NS
8/92	13,900	23,200	53,200	73,600	NS
2/93	13,450	25,000	16,990	88,400	NS
8/93	4,650	103,400	21,560	82,600	72,500
10/93	AS/SVE Initiated --->				
12/93	260	41	1,820	58,300	26,570
5/94	ND[b]	14,620	132	5,637	452
8/94	ND	66	4	320	98
11/94	24	ND	ND	412	ND
2/95	4	ND	ND	ND	ND

(a) FP - Free product.
(b) NS - Not sampled/installed.
(c) ND - Not detected at EPA Method 8020 detection limits.
Note: Wisconsin Administrative Code NR 140 limits (µg/L):

	Enforcement	Preventative Action
Benzene	5	0.5
Toluene	343	68.6
Ethylbenzene	700	140
Xylenes	620	124

AS/SVE was completed in January 1993 to gain additional design criteria for an upgrade for site remediation. Results of these tests indicated that AS/SVE combined with in situ inorganic nutrient delivery would provide an effective remedial technology for the site. In 1993, AS/SVE was implemented to gain faster site closure.

METHODS

Groundwater monitoring parameters included dissolved oxygen (DO), pH, temperature, conductivity, and water levels using calibrated field instruments and colorimetric test kits. Following purging of four wellbore volumes of ground-water, the concentrations of DO, soluble iron, and total iron in bailed groundwater were measured using colorimetric test kits. Temperature, conductivity, and pH meter measurements were also collected from bailed water samples. Samples were collected for analysis of petroleum hydrocarbon concentrations including BTEX by U.S. Environmental Protection Agency (EPA) Method 8020. The AS/SVE was turned off for at least 1 hour prior to collected groundwater measurements and samples.

RESULTS

Standard site visits for Site #1 were employed from 1992 until AS/SVE system operation was discontinued in July 1994. System data evaluation, operation modifications, and data collection were accomplished by field staff visits to the site on a monthly basis. Collected data were used to evaluate and provide guidance for optimization of system operation. Site monitoring data are summarized in Tables 1 and 3. The log of the system operation is reviewed in Table 4.

TABLE 3. Site #1: Groundwater quality summary.

Date		Groundwater Quality Parameters (mg/L)			
		MW-3	MW-7	MW-8	SV-10
10/91	$DO^{(a)}$	2.0	2.0	6.0	2.0
	$Fe^{3+(b)}$	>10.0	2.0	5.0	>10.0
	$Fe^{2+(c)}$	6.0	0.3	2.0	8.0
4/92	AS/SVE Initiated -->				
5/92	DO	1.0	1.0	1.0	3.0
	Fe^{3+}	10.0	2.0	5.0	1.0
	Fe^{2+}	5.0	1.0	2.0	0.2
11/92	DO	1.0	1.0	1.0	5.0
	Fe^{3+}	10.0	10.0	10.0	0.8
	Fe^{2+}	10.0	10.0	10.0	0.3
5/93	DO	2.0	4.0	6.0	6.0
	Fe^{3+}	6.0	6.0	4.0	2.0
	Fe^{2+}	4.0	5.0	2.0	2.0
11/93	DO	2.0	6.0	6.0	6.0
	Fe^{3+}	10.0	10.0	5.0	$NM^{(d)}$
	Fe^{2+}	7.0	1.0	0.4	1.0
5/94	DO	1.0	4.0	5.0	3.0
	Fe^{3+}	6.0	0.1	0.6	1.0
	Fe^{2+}	6.0	0.1	0.6	1.0
11/94	DO	2.0	2.0	4.0	2.0
	Fe^{3+}	7.0	7.0	0.3	0.6
	Fe^{2+}	7.0	7.0	0.2	0.4

(a) DO - Dissolved oxygen.   (c) Fe^{2+} - Dissolved iron.
(b) Fe^{3+} - Total iron.   (d) NM - Not measured.

TABLE 4. Site #1: System operating log.

Date	AS[a] points	Pressure (psi)	Pressure (kPa)	Airflow (cfm)	Airflow (m³/min)	AS cycles (min)	Notes
4/92	1,2,3	8.0	55.2	9.0[b]	0.255[b]	10 on/10 off	System startup
9/92	1,2,3	10.0	69.0	15.0	0.425	10 on/10 off	—
10/92	1,2,3	0.0	0.0	0.0	0.0	Changed to 20 on/10 off	SVE[c] blower failed
11/92	1,2,3	8.0	55.2	9.0	0.255	20 on/10 off	New SVE blower
12/92	1,2,3	11.0	75.8	16.0	0.453	100% on	No off AS cycles
3/93	1,2,3	10.0	69.0	8.0	0.227	100% on	Adjust manifold
6/93	1,2,3	14.0	96.5	12.0	0.340	100% on	—
7/93	1,2,3	15.0	103.4	11.0	0.312	100% on	System down; breaker off
8/93	1,2,3	14.0	96.5	11.5	0.326	100% on	—
9/93	1,2,3	18.0	124.1	9.0	0.255	2 AS points on	#3 AS off

(a) AS - Air sparge.
(b) Estimated airflow.
(c) SVE - Soil vapor extraction.

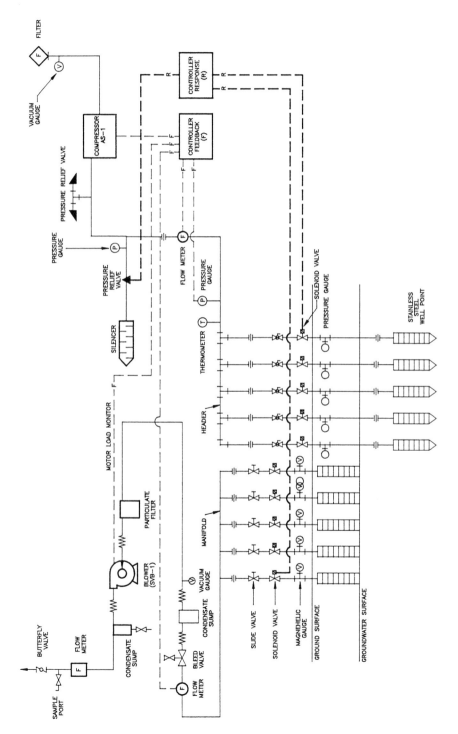

FIGURE 4. Site #2: Process and instrumentation diagram.

Modifications to the Site #2 treatment system, AS/SVE added to complement a P&T system that incorporated inorganic nutrient infiltration, were completed in October 1993. At Site #2, telemetry control using modem/PLC equipment was built into the treatment system upgrade (Figure 4) to allow remote monitoring/adjustments of system performance, troubleshooting of system problems, and correction of problems without physically visiting the site. By having up-to-date monitoring information available on the operation of the treatment system prior to site visits, field staff were better able to anticipate the need for on-site work or repairs. If system problems were noted during remote monitoring, the appropriate on-site response and urgency to schedule could be determined. Site monitoring data are summarized in Tables 2 and 5. The system operation log is reviewed in Table 6.

TABLE 5. Site #2: Groundwater quality summary.

Date		Groundwater Quality Parameters (mg/L)				
		MW-3	MW-4	MW-8	MW-9	MW-15
1/93	$DO^{(a)}$	1.0	1.0	0.8	0.6	$NM^{(d)}$
	$Fe^{3+(b)}$	NM	NM	NM	NM	NM
	$Fe^{2+(c)}$	NM	NM	NM	NM	NM
10/93	DO	1.0	4.0	2.0	1.0	1.0
	Fe^{3+}	NM	NM	NM	NM	NM
	Fe^{2+}	NM	NM	NM	NM	NM
10/93	AS/SVE Initiated -->					
12/93	DO	4.0	5.0	1.0	3.0	1.0
	Fe^{3+}	0.8	0.6	0.4	0.8	NM
	Fe^{2+}	0.3	0.4	0.2	0.4	NM
2/94	DO	NM	5.0	5.0	3.0	2.0
	Fe^{3+}	NM	2.0	2.0	2.0	10.0
	Fe^{2+}	NM	1.0	0.8	0.8	10.0
5/94	DO	5.0	4.0	5.0	5.0	4.0
	Fe^{3+}	0.8	7.0	0.2	0.4	0.2
	Fe^{2+}	0.1	1.0	0.1	0.2	0.1
8/94	DO	2.0	5.0	4.0	5.0	4.0
	Fe^{3+}	0.4	10.0	4.0	10.0	0.8
	Fe^{2+}	0.1	10.0	1.0	10.0	0.6
11/94	DO	6.0	8.0	6.0	6.0	2.0
	Fe^{3+}	10.0	10.0	5.0	10.0	2.0
	Fe^{2+}	5.0	10.0	2.0	10.0	2.0
2/95	DO	5.0	6.0	5.0	6.0	2.0
	Fe^{3+}	3.0	1.0	4.0	10.0	1.0
	Fe^{2+}	1.0	0.4	1.0	7.0	0.2

(a) DO - Dissolved oxygen.   (c) Fe^{2+}- Dissolved iron.
(b) Fe^{3+} - Total iron.   (d) NM - Not measured.

TABLE 6. Site #2: System operating log.

Date	SVE[a] cycle points	AS[b] cycle points	Pressure (psi/kPa)	Airflow (cfm/m³/min)	Nutrient delivery (ND)[c]	Recovery well operation	Notes
10/93	1,4,5,8,9/ 2,3,6,7,10	1,2,5,6,9,11/ 3,4,7,8,10,12	4.0/27.6	46.0/1.30	Zones 2-7; 302 L at 6 mL/min	RW-2: 7.56 L/min; RW-3: 11.3 L/min	System startup
11/93	NC[d]	NC	6.0/41.4	45.0/1.27	132 L added	NC	ND floats sticking
12/93	NC	NC	8.0/55.2	44.0/1.25	Restarted at 6 mL/min	Mercury switches installed	NC
3/4/94	NC	10 & 11 off	9.0/62.1	44.0/1.25	Increased to 10 mL/min	NC	AS points off to observe MW-4
3/10/94	NC	NC	9.0/62.1	42.0/1.19	Zone 9 on; up to 13 mL/min	NC	Nutrient levels low in MW-9
6/94	All points on continuously	10 & 11 on	10.0/69.0	42.0/1.19	Zones 8 & 10 on; down to 6 mL/min	NC	Nutrient levels low by MW-4
7/94	NC	NC	10.0/69.0	40.0/1.13	ND halted	NC	75.6 L of nutrients added
9/94	1 & 3 off	1,2,3,5 off	10.0/69.0	40.0/1.13	Zones 2-7 off; 3 mL/min to zones 8, 9, 10	NC	Western half of site GW[e] clean
10/94	NC	NC	10.0/69.0	40.0/1.13	System stops if >3 cycles/h	NC	Cycle counter for excess ND to GW
12/94	3 on	3 on	10.0/69.0	40.0/1.13	Zone 5 on; up to 10 mL/min	NC	BTEX detect/MW-3

(a) SVE - Soil vapor extraction.
(b) AS - Air sparge.
(c) ND - Nutrient delivery.
(d) NC - No change in operation.
(e) GW - Groundwater.

CONCLUSIONS

While AS/SVE remediation was relatively easy to employ at each of these locations given the site conditions of geology, hydrogeology, and contaminants, the two sites had differences in design complexities that required varying needs for system operation and monitoring. These two sites used either on-site field staff visits or modem/PLC "visits" prior to actual field staff mobilization to the site. Given the different complexities for each site's remediation design, each O/M method was appropriate for site-specific design considerations.

For Site #1, monthly site visits by field staff proved sufficient to maintain reasonable system operation with approximately 90% reliability after minor equipment problems were solved. Monitoring of groundwater quality parameters was important to optimize system performance. Site #2 used a more complex treatment design to correct deficient site conditions and to provide more biologically optimized remediation treatment; therefore remote telemetry monitoring was warranted. Groundwater quality parameters illustrate even better levels for key system performance indicators, such as DO, compared to Site #1. Although the less complex site (Site #1) may have benefitted from the modem/PLC option for site O/M, the less complex, more standard site O/M was adequate to reach target remediation goals in a reasonable time frame given the budgetary constraints of the project. In contrast, the more difficult and complex site conditions presented at Site #2 greatly benefitted from the ability to remotely monitor and adjust system performance during project remediation. Site #2's remote telemetry system has provided more efficient O/M with greater than 95% operating system efficiency compared to Site #1's nontelemetry O/M program.

REFERENCES

Brown, R. 1993. "Section 4: Treatment of Petroleum Hydrocarbons in Ground Water by Air Sparging." *In-Situ Bioremediation of Ground Water and Geological Material: A Review of Technologies*, EPA/600/R-93/124, July 1993, pp. 4-1 - 4-25.

Dupont, R. R., W. Doucette, and R. E. Hinchee. 1991. "Assessment of In Situ Bioremediation Potential and the Application of Bioventing at a Fuel-Contaminated Site." In R. E. Hinchee and R. F. Olfenbuttel (Eds.), *On Site Bioreclamation: Processes for Xenobiotic and Hydrocarbon Treatment*, pp. 262-282. Butterworth-Heinemann, Stoneham, MA.

Hinchee, R. E., and R. N. Miller. 1990. "Bioventing for In Situ Treatment of Hydrocarbon Contamination." *Hazardous Materials Control* 3(5): 30-34.

Hinchee, R. E. 1993. "Section 3: Bioventing of Petroleum Hydrocarbons." *In-Situ Bioremediation of Ground Water and Geological Material: A Review of Technologies*, EPA/600/R-93/124.

Loden, M. E. 1992. *A Technology Assessment of Soil Vapor Extraction and Air Sparging.* EPA/600/R-92/173, September 1992, pp. 1-63.

Miller, R. N., R. E. Hinchee, and C. C. Vogel. 1991. "A Field Scale Investigation of Soil Venting Enhanced Petroleum Hydrocarbon Biodegradation in the Vadose-Zone at Tyndall AFB, Florida." In R. E. Hinchee and R. F. Olfenbuttel (Eds.), *On Site Bioreclamation: Processes for Xenobiotic and Hydrocarbon Treatment*, pp. 283-302. Butterworth-Heinemann, Stoneham, MA.

Newman, B., M. Martinson, G. Smith, and L. McCain. 1993. "Dig-and-Mix Bioventing Enhances Hydrocarbon Degradation at Service Station Site." *Hazmat World* 6(12): 34-40.

Air Channel Distribution During Air Sparging: A Field Experiment

Andrea Leeson, Robert E. Hinchee,
Gregory L. Headington, and Catherine M. Vogel

ABSTRACT

Air sparging may have the potential to improve upon conventional groundwater treatment technologies. However, judging from studies published to date and theoretical analyses, it is possible that air sparging may have a limited effect on aquifer contamination. The basic mechanisms controlling air sparging are not well understood, and current monitoring practice does not appear adequate to quantitatively evaluate the process. During this study, the effective zone of influence, defined as the areas in which air channels form, was studied as a function of flowrate and depth of injection points. This was accomplished by conducting the air sparging test in an area with shallow standing water. Air sparging points were installed at various depths, and the zone of influence was determined visually.

INTRODUCTION

Air sparging involves injecting air under pressure greater than that of the water depth directly into groundwater-saturated aquifer materials. The objective is to force the air through contaminated aquifer materials to provide oxygen for bioremediation and/or strip the contaminants out of the aquifer.

Air sparging may have the potential to improve upon conventional groundwater treatment technologies. However, based on published studies to date and theoretical analyses, it also is possible that air sparging may have a limited effect on aquifer contamination. The basic mechanisms controlling air sparging are not well understood, and current monitoring practice does not appear to be adequate to quantitatively evaluate the process.

The primary objective of this study was to evaluate the zone of influence and distribution at air channels as a function of flowrate and depth of injection points. We accomplished this by conducting an air sparging test in the field in an area with shallow standing water. Air sparging points were installed at various depths, and the zone of influence was determined visually.

SITE CHARACTERISTICS

Site activities were conducted at the Wild Goose Lagoon, Tyndall Air Force Base (AFB), Florida. The wide tidal flats in this area allowed tests to be conducted in shallow standing water. Tidal exchange in this area is minimal, i.e., no more than 1 ft (0.3 m) in any given day during testing. In general, tests were conducted at low tide. Soils are relatively uniform sand down to 30 ft (9 m), at which depth a clay lens is encountered.

METHODS

A series of tests were conducted to examine the zone of influence as a function of flowrate and depth of injection points. All tests were conducted using a stainless steel well point with a 1¼-in. (3.2-cm) inner diameter and 1.5-ft (0.4-m) screen length. The well point was driven to various depths using either a Terraprobe™ or a jackhammer mounted on a platform. The well point was connected to flexible tubing which was weighted to keep it below the water surface. On land, the flexible tubing was connected to polyvinyl chloride (PVC) piping coupled to a 5-hp blower.

During all tests, the appearance of bubbles in overlying counter was recorded and located according to distance and direction from the well point. A qualitative judgment of the airflow on a scale of 1 to 7 was made at each point. The score "1" represented the lowest observed flowrate, a pattern of slow bubbling, where a single small bubble was observed every few minutes. The score "7" represented the highest flowrate, during which a rapid flow of multiple bubbles was observed. In a region close to the injection point, high flow was observed to occur in a manner that precluded mapping of individual points. After air injection was discontinued, the time required for bubbling to cease was recorded. The tests conducted were as follows:

- **Test 1:** Well point was driven to a depth of 6 ft (1.8 m) below the lagoon surface. Air was injected at a flowrate of approximately 2.5 cfm for approximately 2 hours.
- **Test 2:** Well point was driven to a depth of 6 ft (1.8 m) below the lagoon surface. Air was injected at a flowrate of approximately 6.0 cfm for approximately 2 hours.
- **Test 3:** Well point was driven to a depth of 6 ft (1.8 m) below the lagoon surface. Air was injected at a flowrate of approximately 20 cfm for approximately 2 hours.
- **Test 4:** Well point was driven to a depth of 10 ft (3 m) below the lagoon surface. Air was injected at a flowrate of approximately 20 cfm for approximately 2 hours.
- **Test 5:** Well point was driven to a depth of 10 ft (3 m) below the lagoon surface. Air was injected at a flowrate of approximately 20 cfm for approximately 24 hours.

- **Test 6:** Well point was driven to a depth of 17.5 ft (5.3 m) below the lagoon surface. Air was injected at a flowrate of approximately 20 cfm for approximately 2 hours.
- **Test 7:** Well point was driven to a depth of 17.5 ft (5.3 m) below the lagoon surface. Air was injected at a flowrate of approximately 24 cfm for approximately 2 hours.
- **Test 8:** Well point was driven to a depth of 6 ft (1.8 m) below the lagoon surface. Air was injected at a flowrate of approximately 10 cfm for approximately 2 hours. An alternative location was used for this well point to examine possible differences in bubble patterns due to geologic differences.
- **Test 9:** Well point was driven to a depth of 17.5 ft (5.3 m) below the lagoon surface. Air was injected at a flowrate of approximately 31 cfm for approximately 2 hours.
- **Test 10:** Immediately after discontinuing air injection during Test 9, the blower was pulsed twice to examine the effect on bubble pattern.
- **Test 11:** To evaluate short-circuiting, three monitoring wells were installed: one within the radius of influence of the sparge well; one at the edge of the radius of influence; and one outside the radius of influence. The monitoring wells consisted of well points with 1¼-in. (3.2-cm) inner diameter and 5 ft (1.5 m) of screen, driven to a depth of 6 ft below the lagoon surface. Air was injected at a flowrate of approximately 10 cfm for approximately 2 hours. During air injection, airflow rates out of the monitoring wells were measured with a Rockwell Model dry gas meter, accurate to 0.005 cfm.

Care was taken to note and avoid fluidization of the soils. Some localized fluidization was noted near where the air channels appeared, but the fluidized soils were very limited in both extent and depth. Typically only a few inches of soil around and below the air channel surface fluidized. The site was stable, and there was no indication of fluidization deeper than the surficial few inches. Most of this fluidization was noted within 2 ft (0.6 m) of the injection wells. It is recognized that this limited fluidization may have localized impact on air channel formation near the ground surface. However, it is not likely that the overall pattern of air channel formation and zone of influence would be impacted.

RESULTS AND DISCUSSION

Results from Test 1 are presented in Figure 1. In all figures, the various qualitative flowrates are represented by different shapes, with flowrate 1 representing the lowest flow and flowrate 7 representing the highest flow. The area near the injection point where flow was too high to distinguish individual channels is shown. Results from this test indicated a fairly small zone of influence, with maximum bubble appearances approximately 4 ft (1.2 m) from the injection well. Most of the flow was observed within a radius of approximately 1 ft (0.3 m)

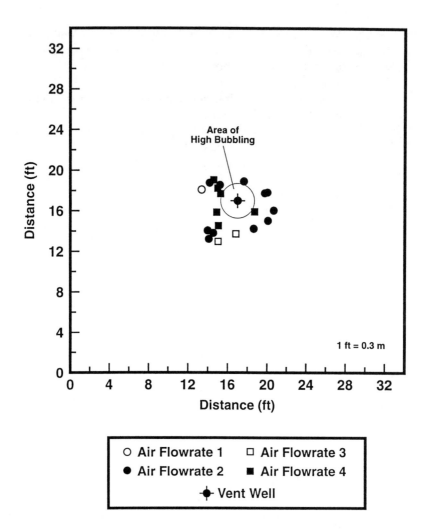

FIGURE 1. Bubble appearance pattern at a depth of 6 ft and a flowrate of 2.5 cfm (2-h test).

from the injection well. In this area, there was excessive churning of the water, and discrete locations of bubble appearance could not be recorded. It should be noted that bubbles appeared at very discrete intervals; the locations in Figure 1 represent the only sites where bubbles were observed. No activity was observed in areas between these locations.

Tests 2 and 3 were conducted at the same depth as in Test 1, but at higher flowrates. Little difference was observed in the bubble patterns between Test 1 (2.5 cfm) and 2 (6.0 cfm). During Test 3 (20 cfm), some differences were observed (Figure 2). Although more channels appeared to form, the increased flowrate did

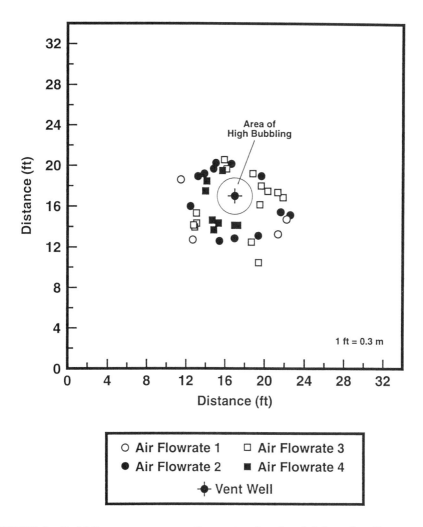

FIGURE 2. Bubble appearance pattern at a depth of 6 ft and a flowrate of 20 cfm (2-h test).

not seem to affect the radial zone of influence. The maximum distance of bubble appearance increased to approximately 6 ft (1.8 m). However, most of the flow still was found within a 1- to 2-ft (0.3- to 0.6-m) radius of the injection well.

Next, tests were conducted to determine whether injection depth would affect the observed bubble pattern. Injection at a depth of 10 ft (3 m) at 20 cfm (Test 4) did not result in a significant difference in bubble appearance. Maximum distance of bubble appearance was approximately 4 ft (1.2 m) from the injection well, and, again, most of the flow was found within a 1- to 2-ft (0.3- to 0.6-m) radius of the injection point.

Injection conditions for Test 4 were used to conduct a 24-hour test to determine whether prolonged injection would result in differences in channeling. Only slight increases were observed in the number of channels formed and the maximum distance from the injection well. No change was observed in terms of the location of the majority of the flow appearing within 1 to 2 ft (0.3 to 0.6 m) of the injection well.

During Test 6, the injection point was driven to 17.5 ft (5.3 m). Significant changes were observed in the number of channels formed and the maximum distance of bubble appearance from the injection point (Figure 3). Bubbles were observed at a distance of up to 16 ft (4.9 m) from the injection point. Pulsed flow seemed to increase the number of channels formed without greatly affecting

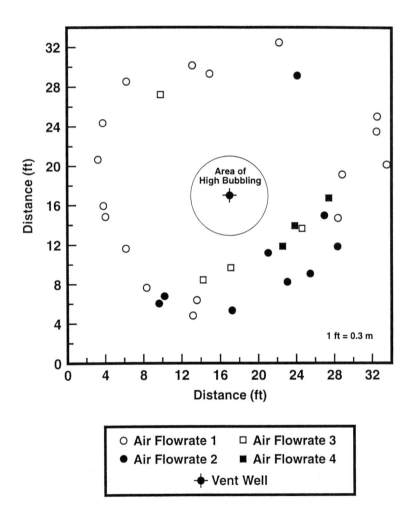

FIGURE 3. Bubble appearance pattern at a depth of 17.5 ft and a flowrate of 31 cfm (2-h test).

the distance of channeling. Results shown in Figure 4 represent bubble patterns after pulsing. Higher flowrates (24 and 31 cfm) at this same location did not significantly affect bubble appearance, but, in general, flowrates of individual channels appeared to increase and slightly more channels were observed. However, the maximum distance from the injection point of bubble appearance did not change significantly.

Test 8 was conducted at a distance of approximately 80 ft (24 m) from the locations of Tests 1 through 7 in order to determine whether geologic differences may result in pattern changes. This test was conducted at a depth of 6 ft (1.8 m) at 10 cfm. Bubble appearance was very similar to that observed in previous tests conducted under the same conditions.

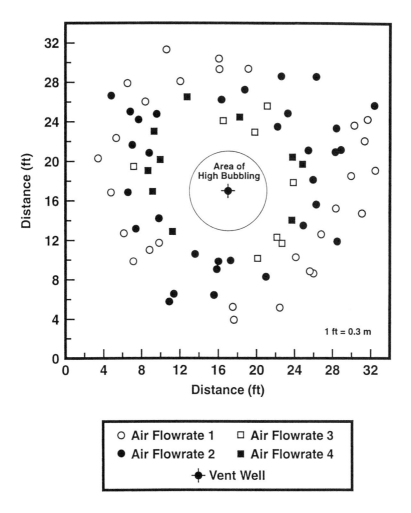

FIGURE 4. Bubble appearance pattern at a depth of 17.5 ft and a flowrate of 31 cfm after flow pulsing.

During testing, bubbles (indicating air channels) were observed for a period of about 10 to 15 minutes. After that initial period, new air channels did not appear, and the location and flow characteristics of the channels looked stable. That is, the channels did not seem to change or move with time.

Tests for short-circuiting indicated that a fairly small flowrate occurred (0.033 cfm) in the monitoring well within the zone of influence of the injection point, in addition to a small flow on the outside of the monitoring well that could not be measured. No measurable flow was observed in monitoring points at the edge of or beyond the zone of influence.

SUMMARY

From these tests, the following conclusions can be drawn:

- The zone of influence of the injection point is relatively small, ranging from 4 to 16 ft (1.2 to 4.9 m).
- The most flow in all tests occurred within a 1- to 2-ft (0.3- to 0.6-m) radius of the injection point, regardless of flowrate or depth of injection.
- The flowrate appeared to have little effect on the zone of influence but did affect the amount of channeling.
- Increased injection depth corresponded to an increased zone of influence.
- Bubbles appeared at very discrete locations, and neither the locations nor the volume of flow from those locations appeared to change with time.

Statistical Analyses of the U.S. Air Force Bioventing Initiative Results

Andrea Leeson, Priti Kumar, Robert E. Hinchee, Douglas Downey, Catherine M. Vogel, Gregory D. Sayles, and Ross N. Miller

ABSTRACT

The U.S. Air Force's Bioventing Initiative has involved conducting field treatability studies to evaluate bioventing feasibility at more than 120 sites throughout the United States. At those sites where feasibility studies produced positive results, pilot-scale bioventing systems were installed and operated for 1 year. The results from the pilot-scale bioventing systems have been used to develop a large database from which to determine the most important parameters to be used in evaluating whether to implement bioventing. Data generated from the Bioventing Initiative were subjected to a thorough statistical analysis to determine which parameters correlate with biodegradation rates. The study involved in situ respiration test data, soil gas permeability test data, and soil chemistry and nutrient data from each site. Results from the Bioventing Initiative demonstrated that some biodegradation occurred at virtually all sites regardless of site conditions. Data collected from the sites demonstrate that even sites with low nutrient levels exhibit significant microbial activity and will therefore respond well to bioventing.

INTRODUCTION

In May 1992, the U.S. Air Force initiated the Bioventing Initiative to examine bioventing at 55 contaminated sites throughout the country. In December 1992, the program was increased to more than 130 sites due to increased demand by Air Force managers. Thus far, data have been collected from 125 contaminated sites at a total of 50 Air Force bases, one Army base, one Naval installation, and one U.S. Department of Transportation installation. Sites are located in 35 states and in all 10 U.S. Environmental Protection Agency (U.S. EPA) regions. The selected sites represent a wide range of contaminant types and concentrations, soil types, contaminant depth, climatic conditions, and regulatory frameworks.

A Bioventing Test Protocol was developed that provided strict guidelines for treatability testing and bioventing system design (Hinchee et al. 1992). The Bioventing Test Protocol was peer-reviewed and was reviewed by U.S. EPA Headquarters and Risk Reduction Engineering Laboratory personnel. Using the Bioventing Test Protocol, initial testing was conducted at each site to determine whether bioventing was feasible. Based on the initial testing, a decision was made whether to install a bioventing system for 1 year of operation. At the majority of sites (95%), a bioventing system was installed for the 1-year operational period. At the end of this time period, each Air Force base could either elect to keep the bioventing system in operation or remove it if the site was deemed to be remediated sufficiently.

Data collected at each site where a bioventing system was installed included results from initial soil and soil gas sampling, in situ respiration testing, and soil gas permeability testing; 6-month in situ respiration testing results; and 1-year soil and soil gas sampling and in situ respiration testing results. A summary of the results to date with potential implications is presented in the following sections.

One primary objective of the Bioventing Initiative has been to develop a large database of bioventing systems to determine the most important parameters to be used in evaluating whether to implement bioventing. Previously, the feasibility of installing bioventing systems was determined based on experience. Although this often has produced satisfactory results, the Bioventing Initiative data were able to supply a statistical basis for making decisions. This effort has produced the largest database of field data collected in a consistent manner, with the same procedures and analyses conducted at each site, making a thorough statistical analysis practical. The statistical analysis involved determining which parameters most influenced biodegradation rates and, thus, bioventing performance.

PROCEDURES FOR STATISTICAL ANALYSIS

Data collected from 120 Bioventing Initiative sites have been analyzed for this study. The study involved in situ respiration test data, soil gas permeability test data, and soil chemistry and nutrient data from each site. Several parameters were measured in the soil samples. The statistical analysis had five specific objectives:

1. To develop a consistent statistical approach for calculating the oxygen utilization and carbon dioxide production rates from the in situ respiration data.
2. To characterize the oxygen utilization rate as a function of parameters measured during initial testing.
3. To characterize the ratio of oxygen utilization rate to carbon dioxide production rate as a function primarily of pH and alkalinity.
4. To characterize soil gas permeability as a function of particle size and moisture content.

Averages for oxygen utilization and carbon dioxide production rates and soil parameters were computed for each site. All subsequent analyses were performed on the site averages. Table 1 displays the parameters included in the statistical analysis, their units, and transformations performed on these parameters whenever necessary.

Data were stored in Statistical Analysis System (SAS) databases, and all statistical manipulations and analyses were conducted using SAS software package. Methods used for characterizing the data and the final regression model are presented in the following sections for each of the listed objectives.

CALCULATION OF OXYGEN UTILIZATION AND CARBON DIOXIDE PRODUCTION RATES

A statistical analysis was conducted to consistently calculate oxygen utilization and carbon dioxide production rates. A linear time-related change in oxygen and carbon dioxide levels that is characterized by a constant (or zero-order) rate is typical of most of the sites. However, in some sites, a two-piecewise linear change is observed. More specifically, oxygen concentration will increase and carbon dioxide levels will decrease linearly, until conditions become limiting and oxygen utilization or carbon dioxide production rates decrease compared to the initial rapid rate.

The two-piecewise regression model, with a slope change at time t_0, was fitted to the oxygen (and carbon dioxide) versus time data at every monitoring point. The piecewise regression model was implemented using the NLIN procedure (nonlinear regression procedure) in the SAS software package and is presented below:

$$R_i = \alpha + \beta t_i \qquad t_i \leq t_0 \qquad (1)$$

$$R_i = \left(\alpha + \beta t_0\right) + \left(\beta + \delta\right)\left(t_i - t_0\right) \qquad t_i > t_0 \qquad (2)$$

for i = 1, 2,..., number of observations at each monitoring point, and where:

R_i = measured i^{th} oxygen or carbon dioxide level at time t_i,
α = oxygen or carbon dioxide level at initial time;
β = rate of change of oxygen or carbon dioxide level with time;
δ = increase or decrease in the rate of change at time t_0;
t_0 = time at which the slope change occurs.

The parameter δ in the above model measures the increase or decrease in the slope at time t_0. Therefore, the statistical significance of δ confirmed the suitability of a two-piecewise model fitted to the data. The rate of oxygen utilization (or carbon dioxide production) was estimated from the slope of the first linear

TABLE 1. Data parameters included in the statistical analysis.

Category	Parameter	Units	Transformation[a]	Acronym
In Situ Respiration Rates	Oxygen utilization rate	%/h	Log	O_2
	Carbon dioxide production rate	%/h	None	CO_2
	Ratio of the carbon dioxide production rate to oxygen utilization rate	No units	Square root	Ratio
Soil Parameters	Soil gas TPH	ppmv	Log	tphsg
	Soil gas BTEX	ppmv	Log	btexsg
	Soil TPH	mg/kg	Log	tphs
	Soil BTEX	mg/kg	Log	btexs
	pH	No units	Log	PH
	Alkalinity	mg/kg as $CaCO_3$	Log	ALK
	Iron content	mg/kg	Log	IRN
	Nitrogen content	mg/kg	Log	NIT
	Phosphorus content	mg/kg	Log	PHO
	Moisture content	% wt	None	MOI
	Gravel	% wt	None	GRA
	Sand	% wt	None	SAN
	Silt	% wt	None	SIL
	Clay	% wt	None and log	CLA
	Soil gas permeability	Darcy	Log	PRM
	Soil temperature	Celsius	None	TMP
Other	Season (time of year)	Day	None	season

(a) Transformation was applied to the parameter for purposes of statistical analysis.

piece, β, whenever δ was statistically significant at the 0.05 significance level. For example, Figure 1 presents the piecewise linear model fitted to oxygen data at a monitoring point at Site FSA-1, AFP 4, where β was estimated to be –1.1%/h.

In cases where δ was not significant at the 0.05 level, a linear regression model of the following form was fitted to the data:

$$R_i = \alpha + \beta t_i \qquad \text{for all } t_i \qquad (3)$$

where the rate of oxygen utilization (or carbon dioxide production) was determined from the slope of the straight line, β.

For cases in which six or fewer observations were available at a monitoring point, or when the oxygen levels exhibited virtually no change over a short initial time period followed by a linear change, the piecewise analysis was not attempted. In such cases, a linear regression model, as described above, was fitted. In these cases, the suitability of the linear model was confirmed by inspection of the model-fit to observed data.

CORRELATION OF OXYGEN UTILIZATION RATE AND ENVIRONMENTAL PARAMETERS

A preliminary analyses on the untransformed data was performed in which a regression model was fitted to the oxygen utilization rate using forward stepwise

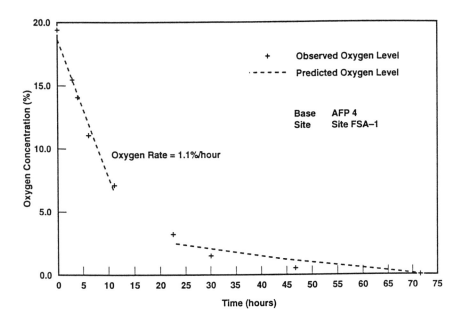

FIGURE 1. Use of piecewise analysis of oxygen utilization data at Site FSA-1, AFP 4.

regression. This model accounted for the effects of the soil parameters and their interactions. To reduce the effect of multicollinearity among the parameters on the fitted model, benzene, toluene, ethylbenzene, and xylenes (BTEX) soil gas and gravel were excluded from the modeling. In other words, BTEX soil gas was highly correlated with soil gas TPH and, therefore, it was concluded that the effect of BTEX soil gas on the oxygen rate can almost completely be explained by soil gas TPH. Also, because the particle size levels added up to a constant value (100%), the effect of gravel was assumed to be redundant in the modeling.

As a result of fitting the regression model on the oxygen utilization rate, it was found that the particle sizes and permeability had a dominating influence on the oxygen rate; that is, low levels of permeability and sand, and high levels of silt and clay appeared to correlate strongly with high oxygen rates.

To determine whether a handful of sites were unduly influencing the statistical modeling, sites with high oxygen utilization rates were examined in detail. Seven sites in the analyses had extremely high oxygen utilization rates, well above average rates from other sites. A two-sample t-test was performed on each parameter (e.g. sand, nitrogen) to determine whether the average value of the parameter over the seven sites was different from the corresponding average for the remaining sites. This analysis revealed statistically significant differences in particle size, soil gas permeability, and soil TPH between the two groups of sites (Table 2). As a result of this analysis, it was determined that the seven sites with extremely high oxygen rates were atypical with respect to their levels of particle size, soil gas permeability, and soil TPH.

To reduce the influence caused by these seven sites on the model for the oxygen utilization rate, the log transformation of the oxygen utilization rate was taken. Additionally, the log transform resulted in more normally distributed data for the oxygen utilization rate. However, sites with oxygen utilization rates near zero get artificial importance as a result of the transformation. To eliminate this artificial effect caused by the log transformation, all the log-transformed values

TABLE 2. Parameters that distinguish the seven sites with high oxygen utilization rates from the remaining sites.

Parameter	Level of Parameter in 7 Sites Relative to Other Sites
Sand	Lower
Silt	Higher
Clay	Higher
Soil gas permeability	Lower
Soil TPH	Lower

of the oxygen rate below −2.5 were censored, that is, set to a constant value of −2.5. Censoring was based on visual inspection of the log-transformed data.

Subsequently, the log transforms of some of the soil parameters were taken if the data for the parameter were not well represented by a normal distribution. Normality in the data was checked using the Shapiro-Wilk test for normality and by observing histograms and normal probability plots.

As a preliminary step to determine the correlation of the soil parameters with the oxygen utilization rate, correlations between the rate and each of the soil parameters were examined. This was conducted to examine strong relationships between oxygen utilization rates and the environmental parameters to assist in developing the statistical model. First, the log transformation of the oxygen utilization rate and some of the soil parameters was taken to obtain more normally distributed data on each parameter (Table 1). After the transformation, the data for each parameter were plotted against the corresponding data for each of the other parameters.

Figure 2 illustrates a typical scatterplot correlation for some of the parameters of interest. Ellipses are drawn on each plot containing 95% of the estimated bivariate distribution. The plots for which the ellipses are narrow represent pairs of elements that have a strong observed correlation. Pairs of elements that are positively correlated have the ellipse with the major axis running from the lower left to the upper right, while negative correlations are indicated by the major axis running from the lower right to the upper left. The magnitude of the correlation can be inferred from the shape of the ellipse by comparing it to the key at the bottom of the figure. In the key, comparable ellipses are displayed for distributions with known correlations of 90%, 60%, 30%, and 0%.

From the bivariate relationships, it was seen that the oxygen utilization rate was most positively correlated with nitrogen, moisture, and soil gas TPH, and negatively correlated with sand and temperature. Among the soil parameters, the correlation coefficient between soil gas BTEX and soil gas TPH is 0.92 and that between pH and alkalinity is 0.75. The correlations between the particle sizes (sand, silt, and clay), moisture, and soil gas permeability also are pronounced.

After taking the log transformation, a second regression model was fitted to the oxygen utilization rate using stepwise regression. Finally, the effect of a cyclic seasonal component on the residuals obtained from the fitted regression model was investigated.

The final regression model for oxygen utilization rate is:

$$\log(O_2) = -2.7 + 0.39 \log (NIT) - 0.108 (MOI) + \qquad (4)$$
$$0.017 \log (TPHsg) * MOI - 0.004 \log (TPHsg) * TMP$$

All of the effects in the above model are statistically significant at the 0.05 significance level. Note that the effects appearing in the model are consistent with the relationships observed in the bivariate setting. The model explains 41% of the variability in the log-transformed oxygen utilization rate; that is, a 64% correlation between the observed and model-predicted log-transformed oxygen rates.

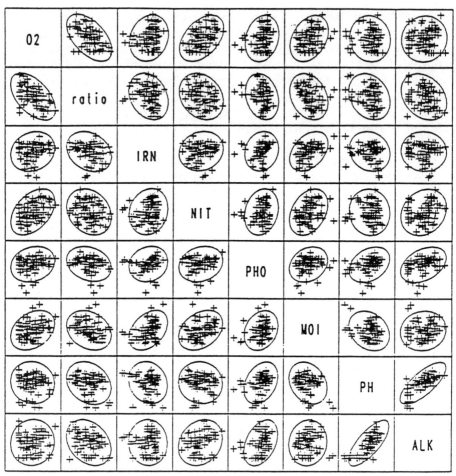

O_2 = log O_2 Rate Ratio = $(CO_2$ Rate/O_2 Rate$)^{1/4}$ IRN = log Iron NIT = log Nitrogen
PHO = log Phosphorus MOI = Moisture PH = log pH ALK = log Alkalinity

	90%	60%	30%	0%
Z1				

Key to Correlation Scatterplots.

FIGURE 2. Oxygen utilization rates, oxygen:carbon dioxide rate ratios, element concentrations, moisture content, pH, and alkalinity site average correlation scatterplot.

The effect of nitrogen on the oxygen utilization rate as predicted by the model is shown in Figure 3. As the nitrogen concentration increases, the oxygen utilization rate increases; however, relatively large changes in nitrogen concentration correlate with only relatively small changes in the oxygen utilization rate. These results indicate that while nitrogen concentration correlates with oxygen utilization rates in the field, the relationship is not strong.

CORRELATION OF OXYGEN UTILIZATION AND CARBON DIOXIDE PRODUCTION RATE RATIOS WITH ENVIRONMENTAL PARAMETERS

Because in situ biodegradation rates are measured indirectly through measurements of soil gas oxygen and carbon dioxide concentrations, abiotic processes that affect oxygen and carbon dioxide concentration will affect measured biodegradation rates. The factors that may most influence soil gas carbon dioxide concentrations are soil pH and alkalinity.

At several sites, oxygen utilization has proven to be a more useful measure of biodegradation rates than has carbon dioxide production. The biodegradation

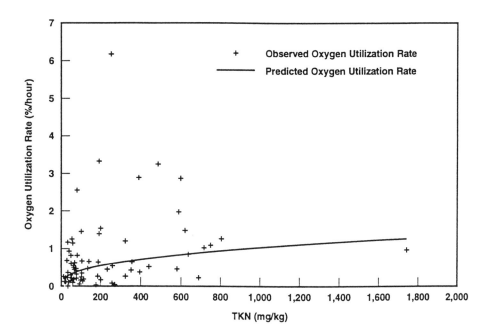

FIGURE 3. Variation of total Kjeldahl nitrogen (TKN) and the effect on oxygen utilization rates based on model predictions with average levels of other parameters.

rate in milligrams of hexane-equivalent/kilograms of soil per day based on carbon dioxide production usually is less than can be accounted for by the oxygen disappearance. At virtually all sites studied as part of the Bioventing Initiative, oxygen utilization rates have been higher than carbon dioxide production rates. A study conducted at Tyndall AFB site was an exception. That site had low-alkalinity soils and low-pH quartz sands, and carbon dioxide production actually resulted in a slightly higher estimate of biodegradation (Miller 1990).

In the case of the higher pH and higher alkalinity soils at Fallon NAS and Eielson AFB, little or no gaseous carbon dioxide production was measured (Hinchee et al. 1991; Leeson et al. 1993). This is possibly due to the formation of carbonates from the gaseous evolution of carbon dioxide produced by biodegradation at these sites. A similar phenomenon was encountered by van Eyk and Vreeken (1988) in their attempt to use carbon dioxide evolution to quantify biodegradation associated with soil venting.

To determine whether pH and alkalinity correlated with carbon dioxide production rates at Bioventing Initiative sites, an analysis of the ratio of oxygen utilization to carbon dioxide production versus soil parameters was performed. Square root transformations of the oxygen utilization and carbon dioxide production rate ratio and log transformation of some of the soil parameters were taken whenever the data were not well represented by the normal distribution.

The statistical methods used to model the ratio of the oxygen utilization rate to carbon dioxide production rate as a function of the soil parameters are similar to those used for the oxygen utilization rate. As a preliminary step, a square root transformation of the ratio and log transformation of some of the soil parameters were taken to obtain more normally distributed data. All the transformations for the soil parameters except clay were consistent with those taken previously to model the oxygen utilization rate. A log transformation of clay was considered as it was more correlated with the ratio.

After applying the transformation, a regression model was fitted to the ratio using forward stepwise regression. The model accounted for the effects of each of the soil parameters (except season) and their interactions. Finally, the effect of a cyclic seasonal component on the residuals obtained from the fitted model was determined.

The final model for the ratio of the carbon dioxide production rate to the oxygen utilization rate is as follows:

$$\left(\frac{CO_2\,rate}{O_2\,rate}\right)^{1/2} = 1.28 - 0.38\log(pH) - 0.095\log(clay) + \tag{5}$$
$$0.0007\log(tphs) * TMP$$

All of the effects in the above model are statistically significant at the 0.05 significance level. The model explains 40% of the variability in the transformed ratio. This amounts to 63% correlation between the observed and model-predicted transformed ratios. The correlation of pH and clay on the ratio as predicted by the model are presented in Figures 4 and 5, respectively.

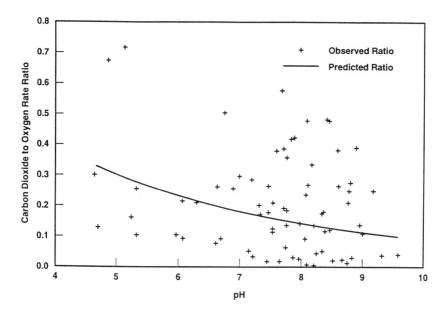

FIGURE 4. Variation of pH and the effect on oxygen utilization to carbon dioxide rate ratio based on model predictions with average levels of other parameters.

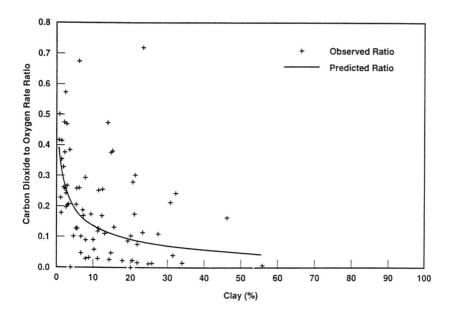

FIGURE 5. Variation of clay and the effect on oxygen utilization to carbon dioxide rate ratio based on model predictions with average levels of other parameters.

CORRELATION OF SOIL GAS PERMEABILITY
WITH ENVIRONMENTAL PARAMETERS

The statistical methods used here are similar to those described previously for the oxygen utilization rate and the ratio. Forward stepwise regression was used to determine a regression model for the log-transformed soil gas permeability. The independent variables of interest in the modeling were the moisture content and the particle sizes (sand, silt, and clay).

The final model describing soil gas permeability is given below:

$$\log(\text{PRM}) = 3.2 - 0.064 \text{ clay} \tag{6}$$

Based on this model, clay alone explains 21% of the variability in the log-transformed soil gas permeability. The correlation of clay with soil gas permeability as predicted by the model is presented in Figure 6. In this figure, the soil gas permeability levels greater than 100 have been censored, that is, set to a constant value of 100. Based on the regression model it is determined that increase in clay by 5 units decreases soil gas permeability by 25% on average.

SUMMARY

Based on the statistical analyses presented in the previous sections, the following overall conclusions are drawn:

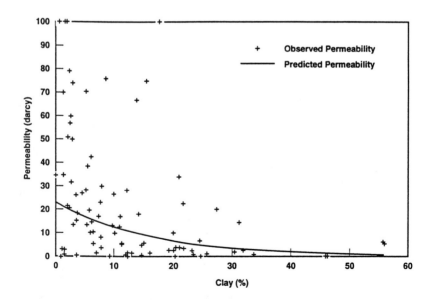

FIGURE 6. Variation of clay and the effect on soil gas permeability based on model predictions.

1. The relationships between the biodegradation rates and the soil parameters are not very strong. However, some correlation with soil parameters do exist based on the statistical modeling. For example, nitrogen, moisture, and the soil gas concentration of TPH appear to correlate with the oxygen utilization rate, but the relationship between nitrogen and oxygen utilization rates appears too weak to suggest any beneficial effect of nitrogen addition.
2. The ratio of the carbon dioxide production rate to the oxygen utilization rate correlates strongly with pH and clay levels in the soil, probably an indication of carbonate and inorganic interaction, and not reflective of biodegradation.
3. Soil gas permeability correlates with each of the particle sizes (sand, silt, and clay) and moisture content; however, the relative effect of clay on permeability is most important.

The Bioventing Initiative has provided a large database of information useful in the design and implementation of bioventing systems. The statistical analysis provides strong guidelines for determining which parameters are of most importance in the bioventing technology. However, this data must be balanced by experience and site-specific data. For example, sites with relatively low soil nitrogen concentrations should not be discarded as a bioventing site for this reason alone, nor should it be assumed that nitrogen addition at these sites will increase oxygen utilization rates. Data collected from Bioventing Initiative have shown that even sites with low soil nutrient concentrations will still exhibit significant microbial activity and will therefore respond well to bioventing.

REFERENCES

Hinchee, R. E., D. C. Downey, and P. Aggarwal. 1991. "Use of Hydrogen Peroxide as an Oxygen Source for In Situ Biodegradation: Part I. Field Studies." *J. Hazardous Materials*, 27:287-299.

Hinchee, R. E., S. K. Ong, R. N. Miller, D. C. Downey, and R. Frandt. 1992. *Test Plan and Technical Protocol for a Field Treatability Test for Bioventing*, Rev. 2. U.S. Air Force Center for Environmental Excellence, Brooks Air Force Base, TX.

Leeson, A., R. E. Hinchee, J. Kittel, G. Sayles, C. Vogel, and R. Miller. 1993 (in press). "Optimizing Bioventing in Shallow Vadose Zones in Cold Climates." *Hydrological Sciences Journal* 38(4).

Miller, R. N. 1990. "A Field Scale Investigation of Enhanced Petroleum Hydrocarbon Biodegradation in the Vadose Zone Combining Soil Venting as an Oxygen Source with Moisture and Nutrient Additions." Ph.D. Dissertation. Utah State University, Logan, UT.

van Eyk, J. and C. Vreeken. 1988. "Venting-Mediated Removal of Petrol from Subsurface Soil Strata as a Result of Stimulated Evaporation and Enhanced Biodegradation." *Med. Fac. Landbouww. Riiksuniv. Gent*, 53(4b):1873-1884.

Assessment of a Biological In Situ Remediation

Hilke Würdemann, Nils Christian Lund, and Gerd Gudehus

ABSTRACT ━━━━━━━━━━━━━━━━━━━━━━━━━━━━━

A field experiment using a bioventing technique has been conducted at the center of contamination at a former gasworks site for 3 years. The emphasis of this investigation is to determine the efficiency of in situ remediation. Due to an extremely heterogeneous distribution of contamination it was impossible to satisfactorily quantify the reduction of hydrocarbons. However, a comparison of highly contaminated soil samples shows a qualitative alteration. The analyses of pollutant composition reveal a significant decrease of low condensed PAHs up to anthracene. The relative increase of high condensed PAHs in the contaminant composition indicates a PAH degradation of 54%. Soil respiration is used to assess the course of remediation. Continuous monitoring of O_2 and CO_2 in the used air leads to an amount of about 2,400 kg of decomposed organics. Large-scale elution tests show a reduction of the sum parameters for the organic pollution of the flushing water of 80%. The PAHs have dropped about 97%. The Microtox test indicates a detoxification of 98%.

EXPERIMENTAL DESIGN

For about 3 years, a biological in situ remediation has been conducted on part of a former gasworks site in Karlsruhe. The test area is located at the center of contamination, where the tar-ammonia separating sump used to be. Below this sump, the contamination of the natural gravel and sand aquifer (average hydraulic conductivity 5×10^{-3} m/s) extends down to a depth of 10 m. The maximum contamination zone was located at a depth of 5 to 7 m. The test area is isolated from its surroundings by sealing walls that reach down to a depth of 17 m into an impervious layer of clay (Figure 1). To enhance the aerobic degradation of hydrocarbons, the water table is lowered to the limits of contamination within the confined area. To obtain a more or less horizontal airflow in the drained subsoil, a network of airlances was sunk into the ground to serve the inflow of injected air and the outflow of spent air. The airstream flows through the unsaturated pores and transports the required O_2 into the soil. The

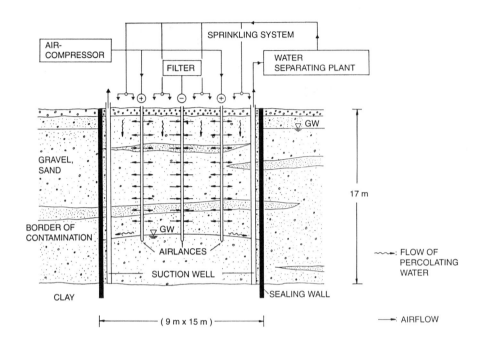

FIGURE 1. Illustration of principal surface and subsurface installations at the experimental site.

O_2 diffuses from the airstream into the soil water. Thus, the O_2 content in the soil water is replenished continuously by diffusion from the airflow. At the surface, an irrigation system creates a vertical seepage flow to supply the organisms with inorganic nutrients and to moisten the soil.

From time to time, remediation was interrupted for 1 to 2 weeks to conduct large-scale flushing of the subsoil with the aim of gaining information on the remaining concentration of elutable contaminants. The pores of contaminated soil were repeatedly flushed by using one of the peripheral wells as an infiltration well and the other as a suction well. Soil flushing was also used to raise soil temperature. In the first year the flushing water was heated with solar energy. In the following 2 years, an oil-fired heater was added to further the increase of temperature. Simultaneously, the flushing water was enriched with nutrients.

MONITORING AND ASSESSING THE PROGRESS OF BIOREMEDIATION

Results of Soil Sampling

Before beginning the experiment, information was collected about the kind, degree, and distribution of contamination by extracting three cores from the field.

Mixed samples were taken from the cores at 1-m intervals for analysis. Gas chromatography with a flame ionization detector was used to analyze 18 polycyclic aromatic hydrocarbons in the carbonsulfide extract of the soil (PAH_{EPA+2}). The amount of organic contamination was determined by measuring the weight of residues after solvent extraction and evaporation (lipophilic organics). If the initial amount of contaminants in the field is calculated from these data, one is faced with a number of problems. Apart from the unevenness of contaminant distribution, there is also a problem with quantifying the total amount of organic contaminants. Although the gravimetric determination of lipophilic organics resulted in a total contamination of 5,000 kg, the total burden of PAHs was just 600 kg. Detailed investigations (determination of the elements C, H, N, O and analysis of the organic carbon) showed the nonspecific parameter, lipophilic organics, to be the most suitable to encompass and quantify the total amount of contaminants, which is important for the evaluation of the degradation efficiency on the basis of a CO_2/O_2 balance (see below). The PAH_{EPA+2} make up only 10 to 20% of the tar oil, which consists of about 10,000 substances (Lauer 1989). Therefore they can only be used as guiding substances.

After 1 year of remediation, a second set of cores was extracted from the site. To minimize the influence of the uneven contaminant distribution, the cores were taken in close proximity to where the original cores were extracted. Despite this, the second set showed a considerably greater range of contamination concentration. While one core showed reduced contamination of 50%, another exhibited seemingly increased contamination. Thus, other means of monitoring the remediation process had to be found (Gudehus et al. 1993). Therefore, a new method was used for the final soil sampling, which gave more detailed information about the degree and distribution of contamination. Using a ground-freezing technique, undisturbed soil cores up to 12 m long were taken from the test area as well as from the contaminated area surrounding the field. While the untreated soil showed partly liquid tar oil, the appearance of the tar oil in the treated soil had changed. Due to the increase of tar oil viscosity, the soil grains stuck together, creating larger soil aggregates. In Figure 2 the concentrations found in the test field are compared to the ones found outside, indicating a significant reduction of PAHs in the soil and in the soil eluate. As a result of biological treatment, the smaller and therefore more soluble substances such as naphthalene or phenanthrene are degraded nearly completely, whereas the highly condensed PAHs remained in the soil (Figure 3).

To evaluate the extent of an in situ biodegradation, Douglas et al. (1993) looked for persistent substances in the contaminant composition, that can be taken as an internal chemical indicator for the original loading of the analyzed soil sample. For the gasworks' specific contamination, PAHs with more than 4 rings proved to be suitable. As long as there were sufficient rather easily degradable substances in the soil, the amount of degradation of highly condensed PAHs was negligible. For the application of this evaluation method it has to be ensured that the analyses of all sets of soil samples are done exactly the same. In the field experiment, the ratio of highly condensed PAHs increased from 15 to 25% on average (Figure 4). This indicates a PAH degradation of 54%. Laboratory experiments with large,

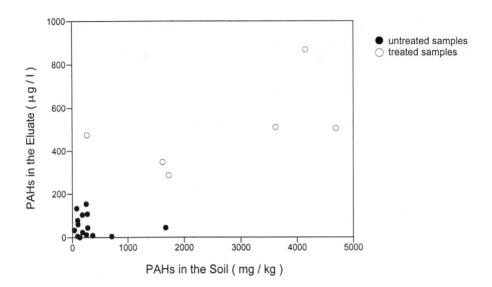

FIGURE 2. Relation between the PAH$_{EPA+2}$ content in the soil and in the eluate: After the biological treatment, the eluate shows an evident reduction of PAH concentration.

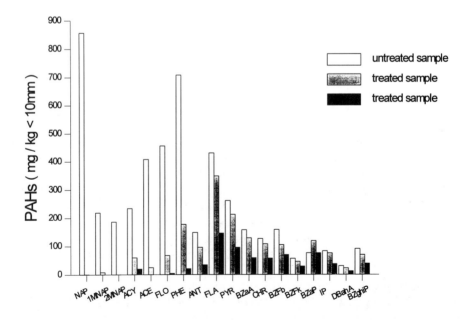

FIGURE 3. PAH composition of the two most highly contaminated soil samples from the test field compared to a highly contaminated sample of untreated soil.

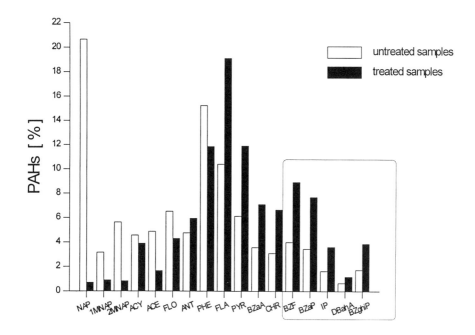

FIGURE 4. Change of the average PAH composition due to biological degradation: The relative increase of PAHs with more than 4 rings from 11 to 25% indicates a PAH degradation of 54%.

undisturbed soil samples showed a significantly higher percentage of degradation. Depending on the kind of measurement, after 2 years of bioremediation, 70 to 90% of the PAHs were degraded (Swiniansky and Gudehus, 1995).

Results of Soil Respiration Measurements

A very important criterion for assessing the course of remediation is soil respiration as a measure of the biological degradation rate. Measurements were made of the O_2 and CO_2 contents in the spent air, from which it was possible to deduce the amount of organic material that had been mineralized. Due to the stoichiometric equation for the mineralization of 1 kg aromatic hydrocarbons, 3 kg of oxygen are required. Under optimized conditions a maximum of 50% of the organic carbon could be transferred into biomass, which would reduce the oxygen demand considerably. Under in situ conditions, an initial, but not continuous increase in biomass is to be expected. Thus, a factor of 3 as a conservative estimate was used to assess the amount of degraded hydrocarbons.

Because of biotic and abiotic processes not involved in the degradation of organics, but which nevertheless contribute to oxygen consumption (e.g., nitrification), it was also necessary to measure the production of carbon dioxide (Würdemann 1990). If aromatic hydrocarbons are completely mineralized and the amount of newly created biomass is negligible, a molar ratio of CO_2 production to

O_2 consumption of 0.85 is to be expected (respiratory quotient). The average value obtained in the field experiment was 0.72. An estimation of the influence of processes not involved with the degradation of organic materials suggested an error of about 10 to 15%. This estimation is based on NO_3^-, SO_4^- and CO_3^- concentrations found in the flushing water.

Because microorganisms degrade possible substrates according to their usefulness and bioavailability, it is conceivable that a significant amount of O_2 might be consumed through the oxidation of humic substances that are naturally present in the soil. However, on-site measurements revealed a close correlation between the degree of contamination and the level of biodegradation activity, suggesting that the degradation of organic constituents other than contaminants is small. Thus the respiration measurements can be used to estimate the amount of degraded hydrocarbons. The data obtained from monitoring O_2 and CO_2 content in the spent air are presented in Figure 5. During the course of 3 years of remediation, about 7,700 kg O_2 and 7,600 kg CO_2 were consumed and produced, respectively, which indicates a mineralization of about 2,400 kg of organic material. This yields a degradation efficiency of about 50% of the total amount of organics, which is a rather rough estimation due to the problems with determining the initial load of the field.

Apart from providing information on the amount of degradation achieved, monitoring O_2 and CO_2 also provides information on the effects of various measures taken to optimize degradation. During the first year of the experimental operation, it was possible to increase the rate of degradation considerably. This increase in bioactivity is reflected in both the O_2 consumption and the CO_2 production rates. At the beginning of the operation, an O_2 consumption of 4 kg/d

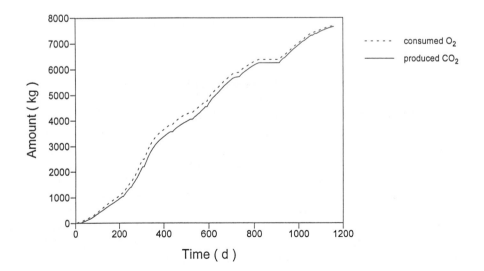

FIGURE 5. Course of the biological remediation: Amount of consumed O_2 and produced CO_2 during 3 years of remediation.

was measured. During the summer of the first year, this was increased to 17 kg/d by optimizing soil aeration and nutrient supply. Parallel to this development, an increase in soil temperature to a maximum of 10°C in the zone of highest activity was registered. This was due to the preheating of injected air and process water and to metabolic heat produced by the degrading microorganisms. During the cold winter months, there was a marked drop in activity, which was explained by a drop in temperature and by a reduction of available substances. In the following 2 years, the activity increased again with increasing ambient temperatures and the temperature of the process water.

Considering the long time required for the remediation, the forced nutrient supply, which increased the degradation rate in the first year significantly, had only a short-term effect on the efficiency of the remediation. This is because the bioavailability of contaminants became the limiting factor of the biodegradation kinetics. Therefore heating the soil, which increases the solubility of contaminants and also the metabolic activity of the microorganisms, was very successful. Because of a relatively small heat loss rate in the summer soil warming proved to be a very effective optimization. To meet the large demand of 5.7 kg oxygen per 1 m^3 soil, it was clearly necessary to lower the groundwater table and to use a venting system for soil aeration. An oxygen supply by water flushing would have extended the remediation time more than 4-fold.

Results of Large-Scale Elution Experiments

Determining the contaminant emissions is an important parameter for assessing the course and progress of the remediation process, because it provides an indication of the hazard potential, which the contaminated site still possesses. Figure 6 shows the course of the chemical oxygen demand (COD) and the dissolved organic carbon (DOC) in samples of water taken from the field during the course of bioremediation. The 10 peaks obtained during large-scale elution experiments are of particular interest. The water used for flushing was repeatedly passed through the contaminated soil (10 to 20-fold flushing of mobile soil pore water volume) and became enriched with contaminants. During the 3 years of bioremediation, the thus obtained COD peaks were reduced by about 83%, while the DOC peaks dropped about 76% of their original value. Over the same period there was a parallel decrease of 97% in the concentration of PAHs (Figure 7). The Microtox test showed an increase of the EC_{20} by a factor of 50, which yields a detoxification of 98% (Stieber et al. 1993). The amount of contaminants lost by the flushing procedure was balanced on the basis of DOC data. About 15 kg of organic carbon were leached with the flushing water. In relation to the amount of 2400 kg of degraded organics, the leached amount is negligible.

CONCLUSION

An exact assessment of the remediation efficiency in the field was difficult due to the extremely heterogeneous subsoil. Investigation of the contaminant

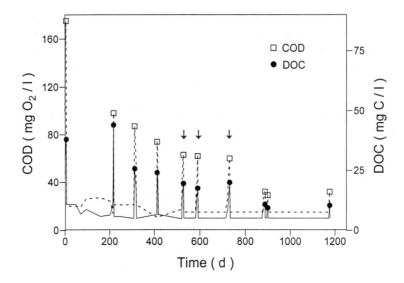

FIGURE 6.   COD and DOC concentration of water samples taken during
3 years of the field experiment. Arrows: Preheating of the flushing water
up to 40°C.

composition confirmed that bioremediation was successful in stimulating the
biodegradation of the more available components of the tar oil. The main factor
limiting the biodegradation kinetics appeared to be the availability of contaminants in the sandy gravelly aquifer. Internal chemical indicators showed
about 54% of the PAHs being degraded after 2½ years of bioremediation. Experiments with undisturbed large samples suggest a potential for the removal of
more than 70% of the PAHs if the remediation is continued. However, the
removal of 54% PAHs already reduced the contaminant emissions considerably.
Large-scale elution tests showed a reduction of 80% for the sum parameters DOC
and COD, and of 97% for the PAHs of the flushing water. Although in some
places the soil still contains relatively high concentrations of PAHs, the hazard
potential of the contaminated site has been reduced considerably. Determining
the amount of contaminants leaving the biologically treated soil under natural
conditions will be an important subject of our further studies.

ACKNOWLEDGMENTS

   The financial and managerial support provided by the Bundesministerium
für Forschung und Technik and the Umweltbundesamt (federal) and by the
Projekt Wasser Abfall Boden and the Forschungszentrum Karlsruhe (state) is
gratefully acknowledged. We also thank the City of Karlsruhe for conceptual and
technical support, especially Prof. Dr.-Ing. habil. D. Maier for his scientific advice

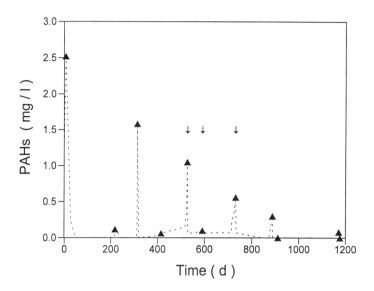

FIGURE 7. PAH concentration of water samples taken during 3 years of the field experiment. Arrows: Preheating of the flushing water up to 40°C.

concerning the evaluation of chemical analyses. We are further obliged to the contractor, Bauer GmbH, Schrobenhausen, for their contribution to the construction and management of the field installations.

REFERENCES

Douglas, G. S., R. C. Prince, E. L. Butler, and W. G. Steinhauer. 1993. "The Use of Internal Chemical Indicators in Petroleum and Refined Products to Evaluate the Extent of Biodegradation." In R. E. Hinchee, B. C. Alleman, R. E. Hoeppel, R. N. Miller (Eds.), *Hydrocarbon Bioremediation.* pp. 219-236. Lewis Publishers, Ann Arbor, MI.

Gudehus, G., J. Swiniansky, and H. Würdemann. 1993. "Biological In Situ Remediation of Sandy Gravelly Gasworks Subsoils." In F. Arendt, G. J. Annokee, R. Bosman, W. J. van den Brink *Contaminated Soil '93.* pp. 1047-1056. Kluwer Academic Publishers. Dordrecht/ Boston/London.

Lauer, K.-H. 1989. "Herkunft von Boden und Grundwasser belastenden Stoffen bei der Stadtgaserzeugung." In *Altlasten auf ehemaligen Gaswerksgeländen.* pp. 62-81. DVGW-Schriftenreihe. Gas Nr. 45.

Stieber, M., F. Haeseler, M. Rommel, F. Seibel, and P. Werner. 1993. "Oekophysiologische Untersuchungen." In *In-Situ-Sanierung kohlenwasserstoffbelasteter Böden.* Abschlußbericht zum BMFT Forschungsvorhaben. Projekt Nr. 1460635A5.

Swiniansky, J., and G. Gudehus. 1995. "Bioremediation of Coal Tar-Contaminated Large Soil Samples in Long-Term Experiments." Submitted for publication.

Würdemann, H. 1990. "Schnelle Beurteilung der aktuellen Sanierungsleistung von Bodenregenerationsmieten durch die In-Situ-Erfassung der biologischen Atmungsaktivität." Master thesis at the Institute of Microbiology. University Braunschweig, Germany.

Using In Situ Bioventing to Minimize Soil Vapor Extraction Costs

Douglas C. Downey, Russell A. Frishmuth,
Steven R. Archabal, Christopher J. Pluhar,
Paul G. Blystone, and Ross N. Miller

ABSTRACT

Gasoline-contaminated soils may be difficult to remediate with bioventing because high concentrations of gasoline vapors become mobile when air is injected into the soil. Because outward vapor migration is often unacceptable on small commercial sites, soil vapor extraction (SVE) or innovative bioventing techniques are required to control vapors and to increase soil gas oxygen levels to stimulate hydrocarbon biodegradation. Combinations of SVE, off-gas treatment, and bioventing have been used to reduce the costs normally associated with remediation of gasoline-contaminated sites. At Site 1, low rates of pulsed air injection were used to provide oxygen while minimizing vapor migration. At Site 2, a period of high-rate SVE and off-gas treatment was followed by long-term air injection. Site 3 used an innovative approach that combined regenerative resin for ex situ vapor treatment with in situ bioventing to reduce the overall cost of site remediation. At each of these Air Force sites, bioventing provided cost savings when compared to more traditional SVE methods.

OVERVIEW

In recent years, bioventing has gained recognition as a state-of-the-art remediation technology for the in situ destruction of fuel hydrocarbons. Bioventing is best suited for less volatile hydrocarbons commonly found in jet fuels, diesel, and heating oils. Bioventing is most efficiently accomplished by continuously injecting low volumes of air into contaminated soil to supply the oxygen required for aerobic biodegradation of fuel residuals while minimizing volatile emissions. However, in the case of soils contaminated with more volatile hydrocarbons (e.g., gasoline), air injection can result in the uncontrolled migration of significant concentrations of volatile organic compounds (VOCs) away from the source area. At a typical retail gasoline station, VOC migration is often unacceptable due to the potential for spreading contamination to adjacent properties or vapor migration into surrounding utility corridors. Under these circumstances, SVE may be required to remove high levels of soil gas VOCs. Using high rates of SVE, the primary mechanism of removal is volatilization. In many regions of the United States, SVE must be accompanied by expensive vapor treatment. When low rates of air injection or vapor extraction are used, in situ biodegradation becomes the primary mechanism of removal.

The primary objective of the remediation projects described in this paper was to minimize contaminant volatilization and vapor treatment costs and maximize in situ biodegradation. The following case studies provide examples of three different approaches for lowering the cost of remediating gasoline-contaminated soils.

SITE 1 – PULSED AIR INJECTION

At Site 1, gasoline-contaminated soils are being remediated using a low rate of pulsed air injection to maintain an aerobic soil environment while minimizing horizontal and vertical vapor migration. This form of bioventing provides a low-cost treatment alternative for sites with deeper soil contamination where upward vapor migration is minimal and some horizontal vapor migration is acceptable.

Site Description

Site 1 is located at Ellsworth Air Force Base (AFB), South Dakota. The site, also referred to as the Building 102 Site, is currently being used as a fueling station and maintenance center for base vehicles. The fueling station was constructed in 1965 with the installation of a 45,000-L gasoline underground storage tank (UST) and a 7,600-L diesel fuel UST. No leaks were detected in the tanks during leak testing performed in October 1990. A release was first noticed during leak-detection monitoring well installation in July of 1991 and occurred in the vicinity of the USTs and fuel loading area. The leaking 45,000-L gasoline UST was subsequently emptied and abandoned (FMG, Inc. 1992). A bioventing pilot study area has been established adjacent to the USTs and a fuel loading area.

The soil profile at this site consists of lean sandy clay to a depth of 2.8 m below ground surface (bgs), and well-graded gravel with interbedded layers of clayey sand to a depth of at least 5.6 m bgs. The entire site is covered with approximately 8 cm of asphalt and 30 cm of concrete. During pilot-scale bioventing, groundwater was encountered at approximately 5.2 m bgs. The primary contaminants at this site are gasoline-related petroleum hydrocarbons that have migrated to the groundwater at a depth of approximately 5.2 m bgs. Free product was observed in three monitoring wells located downgradient of the suspected source area. Laboratory analyses of soils at the site indicated that soils were most contaminated adjacent to the fuel filling area and associated USTs. Soil contamination appeared to be confined to a relatively thin zone extending 1 m above the water table surface. Total petroleum hydrocarbon (TPH as gasoline) concentrations in soil as high as 9,390 mg/kg were detected at a depth of 4.6 to 5.6 m bgs.

Total benzene, toluene, ethylbenzene, and xylenes (BTEX) compounds were also detected at 1,315 mg/kg in soils near the pilot test area (FMG, Inc. 1992).

Bioventing Pilot Tests

An initial bioventing pilot test was completed at the site by Parsons Engineering Science, Inc. (Parsons ES) during late 1993. The following paragraphs describe the final design and installation of the bioventing pilot system and test results at the site. All bioventing pilot tests described in this paper were conducted using the procedures described in the Air Force Center for Environmental Excellence (AFCEE) *Test Plan and Technical Protocol for Bioventing* (Hinchee et. al. 1992).

Test Well Construction. One vent well (VW), three vapor monitoring points (MPs), and a blower unit were installed at the site. The VW was installed with the screened interval extending from 2.5 to 5.5 m bgs to focus airflow in the most contaminated soil interval. The VW was constructed using 5-cm-(2-in)-diameter, schedule 40 polyvinyl chloride (PVC) casing, with 3 m (10 ft) of 0.1-cm slotted PVC screen. Three MPs were installed at the site with screened intervals at 3-m and 4.6-m depths. Each point was constructed using 15-cm sections of 2.5-cm-diameter PVC well screen and 0.6-cm (0.25-in.) PVC riser pipes extending to the ground surface. Figure 1 provides a cross section of the well construction and site geology.

Initial Soil Gas Chemistry. Prior to initiating any air injection, all MPs were purged until oxygen levels had stabilized. Initial oxygen, carbon dioxide, and total volatile hydrocarbon (TVH) concentrations were sampled using portable gas analyzers. Laboratory soil gas analysis revealed that high levels of gasoline vapors (97,000 ppmv) had accumulated in the deeper, more contaminated soils. At all MP screened intervals and at the VW, microorganisms had depleted soil gas oxygen levels (0.5 to 4.1%), indicating the potential for increased microbial activity when oxygen is supplied. Background oxygen levels measured in uncontaminated soils ranged from 19 to 20.1%, indicating that oxygen depletion was directly related to petroleum biodegradation.

Air Permeability/Oxygen Influence. An air permeability test was conducted according to procedures outlined by Johnson et al. (1990). Air was injected into the VW for 1 h at a rate of approximately 1,100 L/min and an average pressure of 70 cm of water. A soil gas permeability value of 1.4×10^{-5} cm^2, typical for gravel and loose sands, was calculated for this site. A radius of pressure influence of at least 9 m was observed at all MP depths. The depth and radius of oxygen influence in the subsurface resulting from air injection into the central VW is the primary design parameter for full-scale bioventing systems. A 15-h period of injection at approximately 280 L/min increased in soil gas oxygen levels to greater than 16% at all MP screened intervals. Based on measured changes in oxygen levels, it was determined that the radius of oxygen influence would encompass the entire source area using air injection rates as low as 280 L/min.

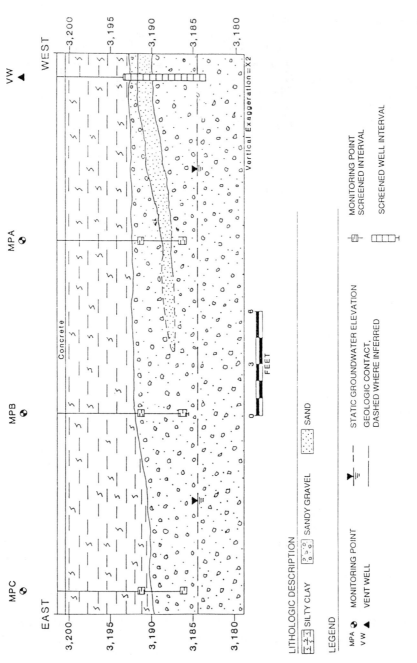

FIGURE 1. Hydrogeologic cross section, Building 102, Ellsworth AFB, South Dakota (1 ft = 0.3 m).

In Situ Respiration Rates. An in situ respiration test was performed by injecting air (oxygen) and approximately 1.5% helium (inert tracer gas) into three MP screened intervals (MPA-4.6, MPB-3, and MPC-4.6) and the VW for a 19-h period. The oxygen loss and other changes in soil gas composition over time were then measured at these intervals. Oxygen, TVH, carbon dioxide, and helium were measured for a period of 47 h following air injection. Oxygen loss occurred at slow but consistent rates, ranging from 0.62% per day at MPB-3 to 1.1% per day at the VW. Based on these initial oxygen utilization rates, an estimated 100 to 200 mg of fuel per kg of soil can be degraded each year at this site. This conservative estimate is based on an average air-filled porosity of approximately 0.13 L per kg of soil, and a ratio of 3.5 mg of oxygen consumed for every 1 mg of fuel biodegraded.

Potential Air Emissions. The long-term potential for vertical migration and air emissions from full-scale bioventing operations at this site is low because of the depth of contamination, the relatively impermeable soils near the ground surface, and the concrete pavement covering the site. Horizontal migration should be minimal because vapors will move slowly outward from the air injection point and should be biodegraded as they move through an expanded soil bioreactor. This phenomenon has been demonstrated and more thoroughly documented by U.S. Environmental Protection Agency (EPA) and Battelle researchers at a Hill AFB bioventing site (Sayles et al. 1992). Because Ellsworth AFB controls the land surrounding the site, liability issues related to possible off-site migration are not a concern.

Ambient air in Building 102 was monitored for TVH changes both before and during air injection to confirm that TVH emissions were not entering the building as the result of air injection at the VW. These monitoring results confirmed that low rates of air injection would not cause vertical vapor migration into the building and would not create health or explosion hazards.

Extended Pilot Testing Design

Air injection was selected as a long-term method of bioventing at this site for two reasons. First, the most contaminated soil interval at the site is located at a depth of 4.6 m to 5.2 m in permeable sands and gravels. Low rates of air injected at this depth would have little chance of causing vertical migration to surface structures. Second, the biological uptake of oxygen at the site was slow, and minimal quantities of oxygen (air) were required to maintain an aerobic environment. After examining test data from permeability, oxygen influence, and respiration testing, pulsed air injection was selected for the site. Pulsed air injection at low flowrates will provide adequate oxygenation of the contaminated soil while limiting the potential for VOC vapor migration at the site.

Respiration and radius of oxygen influence data were used to determine an appropriate pulsing cycle for the site. A minimum soil gas oxygen content of 5% was desired throughout the contaminated soil area to ensure that oxygen would not limit fuel biodegradation. A conservative oxygen supply scenario was developed using the lowest oxygen concentration achieved during oxygen influence testing (16%) and fastest oxygen utilization found during respiration testing (1.1% per day). Using these two test results, it was determined that approximately 10 days of respiration could occur from the time the blower shut off until oxygen would decrease to the 5% target minimum. Based on the oxygen influence test conducted at an air injection rate of 280 L per minute, it was also determined that the oxygen concentrations in the contaminated source area could be increased to at least 16% in an 8-h period of air injection. To ensure aeration of any contaminated soils outside the study area, two 8-h pulses per week were used as a design safety factor. Due to the low injection rate, a 1-HP regenerative blower unit was used for both the initial and extended pilot tests. A relay and timer were installed to provide pulsed operation of the blower.

Cost Advantage over SVE

If a standard SVE system was used to remediate this site and an internal combustion engine (ICE) was required for vapor treatment, the cost for three months of SVE treatment would be approximately $18,000. The cost of equipment and one year of operating and maintaining an air injection bioventing system at this site was approximately $9,000. It is important to point out however, that if vapor treatment was not required at this site, the cost of SVE and bioventing would be nearly identical. If monitoring of extracted vapor was not required, the cost of SVE could be less than air injection bioventing because cleanup could proceed more rapidly using SVE.

SITE 2 — SOIL VAPOR EXTRACTION FOLLOWED BY AIR INJECTION

At Site 2, a UST leak has contaminated sandy soils and the shallow aquifer beneath the Patrick AFB, Florida gasoline service station. Due to the high soil gas vapor concentrations, the shallow depth of contamination, and the highly permeable soils, bioventing using standard air injection techniques would create uncontrolled vapor migration in a highly populated area of the base. To prevent a potentially hazardous situation, Parsons ES implemented a combination of short-term SVE followed by long-term bioventing using air injection. As a part of this project, a performance and cost evaluation of the VR System® ICE vapor treatment system was also completed for AFCEE.

Site Description

This site has been an active gasoline station since 1954. There are currently four 38,000-L USTs at the site. In 1985, leaking fuel lines resulted in the release of at least 2,700 L of unleaded gasoline. In 1990, a site investigation revealed that both the soil and groundwater at this site were contaminated. Soils at this site consist of unconsolidated and poorly to moderately sorted, fine- to coarse-grained quartz sand with shell fragments. Groundwater is encountered at depths fluctuating between 1.2 m and 1.5 m bgs. The contaminated soil area is overlain by a 10-cm-thick asphalt driveway, and the majority of the soil contamination occurs in the capillary fringe. Total BTEX concentrations as high as 2,816 mg/kg were detected during installation of the bioventing test wells, and soil gas vapor concentrations as high as 100,000 ppmv were found in the soils in the spill area.

Test Well Construction. Because the average water table at this site is approximately 1.5 m bgs, a horizontal vent well (HVW) was installed at a depth of 1.2 m in the center of the most contaminated soil area. The HVW provides an advantage in high water table situations because it provides for maximum airflow at minimum pressure drop, and at this site provided the maximum oxygen delivery capability at the lowest construction cost. The HVW was constructed of 10-cm (4-in.) PVC with 0.75-mm slot screen and was 9.2 m (30 ft) in length. The HVW was connected to a 1-HP regenerative blower for initial pilot testing. In addition to the HVW, four vapor MPs were established at distances ranging from 3 m to 11 m from the HVW and were screened in the most contaminated soil interval at 1 to 1.2 m bgs.

Initial Soil Gas Chemistry. In January of 1993, Parsons ES completed an initial soil gas survey in the contaminated soil area and found anaerobic (zero oxygen) conditions, high volatile organics (100,000 ppmv), and elevated carbon dioxide concentrations. Based on these data, the site was selected for a more extensive in situ bioventing pilot test.

Air Permeability/Oxygen Influence Results. An air permeability test was conducted according to procedures outlined by Johnson et al. (1990). Air was injected for 10 min at a rate of 2,000 L per min at an average pressure of 25 cm of water. Steady-state pressures were achieved after only 5 min in this highly permeable soil. A soil gas permeability value of 2.2×10^{-5} cm^2 was calculated for these sandy soils. During this short test, increases in soil gas oxygen were observed at the MP located 11 m from the HVW. Due to the high concentrations of gasoline vapor at the site, air injection was limited to 10 min to prevent undesirable migration into nearby buildings.

In Situ Respiration Test Results. During in situ respiration testing, oxygen utilization occurred at a very consistent rate of 4.3% per day in soils surrounding each of the MPs. Based on this rate of biological oxygen demand, and a soil air-filled porosity of 0.17 L/kg, approximately 2.5 mg of petroleum hydrocarbon per kg of soil could be degraded each day at this site. It is important to note that this rate of biodegradation will occur when oxygen is provided to contaminated soils, regardless of whether oxygen is supplied through soil gas extraction, or air is being injected at the site.

Remediation Approach

Because initial soil vapor concentrations at this site were very high, bioventing through the use of air injection was ruled out due to the potential for vapor migration. Soil vapor extraction was required to significantly reduce soil vapor concentrations before the system could be converted to a standard air injection bioventing system. Several emission control technologies were evaluated based on efficiency, maximum TVH influent concentration capacities, maintenance requirements, and cost over the period necessary for vapor extraction. Based on the technology review, a decision was made to use an internal combustion engine (ICE) vapor extraction system and to evaluate its effectiveness at rapidly reducing soil vapor concentrations and compatibility with long-term bioventing.

High-Rate Vapor Extraction and Combustion. Vapor extraction with combustion is an innovative technology which uses a gasoline-burning internal combustion engine with advanced emission controls to extract and burn hydrocarbon vapors from contaminated soil. Vapors are extracted from the ground by the intake manifold vacuum of the engine. The vapors are then burned as fuel to run the engine. The exhaust gases pass through catalytic converters for final combustion before exiting to the atmosphere.

Equipment Specifications. At this site a VR System® Model V3 ICE was used. The unit is comprised of a Ford 460-in.^{3} (7.2 L) displacement engine and accessories, along with an onboard computer system that automatically adjusts the fuel/air mixture and monitors engine performance. The intake manifold of the engine provides a vacuum source of up to 450 mm of mercury (Hg), and flow-rates of up to 7,000 L/min can be achieved depending on soil conditions and the hydrocarbon concentrations of the extracted soil gas.

Supplemental fuel (propane or natural gas) is used to provide smooth operation of the engine as extracted soil gas vapor concentrations fluctuate. Elimination of supplemental fuel usage can be achieved if the extracted soil gas vapor concentrations provide sufficient fuel to sustain combustion and smooth operation of the engine. Sustained volatile organic levels in excess of 40,000 ppmv (as gasoline) are generally required for unsupplemented operation. By maintaining the proper air-to-fuel ratio, the total hydrocarbon vapor destruction efficiency typically exceeds 99%.

Equipment Performance. The Florida Department of Environmental Protection (FDEP) requires that all SVE units must use a catalytic or thermal oxidation device, or its equivalent (carbon absorption), to reduce VOC emissions by at least 99% during the first 2 months of operation. With minor exceptions, the VR System® unit achieved this level of destruction throughout its 11 weeks of operation. During the extended test period, the average flowrate was reduced from 4,200 L/min to 2,200 L/min due to a seasonally high water table, which reduced the HVW efficiency. Limitations placed on the vacuum reduced the overall efficiency of the V3 unit. Despite these inefficiencies, the primary goals of determining the destruction efficiency, operating cost range, reliability, and maintainability were achieved during the evaluation. A more complete report on the operation of the VR System V3 ICE unit has been prepared for AFCEE (Parsons ES 1994).

Figure 2 illustrates the range of soil gas influent BTEX and TVH concentrations encountered during the test and the significant reduction that occurred as a result of 75 days of soil vapor extraction. The VR Systems ICE provided greater than 99% destruction efficiency for BTEX and greater than 96% destruction efficiency for TVH throughout the test period. After 75 days of extraction, the average soil gas concentration was reduced to approximately 1,600 ppmv or 12% of the lower explosive limit for fresh gasoline. At this reduced concentration, there was little risk of using low-rate air injection for bioventing the remaining fuel residuals at the site.

Long-Term Bioventing via Air Injection

Following 75 days of vapor extraction, the average soil gas TVH concentrations were decreased to less than 1,600 ppmv. A decision was made to proceed with a low rate of air injection because remaining vapors did not pose an explosive hazard and would biodegrade as they migrated toward the perimeter of the site. Ambient air monitoring in nearby buildings during the first 48 h of air

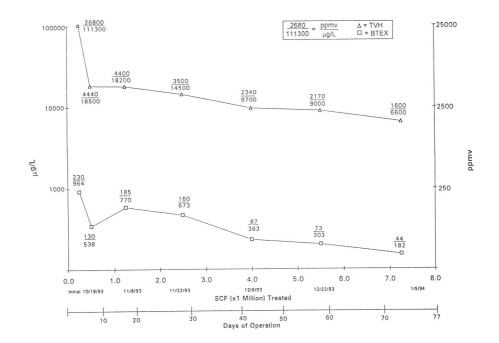

FIGURE 2. Influent BTEX and TVH concentration reduction over total standard cubic feet (SCF) treated.

injection confirmed that vertical vapor migration was not impacting occupied structures.

Air injection was accomplished by reconnecting the 1-HP regenerative blower to the HVW and adjusting the airflow so that an oxygen increase of at least 5% was achieved at the MP furthest (11 m) from the HVW. A continuous air injection of approximately 280 L/min was selected for long-term bioventing of the pilot test area. The system has been operating in the air injection mode for approximately 9 months. Average in situ respiration rates had increased from 2.5 to 2.8 mg of fuel degraded per kg of soil per day after 6 months of air injection.

Ratio of Biodegradation to Volatilization

Based on laboratory analysis of extracted soil gas during the first 75 days of ICE unit treatment, approximately 3,100 kg of hydrocarbon vapors were removed and destroyed. A higher extraction rate could have been achieved if groundwater at the site would not have restricted the soil vapor flow into the HVW. Throughout the 12-month pilot test, oxygen has been supplied to the contaminated soil volume to stimulate in situ biodegradation of fuel residuals. Based on the in situ respiration rate measured at the site of 2.8 mg of fuel per kg of soil per day, and an estimated contaminated soil volume of 700 m^3, approximately 1,100 kg of hydrocarbons should have been biodegraded during the first year of pilot testing. At this site, the ratio of volatilization to biodegradation during the first year of treatment is approximately 3:1.

Cost Advantage over SVE

The conversion of the SVE system to long-term bioventing provided a significant cost savings at this site. During the 11-week test of the ICE unit, the cost per kilogram of TVH destroyed increased from $0.88 to $16.32/kg. The cost increase is due to decreasing soil vapor concentrations and increased supplemental fuel requirements. During this period, the average total operating cost (including rental, supplemental fuel, and analytical) was $345.00 per day. In contrast, the cost of operation, monitoring, and maintaining an air injection bioventing system at this site was $33 per day. By removing the ICE unit after 11 weeks of treatment and converting the system to air injection, approximately $300 per day was saved. Although bioventing may require more time to complete the site remediation, 10 months of bioventing can be completed for the same cost as 1 month of SVE operation at this site.

SITE 3 — COMBINED OFF-GAS TREATMENT WITH VAPOR REINJECTION

Purus Inc. of San Jose, California has developed an innovative vapor treatment system, known as PADRE®, which is particularly suited for combination with in situ bioventing. The objective of this field project was to demonstrate and optimize the combination of these two innovative technologies for the cost-effective remediation of a gasoline-contaminated site at Vandenberg AFB, California. The test program was divided into two phases of operation. The focus of Phase One was the removal of highly concentrated VOCs from the soil gas and the treatment of VOCs using the PADRE® unit. Treated effluent from this vapor treatment unit was recirculated through the soil using a series of perimeter air reinjection or biofilter trenches. Following approximately 16 weeks of soil vapor extraction, average influent VOC concentrations were reduced from over 8,000 ppmv to less than 1,000 ppmv. Based upon the average rates of in situ biodegradation measured at the site, a VOC loading rate of approximately 7 kg per day can be biodegraded by soil bacteria within the soil volumes impacted by the air injection trenches. Phase Two was initiated when the PADRE® system was removed and reduced VOC concentrations were recirculated through the soil and biologically degraded using the biofilter trenches.

Site Description

The site is located at the Base Exchange Service Station (BXSS) on Vandenberg Air Force Base. Vandenberg AFB is located on the south-central coast of California, approximately 140 miles north of Los Angeles. The BXSS was constructed in 1967. Four 38,000-L fuel, and one 950-L waste oil single wall steel USTs were installed at the facility. Two of the original 38,000-L tanks and associated pipes were removed in 1985. The remaining tanks and piping were removed in 1991. The original tanks were replaced with double-wall fiberglass tanks and piping.

Surficial deposits at the site consist of poorly graded fine to medium sands. Under the majority of the site, the sand extends to approximately 4.3 m bgs, where a 0.6-m-thick discontinuous clay layer is encountered. The sand continues beneath the clay to approximately 7.4 m bgs, at which depth another more continuous clay layer is encountered.

During tank and piping removal operations, soil contaminated with fuel hydrocarbon was detected. A limited amount of contaminated soil was excavated during tank removal operations. Several rounds of site assessment activities were conducted to determine the nature and extent of subsurface contamination. Results of these studies indicate that leaks and spills from the former tanks and piping have impacted the soils and groundwater. The primary contaminants are total petroleum hydrocarbons as gasoline (TPH-G) and the associated BTEX components. This contamination is believed to have migrated to the water table at approximately 2.1 to 2.8 m bgs. The majority of the contaminated soil is distributed in a smear zone approximately 1 m thick along the soil/groundwater interface. Soil concentrations of TPH-G up to 22,000 mg/kg were detected. Maximum soil concentrations of benzene, toluene, ethylbenzene, and xylenes were 210 mg/kg, 2,000 mg/kg, 490 mg/kg, 2,900 mg/kg, respectively. Previous investigations have confirmed fuel-related hydrocarbon contamination in site groundwater. Free product has not been encountered; however, a slight sheen has been observed in two wells.

Bioventing Pilot Tests

Test Well Construction. Bioventing pilot tests at this site were completed using a combination of existing monitoring wells and three newly installed vapor monitoring points. In total, 8 wells were available for monitoring soil gas and conducting respiration tests, including one background vapor monitoring point. All wells were screened in the interval of greatest soil contamination within 1 m of the water table. Several wells were located in the vicinity of the reinjection trench and were used to monitor in situ respiration of injected vapors.

Initial Soil Gas Chemistry. Soil gas samples were extracted from existing monitoring wells with screens extending above the water table into contaminated soil, and from newly constructed soil gas monitoring points. Oxygen concentrations of 0% were encountered in existing monitoring wells located in contaminated areas covered with asphalt. Existing wells and monitoring points located in or near grassy areas had depleted oxygen concentrations of 1.0 to 11.6%. Volatile hydrocarbon concentrations ranged from 11,000 to 45,000 ppmv. All soil gas monitoring locations had elevated carbon dioxide concentrations of between 8.5 and 17.0%. The results of this initial soil gas survey indicate that biological activity has reduced oxygen concentrations at the site, particularly where atmospheric diffusion of oxygen is limited by the asphalt surface. Oxygen levels in the background monitoring point were near atmospheric levels at 20.1%.

In Situ Respiration Testing. An in situ respiration test was performed in the existing monitoring wells and newly constructed soil gas monitoring points with low initial oxygen concentrations. Oxygen utilization rates varied from 2.9 to 5%/day. Using a conservative ratio of 1 mg of hydrocarbon degraded for every 3.5 mg of oxygen consumed, approximately 1.6 to 2.7 mg of fuel per kg of soil per day can be degraded at this site under oxygen-stimulated conditions.

Air Permeability Testing. An air permeability test was performed to determine the radius of influence of an air injection vent well. Air was injected into an existing 10-cm-diameter monitoring well at a rate of approximately 1,500 L/min and a wellhead pressure of 88 cm of water. Pressure response and oxygen concentrations were observed in four vapor monitoring points located at distances of 3 to 12 m from the injection well. Due to the rapid response and relatively short time to achieve steady-state conditions, the steady-state method (Johnson et al. 1990) of determining soil gas permeability was selected. Using the steady-state method, soil gas permeability was estimated to be a minimum of 5.9×10^{-6} cm^2.

After 6 h of injecting air at 1,500 L/min, an odor of degraded gasoline was noted around a nearby UST vault lid. A slight positive pressure at UST access hole covers was also observed. To reduce the risk of vapor migration toward the service station and of air emissions, the flowrate to the well was reduced to less than 700 L/min. After a total of only 17 h of air injection, an increase in soil gas oxygen was observed in a monitoring point 12 m from the injection well. Based on this rapid transport of oxygen through the subsurface and experience at similar sandy sites, it was determined that the long-term radius of oxygen influence could exceed 12 m at injection flowrates as low as 280 L/min.

Regulatory Approval

Several regulatory approvals were required before initiating this field demonstration. A test work plan was reviewed and approved by the California Department of Toxic Substances, local water board, and local air pollution control district. Requirements set forth by the air district included intensive monitoring during system startup, biweekly sampling of effluent from the vapor treatment unit and monitoring for potential flux of VOCs into the atmosphere over the top of the biofilter trenches. Total VOC emissions to the atmosphere could not exceed 100 ppmv, and benzene concentrations could not exceed 1 ppmv at any time during the test. A total VOC emission limit of 0.45 kg/h (1 lb/h) also was established.

Full-Scale Bioventing System

Based on the results of the in situ bioventing pilot test, biological degradation of the contaminants would be stimulated by providing the subsurface with oxygen-rich air. A radius of oxygen influence of at least 12 m per well was also demonstrated. The air injection method of bioventing was ruled out at this site due to the potential migration of gasoline vapors to the atmosphere and nearby buildings. Therefore, bioventing was accomplished by extracting soil vapors from the contaminated area and drawing in oxygen-rich soil vapor from surrounding clean soil. Complete aeration of the contaminated soil volume was achieved with 5 vapor extraction wells (VEWs) and a combined extraction rate of 1,100 to 1,400 L/min. Recirculation of the extracted vapors to biologically active soils around the periphery of the site maximizes biodegradation and eliminates the need for long-term, aboveground vapor treatment. The five VEWs have individual flow controls and are connected via a common manifold to a regenerative blower system (Figure 3).

The bioventing system has been integrated with a groundwater treatment system. The groundwater extraction system is dewatering the site, exposing contaminated soil previously below the water table to bioventing treatment. At the time of Phase One startup, the static groundwater level was about 2 m bgs. The water level had dropped 6 months later, through seasonal fluctuation and dewatering, to approximately 3 m bgs.

Two air injection or biofilter trenches were constructed to reinject and complete the biodegradation of vapors. With the trenches oriented around the perimeter of the site, the injected gas is drawn toward the nearby vapor extraction wells. Past research has shown that injected air prefers lateral migration due to the anisotropy of sedimentary materials (AFCEE 1994). Biofilter trenches were constructed by excavating to a total depth of 1.8 m and placing a 5-cm (2-in.) PVC well screen and filter pack at the bottom of each trench. The design of the

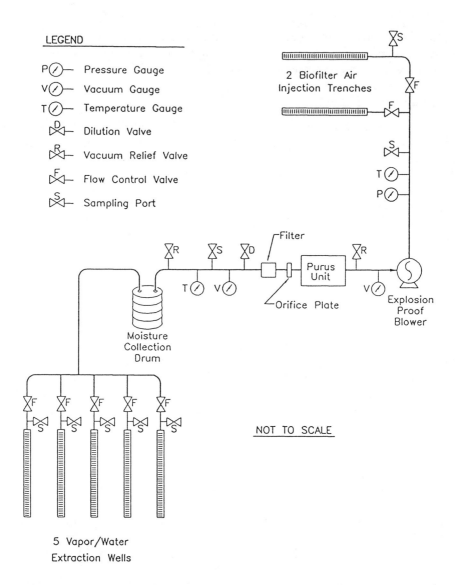

FIGURE 3. Phase One flow diagram — BX service station bioventing, Vandenberg AFB, California.

air injection trenches was based on the available soil volume around the site and biodegradation rates of approximately 1.6 to 2.7 mg of TPH-G per kg of soil per day (observed during pilot testing). Assuming that vapor injected into the bio-filter trench will move horizontally at least 4.6 m from the horizontal injection well, a soil volume of 1,500 m³ was designed to assimilate approximately 7 kg of fuel vapor per day. A loading rate of 7 kg per day can be achieved through various combinations of flow and vapor concentration. Because bioventing pilot tests indicated that site soils could be oxygenated at flowrates of 280 L/min per well, a total design flow of 1,100 to 1,400 L/min was selected. At the 1,100 L/min flowrate, vapor concentrations of approximately 4 mg/L or 1,000 ppmv could be biodegraded within the available biofilter volume. (This assumes an average molecular weight of 100.)

During the bioventing pilot test, soil vapor concentrations as high as 45,000 ppmv were detected in soil vapor monitoring points. During the initial months of operation, these high soil vapor concentrations would exceed the treatment capacity of the biofilter trenches. The Purus PADRE® system was selected to provide short-term treatment of these VOCs until average extracted soil gas concentrations could be reduced below the 1,000-ppmv biofilter design load.

The PADRE® system was designed for onsite capture and recovery of VOC vapor emissions from industrial air vents, industrial water treatment processes, and site remediation operations. The principles of regenerative resin operation have been described in other publications (Blystone et al. 1992 and 1994). This vapor treatment system consists of two modular adsorbent resin beds. The design allows one bed to be online treating influent air, while the other bed is undergoing a desorption cycle. The beds are automatically switched back and forth between adsorption and desorption cycles by an on-board control system. During the desorption cycle, all of the organic contaminants trapped in the adsorbent material are removed, condensed, and transferred as a liquid to a storage tank. The recovered compounds are often reclaimed for recycling or disposal. The condenser system used liquid nitrogen and has two stages, one set at 2°C for water condensation and the other at −45°C to capture compounds with low boiling points. These synthetic adsorbents have a high tolerance to water vapor, allowing processing of airstreams having relative humidities greater than 90% with little impact on adsorption efficiencies. The system is skid-mounted and comes equipped with a modem for remote monitoring and control.

Phase One Operations

The Phase One design combined the advantages of several treatment technologies: (1) bioventing using low rates of vapor extraction eliminated the risks of hydrocarbon vapor migration while stimulating in situ biodegradation; (2) treating more concentrated soil vapors with the PADRE® system during Phase One of operation provided a rapid removal of easily removed contamination; (3) recirculating vapor through biofilter trenches eliminated the need for costly air permitting; (4) discharging to the biofilter trench also increased the efficiency of the PADRE® system by allowing some breakthrough of the resin to occur before regeneration of each bed, which can reduce electrical and liquid nitrogen costs by extending the time between bed regeneration; and (5) as soil vapor hydrocarbon concentrations decreased, the operation of the vapor treatment system became less cost efficient, and Phase Two was initiated to maximize in situ bioremediation through vapor reinjection.

A schematic of the Phase One system is shown on Figure 3. Flow control valves were used to adjust the amount of flow from each VEW and the hydrocarbon influent to the vapor treatment unit and to each biofilter trench. Sampling ports at the VEWs allowed individual monitoring of soil gas hydrocarbon and oxygen concentrations. Based on this information, flow from each well could be adjusted to control the unit's influent and to maintain aerobic conditions in soils surrounding each VEW.

Initial soil gas concentrations of hydrocarbon and oxygen at the VEWs are included in Table 1. There was insufficient oxygen for aerobic biodegradation at VEWs 1 through 4 at the start of the test. After 18 days of operation, the soils surrounding each VEW were highly oxygenated and suitable for aerobic biodegradation of fuels. Hydrocarbon concentrations were significantly reduced in VEWs 3 and 4; soils surrounding VEWs 1 and 2 appeared to be the primary sources of contamination limited to 1,100 L/min. Airflow was reduced to 550 L/min when more concentrated vapors from VEWs 1 and 2 were extracted. Flow was later increased as overall soil gas concentrations decreased. In an attempt to recover and treat as much hydrocarbon vapor with the unit as possible before initiating Phase Two, the vapor extraction rate was eventually increased to 1,400 L/min.

During approximately 110 days of operation, the PADRE® system recovered approximately 2,200 L of fuel and 270 L of water from the extracted soil vapor. Total VOC removal efficiencies of greater than 98% were achieved throughout most of Phase One operation. This level of treatment efficiency maintained at flowrates of 550 to 1,400 L/min and influent VOC concentrations of 4,300 to 13,000 ppmv, as shown in Table 2.

A total of 22,848 kilowatt-h of electricity (includes blower) were used for Phase One operations. Assuming a cost of 6 cents per kilowatt h, the total electric cost was $1,371. Twenty-two dewars of liquid nitrogen were consumed during Phase One. At a cost of approximately $80 per dewar including delivery, $1,760 was spent on nitrogen. Startup of Phase One required an engineer on site for

TABLE 1. Vapor extraction well soil gas analyses, Vandenberg AFB, California.

Date	Vapor Extraction Well	Total Hydrocarbons (ppmv)	Percent Oxygen (%)
1/5/94	VEW 1	54,000	1.0
Pre-startup	VEW 2	9,000	2.0
	VEW 3	5,200	1.5
	VEW 4	8,000	0.0
	VEW 5	94	13.0
After 18 days of	VEW 1	9,000	16.0
treatment	VEW 2	3,600	20.2
	VEW 3	700	20.8
	VEW 4	580	20.5
	VEW 5	260	20.8

TABLE 2. Phase One — BX service station air monitoring, Vandenberg AFB, California.

Date		Purus Influent (ppmv)	Biofilter Trench Influent (ppmv)	Average Flux Monitoring Point Concentration (ppmv)[a]	Total Site Emissions (kg/h)
				Background Flux	Background Flux
1/5/94	Benzene	—[b]	—	<0.002	
	TVH	—	—	0.75	6.4×10^{-4}
2/18/94	Benzene	220	<0.003	<0.013	
	TVH	13,000	64	7.0	1.3×10^{-2}
3/21/94	Benzene	96	<0.002	<0.002	
	TVH	4,000	50	0.25	5.7×10^{-4}
4/14/94	Benzene	60	0.14	<0.002	
	TVH	3,000	430	0.22	1.1×10^{-4}
5/24/94	Benzene	35	0.004	<0.002	
	TVH	4,300	71	0.076	7.8×10^{-5}

(a) Values such as <0.002 indicate the concentration of analyte was less than the detection limit.
(b) — = Not required/not applicable.

1 week at an approximate cost of $2,500. Operation and maintenance of the system required a daily 2-h visit to the system by a technician at an approximate cost of $300 per week, or a total Phase One cost of $4,500. During long-term operations, this cost can be significantly reduced when a modem is used to monitor and control the system. Disposal costs for condensed hydrocarbons were minimal because the product was of high enough quality to be recycled. The total treatment cost using the vapor treatment unit, including rental, was approximately $23 per kg ($10.60 per lb) of hydrocarbon removed.

Sampling for Atmospheric Emissions

To ensure that hydrocarbon vapors reinjected into the biofilter trenches are being biodegraded rather than escaping to the atmosphere, flux monitoring is being conducted at five locations above the trenches using U.S. EPA (1986) guidelines. Flux sampling consists of placing the open end of a hemispheric chamber on the ground surface and slowly purging it with analyte-free air as hydrocarbons emitted from the ground also enter the chamber. Samples drawn from these chambers are then analyzed in the laboratory for total VOCs and benzene using EPA Method TO-3. The emission area was assumed to be localized to a uniformly emitting, 9-m-wide surface, extending the 108-m length of the air injection trenches.

Permission to conduct this demonstration was contingent upon compliance with discharge limits set by the local air board. Table 2 provides a summary of flux monitoring data and hourly emission estimates. At no time during the demonstration have actual emissions approached regulatory discharge limits. The highest total site flux rate for the site was 13 g/h and benzene concentrations have never exceeded 0.6 ppmv.

Phase Two — Reinjection Only

Phase Two testing began on 1 June 1994 when average extracted soil vapor concentrations were reduced to approximately 1,000 ppmv and the vapor treatment system was taken off line. Based on in situ respiration testing conducted during Phase Two, soil bacteria at this site are biodegrading an average of approximately 2 mg of fuel per kg of soil per day. During the initial 2 months of Phase Two operation, an average VOC loading rate of 6 to 7 kg per day entered the biofilter trench. Based on laboratory analysis of flux samples, the average flux of VOCs to the atmosphere during Phase Two has been only 0.3% of the VOC loading into the biofilter trench. During Phase Two, benzene has not been detected above 0.006 ppmv in any of the flux monitoring points.

Site 3 Summary

During Phase One testing, approximately 1,600 kg of hydrocarbons were removed from the soil using a combination of SVE and treatment with the PADRE® regenerative resin system. This system achieved an average total VOC removal rate in excess of 98% at a total cost of approximately $23 per kg of fuel recovered. The combination of vapor extraction and PADRE® treatment achieved the objectives of significantly reducing average soil vapor concentrations, increasing soil gas oxygen levels, and complying with air discharge limits. Throughout Phase One and Phase Two, in situ biodegradation was also occurring at the site. Based on the average rate of biodegradation, and the estimated 2,300 to 3,100 m^3 of contaminated soil at the site, between 1,550 and 2,360 kg of fuel should have been biodegraded during the first 200 days of operation.

During the first 2 months of Phase Two operation, the biofilter trench has resulted in significant biological degradation of fuel vapors and minimal flux emissions to the atmosphere. Average loading rates of 7 kg per day (approximately 2.7×10^{-4} lb/ft^3) have been biodegraded, with average atmospheric emissions of less than 16 g per day, based on intensive flux monitoring.

Cost Advantage over SVE

This combination of SVE, off-gas treatment, and in situ bioventing resulted in significant cost savings when compared to the SVE/off-gas treatment option. Because "breakthrough" of the resin was acceptable using the reinjection system, the PADRE® required fewer regeneration cycles each day. This innovation resulted in an estimated 20% savings in operating costs or approximately $150 each month. The most significant savings occurred when the PADRE® had achieved its objective of reducing vapor concentrations to less than 1,000 ppmv and Phase Two bioventing began. During the final 8 months of full-scale testing, the in situ bioventing system operated at an average cost of $140 per day. This cost included intensive monthly soil flux monitoring, laboratory analysis of flux sampling, and 6-month and 1-year in situ respiration testing. If the SVE system and PADRE® had continued to operate at the site, the cost of operation would have exceeded $290 per day.

GENERAL CONCLUSIONS

Three case studies have been presented to demonstrate how in situ bioventing can be used to replace or supplement SVE for remediating gasoline-contaminated soils. Two site-specific factors will generally determine how bioventing and/or SVE will be most effectively implemented on a site. First, the physical and chemical characteristics of a site, such as depth of contamination, surface structures, property boundaries, and magnitude of vapor contamination, will determine if bioventing through air injection alone will be a safe and effective solution. Under favorable conditions, such as existed at Site 1, bioventing through air injection will provide a very cost-effective method of remediation. The second determining factor is the air emission limit mandated by local regulatory authorities. Sites that are not suited for air injection, and have strict emission limits, will require some form of SVE and off-gas treatment. Innovative combinations of SVE and bioventing, such as those used at Sites 2 and 3, can significantly reduce the length of time (and cost) for SVE and off-gas treatment. In locations that do not require off-gas treatment, a low rate of SVE will often be the safest method of remediation for gasoline-contaminated sites. Low-rate SVE will control vapor migration toward a safe discharge, while minimizing volatilization and maximizing in situ biodegradation.

ACKNOWLEDGMENTS

Funding and technical direction for these projects was provided by the Air Force Center for Environmental Excellence (AFCEE) Technology Transfer Division. Significant project support was also provided by the environmental staffs of Ellsworth, Patrick, and Vandenberg Air Force Bases.

REFERENCES

AFCEE. 1994. *Bioventing Performance and Cost Summary.* Prepared by Engineering-Science, Inc. and Battelle for the Air Force Center for Environmental Excellence, Brooks AFB, TX.
Blystone, P. G., B. Mass, and W. R. Haag. 1992. "VOC Recovery From Air Streams Using Specialized Adsorbents: A New Economical Recycling Option." In *Proceedings of the Ind.*

and Eng. Chem. *Division Special Symposium on Emerging Technologies for Hazardous Waste Management*, Vol. 1, American Chemical Society, Atlanta, GA.

Blystone, P. G., H. R. Goltz, and J. Springer, Jr. 1994. "Recovery and Reuse of MEK from Paint Stripping Operation Emissions Using Specialized Adsorbents." Paper presented at 87th Annual Meeting, Air and Waste Management Association, 94-TA39A.03, Cincinnati, OH.

FMG, Inc. 1992. *Final Survey Report for Project No. 91-7087-1, Fuel Spill Contamination Survey, Building 102 Base Fuel Station.* November, 1992.

Hinchee, R. E., S. K. Ong, R. N. Miller, D. C. Downey, and R. Frandt. 1992. *Test Plan and Technical Protocol for a Field Treatability Test for Bioventing.* Prepared for the Air Force Center for Environmental Excellence, Brooks AFB, TX.

Johnson, P. C., M. W. Kemblowski, and J. D. Colhart. 1990. "Quantitative Analysis for the Cleanup of Hydrocarbon-Contaminated Soils by In Situ Venting." *Groundwater* 28(3).

Parsons Engineering-Science. 1994. *A Performance and Cost Evaluation of Internal Combustion Engines for the Destruction of Hydrocarbon Vapors from Fuel-Contaminated Soils.* Prepared for the Air Force Center for Environmental Excellence, Brooks AFB, TX.

Sayles, G. D., R. C. Brenner, R. E. Hinchee, C. M. Vogel, and R. N. Miller. 1992. "Optimizing Bioventing in Deep Vadose Zones and Moderate Climates: Hill AFB Bioremediation of a JP-4 Spill." *Bioremediation of Hazardous Wastes.* U.S. Environmental Protection Agency, EPA/600/R-92/126.

U.S. EPA. 1986. *Measurement of Gaseous Emission Rates from Land Surfaces Using an Emission Isolation Flux Chamber.* U.S. Environmental Protection Agency, EPA/600/8-86/008.

Pressure Dewatering: An Extension of Bioventing Technology

H. James Reisinger, Stewart A. Mountain,
Paul A. Montney, Aaron S. Hullman,
and Andrew W. Darnall

ABSTRACT

In the course of bioventing, air is injected into the subsurface under pressure. This application of pressure locally depresses the water table (i.e., pressure dewatering). Pressure dewatering and subsequent gravity drainage have a number of positive impacts that extend the overall utility of the bioventing technology. Water-table depression exposes a greater portion of the subsurface to the injected air. This then not only increases the pore volume open for air distribution, thereby increasing the radius of influence and zone of remediation, but also opens the smear zone to airflow, which allows for increased biodegradation of this significant secondary source. In the course of operating full-scale bioventing systems, improvement in groundwater quality has been observed at higher rates than could be attributed to vadose zone remediation alone. Data generated in the course of monitoring these systems have shown that a factor responsible for this improvement is water-table depression as a result of pressure application and a concomitant increase of biological activity in the smear zone.

INTRODUCTION

Over the past several years, bioventing has become one of the most widely applied and cost-effective means of remediating vadose-zone soils impacted with petroleum hydrocarbons. This process employs indigenous aerobic heterotrophic microorganisms to degrade petroleum hydrocarbons. Introducing oxygen, the terminal electron acceptor, stimulates the degrader population.

Because bioventing has been in full-scale use for several years, a relatively large operational database has been developed. In its infancy, bioventing was recognized most often as a vadose zone remediation tool. However, there has been some suggestion that air injection into the vadose zone also provides oxygen for organisms in the shallow saturated zone; thus, in situ groundwater bioremediation is also occurring. Simple mass transfer calculations, however, show that the mass of oxygen supplied to the saturated zone by injecting air into the vadose zone is minimal and is certainly inadequate to sustain a significant level of bioremediation. Injection of air containing 21% oxygen results in 21% oxygen in the vadose zone atmosphere above the water table. Diffusion, the primary mechanism that transfers this oxygen from the vadose zone to the saturated zone, allows only a small mass of oxygen to be used for biodegradation. In the following stoichiometric relationship for aerobic biodegradation of a representative hydrocarbon, hexane, 9.5 moles of oxygen are consumed for each mole of hydrocarbon degraded:

$$C_6H_{14} + 9.5\ O_2 \rightarrow 6\ CO_2 + 7\ H_2O \qquad (1)$$

On a mass basis, this equates to one mass unit of hydrocarbon degraded for every 3.5 mass units of oxygen consumed. Therefore, in any unit volume, only 3.03 mg/L of hydrocarbons may be biodegraded from a maximum initial dissolved oxygen concentration of 10.6 mg/L at saturation and 13°C. Only a small amount of biodegradation would occur. At its conclusion, the groundwater would be devoid of oxygen and considered anaerobic, i.e., very little hydrocarbon would have been biodegraded.

Chiang et al. (1989) and Newman and Kimball (1991) have demonstrated the limits of oxygen diffusion in situ. Newman and Kimball, for example, used hydrogen peroxide to provide DO to the groundwater within a dissolved hydrocarbon plume. The resulting DO gradients were reported to be as large as 16 mg/L per ft in both the downgradient (horizontal) and vertical directions. Thus, with no mixing of the groundwater, the rate of oxygen diffusion through the saturated zone significantly limits the rate of aqueous-phase biodegradation.

Full-scale bioventing system operational data, however, have shown that dissolved-phase hydrocarbon concentrations decreased much more rapidly than oxygen diffusion from the vadose zone could explain alone. Increased source removal through pressure dewatering of the smear zone appears to be one of the mechanisms responsible for the improved groundwater quality.

PRESSURE DEWATERING CONCEPTS

A large percentage of hydrocarbon released to the subsurface accumulates in the vadose zone as a soil residual, but some of the initially released volume may accumulate on the water table (or more appropriately the capillary fringe) as a separate phase. Most petroleum fuels are less dense than water; thus, they float on the groundwater table. The seasonal fluctuation of most water tables, caused by variable infiltration and recharge rates, creates a high hydrocarbon concentration zone in this area of fluctuation, typically deemed the smear zone. The thickness of the zone is generally considered to approximate the seasonal water-table fluctuation. Within this smear zone there exists funicular and pendular hydrocarbon that fails to drain under a normal gravity drainage scenario. This zone then contains a large mass of hydrocarbon that is in intimate contact with the groundwater and acts as one of the strongest secondary hydrocarbon sources in many groundwater systems.

During bioventing, air injection increases pressure in the injection point, which is then disseminated into the vadose zone. This pressure is generally applied to a level adequate to optimally distribute the injected air through the vadose zone, but at a level less than that required to fracture the vadose soils. Typical injection pressures range from 1.00 to 27.56 kPa. Because water is generally considered to be incompressible, applying pressure to the water-table surface depresses the water proportionally to the injection pressure. In less-permeable soils, greater pressures must be applied to achieve adequate air distribution, which can result in relatively large water table depressions. Figure 1 depicts the contrast between a conceptual resting water table and a pressure-depressed water table.

Pressure about a single point decays radially as a function of distance from the point in the absence of preferential flow paths and matrix heterogeneities (Johnson et al. 1990). The permeability of the formation controls the rate of decay as a function of time. The propagation of pressure in a low permeability formation is relatively small but is higher in a high permeability formation. Therefore, a radial water-table depression develops about a pressure injection point. This depression dewaters a portion of the smear zone and saturated zone proportionally to the pressure applied at the injection point. When pressure is applied, the smear zone, located at the surface of the water table, is the first area dewatered. Pressure dewatering of the smear zone increases the volume of soil into which air can be injected; consequently, it increases the volume that can be biodegraded through bioventing. Removing hydrocarbons from the smear zone, which contains high hydrocarbon concentrations, improves groundwater quality by source removal. Seasonal water-table decline, coupled with pressure dewatering, further enhances this process by allowing even more of the smear zone to be treated.

CASE HISTORY

The subsurface of a site in the southern Piedmont physiographic province (Figure 2) was impacted with petroleum hydrocarbon as a result of misdelivery of about 26,500 liters of fuel oil. The soil beneath the site consists of sandy, silty clay with interbedded lenses of coarse sand and gravel. Groundwater exists at a depth of about 4.6 to 6.1 m and seasonally fluctuates about 2 m. The area of impacted soil was about 1,720 m^2 and had a volume of 2,665 m^3; the estimated mass of hydrocarbon in the impacted soil was 19,396 kg. After several years of groundwater extraction and treatment, a bioventing system was installed. The system consists of seven air injection points and eight soil vapor extraction points. Initial dissolved phase total petroleum hydrocarbon concentrations ranged from less than detectable to about 0.5 mg/L.

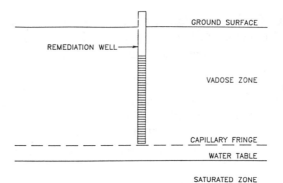

STATIC CONDITIONS

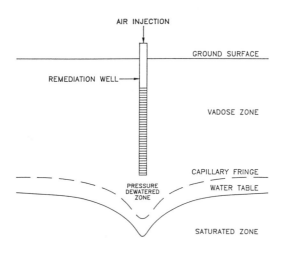

PRESSURIZED CONDITIONS

FIGURE 1. Pressure dewatering concept.

After five quarters of bioventing system operation, approximately 15,345 kg of total petroleum hydrocarbons, through biodegradation in the vadose zone, had been biodegraded in situ. This amount contrasts with the 37.72 kg removed through venting (Figure 3) and the 55.07 kg removed by phase-separated hydrocarbon (PSH) recovery over the same period. Throughout operation, biodegradation rates ranged from 7.57 to 22.93 mg/kg.day as site-wide hydrocarbon concentration weighted averages. These rates were determined quarterly by in situ respiration testing. The data generated to ascertain the source of this variability revealed that, in the early stages of operation, the rates were relatively consistent as a function of depth. As the course of remediation progressed, the monitoring points that were set at a depth interval just above the water table

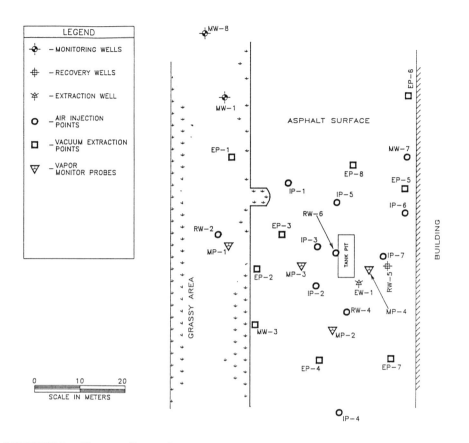

FIGURE 2. Site configuration.

and were submerged in the capillary fringe for part of the year, obviously placing them within the smear zone, began to exhibit higher rates. Although these points were submerged during high water-table periods, the highest biodegradation rates were observed in these same points during the lowest water-table period. These rates provide evidence that the greater the exposure of the smear zone, the more hydrocarbon is removed from this significant source. Therefore, the pressure dewatering caused by bioventing results in significantly greater hydrocarbon mass removal.

Quarterly water-level monitoring showed significant water-table depressions in the vicinities of the air injection points. Figure 4 shows the net water-table depression as the difference in elevation between static and operating conditions. These data show that the maximum depth of depression is about 0.3 m at a positive pressure of approximately 21 kPa and that the zone of depression is approximately radial (approximate radius of 12 m). Water-table depression is readily apparent in the vicinities of all the injection points. Around the extraction points that are also incorporated in the bioventing system, the water table

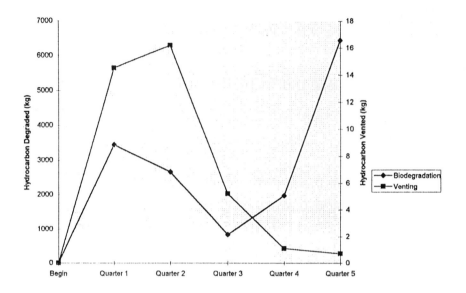

FIGURE 3. Summary of hydrocarbon removal (kg) via biodegradation vs. venting.

has been raised (Figure 4) in proportion to the negative pressure applied. These mounds in the water table demonstrate the ability of a bioventing system to assist in providing hydraulic control of the impacted groundwater plume. Figure 5 shows the distribution of positive pressures, as measured in tri-depth monitoring points, injection points, extraction points, and monitoring wells. The data in this figure illustrate the strong correlation between pressure and water-table depression. At this site, the bioventing system operation has resulted in depressions of the water table over the entire impacted area (i.e., tankfield vicinity).

In addition to the significant mass of hydrocarbon biodegraded in the vadose zone, the data generated through monitoring suggest that the groundwater quality has generally improved. These data, however, have been highly variable. The dissolved-phase hydrocarbon concentrations appear to be changing with fluctuations in the water table, as the data generated from MW-3, which is at the edge of the impacted area, make readily apparent (Figure 6). When the water table is at the peak of its hydrograph (i.e., March 1994), dissolved-phase concentrations are higher; when the water table falls, the concentrations decrease concomitantly,

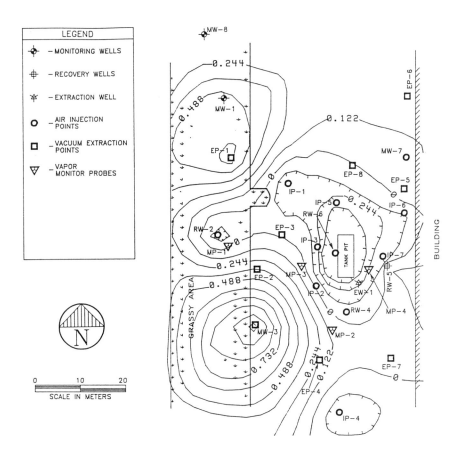

FIGURE 4. Net water table depression (m).

in many instances to levels that are less than detectable. There does, however, appear to be a net decrease in the overall dissolved-phase hydrocarbon concentration. The overall improvement in groundwater quality appears to be a result of the removal of the hydrocarbon source from the smear zone during periods when the water table is lower. The seasonal water-table fluctuation opens the smear zone to oxygen injection, and pressure dewatering exposes an even greater portion of the smear zone. Increased rates of biodegradation and overall hydrocarbon removal during the low water-table periods support this conclusion.

Pressure dewatering has not only enhanced bioremediation in the smear zone and concomitantly improved groundwater quality, but also increased the rate of PSH recovery. Before bioventing was initiated, very little PSH was recovered. In fact, when bioventing began, no PSH was observed in any of the wells. Since applying pressure to the water table through bioventing, the rate of PSH accumulation and recovery has constantly increased (Figure 7). This

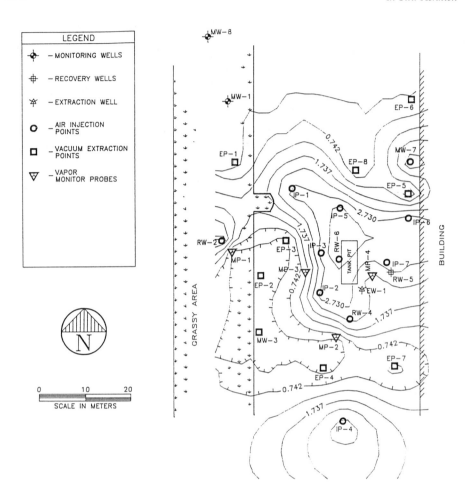

FIGURE 5. Positive pressure (kPa) contour (3-m-depth interval).

increase is directly attributable to the effects of applying pressure and the resulting smear zone exposure. Applying pressure to the pores in which PSH resides also results in pressure drainage. Since physical PSH recovery removes hydrocarbon from the subsurface more rapidly than any other form of remediation and most of the PSH is from the smear zone, this observation represents a significant extension of bioventing.

CONCLUSIONS

Air injection associated with bioventing results in depression of the water table, which in turn results in exposure of the smear zone, a unit that typically serves as a significant secondary source of dissolved-phase hydrocarbon.

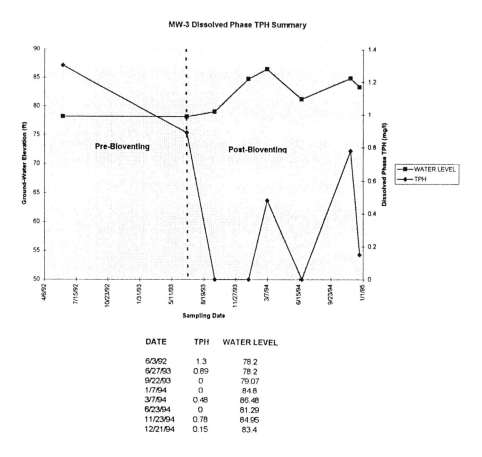

FIGURE 6. Summary of dissolved-phase hydrocarbon and water level in MW-3.

Increased smear zone exposure provides for introduction of oxygen and removal of hydrocarbon via biodegradation over a larger area of the subsurface. Removing this source improves groundwater quality without direct groundwater remediation (i.e., groundwater extraction and treatment) and allows intrinsic bioremediation to occur more rapidly. Therefore, injecting air into the vadose zone at an optimal pressure and flowrate exposes as much of the smear zone as is possible or practical. Pressure dewatering not only provides for enhanced smear zone biodegradation, but also increases the rate of PSH recovery from the smear zone. Pressurization of the vadose, however, must be approached with caution. Overpressurization can result in fracturing and creation of preferential flow paths. It can also redistribute the dissolved-phase hydrocarbon plume. The water-table mounds that vacuum extraction creates, however, can be used to control this redistribution. In summary, pressure-induced dewatering appears to be a controllable, cost-effective extension of bioventing that can result in significant groundwater quality improvement without direct groundwater remediation.

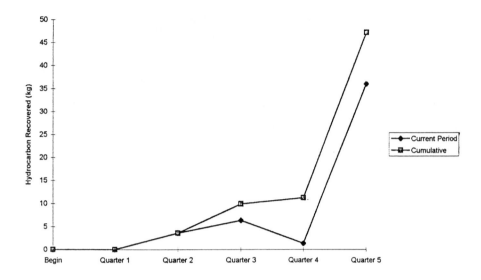

Time	Removal Current Period	Removal Cumulative
Begin	0	0
Quarter 1	0	0
Quarter 2	3.6	3.6
Quarter 3	6.28	9.88
Quarter 4	1.32	11.2
Quarter 5	36	47.2

FIGURE 7. Summary of hydrocarbon removal (kg) attributable to phase-separated recovery.

REFERENCES

Chiang, C. Y., J. P. Salanitro, E. Y. Chiang, J. D. Colthart, and C. L. Klein. 1989. "Aerobic Biodegradation of Benzene, Toluene, and Xylene in a Sandy Aquifer: Data Analysis and Computer Modeling." *Ground Water*, 27(6):823-834.

Incopera, F. P., and D. P. Dewit. 1990. *Fundamentals of Heat and Mass Transfer*. 3rd ed. John Wiley and Sons, New York, NY.

Johnson, P. C., C. C. Stanley, M. W. Kemblowski, D. L. Byers, and J. P. Colthart. 1990. "A Practical Approach to the Design, Operation, and Monitoring of In Situ Soil Venting Systems." *Ground Water Monitoring Review* X(2):159-178.

Newman, W. A., and G. Kimball. 1991. "Dissolved Oxygen Mapping: A Powerful Tool for Site Assessments and Ground Water Monitoring." *Proceedings of the Fifth National Outdoor Action Conference on Aquifer Resaturation, Ground Water Monitoring, and Geophysical Methods*, May 13-16, 1991. Las Vegas, NV.

Verschueren, K. 1983. *Handbook of Environmental Data on Organic Chemicals*. 2nd ed. Van Nostrand Reinhold Company, New York, NY.

Long-Term Bioventing Performance in Low-Permeability Soils

Michael B. Phelps, Frederick T. Stanin, and Douglas C. Downey

ABSTRACT

Short-term and long-term bioventing treatability testing has shown that in situ air injection and extraction is a practical method for sustaining increased oxygen levels and enhancing aerobic biodegradation of petroleum hydrocarbons in low-permeability soils. At several test sites, initial physical parameter analysis of soils and air permeability tests indicated that impacted soils (fine sandy silts and clays) had low air permeabilities. Measurements of depleted soil-gas oxygen levels and increased soil-gas carbon dioxide levels indicated that the natural process of aerobic biodegradation of petroleum hydrocarbons was oxygen-limited. Initial treatability testing consisted of air permeability tests to measure the permeability of the soils to air and in situ respiration tests to measure the rates at which native microorganisms could biodegrade the contaminants when provided with sufficient oxygen. During the long-term treatment period, active air injection or extraction systems were operated for 1 year or longer. Soil gas was periodically monitored within the treatment zone to evaluate the success of the bioventing systems in increasing soil-gas oxygen levels in the low-permeability soils. Follow-up respiration tests and soil and soil-gas sampling were conducted to evaluate changes in respiration rates and contaminant concentrations with time.

INTRODUCTION

Bioventing is the stimulation of natural aerobic biodegradation of petroleum hydrocarbons in soil by direct air injection or vacuum induction through air extraction (Hoeppel et al. 1991, Dupont 1993). Unlike soil vapor extraction (SVE) processes, bioventing utilizes very low air flowrates, which are optimized to provide enough oxygen for microbial respiration within the treatment zone while minimizing volatilization. Because bioventing can be implemented as an air injection process and contaminants are degraded in situ, treatment costs often are much lower than with SVE processes.

From 1992 through 1995, the U.S. Air Force (USAF) has been applying bioventing technology at over 130 sites at USAF installations located in all 10 regions
of the U.S. Environmental Protection Agency (EPA) (Miller at al. 1993). Prior to
implementing this field initiative, the USAF developed a technical protocol document, which serves as the primary reference for field procedures and data collection (Hinchee et al. 1992). This protocol document was reviewed and endorsed by
the EPA's Risk Reduction Engineering Laboratory in Cincinnati, Ohio.

During implementation of the USAF Bioventing Initiative project, several sites
with low-permeability soils were identified for treatability testing. This paper
presents results obtained from treatability tests conducted at two sites, designated
Site One and Site Two, both located at USAF bases in northern California. Site
One and Site Two were the former locations of underground storage tanks used
to store heating oil and diesel fuel, respectively. Remedial investigation data
for both sites, including soil physical parameters and contaminant concentrations,
are shown in Table 1.

AIR PERMEABILITY TESTS

Air permeability (k) describes the ease with which air will flow through the
soil and is usually expressed in units of darcies (1 darcy $\approx 10^{-8}$ cm^2). Although
air permeability can be estimated from the saturated hydraulic conductivity of the
soil or from laboratory methods using in situ or ex situ soil samples, field test
methods are preferred. Field test methods are able to account for the macro
effects of soil moisture content, surface leakage, anisotropy, heterogeneity, and
fractured media. Procedures for conducting field air permeability tests (AP tests)
are well documented (Johnson et al. 1990).

Also important in the design of bioventing or SVE systems is the radius of
influence (Ri) of an injection or extraction well. In its simplest interpretation, the
radius of influence is the distance from an air injection or extraction well where
some level of remediation is occurring. For bioventing systems, this distance
typically is either assumed to be the maximum distance at which some increase
in oxygen is observed or is inferred from the pressure/vacuum response.

TABLE 1. Remedial investigation data summary.

Location	Volume of Impacted Soil (m³)	Clay & Silt Fraction (%)	Average Soil Moisture Content (% by wt)	TPH Concentration (max)[a]	
				Soil (mg/kg)	Soil Gas (ppmv)
Site One	1,200	70 to 90	18.2	1,200	760
Site Two	3,100	18 to 99	18.3	17,240	380

(a) TPH; total petroleum hydrocarbons (calibrated relative to diesel fuel for soil and jet
     fuel for soil gas).

At sites with low-permeability soils, closer well spacing typically must be used with SVE systems because the vacuum decreases rapidly with distance and mass removal is directly related to the magnitude of the induced vacuum and volume of airflow. However, in a bioventing application using air injection, remediation is dependent only on providing oxygen above the biological demand. Oxygen levels in soil gas of only 5% by volume are considered sufficient to ensure aerobic biodegradation. Soil-gas exchange rates of less than one pore volume per day usually are sufficient (Hinchee & Miller 1991). In addition, long-term increases in the effective radius of influence beyond the initial estimate could be expected due to diffusion of oxygen in the subsurface.

Table 2 summarizes the average soil air permeability and radius of influence from initial field air permeability tests conducted at Site One and Site Two. As expected, the air permeability measured at each site was within the range typical for fine sandy clays and fine sandy silts, consistent with the soil descriptions from the field soil boring logs and the results of grain-size distribution tests. Nevertheless, the radius of influence from one injection or extraction well was large enough at each site to aerate most of the contamination zone.

For the initial air permeability test conducted at Site One, air was extracted from the central vent well. After 11 months of air extraction at Site One, the system was converted to an air injection system. Subsequently, an additional air permeability test was conducted using air injection in order to evaluate the long-term impact of venting on the permeability of the soils. The air injection flowrate for the additional test was 1.7 m³/min (60 ft³/min), approximately equal to the flowrate used during the initial extraction test. A comparison of the air permeabilities calculated from the steady-state response of the soil during both tests is shown in Figure 1.

The results suggest that long-term venting has increased the permeability of site soils due to the effects of fracturing and formation of preferential flow pathways, which would also tend to increase the radius of influence and oxygen diffusion. The results also suggest that long-term air injection has promoted soil desiccation and increased the air-filled porosity. The common problems in air extraction systems of upwelling of groundwater and migration of soil moisture toward the extraction well, leading to decreases in air-filled porosity and air permeability, are avoided with air injection systems.

TABLE 2. Initial air permeability test results.

Location	Average Air Permeability (10^{-8} cm²)	Radius of Influence (m)	Wellhead Pressure/(Vacuum) (kPa)	Well Flowrate (m³/min)	Depth to Top of Screen (m)
Site One	2.0	15	(21)	1.8	1.5
Site Two	1.8	17	12	0.93	3.0

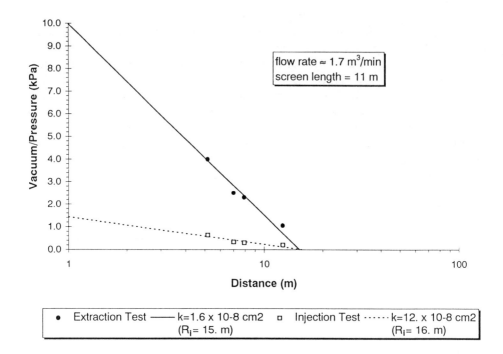

FIGURE 1. Comparison of test methods for measuring air permeability at Site One.

IN SITU RESPIRATION TESTS

At each site, an initial in situ respiration (ISR) test was conducted to measure oxygen uptake by indigenous microorganisms in the soil. Using observed oxygen-utilization rates, rates of biodegradation by microorganisms were calculated (Hinchee & Ong 1992). The initial ISR test at Site One was conducted immediately following the air permeability test and after site soils were sufficiently aerated. For the initial ISR test at Site Two, a mixture of air and helium (2% to 4% by volume) was injected for a fixed period of time into discrete vapor monitoring points.

Helium is used as a tracer gas and also for quality control purposes to assess potential system leaks or short circuits to the surface. The use of a tracer gas for low-permeability soils is particularly important. Constant tracer gas levels in soil-gas samples collected during testing verifies that sufficient aeration of the soil volume has been achieved and that oxygen depletion is not the result of the influx of oxygen-depleted soil gas from outside the zone of aeration.

Initial soil-gas oxygen and carbon dioxide levels, oxygen-utilization rates (in situ respiration rates), and biodegradation rates for Site One and Site Two are shown in Table 3. As expected, the soil-gas oxygen levels are initially depleted and carbon dioxide levels are elevated, indicating active microorganism

TABLE 3. Initial in situ respiration test results.[a]

Location	Initial Soil Gas Measurements		Oxygen Utilization Rate (% per hour)	Biodegradation Rates (mg/kg per year)[b]
	Oxygen (%)	Carbon Dioxide (%)		
Site One	0.0 to 8.4	4.4 to 7.8	0.24 to 0.36	750 to 900
Site Two	0.0 to 8.0	1.2 to 8.5	0.09 to 1.2	100 to 1,100

(a) Measurements are the range of values for all site monitoring points.
(b) mg TPH per kg soil per year.

populations in the low-permeability soils. At Site Two, helium concentrations in soil-gas samples remained relatively constant during the tests (no helium was injected at Site One). ISR rates and biodegradation rates measured at the two sites were typical of those measured at other sites with higher permeability soils. It is important to realize that rates measured during ISR tests are *potential* rates, and that achieving these rates will be dependent on the ability to sustain increased oxygen levels in the soils during extended bioventing.

LONG-TERM RESULTS

One of the primary goals of the USAF Bioventing Initiative is to evaluate the long-term performance of the bioventing systems by periodic soil-gas monitoring, repeated ISR tests, and confirmatory soil and soil-gas sampling. Measurements of long-term performance for Site One and Site Two are summarized in Table 4.

At these sites, increases in oxygen levels within the first few days or weeks of operation were above 5% by volume and were sufficient to sustain biodegradation at all monitoring points. The previously measured air permeabilities appear

TABLE 4. Measurements of long-term performance.

Location	Oxygen in Soil Gas		Oxygen Utilization Rates		TPH in Soil (max)[b]		TPH in Soil Gas (max)[b]	
	Initial (%)	Interim[a] (%)	Initial (% per h)	12 months (% per h)	Initial (mg/kg)	12 months (% per h)	Initial (ppmv)	12 months (ppmv)
Site One	0.0 to 8.4	4.0 to 16.3	0.24 to 0.36	0.1 to 0.33	1,200	not yet sampled	760	170
Site Two	0.0 to 8.0	20.1 to 20.8	0.09 to 1.2	0.0 to 0.76	17,240	3,150	380	45

(a) Measurements taken after 30 hours and 3 weeks of venting for Site One and Site Two, respectively.
(b) TPH: total petroleum hydrocarbons (calibrated relative to diesel fuel for soil and jet fuel for soil gas).

to have been sufficient to provide oxygen in the subsurface through either advection or diffusional processes. Oxygen utilization rates measured after 1 year of treatment were of the same order of magnitude as those measured initially, probably due to the significant contamination levels remaining in the soils, and do not appear to have been limited by any long-term changes in nutrient or moisture levels. Significant decreases in soil and soil gas contamination after 1 year also were observed.

CONCLUSIONS

Long-term bioventing treatability testing at two sites has provided evidence that significant volumes of soil with low permeabilities can be remediated with single-well air injection systems. Follow-up air permeability tests after extended venting indicated that soil air permeability may increase over time due to formation of preferential flow pathways and soil desiccation. Repeated respiration tests indicated that aerobic biodegradation is continuing to occur in contaminated soils after 1 year of treatment. Soil and soil-gas sampling after 1 year of bioventing indicated that decreases in contaminant levels in soil and soil gas were achieved.

REFERENCES

Dupont, R. Ryan. 1993. "Fundamentals of Bioventing Applied to Fuel Contaminated Sites." *Environmental Progress* 12(1): 45-53.

Hinchee, Robert E., and R. N. Miller. 1991. "Bioventing for In-Situ Remediation of Jet Fuel." *Proceedings of Air Force Environmental Restoration Technology Symposium.*

Hinchee, R. E., and S. K. Ong. 1992. "A Rapid In Situ Respiration Test for Measuring Aerobic Biodegradation Rates of Hydrocarbons in Soil." *Journal of the Air & Waste Management Association* 42(10): 1305-1312.

Hinchee, R. E., S. K. Ong, R. N. Miller, D. C. Downey, and R. Frandt. 1992. *Test Plan and Technical Protocol for a Field Treatability Test for Bioventing.* Prepared for Air Force Center for Environmental Excellence (Brooks AFB, TX).

Hoeppel, R. E., R. E. Hinchee, and M. F. Arthur. 1991. "Bioventing Soils Contaminated With Petroleum Hydrocarbons." *Journal of Industrial Microbiology* 8(3): 141-146.

Johnson, P. C., M. W. Kemblowski, and J. D. Colthart. 1990. "Quantitative Analysis for the Cleanup of Hydrocarbon-Contaminated Soils by In-Situ Soil Venting." *Groundwater* 28(3): 413-429.

Miller, R. N., D. C. Downey, V. A. Carmen, R. E. Hinchee, and A. Leeson. 1993. "A Summary of Bioventing Performance at Multiple Air Force Sites." *Proceedings of the 1993 NWWA/API Conference, Petroleum Hydrocarbons and Organic Chemicals in Groundwater: Prevention, Detection, and Restoration.*

Experience with Bioventing at Wood-Preserving Sites

Jeff L. Gentry and Thomas J. Simpkin

ABSTRACT ━━━━━━━━━━━━━━━

The nature of the contamination and the regulatory framework of wood-preserving sites are unique. Evaluating and applying bioventing are, therefore, different than at petroleum hydrocarbon-contaminated sites. Average biodegradation rates measured from in situ respiration tests and operational data at three wood-preserving sites ranged from 2.1 to 6.3 mg/kg soil/day. This is in the low range of rates from published data on bioventing at petroleum hydrocarbon-contaminated sites. A significant factor in bioventing at wood-preserving sites is the physical characteristics of the wastes. The presence of both dense, nonaqueous-phase liquids (DNAPLs) and light, nonaqueous-phase liquids (LNAPLs) at two of the sites required dewatering in conjunction with bioventing to expose the majority of the contamination. The remedial objective at the three sites ranged from reducing contaminant mass, to reducing site risk and reducing contaminant levels so that groundwater would achieve drinking water standards. Full-scale application of bioventing is planned for 1995 at the site with mass reduction as the objective. A long-term bioventing test is being performed at the second site to evaluate the ability of bioventing to reduce levels of carcinogenic compounds, and thus risk. At the third site, bioventing is not included in the final remedy because the chances of achieving the drinking water standards are very small.

INTRODUCTION

Bioventing is a bioremediation technology that has the potential to remediate organic wood-preserving contaminants, i.e., polycyclic aromatic hydrocarbons and pentachlorophenol (PAHs and PCP), depending on the characteristics of the site and the remedial objectives. Bioventing programs have been implemented at three wood-preserving sites to evaluate the feasibility of bioventing to meet site specific remedial objectives. This paper summarizes the studies conducted at these three site and highlights the differences and similarities in the implementation of the bioventing programs.

Bioventing at wood-preserving sites differs from that at petroleum hydro-carbon sites for the following reasons:

- Wood-preserving contaminants (PAHs and PCP) are generally more difficult to biodegrade than petroleum hydrocarbon contaminants.
- Both LNAPLs and DNAPLs may be present, so that the contamination may be smeared through the vadose zone, floating on the groundwater table, smeared through the saturated zone, and possibly occur as a DNAPL above a confining layer. Mobile LNAPL and DNAPL should be recovered prior to implementation of bioventing. Dewatering also may be required to expose the contamination below the water table for bioventing to be effective.
- The high-molecular-weight PAHs and PCP are carcinogenic, which may influence the remedial objectives.
- Wood-preserving sites generally fall under CERCLA or RCRA jurisdiction. Regulatory agencies can have significant latitude in establishing remedial objectives under these programs.

SUMMARY OF BIOVENTING PROGRAMS

The three bioventing programs are summarized in Table 1. All three of the sites were located in the arid west of the United States.

The pilot study conducted at Site A was conducted in 1989, prior to the standardization of many of the current bioventing methodologies. Consequently, some of the methods used were not consistent with latter methods. Mobile DNAPL was first removed from the study area at this site. Horizontal drains (each 40 m long and spaced 18.3 m apart) were used to dewater and deliver air to the shallow alluvial aquifer (about 3.1 m to bedrock) for the bioventing. Air was injected into two of the drains and extracted from the third.

Bioventing at Site B was targeted at only the vadose zone, since groundwater contamination (which is at 2.4 m) is being handled under a different program. A soil gas survey was conducted, followed by an in situ respiration test, both using existing monitoring wells on site. A longer term (approximately 2-year) bioventing test is currently being performed using a single air injection well and a series of monitoring points. The objective of the test is to evaluate the ability to achieve risk-based treatment levels for the carcinogenic PAHs.

Site C is somewhat unique in that an LNAPL is present in the shallow alluvial aquifer. It is likely that a DNAPL was also present at one time, since contamination is generally found the entire depth (up to 3.66 m below grade) of the shallow aquifer. The mobile LNAPL was removed and the test area was dewatered to expose as much of the contamination as possible during the short-term bioventing test. The remedial objective for the bioventing at this site was to obtain as much mass removal as is practically possible. Mass removal should reduce the potential for further migration of the contamination to other aquifers and was a general objective of the state RCRA authority.

STUDY RESULTS

Soil gas surveys were conducted at Sites B and C prior to initiation of the respiration tests. The results of these surveys showed intrinsic soil gas oxygen contents ranging from zero to 11%. Evaluating the intrinsic soil gas oxygen content is important in developing a bioventing program because it suggests where a bioventing system would be beneficial. If the rate of oxygen uptake from contaminant biodegradation is low compared to the rate of oxygen replenishment to the subsurface through diffusion or other forces, such as changes in barometric pressure or groundwater elevations, the intrinsic soil gas oxygen levels may be naturally high (uniformly greater than about 5%) and not limit biodegradation. In such situations, bioventing would not be of any benefit over the intrinsic bioremediation already taking place.

In situ respiration tests using the procedures developed by Hinchee and Ong (Hinchee and Ong 1992) were conducted at Sites B and C. The data from these sites are summarized on Table 2. Biodegradation rates were calculated from the respiration rates using the mineralization stoichiometry of naphthalene and assumed aquifer characteristics as presented by Hinchee and Ong (1992).

The bioventing pilot test at Site A was conducted prior to developing the in situ respiration test by Hinchee and Ong. At this site, biodegradation rates were estimated based on the composition of the off-gas from the blower and the known flowrate.

The average rates of biodegradation with bioventing estimated at these three wood-preserving sites ranged from 2.1 to 6.3 mg/kg/day. Most of these readings were taken in areas of fairly high contamination. For example, at Sites A and C

TABLE 1. Summary of bioventing programs.

Site	Media of Interest	Remedial Objective	Summary of Study
A	Vadose zone and shallow groundwater, DNAPL present at base of shallow aquifer.	Treat to extent necessary to achieve drinking water standards in the groundwater.	Large-scale (130 by 130 ft [40 by 40 m]) pilot study following mobile DNAPL recovery and dewatering. Study conducted for 1 month. Horizontal drains used to dewater and deliver air.
B	Vadose zone, groundwater being handled as a separate program.	Treat to risk-based levels for carcinogenic PAHs.	In situ respiration tests conducted using existing wells, longer term bioventing pilot currently under way.
C	Vadose zone and shallow groundwater, LNAPL present on groundwater, minimal DNAPL remaining.	As much mass removal as practically possible.	Short-term bioventing test conducted to evaluate respiration rates and physical features of system; dewatering used in the area being treated.

TABLE 2. In situ respiration test results.

Site	O₂ Uptake (% O₂/day)	Biodegradation Rate (mg/kg/day)
Site A	NA	6.3
Site B Average	2.6	2.1
Number of Locations	3	
Number of Tests	1	
Site B Standard Deviation	0.54	
Site C Average	3.4	2.7
Number of Locations	14	
Number of Tests	3	
Site C Standard Deviation	1.6	

they were taken after mobile NAPL removal so residual NAPL levels were present. These rates are on the low end of the range of biodegradation rates reported for bioventing at petroleum hydrocarbon sites (1 to 19 mg/kg/day, Hinchee and Ong 1992), but are consistent with those reported by McCauley et al. 1994 at another wood-preserving site. The lower rates at wood-preserving sites may be a result of the generally lower biodegradability of the contaminants associated with wood preserving.

The lower rates of biodegradation observed at these wood-preserving sites, and the relatively high levels of intrinsic soil gas oxygen levels measured at Site B, could suggest that a passive bioventing approach (Foor et al. 1994) could be effective at wood preserving sites. There may be enough natural or passive exchange of oxygen between the soil gas and the atmosphere that oxygen levels are naturally high enough to maintain biodegradation without actively injecting or extracting air.

It should be noted that none of the three tests were conducted for longer than 1 month. Consequently, it is not possible to predict the long-term biodegradation rates from these data. The rates could increase in heavily contaminated zones because of increases in biomass, but they could also decrease as the more readily biodegraded components of the wood-preserving wastes are degraded. The long-term pilot test at Site B may provide additional insight into the long-term biodegradation rates.

DISCUSSION

The relatively low rates of biodegradation observed with bioventing at wood preserving sites have significant implications for the full-scale application of the technology. Assuming a typical biodegradation rate of 3 mg/kg/day, approximately 1,100 mg/kg of contaminants could be biodegraded per year, assuming the rate remains constant. At sites that originally contained mobile NAPL, the residual contamination remaining after mobile NAPL removal could be as high as 20,000 mg/kg. Concentrations over 5,000 mg/kg total hydrocarbons are not uncommon. Thus, it could take from 4.5 to 18 years to biodegrade the 5,000 to 20,000 mg/kg of contamination often encountered at wood-preserving sites.

The status and future of bioventing at the three sites varies depending on the original remedial objective at the site. At Site A, where the remedial objective was to achieve drinking water standards in the aquifer, it has been determined that this objective is not likely to be achievable with bioventing in a reasonable time period. Site A contained mobile DNAPL so that full-scale dewatering would be required to expose all of the contaminated soil. It is not likely that the dewatering would be complete, so that there might be pockets of residual contamination that would not be treated because air could not move through the saturated pockets. These pockets could serve as a long-term source of contamination to the groundwater and result in contaminant levels greater than drinking water standards.

For Site B, the remedial objective was to reduce site risk by reducing the concentration of carcinogenic PAHs in subsurface soil to an acceptable risk level. Because carcinogenic PAHs are higher-molecular-weight PAHs, which have been shown to be less biodegradable, an extended pilot study is being conducted to assess the effectiveness of bioventing on carcinogenic PAHs. Subsurface soil PAH concentrations will be measured before and after the test to determine the effectiveness of bioventing on PAH compounds. In situ respiration tests will be conducted to monitor system performance. Additional tests are planned to assess whether additional systems to control soil moisture content and nutrient levels are effective in increasing in situ respiration rates.

For Site C, the results of the in situ respiration tests were considered sufficient evidence that bioventing will produce a significant contaminant mass removal. Because remediation goals are not compound-specific, this site is proceeding directly into a full-scale bioventing system. The design for the full-scale system has been completed, and construction will begin in 1995. The full-scale bioventing system will follow a mobile LNAPL recovery system. It will include dewatering using horizontal drains and air injection using either horizontal drains or wells. The full-scale operation will continue until the respiration tests suggest that active bioventing is no longer beneficial.

REFERENCES

Foor, D. C., T. Zwick, R. Hinchee, R. Hoeppel, C. Kybur, and L. Bowling. 1994. "Passive Bioventing Driven by Natural Air Exchange." *Proceedings of NWWA/API Conference on Petroleum Hydrocarbons and Organic Chemicals in Ground Water.* pp. 305-315.

Hinchee, R. E., and S. K. Ong. 1992. "A Rapid In Situ Respiration Test for Measuring Aerobic Biodegradation Rates of Hydrocarbons in Soil." *Journal of the Air and Waste Management Association* 42:1305-1312. October.

McCauley, P. T., R. C. Brenner, F. V. Kremer, B. C. Alleman, D. C. Beckwith. 1994. "Bioventing Soils Contaminated with Wood Preservative." *Symposium on Bioremediation of Hazardous Wastes: Research, Development, and Field Evaluations.* San Francisco, CA, June.

Odor Stabilization in Waste Disposal Sites

Reinhard Göschl

ABSTRACT

Any cutting operations into old waste disposal sites for the purpose of site remediation or restoration must be preceded by preventive measures to contain odor emissions. A new patented process induces biological changes in a waste disposal site before it is opened. Warm air saturated with aerobic bacteria is forced into the site where it stops anaerobic processes and initiates an aerobic decomposition process. Residual gas is sucked off and reduced by means of a biofilter. The biological reduction of methane by biofilter has been demonstrated. The process provides for a special pattern of air conduction to avoid the formation of channels in the site and to control entrained leachate. Implementation of the process involves driving steel air pipes into the site and installation of a compressor plant with biofilters. After only 10 days of operation of this odor stabilization system, the site can be opened and the necessary action executed. A facility of this type was started up at Ludwigsburg, Germany in August 1994 and has been operating since in full compliance with specified requirements. The findings resulting from scientific monitoring of its operations, including measurements recorded at regular intervals, will be presented in greater detail.

INTRODUCTION

The biological reactions occurring inside waste disposal sites produce gases which, mainly because of their odor, are offensive to the ambient environment. Opening of old disposal sites allows such gases to escape, causing an enormous odor problem. Because space is scarce in Europe, waste dumps often are located close to residential areas. Carrying on work at opened sites without odor control measures is difficult or all but impossible as this leads to massive protests from nearby residents. Minimization of odor emissions is therefore the primary task in the remediation or restoration of waste disposal sites. The quantity of odor produced depends more on the material disposed and its moisture content than on the age of the material. The biological anaerobic decomposition process in the disposal site leading to odor formation starts soon after tipping of the material.

Such decomposition processes continue for decades and can be prevented or reduced only by lack of moisture or the absence of organic material. Experience gained in other projects shows that odor-restricting measures are necessary even in waste disposal sites with a high content of demolition waste, low filling height, and relatively dry contents. Control measures aimed at reducing odor emissions and microorganism concentrations must be taken prior to opening an old waste disposal site, particularly when a site holds residential and commercial waste with a relatively high portion of biogenic material.

THE BASIC PRINCIPLE

Odor is minimized very quickly or its substance is changed when the microbiological conditions within the waste disposal site are changed. The anaerobic bacteria that cause the odor emissions cannot exist in the presence of oxygen, injection of which therefore reduces or stops the production of odor and leads to the development of an aerobic decomposition process. Landfill gases — primarily methane — are formed by microbiological decomposition under anaerobic conditions. The deposited material is acidic and its fermentation produces both gases and offensive odors.

The problem is solved by driving air pipes into the site, both pipes through which oxygen-rich gas is forced into the dumped material and pipes through which landfill gas is drawn off (Figure 1). Before the oxygen-rich air is blown through the pipes it is passed through a biofilter that includes a container filled with decomposing organic waste. The landfill gas drawn off the site is pulled through another container filled with the same type of material. As the oxygen-rich feed gas flows through the decomposing organic waste it heats up to approx. 50 to 60°C and becomes saturated with water vapor. At the same time, the air is enriched with organic bacteria that thrive best under aerobic conditions. These bacteria are fed into the landfill, where they effectively stabilize odors and transform the deposited material. The decomposing organic waste through which the landfill gas is passed acts as a filter and absorbs any offensive odors that are still present in the gas.

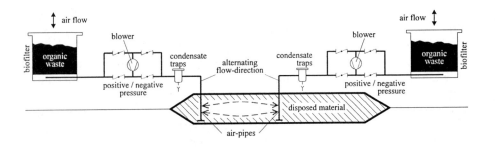

FIGURE 1. Principle of odor stabilization.

A major problem in odor stabilization is water retention. A 12- to 15-year-old waste disposal site lined with impermeable material is very moist inside. This moisture is entrained when the gas-air mixture is sucked off, condenses in the pipes, causes problems inside the compressors, and blocks air ducts. With the new process, water retention is controlled by reversing, at 1-hour intervals, the flow direction of the air injected through the air pipes. The flow direction is changed by reversing valves switching the air pipes at 1-hour intervals from positive mode (forcing air into the waste disposal site) to negative mode (drawing off waste gas) and vice versa. The air pipes (steel pipes with a diameter of 7.6 cm and 3.5 m long) are driven full length into the disposal site in a grid-like pattern, 5 to 6 m apart, over an area of between 1,200 and 1,500 m². Reversal of the air-flow every hour largely avoids channelization inside the waste disposal site and ensures an adequate supply of oxygen to the disposed waste.

Air pipes are pressed into the waste disposal site by means of a vibratory hammer. To avoid blocking of the pipes, air supplied by a mobile compression unit is passed through flexible tubing and blown through the openings of the air pipes. Tubing linking the air pipes with the compressor unit is attached with quick-fitting couplings. It takes 10 to 15 minutes to install one air pipe. Tubing must be sloped to make sure that condensate will always run off toward the air pipes. The entire compression unit is housed in one mobile container, the biofilters in 8 mobile 20-ft (6-m) containers. Air pipes and tubing as well as valves and compressors are made of commercial quality steel. The ductwork is fitted with safety devices to prevent explosions. After 1½ years of operation there are no signs of corrosion. The blowers are of the rotary piston type with an adjustable driving motor, which allows matching the air volume blown in or drawn off to the number of air pipes in operation. Each blower is designed for a maximum capacity of 2,000 m³/hour. The material in the biofilters is a combination of 4 different types of organic waste (bark, wood chips, raw compost, finished compost). The different materials are not mixed but are placed layer upon layer.

High methane peaks are recorded during the first 4 days after aeration begins. After 4 days the change from anaerobic to aerobic conditions within the area to be excavated is completed and emissions show greater uniformity.

The biofilters and the treated section of the waste disposal site are in an equilibrium with regard to the water balance: the water entrained is required to wet the biofilters; the high temperature inside the biofilters transforms the moisture into vapor and returns it to the waste disposal site. During 1 full year of operation it was not ever necessary to regulate the water content in the biofilters by external intervention, let alone change the filter media.

RESULTS OF MEASUREMENTS

The data shown below were obtained from measurements taken at the site of the Burghof demonstration project in the rural district of Ludwigsburg in southern Germany. This project involved restoration of an old 5 million m³ waste disposal site ("landfill-mining") where odor containment was a crucial requirement. Intensive scientific monitoring has yielded an abundance of data demonstrating the effectiveness of this biological stabilization process.

Odor Measurements

Regular odor measurements over 1 year based on the olfactometric principle of Verein Deutscher Ingenieure (VDI; a German standard) confirmed the effectiveness of the process. The results were compared against the odor emissions that occur when fresh residential waste is tipped. The mean values are shown in Table 1. The level of odor emissions (OE) caused by the excavation of old material was reduced dramatically after the treatment. Even after excavation and transportation to the treatment plant only slight odor emissions were recorded.

Emissions of Landfill Gas

The odor stabilization system is designed to achieve a drastic reduction of landfill gas concentrations in the exhaust air. Landfill gas concentrations were measured regularly with a flame ionization detector (FID) at the following emission sites: biofilter, area being excavated, and treatment plant. Table 2 shows these data.

Continuous measurements at the exhaust duct of the odor stabilization system and daily measurements at the biofilters clearly demonstrated that the methane peaks recorded at the exhaust were buffered or eliminated by the biofilters (see Figure 2). Methane emissions from the biofilters are continuous and uniform. Breakdown of filter action during or after placement of new air pipes has not been observed. This is explained first by the adequate dimensioning of the biofilters and then by the biological transformation processes that also occur in the biofilters, leading to a reduction of CH_4 emission to CO_2. This reduction is caused by the fast change in biological conditions in the site as illustrated by Figure 3.

TABLE 1. Results of odor measurement (mean values where OE is odor emissions).

Type of Measurement	Average Annual OE/m^3
Odor emitted by biofilter (when plant is not in operation)	30
Waste air from biofilter (plant in operation)	62
Excavation section 1 (right at the excavation site)	72
Excavation section 2 (area not being excavated at the time measurements were made)	74
For comparison: Fresh residential waste	3,264

TABLE 2. Data from measurements of landfill gas (with FID, mean values).

Type of Measurement	Landfill Gas Concentration in ppm
Exhaust air from biofilter	50
Area excavated	200
Treatment plant	70

Within just a few minutes methane and CO_2 concentrations decline while the oxygen content in the site's free pore volume rises.

Measurement of Microorganism Concentrations

Another objective in using odor stabilization systems is the reduction of microorganism emissions from the area excavated, which are believed to be caused by a reduction of biological activity in the waste disposal site. This is currently a subject of further research. Intensive microorganism measurements were carried out in August and September 1994, the mean values of which were compared against a control sample taken in woodland at a distance of about 300 m from the waste disposal site.

It can be seen that the concentrations of bacteria thriving under aerobic conditions and of fungi ranged between 10^2 and 10^3 KBE/m^3 of air (Table 3). Without

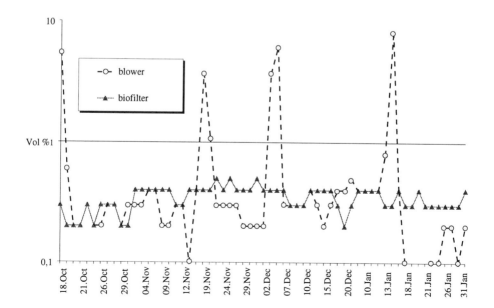

FIGURE 2. CH_4 concentrations October 1993 to January 1994.

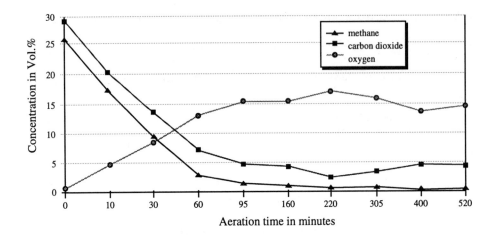

FIGURE 3. Change in landfill gas concentration in the site on aeration.

exception, the results are at very low levels and only slight differences were
found compared with the control sample. The expert opinion concludes that
workers at that site, with very high probability, are not exposed to higher microorganism concentrations than other workers employed in waste and recycling
operations.

SUMMARY

The odor stabilization system for waste disposal sites enables working in
contaminated areas after a short time and at low cost. Transformation of a waste

TABLE 3. Microorganism concentrations (mean values) in KBE (microorganism
concentration units)/m³ air.

Type of Microorganism	Control Sample	Area Excavated
Total number of germs		
Special impinger	3.3×10^2	6.5×10^3
RCS plus	7.8×10^2	1.1×10^3
Staphylococcus aureus	—	—
Anaerobic sporifers	—	—
Enterobacteriaceae	—	—
Total fungi		
Special impinger	6.8×10^2	2.4×10^3
RCS plus	7.9×10^2	2.2×10^3
Aspergillus fumigatus	—	6.8×10^2

disposal site from anaerobic conditions to aerobic conditions and the associated reduction of emissions (odor, methane, microorganisms) has been demonstrated successfully and continuously over almost two years of operation.

An international patent application for the process has been filed. The cost of treating excavated material for odor stabilization is approximately DM 2.20 (US$ 1.60) per m^3 of excavated material. This cost includes capital expenditure and operating costs as well as personnel and energy costs. This odor stabilization system is now a mandatory requirement prescribed by the German supervisory authorities for opening of waste disposal sites.

Cold Climate Bioventing with Soil Warming in Alaska

Gregory D. Sayles, Andrea Leeson, Robert E. Hinchee,
Catherine M. Vogel, Richard C. Brenner, and Ross N. Miller

ABSTRACT

In the heart of Alaska, a 3-year field study was conducted of bioventing in conjunction with several soil warming methods. The contamination was JP-4 jet fuel. The soil warming methods evaluated, chosen for their apparent low cost, were (1) application of warm water at a low rate, (2) enhanced solar warming by covering the surface with clear plastic in the summer and covering the surface with insulation in the winter, and (3) buried heat tape. The warm water and buried heat tape methods performed best, maintaining summer-like 10 to 20°C temperatures in the test plots year round, compared to the temperature of the unheated control plot, which dipped to −1°C in the winter. The solar/insulation warming method showed a modest improvement in temperature over the unheated control test plot. The annual average temperatures of the warm water, heat tape, solar, and control plots were 16.9, 14.5, 6.1, and 3.5°C, respectively. The biodegradation rates, measured by in situ respirometry, were higher in plots with higher temperatures and followed the Arrhenius relationship. Despite the low temperature, significant biodegradation was observed in the unheated plot during the winter.

MOTIVATION

Bioremediation in cold climates was shown to be feasible in several previous studies (e.g., Carss et al. 1994, Kellems & Hinchee 1994, and Reynolds et al. 1994). The bioventing process stimulates in situ bioremediation of contaminated unsaturated soil by supplying air, and thus oxygen, to oxygen-deprived soil microbes (Wilson & Ward 1986, Dupont et al. 1991, Hoeppel et al. 1991, Dupont 1993). The goal of bioventing is to supply the oxygen demand of the biodegradation process and to minimize volatilization of contaminants. Thus, air injection rates are relatively low, typically less than 1 pore volume per day. Previous studies have shown that in situ oxygen utilization rates measured during bioventing feasibility studies in cold climates could be as high as rates measured in moderate climates (Ong et al. 1994). Previous work (Miller et al. 1991) demonstrated that an Arrhenius relationship can describe the relationship between biodegradation rates associated with bioventing and soil temperature. Most shallow contaminated soils experience annual variations in temperature. The average rate of biodegradation from bioventing could, therefore, be increased if the average temperature of the soil was increased.

The goal of this study was to evaluate bioventing in a cold climate in conjunction with several low-intensity, low-cost soil warming methods. The soil warming methods were evaluated for their ability to maintain greater than average soil temperatures and rates of biodegradation due to bioventing relative to an unheated bioventing control. During the study, several updates of results were presented (Sayles et al. 1992, Leeson et al. 1993, Sayles et al. 1994). This paper covers the temperature and rate data from the entire study.

SITE DESCRIPTION

The test site was located at Eielson Air Force Base, near Fairbanks, Alaska, in a flat, open field adjacent to a JP-4 jet fuel storage and pump house (Site 20). At this location, groundwater is approximately 7 ft (2 m) below ground surface (bgs) and there is no permafrost. The area receives approximately 20 in. (51 cm) per year of precipitation, and the air temperature varies from −30 to 30°C with an average annual air temperature of approximately 0°C. Jet fuel contamination of the field presumably occurred via leaks in the underground fuel distribution piping that crosses the field. Soil characteristics prior to bioventing are summarized in Table 1. Soil gas measurements were taken at many locations and depths in July 1991. The low soil gas O_2 and high CO_2 concentrations measured indicated that the site was biologically active, but that the activity was oxygen limited. Thus, introducing air into the contaminated vadose zone would be beneficial.

TABLE 1. Initial (pre-venting) characteristics of Eielson AFB bioventing site.

Soil	
Total petroleum hydrocarbons[a]	0.2 - 5,100 mg/kg
Contaminated vadose zone interval	2 - 7 ft (water table)
Total Kjeldahl nitrogen	100 - 450 mg/kg
Total phosphorous	260 - 750 mg/kg
Soil Gas	
O_2	0 - 13%
CO_2	10 - 18%
Total volatile hydrocarbons	600 - 40,000 ppmv

(a) Measured as the sum of C-5 to C-15 hydrocarbons by purge-and-trap gas chromatography with a flame ionization detector.

The soil properties were measured from soil samples taken at many locations and depths during the bioventing system installation in August 1991.

METHODS

The test area was established by installing a relatively uniform distribution of vertical air injection wells and constructing four 50-ft (15-m)-square test plots within this test area. A plan view of the entire test system is shown in Figure 1, and a typical cross section of a test plot is shown in Figure 2. Three soil warming methods — application of warm water, enhanced solar warming, and buried heat tape — and an unheated control, were installed in separate test plots. The test plot designs, including warming methods, are summarized in Table 2. Except for the warm water plot, soil warming and bioventing were conducted in all test plots from the start date (Table 2) until July 1994. Bioventing continued in the

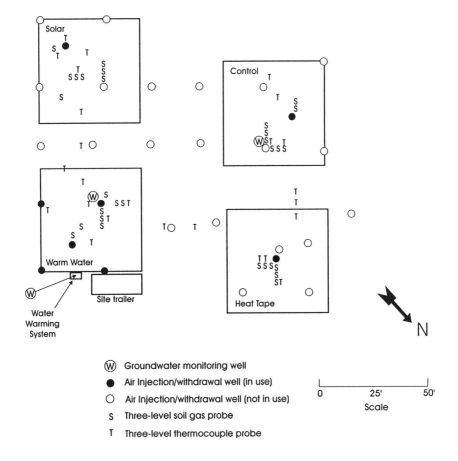

FIGURE 1. Plan view of the bioventing installation at Eielson AFB.

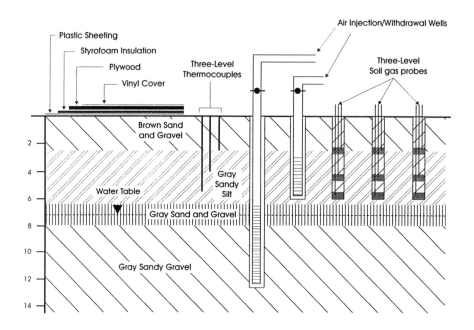

FIGURE 2. A characteristic cross section of a test plot. Soil warming mechanisms are not shown. The surface coverings shown do not apply to the control plot that had no covering or to the solar plot during spring through fall when it was covered with clear plastic.

warm water plot until July 1994, although soil warming was discontinued in July 1993. Thus, the warm water plot became another unheated control during its final year of operation.

Except for the warm water plot, the test plots required only one injection well in operation to meet oxygen demands. Five injection wells were used in the warm water plot to maintain adequate oxygen levels (Figure 1), apparently due to the excess water in the plot from warm water application. The initial air injection wells installed in August 1991 were screened from 3 to 6 ft (0.9 to 1.8 m) bgs (Figure 2). Additional air injection wells were installed in September 1992, screened from 6.5 to 13 ft (2 to 4 m) bgs, to aerate the capillary fringe where most of the contamination was found. The wells near the center of each plot (Figure 1) were installed in 1991. The wells indicated as "in use" in the solar, control, and heat tape plots were installed in 1992. The well in use in the center of the collection of wells in the warm water plot was installed in 1992; the others were installed in 1991. The total (site) air injection rate was approximately 25 ft³ (0.7 m³)/min.

Soil gas composition and soil temperature were monitored regularly. Three-level soil gas monitoring points were distributed throughout the plots (Figures 1 and 2). Soil gas was sampled weekly and its composition (O_2, CO_2, and total volatile hydrocarbons) was measured with portable GasTech analyzers. At various locations (Figures 1 and 2), three-level temperature probes (3 thermocouples)

TABLE 2. Test plot designs and soil warming start and end dates (all bioventing ended in July 1994).

Name	Soil Warming Design	Estimated Heating Rate	Start Date	Heating End Date
Warm water	Groundwater was pumped through an underground in-line heater then onto the plot through a closed loop of soaker hoses. The hoses were buried 2.5 ft (0.8 m) below ground surface in drainage tile in parallel ditches 10 ft (3 m) apart. Approximately 1 gal (3.8 L)/min was pumped and applied at approximately 35°C.	170 W/plot = 0.07 W/ft^2 (0.09 m^2)-plot	Sept. 1991	July 1993
Solar	Clear plastic was placed across the entire surface of the plot, spring through fall, and replaced with insulation, fall through spring (Figure 2).	Unknown	Sept. 1991	July 1994
Heat tape	Heat tape was buried 3 ft (0.9 m) below ground surface in parallel trenches 5 ft (1.5 m) apart.	6 W/ft-tape = 2,580 W/plot = 1.0 W/ft^2 (0.09 m^2)-plot	Sept. 1992	July 1994
Control	No warming.	None	Sept. 1991	N/A

were installed to monitor soil temperature as a function of warming method, position, and time. Typically, temperatures were noted every 2 days.

Approximately quarterly, an in situ respiration test (Ong et al. 1991) was conducted to determine the O_2 utilization rate at each soil gas monitoring point. The rate of oxygen use (%/h) was converted into an estimated rate of petroleum degradation (mg hexane/kg soil/day) by assuming a stoichiometry of biodegradation (Leeson et al. 1993). Thus, the instantaneous rate of biodegradation was measured as a function of warming method, position, and time.

An uncontaminated area northeast of the site was used to measure background soil temperature and in situ respiration rates. The respiration rate measured in the background area, i.e., the intrinsic oxygen use rate of the site soil, was insignificant.

RESULTS AND DISCUSSION

During blower operation, air injection provided adequate soil gas oxygen levels at virtually all times. Average oxygen levels in all plots were almost always >12% and always above 8%. All of these levels should not have limited the rate of microbial activity.

Two of the soil warming methods had a strong influence on soil temperature. Figure 3 displays the average temperature of each plot and at an uncontaminated background location as a function of time during the study. The average temperature of a test plot was calculated as the arithmetic mean of the temperatures measured from all the thermocouples in the test plot. The temperature of the warm water plot was maintained in the range of 10 to 25°C (mostly 15 to 20°C) compared to the contaminated (unheated) control plot where the minimum winter temperature was roughly 0°C. The annual averaged temperatures of the warm water plot and the unheated control plot were 16.9 and 3.5°C, respectively. When heating the warm water plot was terminated in July 1993, its temperature followed the temperature of the unheated control plot closely, as expected.

Heating by buried heat tape (heat tape plot) was successful at maintaining the average temperature between 10 and 22°C year round. The maximum temperature achieved in this plot in the summer was about 8°C higher than that maintained in the winter because, although the heat input was constant, the ambient temperature was much higher in the summer. The annual average temperature of the plot was 14.5°C.

The impact of the solar heating strategy on soil temperature was not as dramatic. The average temperature as a function of time of the solar plot roughly mimicked the temperature of the contaminated control plot. However, during the summer of 1992, the solar plot was roughly 5°C warmer than the control plot, and in the early summer of 1992 and 1993, the plot warmed up several weeks earlier than the control plot. The insulation applied during the winter was marginally successful at best, providing a 1 to 2°C temperature elevation in the solar plot relative to the control plot. The annual average of the temperature of the solar heated plot was 6.1°C.

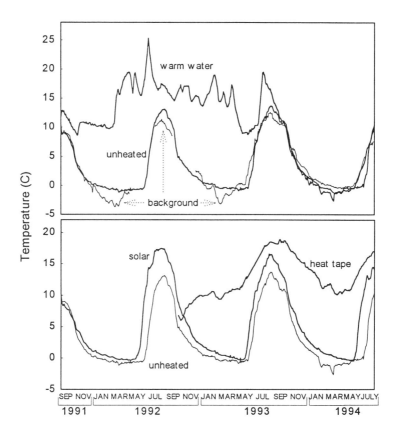

FIGURE 3. Average temperature of each test plot and uncontaminated background location versus time.

Although the unheated control plot was somewhat warmer than the uncontaminated background in the first two winters (Figure 3), the annual average temperatures of the two sites were roughly equal at 3.5°C.

The instantaneous average rates of biodegradation in each plot seem to reflect their respective average temperatures. The average rate in a test plot was calculated as the arithmetic mean of the rates measured by in situ respirometry using all soil gas monitoring points in the test plot. The average rate in each plot as a function of time is shown in Figure 4. The warm water and heat tape plots maintained rates 2 to 3 times greater than the unheated control plot year round. The small difference in temperature between the solar and the control plots (see Figure 3) was reflected in the small difference in the respective rates measured in these plots. Rates in the heat tape plot during 1994 could not be measured because of high moisture levels in the vadose zone of that plot.

It is commonly believed that bioremediation systems should be shut down for the winter in any cold climate because it is assumed that microbial activity becomes insignificant at these low temperatures. However, the rate was greater

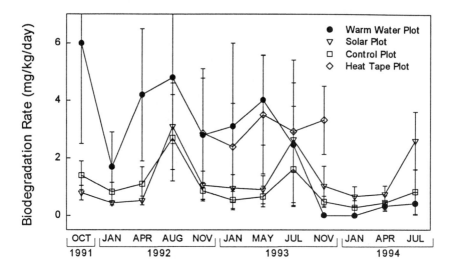

FIGURE 4. Average rate of biodegradation, as measured by in situ respirometry, of each plot versus time. Error bars represent one standard deviation.

than zero in the unheated control plot (roughly 0.5 mg/kg/day) in the middle
of the winters of 1992 and 1993 when the average temperature of the plot was
roughly 0°C (Figure 3). This rate is not insignificant. For example, assuming
that the above rate applies for November through April each year, as observed,
operating the system during this time allows the additional degradation of over
90 mg/kg/year relative to shutting the system down.

In the winter of 1993-4, after heating the warm water plot was discontinued,
the rate observed in the plot was practically zero (Figure 4). Apparently, the
character of the soil microbial consortia in that plot had changed during the
2 years of continuous warm temperatures to one that was no longer active at
temperatures near 0°C. During the warm months, the rate of this plot was similar
to others plots of similar temperature.

If the rates of biodegradation attained in the test plots are truly temperature
dependent (and the temperatures are not near the temperature associated with
the microbial maximum growth rate), then the relationship between rate and
temperature should be described by the Arrhenius equation (Fried et al. 1977).
Using the data from Figures 3 and 4, an Arrhenius plot was constructed by
plotting the logarithm of the average rate versus inverse average temperature
(Figure 5). Although there is considerable scatter in the data, a linear relationship
with negative slope is apparent. Thus, higher temperatures did indeed provide
higher rates. A least-squares fit of the data in Figure 5 yields the following rate
versus temperature model:

$$\text{Rate (mg/kg/day)} = 4.1 \times 10^{12} e^{-8100/T}$$

where temperature T is in units of Kelvin. This model is consistent with that of an earlier bioventing field study (Miller et al. 1991).

CONCLUSIONS

The application of warm water at a low rate and the use of buried heat tape were the most successful methods of soil warming evaluated. The temperature of the plot with solar warming in the summer and insulation in the winter was modestly higher than the unheated control. This positive, though humble, result obtained using the solar/insulation approach is nonetheless encouraging for application of this strategy in cold climates at lower latitudes where the flux of sunlight is higher. The elevated temperatures observed in the heated plots resulted in higher oxygen uptake/biodegradation rates. Although the rates were higher in the warmer plots, the rate obtained in the unheated control plot was significant, even in the winter.

ACKNOWLEDGMENTS

This work was funded in part by the U.S. Environmental Protection Agency Bioremediation Field Initiative, the U.S. Air Force Armstrong Laboratory, the U.S. Air Force Center for Environmental Excellence, and Eielson Air Force Base.

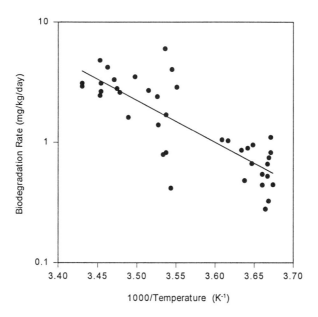

FIGURE 5. Arrhenius plot of the logarithm of rate versus inverse temperature. The line is a linear regression fit of the data ($r^2 = 0.7$).

REFERENCES

Carss, J. G., J. G. Agar, and G. E. Surbey. 1994. "In-Situ Bioremediation in Arctic Canada."
In R. E. Hinchee, B. C. Alleman, R. E. Hoeppel, and R. N. Miller (Eds.), *Hydrocarbon Bio-remediation*, pp. 323-328. Lewis Publishers, Boca Raton, FL.

Dupont, R. R. 1993. "Fundamentals of Bioventing Applied to Fuel Contaminated Sites."
Environ. Prog. 12(1):45-53.

Dupont, R. R., W. J. Doucette, and R. E. Hinchee. 1991. "Assessment of *In Situ* Bioremediation
Potential and the Application of Bioventing at a Fuel-Contaminated Site." In R. E. Hinchee
and R. F. Olfenbuttel (Eds.), *In-Situ Bioreclamation*, pp. 262-282. Butterworth-Heinemann,
Stoneham, MA.

Fried, V., H. F. Hameka, and U. Blukis. 1977. *Physical Chemistry*, pp. 640-643. Macmillan
Publishing Co., Inc., New York, NY.

Hoeppel, R. E., R. E. Hinchee, and M. F. Arthur. 1991. "Bioventing Soils Contaminated with
Petroleum Hydrocarbons." *J. Indust. Microbiol.* 8: 141.

Kellems, B. L., and R. E. Hinchee. 1994. "Review of Bioremediation Experience in Alaska."
In R. E. Hinchee, B. C. Alleman, R. E. Hoeppel, and R. N. Miller (Eds.), *Hydrocarbon Bio-remediation*, pp. 438-443. Lewis Publishers, Boca Raton, FL.

Leeson, A., R. E. Hinchee, J. Kittel, G. Sayles, C. M. Vogel, and R. N. Miller. 1993. "Optimizing
Bioventing in Shallow Vadose Zones and Cold Climates." *Hydrological Sci.* 38(4): 283-295.

Miller, R. N., R. E. Hinchee, and C. M. Vogel. 1991. "A Field-Scale Investigation of Petroleum
Hydrocarbon Biodegradation in the Vadose Zone Enhanced by Soil Venting at Tyndall
AFB, Florida." In R. E. Hinchee and R. F. Olfenbuttel (Eds.), *In-Situ Bioreclamation*, pp.
283-302. Butterworth-Heinemann, Stoneham, MA.

Ong, S. K., R. E. Hinchee, R. Hoeppel, and R. Schultz. 1991. "In-Situ Respirometry for Deter-mining
Aerobic Degradation Rates." In R. E. Hinchee and R. F. Olfenbuttel (Eds.), *In-Situ
Bioreclamation*, pp. 541-545. Butterworth-Heinemann, Stoneham, MA.

Ong, S. K., A. Leeson, R. E. Hinchee, J. Kittel, C. M. Vogel, G. D. Sayles, and R. N. Miller.
1994. "Cold Climate Applications of Bioventing." In R. E. Hinchee, B. C. Alleman, R. E.
Hoeppel, and R. N. Miller (Eds.), *Hydrocarbon Bioremediation*, pp. 444-453. Lewis Publishers,
Boca Raton, FL.

Reynolds, C. M., M. D. Travis, W. A. Braley, and R. J. Scholze. 1994. "Applying Field-Experi-ment
Bioreactors and Landfarming in Alaskan Climates." In R. E. Hinchee, B. C. Alleman,
R. E. Hoeppel, and R. N. Miller (Eds.), *Hydrocarbon Bioremediation*, pp. 100-106. Lewis
Publishers, Boca Raton, FL.

Sayles, G. D., A. Leeson, R. E. Hinchee, R. C. Brenner, C. M. Vogel, and R. N. Miller. 1992.
"In-Situ Bioventing: Two U.S. EPA and Air Force Sponsored Studies." *In-Situ Treatment of
Contaminated Soil and Water*, pp. 207-216. Air and Waste Management Association,
Pittsburgh, PA.

Sayles, G. D., A. Leeson, R. E. Hinchee, R. C. Brenner, C. M. Vogel, and R. N. Miller. 1994.
"Bioventing of Jet Fuel Spills 1: Bioventing in a Cold Climate with Soil Warming at Eielson
AFB, Alaska." *Symposium on Bioremediation of Hazardous Wastes: Research, Development and
Field Evaluations*, pp. 15-21. U.S. Environmental Protection Agency, EPA/600/R-94/075.

Wilson, J. T., and C. H. Ward. 1986. "Opportunities for Bioremediation of Aquifers Con-taminated
With Petroleum Hydrocarbons." *J. Indust. Microbiol* 27:109-116.

Effects of Flowrate and Temperature During Bioventing in Cold Climates

Brent J. Moore, James E. Armstrong,
Jim Barker, and Paul E. Hardisty

ABSTRACT

A bioventing project was performed at a natural gas processing plant site in west central Alberta, where a light, nonaqueous-phase liquid (LNAPL) plume of natural gas condensate covers an area of approximately 65,000 m². Bioventing was tested in two phases using an existing soil vapor extraction (SVE) installation. The first phase was a flowrate variation test, during August 1993 to November 1993. The blower extraction rate was varied to determine the optimum air extraction rate at which biodegradation was maintained and volatilization was minimized, in order to reduce potential off-gas treatment costs. At the lowest extraction rate of 24 L/s the hydrocarbon mass removed due to biodegradation was 50 kg/day, with only 4 kg/day of extracted off-gas. The second phase of the test consisted of respiration testing from December 1993 to May 1994 to monitor biodegradation rates during winter. It is widely believed that biodegradation rates drop at low temperatures. However, the biodegradation rate was relatively high during the winter, averaging 20 mg of hydrocarbon/kg of soil per day, at in situ temperatures of 5 to 8°C.

INTRODUCTION

A field study was conducted to demonstrate the application of bioventing to clean up vadose zone contamination by natural gas condensate. Bioventing is a technology which supplies oxygen to naturally occurring bacteria within contaminated soils in the unsaturated zone. Bacteria consume oxygen during aerobic biodegradation, while degrading the residual hydrocarbons into CO_2 and water. Oxygen can be supplied either through vapor extraction or air injection. The advantage of vapor extraction over air injection bioventing is that air injection bioventing may force hydrocarbon vapors into adjacent property. However, the off-gases may require treatment prior to atmospheric release, which can be costly.

The major goal of the study was to investigate the applicability of bioventing as a year-round remediation technique in a northern climate. It is generally believed that biodegradation is limited at low temperatures. However, at Strachan the yearly temperature range is small, ranging from approximately 5 to 10°C. Because biodegradation was observed during the summer at Strachan, the small annual temperature range at the site indicated that winter biodegradation rates should also be significant. The biodegradation rate was monitored for 5 months during winter to observe low-temperature effects.

A second goal was to determine the optimum air extraction rate at which biodegradation could be maintained and off-gas hydrocarbons extracted to the atmosphere minimized. A flowrate variation test was conducted to observe the effects of variable air extraction on biodegradation and volatilization.

BACKGROUND

The site is located at the Gulf Strachan Gas Plant, which is 200 km northwest of Calgary, Alberta, Canada. The main contamination at the plant is a free-phase natural gas condensate plume estimated to cover an area of 65,000 m². Natural gas condensate is the portion of gas at reservoir temperature and pressure which reverts to a liquid upon production. Condensate at this facility is composed mainly of light hydrocarbons (C_5 to C_{12}), but may contain some C_{12} to C_{22} components. The plume and selected wells within the 11,000 m² test area are shown in Figure 1.

In the study area, the Quaternary sediments comprise 2 to 2.5 m of clayey silt till deposited above 8 m of glaciofluvial sand and cobbley gravel. The groundwater surface generally lies around 7 to 8 m below ground. Seasonal groundwater surface fluctuations have resulted in smearing of the condensate, so that much of the original contaminant volume has been trapped as residual saturation over an approximate 1 m thickness in the unsaturated zone. This trapped condensate is the contaminant source targeted by the bioventing program. Details of the contaminant situation and bioventing program are given in CAPP (1994) and Hardisty et al. (1994).

FLOWRATE VARIATION TEST

The first bioventing experiment involved operating a vapor extraction blower at four different flowrates over a 4-month period. The goal was to determine if the air flowrate could be optimized to sustain a high rate of biodegradation while minimizing volatilization. During the test the O_2 and CO_2 concentrations were monitored in the extraction well and at four monitoring wells as biodegradation indicators. Volatilization was monitored by measuring the effluent hydrocarbon concentration. After operating the blower at 350 L/s for 3 days to fully aerate the subsurface, the blower extraction rate was set at 118 L/s flowrate for 7 days, 76 L/s for 23 days, 42 L/s for 27 days, and then reduced to 24 L/s for 63 days.

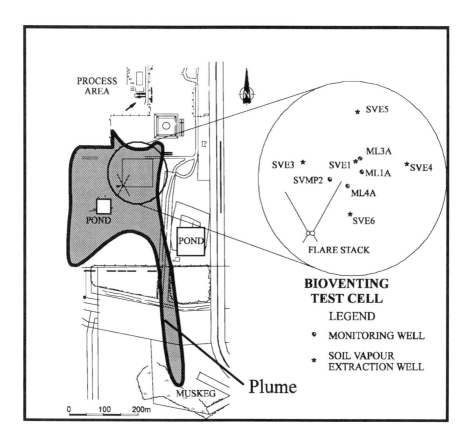

FIGURE 1. Bioventing test cell.

Observations

Following an initial drop from 21% O_2 at the beginning of the test, the O_2 concentrations at the extraction well remained relatively consistent throughout the test, near 15%. The CO_2 concentrations rose from near 0% at the test beginning, and stayed near 5% throughout. The hydrocarbon concentrations in the extracted vapors were variable, and dropped from 800 to 550 ppm during the test.

As the air flowrate was reduced, the rate of mass removal due to biodegradation rate dropped from approximately 210 kg/day to 51 kg/day, and the rate of mass removal due to volatilization dropped from 25 to 4 kg/day (Table 1). However, the proportion of mass removed due to biodegradation increased relative to volatilization by approximately 33%. Therefore, significant mass removal rates were observed while maintaining a low level of off-gas output, minimizing the need for off-gas treatment.

Biodegradation mass removal was calculated by assuming that the difference between the off-gas O_2 concentration and the background O_2 levels (approximately 20%) was due to oxygen depletion during biodegradation. The observed drop in

TABLE 1. Hydrocarbon mass removal during bioventing from SVE-1.

Flow-rate, (L/s)	Duration (days)	O_2 in Effluent (%)	Average Hydrocarbon Concentration (ppmv)	Removal by Volatilization		Removal by Biodegradation	
				Rate (kg/day)	Total (kg)	Rate (kg/day)	Total (kg)
118	7	15	800	25	170	210	1,500
76	23	13	900	21	490	188	4,300
42	27	13	700	6	240	104	2,800
24	63	14	550	4	250	51	3,200
					1,150		11,800

O_2 concentration in the extraction well (SVE-1) was converted to a mass of O_2, and multiplied by the air extraction rate. It was assumed that for every 3.5 g of O_2 consumed, 1 g of hydrocarbon is biodegraded (Hinchee and Miller 1992). The volatilized mass was calculated from the extraction rate multiplied by the average off-gas concentration. Overall, it is estimated that approximately 1,150 kg of condensate were removed by volatilization during the 4-month experiment, compared to 11,800 kg removed by biodegradation.

The steady O_2 concentrations at the extraction well indicated that reducing the air extraction rate did not affect the in situ oxygen concentrations. This may be due to the fact that the extraction well is extracting soil vapor from both contaminated and uncontaminated soils. However, the monitoring well data indicate that oxygen concentrations within the zone of residual contamination were actually much lower than the concentrations observed in the effluent. A plot of the O_2, CO_2, and hydrocarbon variations over time in the monitoring well with the greatest response, ML-4A, is shown in Figure 2. During the lower flowrates of the third and fourth stages, the O_2 concentrations were approximately 4%, which were beginning to approach anaerobic conditions (<2% oxygen). These results show the importance of monitoring well data in addition to monitoring the SVE effluent.

Figure 2 also shows that CO_2 concentrations were inversely related to the O_2 concentrations, rising from near zero at the beginning of the first stage to a high of approximately 15% during the fourth stage of the test. The hydrocarbon concentrations were dynamic, ranging from 2,000 to 5,000 ppmv. An unexpected sharp rise in hydrocarbon concentration occurred near the end of the test, which may be due to a slug of hydrocarbon vapor moving through the monitoring well area. Possible toxic effects to the bacteria from the higher hydrocarbon concentrations may possibly explain the rise in O_2 and drop in CO_2 which followed the appearance of the slug.

RESPIRATION TESTING

Until very recently, it was commonly believed that biodegradation did not occur at low temperatures. Recent work by Ong et al. (1994) shows that appreciable biodegradation rates have been observed in Alaska, as high as 10 mg/kg per day. To the author's knowledge, no studies have ever been conducted on cold weather bioventing in Canada. To observe the effect of a decreasing subsurface temperature on the biodegradation rate, 12 respiration tests were run during the winter. A respiration test has two parts: an aeration period, during which the soil O_2 and CO_2 concentrations are brought to atmospheric levels (approximately 21 and 0.03%, respectively), followed by a blower shutdown period. In the latter period, biodegradation causes the O_2 concentrations to diminish, and the CO_2 concentrations to increase. The rates at which the O_2 and CO_2 concentrations change are used to infer the rate of biodegradation.

Biodegradation Rates

The biodegradation rate during respiration testing was calculated by converting the rate of O_2 consumption following blower shutdown. At the more highly contaminated monitoring wells, an O_2 consumption of 10% in two hours was commonly observed throughout the winter. Using the calculation method described by Miller et al. (1993) and others, the average rate of biodegradation ranged from 3 to 39 mg hydrocarbon/kg of soil per day at the four different monitored wells (Armstrong et al. 1994). The variability in biodegradation rates appears to result from a large range in the in situ hydrocarbon concentrations.

Using conservative estimates of the radius of soil vapor extraction influence (45 m) and thickness of contamination (1 m), and an estimated average

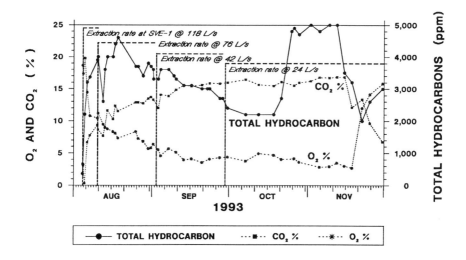

FIGURE 2. O_2, CO_2, and hydrocarbon variations over time in ML-4A.

biodegradation rate of 20 mg/kg per day, a biodegradation removal rate of 190 kg of hydrocarbon per day was calculated.

The winter mass removal rate is similar to the August 1993 mass removal rate of approximately 200 kg/day due to biodegradation. This was expected, as the August 1993 in situ temperature was also similar, about 8°C.

Effect of Temperature on Biodegradation Rate

The rate of biodegradation did not appear to be limited by the relatively low in situ temperatures, which ranged from 8 to 5°C (Figure 3). Atmospheric air temperatures at the site dropped as low as −35°C over the same time. A direct relationship between in situ temperature and biodegradation rate was not observed. As the temperature began to rise toward the end of the test, the bio-degradation rate continued to drop. This drop was likely due to a depletion of the residual source hydrocarbons because the biodegradation rate has continued to drop through early 1995, despite relatively constant temperatures.

SUMMARY AND CONCLUSIONS

Bioventing was shown to be capable of removing hydrocarbon mass from the unsaturated zone at rates as high as 200 kg/day. This mass removal rate was observed during both active bioventing in August 1993, and during respiration testing from December 1993 to May 1994. Biodegradation rates were observed to

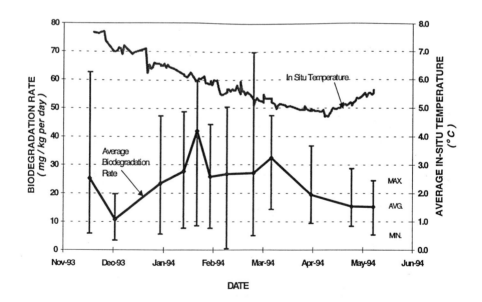

FIGURE 3. Biodegradation rate and in situ temperature over time.

remain consistently high throughout the winter, averaging approximately 20 mg/kg per day, at in situ temperatures between 5 to 8°C. By comparison, Ong et al. (1994) report that average biodegradation rates at warmer sites in Nevada and Florida, were 4.8 and 8.0 mg/kg per day, respectively.

The reason for the rapid biodegradation at Strachan at relatively low temperatures is not clear. A possible explanation is that the bacterial population may be acclimated to the small range of temperature which occurs at the depth of contamination. Further study is needed in this area.

The air extraction test showed that at a low extraction flowrate of 24 L/s, a significant hydrocarbon mass removal rate due to biodegradation was observed (50 kg/day). At the same flowrate, only 4 kg/day of hydrocarbon was off-gassed. Therefore bioventing can be used with vapor extraction (as an alternative to air injection bioventing) while requiring minimal off-gas treatment, thereby reducing operating costs.

REFERENCES

Armstrong, J. E., B. J. Moore, P. E. Hardisty, V. Kuhnel, and D. Stepan. 1994. "A Field Study of Soil Vapour Extraction and Bioventing." In *Proceedings of the GASReP Symposium of Groundwater and Soil Remediation.* Calgary, Alberta, Canada.

Canadian Association of Petroleum Producers (CAPP). 1994. "Soil Vapour Extraction and Bioventing Program Summary Report: 1993 to Spring 1994." Unpublished report prepared by Komex International Limited, June 1994.

Hardisty, P. E., D. Stepan, and D. Anderson. 1994. "Demonstration of Subsurface Remedial Technologies for Gas Industry Contamination." *Proceedings WEF Conference on Innovative Solutions for Contaminated Sites,* Miami, March 1994.

Hinchee, R. E. and R. N. Miller. 1992. "Bioventing for In Situ Remediation of Petroleum Hydrocarbons." *Proceedings of Bioventing and Vapor Extraction: Uses and Applications in Remediation Operations.* Air and Waste Management Association. Satellite Seminar, April, pp. 37-48.

Miller, R. N., D. D. Downey, V. A. Carmen, R. E. Hinchee, and A. Leeson. 1993. "A Summary of Bioventing Performance at Multiple Air Force Sites." *Proceedings of the 1993 Petroleum Hydrocarbons and Organic Chemicals in Ground Water: Prevention, Detection, and Restoration,* Houston, TX.

Ong, S. K., A. Leeson, R. E. Hinchee, J. Kittel, C. M. Vogel, G. D. Sayles, and R. E. Miller. 1994. "Cold Climate Applications of Bioventing," In R. E. Hinchee, B. C. Alleman, R. E. Hoeppel and R. E. Miller (Eds.), *Hydrocarbon Remediation.* Lewis Publishers, Ann Arbor, MI. pp. 444-453.

The Influence of Temperature on Bioventing

Thomas J. Simpkin, Gar Carothers, Roderick W. Hoffman, Robert Elder, and Bryan F. Collver

ABSTRACT

This paper discusses 2 years of operations of a full-scale bioventing demonstration system on a manmade gravel pad on the North Slope of Alaska. The pad was contaminated primarily with diesel fuel. The relationship between biodegradation rates and temperature are the focus of the paper. The North Slope gravel pad was thawed from the end of June to about the end of September. Even during the thawed period, soil temperatures were low, peaking at 7°C in mid July to early August. Despite the low temperatures, relatively high rates of microbial respiration were measured; typically in the range of 3 to 10% O_2/day, but as high as 28% O_2/day. Respiration rates varied over the summer and appeared to be influenced by the pad temperature. With the exception of the respiration rates measured early in the summer, the relationship of rate and temperature appeared to follow the Phelps temperature/rate expression. The rates measured early in the summer were typically greater than predicted by the Phelps expression.

INTRODUCTION

Past operations of petroleum production facilities on the North Slope of Alaska have, in some instances, resulted in the hydrocarbon contamination of gravel pad soils. Bioventing is one potential remediation alternative for these gravel pads. A full-scale bioventing demonstration system has been installed at one such gravel pad to evaluate the applicability of bioventing and to initiate pad remediation.

Unique site conditions, including a shallow gravel pad, a short remediation season, and low remediation season temperatures created engineering challenges for the application of bioventing. The gravel pad at this site is composed of pit-run gravel (sand and gravel alluvium with approximately 10% fines). The pad varies in thickness from 0.9 to 1.5 m. It is elevated slightly above most of the surrounding terrain so that it drains relatively well. However, after snow melt or rainfall, low spots on the pad may accumulate water and increase the water content of the soils to above saturation.

It is believed that handling fuels resulted in contamination of the pad with, primarily, diesel fuel. The total petroleum hydrocarbons (TPH) (by EPA method 418.1) of soil samples from the pad ranged up to 12,000 milligrams per kilogram (mg/kg) (dry weight of soil), with most of the samples collected during bioventing well installation ranging from 1,000 to 8,000 mg/kg. The diesel range organic hydrocarbons (by EPA method 8100M) were in a similar range.

A bioventing pilot study was conducted during the summer of 1992. Based on the favorable results of this study, a full-scale bioventing system was installed in 1993 and was expanded in 1994.

METHODS

The bioventing system consisted of a series of shallow bioventing wells connected to a central blower skid. The bioventing wells were spaced at 7.6 m, with an expected radius of influence of about 4.5 m. Fourteen wells were installed in 1993 with an additional nine wells in 1994. Each bioventing well was connected directly to two regenerative blowers using ¾-inch reinforced plastic tubing. Air flow rates to the wells ranged from 0.62 to 0.85 L/s. Figure 1 presents a typical bioventing well installation. Both extraction and injection wells were used for this application. The original intent was to try to improve airflow distribution in the subsurface by using coupled air injection and extraction. However, because of the presence of water in the pad, the extraction wells were placed in areas that had significant water in an attempt to assist in drying the pad. The extraction wells were connected to 55-gal (208-L) knockout drums.

A total of 25 monitoring points were installed by the end of the 1994 season to evaluate the distribution of oxygen in the subsurface and the microbial respiration rate. Monitoring points consisted of hand-driven, 0.10-m-long KVA shield points, connected to 3/16-inch tubing and placed 0.76 m below grade. Three thermistors were installed throughout the pad at a depth of 0.76 m below grade in 1-in. (2.5 cm) polyvinyl chloride (PVC) pipes. Soil temperature was recorded using a multimeter to measure the resistance at the thermistor leads.

The system began operation on June 26, 1993 and continued until October 1, 1993. Operations were restarted July 9, 1994, and continued until September 9, 1994. Operations were discontinued twice because of excessive water in the pad. For example, in August of 1994, significant rains resulted in ponding of water in some locations and a high water content in the pad. Airflow stopped in a number of wells, and water production greater than the capacity of the knock out drums occurred in others.

System monitoring consisted of periodically measuring pressure and flow at each well head, pressure and soil gas oxygen at each monitoring point, and soil temperature. Respiration rate tests were performed 4 to 5 times each season on a limited number (between 4 and 12) of monitoring points. Oxygen was measured using a GasTech Model 1314 SMPN gas analyzer. Respiration rate test

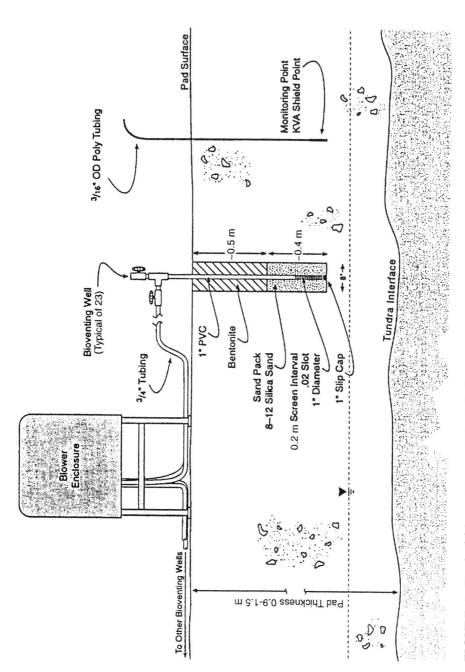

FIGURE 1. Typical bioventing well installation.

procedures were consistent with those provided by Hinchee and Ong (1992). Injection of air was stopped and the oxygen content in a select number of monitoring points was measured periodically over a period of 2 to 3 days. At least five data points were collected. The rate was determined by linear regression of the oxygen concentration with time.

RESULTS

The average pad temperature in the three thermistors placed at 0.76 m below grade over the two summers is shown in Figure 2. The temperature started to climb above freezing in mid June and peaked between 5 and 7°C in mid July to early August. From early August to the end of September, the temperature dropped steadily.

Respiration rates measured in the pads exhibited significant spatial variability. The rates varied from a high of 28% O_2/day to a low of about 1% O_2/day. On one test day (August 3, 1994), the respiration rates varied from 1 to 9.6% O_2/day. Variation may be due, in part, to contaminant concentrations, although the correlation is not very good (see Figure 3).

The respiration rates measured over the two seasons are presented in Figure 4 for four monitoring points. In general, the respiration rates followed the same pattern as the average pad temperature. However, there were a number of outliers, especially early in the season.

From plots such as Figure 2, it appears that the respiration rate is related to temperature. To further evaluate the relationship between respiration rate and temperature, the Phelps equation was used (Grady and Lim 1980):

$$R_t = R_7 \times \theta^{(t-7)} \qquad (1)$$

where R_t = Rate at temperature t
       R_7 = Rate at 7°C
       θ = Thermal coefficient

This type of expression is often used to define biological treatment processes. The values of R_7 and θ were determined by plotting (t–7) versus log (R_t) and calculating a linear regression using data from four monitoring points that had sufficient data (7 or more readings) from 1993 and 1994. Figure 5 is the plot for Monitoring Point 3 along with the linear regression line. The value of R_7 ranged from 10.0 to 14.9, with an average of 12.4. A rate at 7°C was selected rather than the more standard 20°C because 20°C is out of the range of these data. Values of θ ranged from 1.16 to 1.28 with an average of 1.23.

Figure 6 is a plot of this expression with the average value θ and the average, minimum, and maximum values of R_7. The actual data from Monitoring Point 3 are shown on this figure. Most of the data from Monitoring Point 7 fit the expression fairly well. There do appear to be a number of outliers that have rates greater than predicted by these expressions. These outliers were all from early

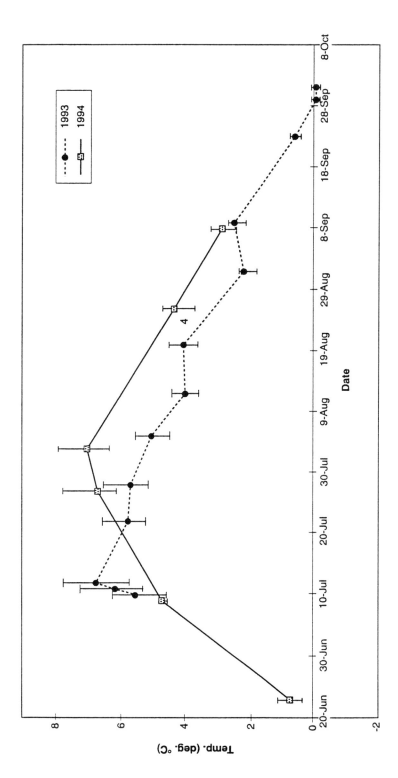

FIGURE 2. 1993 and 1994 gravel pad temperatures at 2.5 ft (0.76 m) below grade.

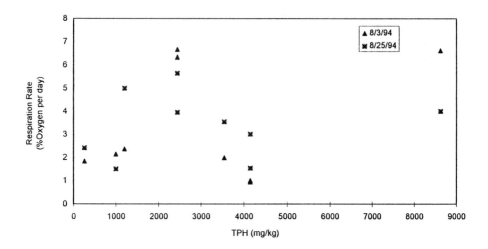

FIGURE 3. 1994 respiration rate versus TPH.

in the season (before July 12). It is unclear why the rates from early in the season are higher than expected, but it may be related to the altered metabolic activity of the microorganisms soon after they thaw.

Other factors, such as nutrient levels, moisture, and microbial population makeup and mass, may have also have impacted the observed respiration rates

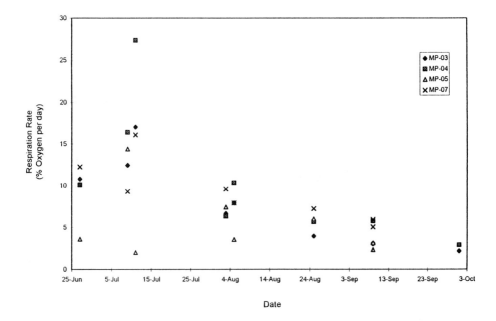

FIGURE 4. Respiration rates for 1994 in four monitoring points.

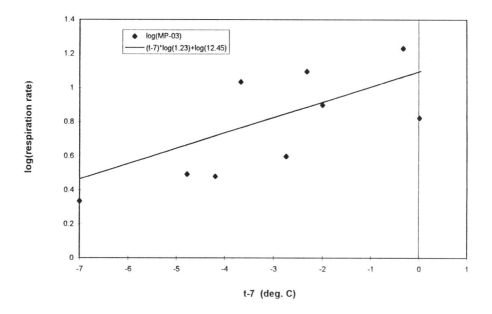

FIGURE 5. **Log temperature model (MP-03).**

and may explain part of the variations observed. Data may be collected in subsequent years to evaluate these factors.

DISCUSSION

The relationship between temperature and respiration rate can be used to estimate the benefit of soil heating. For soils in the area of MP03, it appears that an average respiration rate of about 6.5% O_2/day would be obtained without heating. This is equivalent to a hydrocarbon biodegradation rate of 5.2 mg/kg/day (assuming hexane equivalence, Hinchee and Ong 1992). Over a 90-day summer season, about 468 mg/kg of hydrocarbon would be degraded each year. Consequently, it may take 5 years to completely biodegrade 2,500 mg/kg of contamination. If the soil could be warmed to a constant temperature of 10°C, the respiration rate is predicted to be 23% O_2/day, using the temperature/rate expression above. Over 90 days, 1,600 mg/kg of hydrocarbon would be biodegraded at this temperature, so that it would take 2 years to completely biodegrade 2,500 mg/kg. This is a significant increase in the amount of hydrocarbon removed each year. However, it could be difficult and expensive to achieve such a temperature increase. If a constant increase in temperature of 2°C could be achieved with a low-cost, passive solar warming system, an additional 380 mg/kg of contamination could be biodegraded each year. A more in-depth evaluation of the cost of warming the soil versus the benefits of decreasing the remediation period must

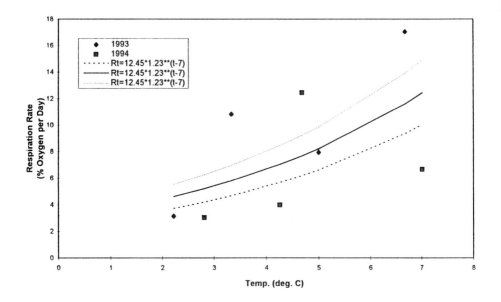

FIGURE 6.   Temperature and respiration rates, MP-03 and temperature relationship.

be performed to justify the expense of soil warming. As long as North Slope pads are being operated for oil production, remediation periods of up to 5 years are acceptable.

REFERENCES

Grady, C.P.L., and C. Lim. 1980. *Biological Wastewater Treatment.* Marcel Dekker, Inc., New York, NY.

Hinchee, R. E., and S. K. Ong. 1992. "A Rapid In Situ Respiration Test for Measuring Aerobic Biodegradation Rates of Hydrocarbons in Soil." *J. Air and Waste Manage. Assoc.* 42(10): 1305-1312.

Effects of Soil Moisture on Biodegradation of Petroleum Hydrocarbons

Hoi-Ying Holman and Yvonne W. Tsang

ABSTRACT

Soil water content has been shown empirically to affect the rate of degradation of petroleum products by indigenous microorganisms in a highly polluted soil. The kinetics of degradation under different soil water content were evaluated by measuring $^{14}CO_2$ produced and released by microbes as they metabolized n-[1-^{14}C]hexadecane, [*methyl*-^{14}C]toluene, [*ring*-^{14}C]toluene, [1-^{14}C]naphthalene, [9-^{14}C]phenanthrene, and [*side ring*-^{14}C]anthracene. Measurements from batch kinetic experiments showed that the degradation of ^{14}C-labeled petroleum compounds depends strongly on soil water content for the silt loam soil tested. The dependency, however, is compound specific, and very likely soil specific as well, although only one soil type was tested here. For aromatic hydrocarbons, a soil water content between 50% and 70% of field capacity appears to be optimum for the biodegradation process to proceed at a maximum rate. The fit of $^{14}CO_2$ measurements to a first-order kinetic model also depends on the complexity of the hydrocarbons and the soil water content. For simple monoaromatic and diaromatic hydrocarbons, such as toluene and naphthalene, a first-order kinetic model provides a good fit to their mineralization data over a range of soil moisture content. For larger polycyclic aromatic hydrocarbons (PAHs), such as phenanthrene and anthracene, the model provides a good fit only at low soil water contents. Microbial observations were also conducted concurrently with the biodegradation kinetic experiments to examine qualitatively the effects of soil moisture on soil microbial communities. Results show a dramatic difference in characteristics of microbial communities from different water content, which corroborate with the mineralization measurements.

INTRODUCTION

Soil water content is a major environmental parameter in the vadose zone that can vary significantly in response to precipitation and changes in groundwater table elevations. Changes in soil water content are accompanied by changes in the redox potential of soil, motility and biomass of microorganisms, and the availability and transport of gases and nutrients in soil (Harris 1981; Sommers 1981, Sims et al. 1993). It has been observed that soil water content affected the degradation of petroleum hydrocarbons in land treatment systems (Umfleet et al. 1984) and in soil aeration processes (Hinchee and Arthur 1991), although Dibble and Bartha (1979) reported no measurable difference in oily sludge biodegradation in a sandy loam within the range of 20 to 80% water saturation. In this study, we have measured the effect of soil moisture content on the extent of degradation of different petroleum hydrocarbon components for a silt loam soil. Our results help to characterize the natural biodegradation processes and provide additional information that is crucial for the design of systems for the enhanced biodegradation of petroleum compounds in the subsurface environment.

APPROACH

The experimental study was designed to measure the kinetics of biodegradation of petroleum products in a soil at different water contents. This study consisted of a batch mineralization experiment; additional studies not reported here included a biometer experiment and a microcosm experiment conducted inside a partially saturated soil column. The batch mineralization experiment used soil at different moisture contents inside gastight serum vials to quantify the extent and rate of mineralization of petroleum hydrocarbons at different soil water contents. Microbial observations were made throughout the batch mineralization experiment to examine effects of water content on soil microbial communities.

For simplicity, petroleum products were represented by five different organic compounds, each representing a distinct group of petroleum products that have been shown to biodegrade readily. Here, n-hexadecane represented the long-chain aliphatic components; toluene the volatile, slightly water-soluble monoaromatic components; naphthalene the volatile, slightly water-soluble diaromatic components; phenanthrene the slightly water-soluble nonvolatile polyaromatic components; and anthracene the almost water-insoluble nonvolatile polyaromatic components.

To quantify the kinetics of mineralization of petroleum products, ^{14}C-labeled substrates were used. $^{14}CO_2$ produced and released by microbes was trapped and counted by a liquid scintillation counter. Intermediate products produced by the microbes were analyzed by gas chromatography and high-performance liquid chromatography. In this paper, we summarize the effects of soil-water content on the kinetics of biodegradation of petroleum hydrocarbons from the batch mineralization experiment.

MATERIAL AND METHODS

Soil and Groundwater Samples

Silt loam vadose soil was collected, air-dried, and ground to pass a 1.7-mm sieve. The soil had a clay content of 18%, a silt content of 48% and a sand content of 34%. It had a pH of 7.9, an organic carbon content of 0.2%, a cation-exchange capacity of 111 meq/kg of dry soil, and a C:N ratio of 5.5. The soil had a maximum (water) retention capacity of 44.8%, and a field capacity of 34.9% (Brady 1990). When air-dried, its moisture content was 4.4%. The water-potential/water-content relationship was determined using techniques in Klute (1986). For air-dry soil and soil with a water content of 30%, 50%, and 70% of the maximum retention capacity, the corresponding matrix potential (from the initial drainage curve) was ≤ -10.0 MPa, -0.5 MPa, -0.025 MPa, and ≥ -0.01 MPa. Hydrocarbon sorption isotherms were measured for n-hexadecane, toluene, naphthalene, anthracene, and phenanthrene using the ^{14}C-labeled batch method described by Guerin and Boyd (1992). Results can be found in Holman et al. (1995). Groundwater was filtered through an activated charcoal cartridge and a 0.2-μ sterile filter. This treated water was further buffered to pH 7.3 and stored at 4°C until use.

Petroleum Products and Radiochemicals

Diesel oil used in this experiment was a mixture of hydrocarbons that could be represented by toluene, naphthalene, phenanthrene, anthracene, and n-hexadecane. To quantify the progress of mineralization of these five hydrocarbons, n-[1-^{14}C]hexadecane, [*methyl*-^{14}C]toluene, [*ring*-^{14}C]toluene, [1-^{14}C]naphthalene, [9-^{14}C]phenanthrene, and [*side ring*-^{14}C]anthracene were mixed individually into diesel oil in nanomolar amounts; the resulting radioactivity levels were approximately 8.8×10^5 dpm/mL of oil.

Preparation of Microcosms

To represent a highly polluted soil, 5 mL of sterile, nonlabeled diesel oil was injected into 50 g of air-dry soil inside each 250-mL airtight sterile vial. These vials were put on an orbital (25 rpm) shaker and kept at 21°C in the dark for 2 weeks. At the end of the second week, microcosms were prepared from these vials for each of four different soil water contents by adding the desired amount of autoclaved groundwater to the vials. The four soil water contents were air-dry, 30%, 50%, and 70% of the maximum retention capacity. Triplicates were prepared for each soil water content. Sterile controls were prepared by autoclaving the soil for 40 min on two consecutive days.

^{14}C-Labeled Hydrocarbon Mineralization Assays

All 250-mL vials were placed again on the shaker and kept in the dark for 3 weeks. During this time, background ^{14}CO$_2$ inside the vials (i.e., prior to the application of ^{14}C-labeled compounds) was trapped and counted. At the end of the third week, 0.3 mL of diesel oil labeled with individual compounds was injected into each of the vials, except for the no-spike controls. (For the no-spike controls, 0.3 mL of diesel oil without any labeled compounds was injected into each vial of soil.) The vials were again incubated at 21°C on the rotary shaker in the dark. Mineralization of petroleum hydrocarbons was quantified by trapping the $^{14}CO_2$ on pleated filter paper (i.e., filter paper fan) saturated with 0.9 mL of 2N NaOH solution. The pleated filter paper was inserted into a center-well that was suspended from the cap of the vial. During the early phase of the mineralization experiment, pleated filter papers were retrieved daily from the vials and transferred to scintillation vials containing scintillation fluid. The $^{14}CO_2$ trapped on the filter papers was then counted by the liquid scintillation counter. The sampling frequency decreased as experiment progressed. At the end of the experiment, 10 mL of 4N H_2SO_4 was injected into the vial. After overnight degassing, filter papers were again retrieved.

The loss of $^{14}CO_2$ and the volatile toluene and naphthalene during removal of pleated filter paper were evaluated quantitatively. Repeated trials showed (1) a negligible decrease of $^{14}CO_2$, (2) a toluene decrease of less than 1%, and (3) a negligible decrease of naphthalene per vial when caps were removed for 10 s. Because filter paper replacement generally took less than 5 s, the loss of $^{14}CO_2$ and volatile hydrocarbons during filter paper replacement was considered negligible in this study. Details of the test can be found in Holman et al. (1995).

The mineralization data for each compound, expressed as the percentage P of the initial activity (at time t_o) that was converted to $^{14}CO_2$ by time t, were fitted to a first-order equation of the following form:

$$P = P_{max} (1 - e^{-k(t-t_o)})$$ (1)

where P_{max} is the maximum percentage mineralized, and k is the first-order proportionality constant. Equation (1) presumes that biomass remains constant over time, and all substrates are freely available to microorganisms.

Microbial Observations

Throughout the batch mineralization experiment, standard protocols were used to characterize microorganisms in the soil samples. Details were reported in Holman et al. (1995). Near the end of the batch mineralization experiment, additional buried slide analyses were performed on soil from each of the 250-mL vials. Our goal was to gain an insight into effects of soil moisture on the population characteristics (type, density, form, arrangement, biomass, biovolume) of the soil microbe communities.

RESULTS AND DISCUSSION

Figures 1 and 2 show the percent conversion of ^{14}C-labeled compounds as a function of time t after the ^{14}C-labeled compounds were injected into soil samples

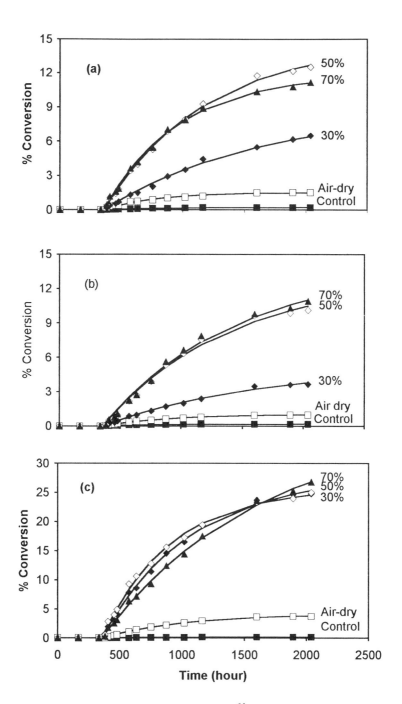

FIGURE 1. Time courses of mineralization of ^{14}C-labeled petroleum hydrocarbons in silt loam: (a) [*methyl*-^{14}C]toluene, (b) [*ring*-^{14}C]toluene, (c) [1-^{14}C]-naphthalene. Soil water contents are (□) air-dry, (♦) 30%, (◊) 50%, and (▲) 70%. (–) indicates fit of the first-order model to the data.

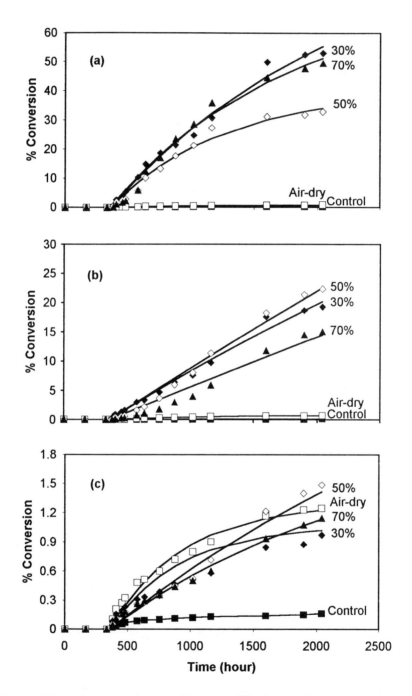

FIGURE 2. Time courses of mineralization of ^{14}C-labeled petroleum hydrocarbons in silt loam: (a) [9-^{14}C]phenanthrene, (b) [*side ring*-^{14}C]anthracene, (c) *n*-[1-^{14}C]hexadecane. Soil water contents are (□) air-dry, (♦) 30%, (◊) 50%, and (▲) 70%. (–) indicates fit of the first-order model to the data.

at $t_0 = 360$ h. Data show that the biotic mineralization of petroleum hydrocarbons depends markedly on soil water content. However, the abiotic mineralization (sterile controls) data for all four water contents collapse on the same curve and are therefore not sensitive to water content. The magnitude of abiotic mineralization is also insignificant compared to the biotic mineralization. Solid lines on these figures represent the fit of the first-order equation to the data; values of the fitting parameters are presented in Table 1. Each data point in the figure represents the mean of triplicate experiments. Triplicate measurements about each data point were generally within 20% of their mean value.

TABLE 1. Parameters fitted to the mineralization data based on the first-order model, $P = P_{max} (1 - e^{-k(t-t_o)})$, with $t_o = 360$ h.

Representative Petroleum Hydrocarbon	Soil Water Content	First-Order Model Parameters	
		P_{max} (%)	k (10^{-3} h^{-1})
[*methyl*-^{14}C]toluene	air dry	1.54	2.38
	30%	9.35	0.72
	50%	14.61	1.21
	70%	11.87	1.50
[*ring*-^{14}C]toluene	air dry	1.05	1.72
	30%	5.20	0.78
	50%	13.01	0.98
	70%	13.95	0.93
[1-^{14}C]naphthalene	air dry	4.22	1.45
	30%	28.00	1.40
	50%	25.80	1.80
	70%	36.30	0.80
[9-^{14}C]phenanthrene	air dry	0.83	1.50
	30%	95.10	0.52
	50%	40.50	1.10
	70%	73.00	0.72
[*side ring*-^{14}C]anthracene	air dry	0.81	1.40
	30%	92.90	0.15
	50%[a]	314.00	0.04
	70%[a]	410.00	0.02
n-[1-^{14}C]hexadecane	air dry	1.30	1.71
	30%	1.07	1.18
	50%	4.04	0.26
	70%	2.04	0.48

(a) Mechanisms other than those accounted for in the first-order equation are suspected to be in operation in these cases.

Figure 1a shows that the amount of $^{14}CO_2$ produced from [*methyl*-^{14}C]toluene by microorganisms increases with soil water content. Increasing the soil water content from air dry to 50% of the maximum retention capacity resulted initially in a six-fold increase in the amount of $^{14}CO_2$ production, and a larger than ten-fold increase at later times. Above 50% soil water, the $^{14}CO_2$ production from [*methyl*-^{14}C]toluene ceased to increase with water content. Similar results were observed in mineralization assays using [*ring*-^{14}C]toluene as the substrate (Figure 1b). Notice that the first-order fit to the measurement was excellent for all soil water concentrations. We interpret this as an indication (1) that the 2-week petroleum and 1-week moisture enrichment time had produced such a high initial microorganism density that the change in biomass during the $^{14}CO_2$ measurement period was insignificant; and (2) that the diffusion of dissolved toluene molecules from inaccessible sites to sites accessible to microbes was quick (compared with the mineralization process) so that one could assume that the substrate was available freely to the toluene-degrading microbes. The first interpretation was confirmed by colony counting, which showed that for a given soil water content there was an insignificant increase in biomass throughout the experiment. Values of P_{max} for [*ring*-^{14}C]toluene and [*methyl*-^{14}C]toluene showed a general increase with increasing soil water content, but the relation breaks down above 50% soil water content. This is possibly because at moisture contents above 50% of maximum retention capacity, water may interfere with O_2 movement into and through the soil, and thus restrict microbial activities. Observations from contact slides, direct microscopy, and culture counts showed that the biomass of microorganisms did indeed increase with water content until it exceeded 50%.

Biodegradation of toluene begins with oxidation of either the methyl group or the aromatic ring. It is generally believed that these two degradation pathways are accomplished by different microbial populations. The production of $^{14}CO_2$ from both the [*ring*-^{14}C]toluene and [*methyl*-^{14}C]toluene in our experiments, as well as the similarities between their cumulative mineralization curves, imply that (1) microbial populations participating in these two different oxidizing processes are both present in our soil samples, and (2) these different populations respond to the change of soil water content in a very similar fashion.

Figure 1c shows that the mineralization of [1-^{14}C]naphthalene mineralization followed a trend of increasing mineralization with soil water content. The first-order fit to the data is also good.

Results for [9-^{14}C]phenanthrene and [*side ring*-^{14}C]anthracene generally showed a larger $^{14}CO_2$ production at moderate moisture contents (Figures 2a and 2b). Unlike toluene and naphthalene, the trend between the $^{14}CO_2$ production and soil water content were ambiguous. The first-order model could provide a good fit to the mineralization data only when water content was low. At higher water contents, the model deviated from the data. The poor fit of the first-order model to the $^{14}CO_2$ produced at early time from [9-^{14}C]phenanthrene occurred when water content was 70%; for [*side ring*-^{14}C]anthracene the water content was at 50% and 70%. The failure of the first-order model to fit these data at a higher soil water content may arise from many factors. Two possible factors are (1) at high water content, the extent of mineralization by microorganisms is governed by desorption/dissolution and diffusion of these large organic molecules (of extremely low solubility) from inaccessible micropores to sites containing microorganisms; and (2) excess soil water delays the movement of O_2 to the microorganisms, leading to an accumulation of intermediate products (during the extensive metabolism) for some time before they are converted to $^{14}CO_2$.

The overall increase of $^{14}CO_2$ production with increasing soil water content seems consistent with results from microbial observations. The culture counts showed that the bacteria population increased from 3.2×10^5 cfu/g soil to 4.3×10^6 cfu/g soil as the water content increased from 30 to 70%. The fungi's population, on the other hand, remained almost constant; however, its biomass increased about ten-fold. Results from buried slide analysis also showed that, compared to low water content, hyphae of fungi at moderate to higher water content generally branched extensively. Bacteria colonies surrounding the hyphae of fungi also increased significantly.

Unlike aromatic hydrocarbons, the mineralization of *n*-[1-^{14}C]hexadecane seems not to be affected by water content in soil (Figure 2c). One of the possible explanations is the solubility difference between aromatics and hexadecane. Compared to aromatics, the aqueous solubility for hexadecane is extremely low. Thus, the flux of hexadecane from the oil phase to water phase was so low that the amount of water may be of little consequence for mineralization.

To assess effects of volatilities of aromatic hydrocarbons on the extent of mineralization, mineralization data shown in Figures 1a through 2b were also compared between compounds. Results show that the amount of $^{14}CO_2$ produced from volatile hydrocarbons was less than the amount from nonvolatile organics, suggesting competing processes of volatilization and biodegradation in our soil.

CONCLUSIONS

Data reported in this technical note demonstrate that soil water can accelerate the degradation of petroleum hydrocarbons in soil by at least an order of magnitude. For monoaromatic and diaromatic hydrocarbons, production of $^{14}CO_2$ from degrading hydrocarbons increases dramatically with soil water content up to about 50% of maximum retention capacity. This relationship breaks down at higher soil water contents. For larger hydrocarbons, such as PAHs, the production of $^{14}CO_2$ increases markedly in the presence of soil water, but no simple relation between $^{14}CO_2$ production and soil water content is evident. Because of the extremely low solubility of the long-chain aliphatic hydrocarbons, the biotic mineralization is little affected by the soil water content. The more extensive mineralization of the semivolatile and nonvolatile aromatics suggests the presence of competition between volatilization and biodegradation in our soil. In addition, the first-order model succeeded in describing mineralization kinetics of monoaromatic and diaromatic hydrocarbons for all soil water contents. For PAHs, the model can represent the mineralization processes only for soil water contents below 50%. That the extent of biotic mineralization generally increases with soil water content is supported by concurrent microbial observations. These results can help in the understanding of natural biodegradation processes and provide important information for the design of systems for enhanced biodegradation of petroleum compounds in the subsurface environment.

REFERENCES

Brady, N. C. 1990. *The Nature and Properties of Soils.* Macmillan Publishing Company, New York, NY.

Dibble, J. T. and R. Bartha. 1979. "Effect of environmental parameters on the biodegradation of oil sludge." *Applied and Environmental Microbiology* 37:729-739.

Guerin, W. E., and S. A. Boyd. 1992. "Differential bioavailability of soil-sorbed naphthalene to two bacterial species." *Applied and Environmental Microbiology* 58:1142-1152.

Harris, R. F. 1981. "Effect of water potential on microbial growth and activity." In J. F. Parr, W. R. Gardner and L. F. Elliott (Eds.), *Water Potential Relations in Soil Microbiology*, pp. 23-96.

Hinchee, R. E. and M. Arthur. 1991. "Bench scale studies of the soil aeration process for bioremediation of petroleum hydrocarbons." *Applied Biochemistry and Biotechnology* 28(9):901-906.

Holman, H.-Y., Y. W. Tsang, and V. A. Wolff. 1995. *Effects of Soil Moisture on Biodegradation of Petroleum Hydrocarbons in a Silt Loam.* Report LBL#36993, Lawrence Berkeley Laboratory, Berkeley, CA.

Klute, A. (Ed.). 1986. *Methods of Soil Analyses.* Vol. 1, 2nd ed., American Society of Agronomy, Inc., Soil Science Society of America, Inc., Madison, WI.

Sims J. L., R. C. Sims, R. R. Dupont, J. E. Matthews, and H. H. Russell. 1993. *In Situ Bioremediation of Contaminated Unsaturated Subsurface Soils.* U.S. Environmental Protection Agency Technical Report, EPA/540/S-93/501, R. S. Kerr Environmental Research Laboratory, Ada, OK.

Sommers, L. E., C. M. Gilmour, R. E. Wildung, and S. M. Beck. 1981. "The effect of water potential on decomposition processes in soils." In J. F. Parr, W. R. Gardner, and L. F. Elliott (Eds.), *Water Potential Relations in Soil Microbiology*, pp. 97-118.

Umfleet, D. A., R. C. Sims and A. Pano. 1984. "Reclamation of PAH contaminated soils." *Presentation Made at Environmental Engineering 1984 Specialty Conference*, ASCE, Los Angeles, CA. June 25-27.

Soil Moisture Effects During Bioventing in Fuel-Contaminated Arid Soils

Thomas C. Zwick, Andrea Leeson, Robert E. Hinchee,
Ron E. Hoeppel, and Leon Bowling

ABSTRACT

This study evaluated the effects of soil moisture addition on microbial activity during bioventing of dry, sandy soils at the Marine Corps Air Ground Combat Center (MCAGCC), Twentynine Palms, California. Soils at the site have been contaminated to a depth of approximately 80 ft (24 m) with gasoline, JP-5 jet fuel, and diesel fuel. Based on the low soil moisture measured at the site (2 to 3% by weight), it was determined that soil moisture may be limiting biodegradation. To evaluate the effect that moisture addition had on microbial activity under field conditions, a subsurface drip irrigation system was installed above the fuel hydrocarbon plume. Irrigation water was obtained from two monitoring wells on the site, where groundwater was approximately 192 ft (59 m) below ground surface. Advancement of the wetting front was monitored. In situ respiration rates increased significantly after moisture addition. The results of this study provide evidence for the potential applicability of moisture addition in conjunction with bioventing for site remediation in arid environments. Further work is planned to investigate optimization of moisture addition.

INTRODUCTION

The study site, located at the Marine Corps Air Ground Combat Center (MCAGCC) Twentynine Palms, California, formerly was used to store fuels including gasoline, JP-5 jet fuel, and diesel fuel for the Crash Fire Rescue Training Facility. The fuel was stored aboveground in a fuel bladder that was surrounded by a 5-ft (1.5-m)-high earthen berm. Over several years, fuel releases resulted in soil contamination to a depth of approximately 80 ft (24 m). Soil concentrations of total petroleum hydrocarbon (TPH) at the site range from 1,000 to 9,970 mg/kg (Jacobs 1993; Battelle 1995).

Surface soils at the site consist mainly of slightly silty sands and medium- to coarse-grained sands (Jacobs 1992). The vadose zone, which extends to approximately 185 ft (56 m), consists of uniformly distributed biotite sands and slightly silty sands (Jacobs 1992). Soil pH ranges from 9 to 10. The average bulk density and porosity of the soil were 1,600 mg/m^3 and 0.35, respectively. Prior to site irrigation, soil moisture from the surface to approximately 100 ft (30 m) deep ranged from 2.0 to 3.3% by weight (Battelle 1995). Annual precipitation for Twentynine Palms is approximately 4 in. (10 cm).

Soil gas monitoring points and vent wells were installed within the hydrocarbon plume. Soil gas oxygen and carbon dioxide concentrations were monitored over several months in soil gas monitoring points. Oxygen concentrations were depressed (12 to 18%); however, these levels were not sufficiently low to be limiting microbial activity. In situ respiration rates were low and oxygen consumption during the in situ respiration test generally leveled off at concentrations of 12 to 18%. Based on the low soil moisture levels and low oxygen utilization rates, it was determined that soil moisture may be the factor limiting hydrocarbon biodegradation.

A subsurface irrigation system was installed and the site was irrigated to evaluate the effect of increased soil moisture on microbial activity. Site irrigation was initiated during November 1994. The effect of moisture addition on microbial activity was evaluated by conducting in situ respiration tests during December 1994 through January 1995.

METHODOLOGY FOR FIELD TESTS

Bioventing System Installation and Monitoring

The bioventing system installed included the following components: soil gas monitoring points; vent wells; a soil moisture monitoring system including two neutron probe access tubes (NPATs); and eight high-pressure, vacuum lysimeters. Construction details of these installations may be found in Battelle (1995). Irrigation water was obtained from two monitoring wells at the site where groundwater was approximately 192 ft (59 m) below ground surface (bgs). Irrigation water was pumped to irrigation lines installed approximately 2 ft (0.6 m) deep over a 75-ft × 75-ft (23-m × 23-m) area. The irrigation lines consisted of 0.5-in. (1.3-cm)-diameter microtubing with 0.5-gal (1.9-L) pressure-compensated emitters placed every 12 in. (30 cm) on each line. Approximately 30 lines, each 75 ft (23 m) in length, were placed approximately every 2.5 ft (0.8 m) within the 75-ft × 75-ft (23-m × 23-m) area.

Soil gas concentrations were analyzed in the field using hand-held portable field monitoring equipments. Hydrocarbons were analyzed with a GasTech TraceTechtor™ Portable Hydrocarbon Vapor Test and oxygen and carbon dioxide were analyzed with a GasTechtor Portable Carbon Dioxide/Oxygen Indication Model 32520X.

Advancement of the wetting front was monitored using a Model 503 DR Hydroprobe® neutron depth moisture gauge and high pressure/vacuum lysimeters.

The neutron probe count data were compared to a calibration curve to determine soil moisture by weight in the soil profile.

Field Methods for Evaluation of the Effect of Moisture Addition

Prior to site irrigation, air was injected into a single vent well for approximately 6 weeks. Air injection was terminated and an in situ respiration test was initiated. The respiration test consisted of periodic monitoring of soil gas concentrations of oxygen, carbon dioxide, and TPH to quantify oxygen utilization and carbon dioxide production rates as described in Hinchee et al. (1992).

Site irrigation was conducted November 3 to 8 and November 29 to December 5, 1994. During the two irrigation periods, 50,000 and 150,000 gal (189,270 and 567,810 L) of water, respectively, were applied. No air was injected during site irrigation. Soil gas concentrations of oxygen, carbon dioxide, and TPH were monitored periodically during the period of November 6 to 29, 1994. During irrigation, soil moisture was monitored using the Hydroprobe®, lysimeters, and soil moisture gypsum blocks.

Following irrigation, air was injected into a single vent well for approximately 1 month. Air injection was then discontinued and a second in situ respiration test was conducted as described previously. During this time period, the soil moisture wetting front also was monitored.

RESULTS AND DISCUSSION

Oxygen utilization and carbon dioxide production at monitoring point 18-MP-A-10′ is illustrated in Figure 1. Results obtained at this monitoring point are typical of results at other monitoring points within the hydrocarbon plume. During the pre-irrigation respiration test (June 1994), microbial activity was very low, with soil gas oxygen concentrations declining from approximately 20% to near pre-air injection levels (12 to 18%) over a 3-month monitoring period (Figure 1). Irrigation was initiated in an attempt to stimulate microbial activity.

Figure 2 compares percent moisture by weight measured on November 2, 1994 (pre-irrigation) and on January 18, 1995 (post-irrigation). Moisture content increased dramatically to depths of approximately 40 ft (12 m). At monitoring depths below 40 ft (12 m), no significant change in moisture content was observed (Figure 2). To date, no soil-pore water was observed in any of the lysimeters which were placed at depths of 25, 50, 100, and 150 ft (7.6, 15.2, 30.4, and 45.7 m).

Moisture content increase corresponded to increased microbial activity within the hydrocarbon plume. After initiation of irrigation, oxygen concentrations rapidly dropped with a corresponding peak in carbon dioxide (Figure 1). Air injection was reinitiated at this time for approximately 1 month, followed by a second in situ respiration test. During the post-irrigation respiration test, oxygen utilization was significantly more rapid than in pre-irrigation tests. A comparison

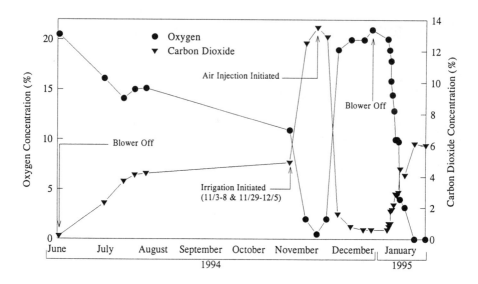

FIGURE 1. Soil gas concentrations of oxygen and carbon dioxide at monitoring point 18-MP-A-10′.

of results at monitoring point 18-MP-A-10′ showed nearly an order of magnitude increase in the oxygen utilization rate from 0.21%/day pre-irrigation to 1.9%/day post-irrigation (Figure 3).

Biodegradation rates were determined by methods reported by Hinchee et al. (1992). The biodegradation rate estimates are based on oxygen utilization rates (change of oxygen [%] per day), and are reported in terms of milligrams of hexane-equivalent per kilograms of soil per day. As observed at monitoring point 18-MP-A-10′, site irrigation resulted in an increase in biodegradation rates at all monitoring points (Table 1). At 18-MP-A, pre-irrigation biodegradation rates ranged from 0 to 0.17 mg/kg/day while post-irrigation rates ranged from 0.06 to 1.5 mg/kg/day.

Significant increases in biodegradation rates were also observed at 18-MP-B and 18-MP-C following site irrigation; however, the increases were relatively small in comparison to 18-MP-A. At the 25-ft depth in 18-MP-B, rates increased from 0.08 to 0.32 mg/kg/day. At the 20-ft depth in 18-MP-C, rates increased from 0.04 to 0.39 mg/kg/day. Biodegradation rates at these monitoring points may be low due to lower contaminant levels. Based on soil analysis data, these monitoring points are in areas of lower soil contamination in comparison to 18-MP-A.

Using the biodegradation rates observed at monitoring point 18-MP-A-10′, if the bioventing system were operated for 2 years without irrigation, approximately 125 mg/kg hydrocarbons would be removed. However, operating the same system for 2 years with irrigation, approximately 1,100 mg/kg hydrocarbons would be removed. These results illustrate the potential decrease in remediation time through enhanced microbial activity.

COST ANALYSIS

This cost analysis assumes a hydrocarbon plume of approximately 14,000 yd³ and average soil TPH concentration of 2,000 mg/kg. Total remediation time is estimated to be four years based on a biodegradation rate of 550 mg/kg/year, the rate observed at monitoring point 18-MP-A-10' following site irrigation. Based on actual costs incurred to date and projected cost to bioremediate the site, the estimated cost for site remediation with irrigation is $31/yd³ (Table 2).

As shown in Table 2, the costs are broken into three categories: (1) bioventing; (2) installation of irrigation system; and (3) system design, irrigation, and monitoring of irrigation water. The total cost to remediate the site with irrigation is estimated at $450,000. Of the total cost, 49% is associated with bioventing and operation/maintenance; 6% is associated with installation of the irrigation system, and 46% is associated with the system design, irrigation, and operation/ monitoring of the irrigation water. Much of the cost of the irrigation system is associated with the neutron probe monitoring. This monitoring was driven by regulatory requirements and probably is not necessary at many sites.

SUMMARY AND CONCLUSIONS

Based on both oxygen utilization and carbon dioxide production rates, bio-degradation rates significantly increased following site irrigation in all three areas

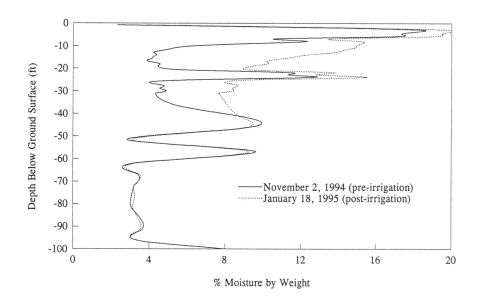

FIGURE 2. Percent moisture versus depth pre- and post-irrigation, where 1 ft = 0.3 m.

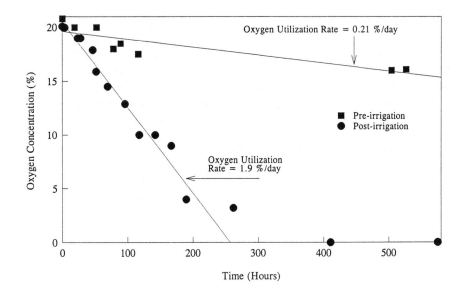

FIGURE 3. Pre- and post-irrigation in situ respiration results at monitoring point 18-MP-A-10'.

of the test plot where soil gas monitoring points had been installed. Rate increases were most notable in monitoring point 18-MP-A. Based on soil analysis data, high hydrocarbon contamination is present within this area of the site. Less contamination is present from 18-MP-A toward 18-MP-B and 18-MP-C, perhaps explaining the lower biodegradation rates observed at these points.

The data clearly demonstrated that biodegradation rate increases are directly correlated with soil moisture; biodegradation rates and soil moisture decreased

TABLE 1. Biodegradation rates pre- and post-irrigation for Site 18, MCAGCC, Twentynine Palms, CA.

Sample Location	Depth, ft	Pre-Irrigation Biodegradation Rate (mg/kg/day)	Post-Irrigation Biodegradation Rate (mg/kg/day)
18-MP-A	10	0.17	1.5
	30	0.08	1.0
	50	0.00	0.06
18-MP-B	25	0.08	0.32
18-MP-C	20	0.04	0.39

TABLE 2. Bioventing and irrigation cost analysis for Site 18, MCAGCC, Twentynine Palms, CA.

Component	$K[a]	$/yd³[b]
Bioventing		
Drilling	75	5
Installation	25	2
Operation & Maintenance (4 y)	120	8
Installation of Irrigation System	25	2
System Design, Irrigation, and Monitoring		
Drilling	35	2
Materials & Labor	45	3
Operation & Maintenance (4 yrs)	125	9
Total Bioventing & Irrigation Cost	450	31

(a) U.S. dollars.
(b) 1 yd = 0.91 m.

with increasing depth. Essentially no biodegradation rate increase was observed at the 50-ft depth where, based on neutron probe counts, soil moisture had not increased.

Based on the results obtained in this study, the follow-on task has been designed to further define the contaminant plume and install additional monitoring points. Additionally, attempts will be made to increase soil moisture within the contaminant plume at depths of 50 to 90 ft (15.2 to 27.4 m).

Based on cost incurred and projected cost to remediate the site, a significant portion (46%) of the costs are for irrigation and monitoring of the wetting front. Although the Hydroprobe® has been demonstrated to be a very reliable tool for monitoring of the wetting front, it is important to point out that there are significant costs associated with acquisition, calibration, and use of the neutron probe. Operation and maintenance of the irrigation system and monitoring of the wetting front over the 4 years estimated for cleanup of the site add approximately $9/yd³. The total estimated cost per cubic yard to remediate this site with irrigation is estimated at $31.

REFERENCES

Battelle. 1995. *Site Characterization, Design, and Installation of a Demonstration-Scale Irrigation System at Site 18 at the Marine Corps Air Ground Combat Center, Twentynine Palms, California.* Prepared for Southwest Division Naval Facilities Engineering Command, San Diego, CA.

Hinchee, R. E., S. K. Ong, R. N. Miller, D. C. Downey, and R. Frandt. 1992. *Test Plan and Technical Protocol for a Field Treatability Test for Bioventing*. Report to U.S. Air Force Center for Environmental Excellence, Brooks AFB, TX.

Jacobs Engineering Group, Inc. 1992. "Draft Hydrogeologic Assessment Report, Site 18A, MCAGCC, Twentynine Palms, CA." Report prepared for Southwest Division Naval Facilities, Engineering Command, San Diego, CA under Contract #N68711-89-D-9296. CTO #0127.

Jacobs Engineering Group, Inc. 1993. "Site Investigation/Removal Action (Phase III), Sites 17, 18, and 19, MCAGCC Twentynine Palms, CA." Technical Memorandum Preliminary Draft. Report prepared for Southwest Division Naval Facilities, Engineering Command, San Diego, CA under Contract #N68711-89-D-9296. CTO #0240.

In Situ Vacuum Extraction/Bioventing of a Hazardous Waste Landfill

Deborah M. Heuckeroth, Michael F. Eberle, and Michael J. Rykaczewski

ABSTRACT ────────────────────────

In situ vacuum extraction (VE)/bioventing of volatile and semivolatile organic compounds (VOCs and SVOCs) was performed at an inactive hazardous waste landfill in the northeast United States. A VE system was used to extract VOCs from a horizontal well (trench), thereby delivering oxygen to the subsurface to biodegrade VOCs and SVOCs in situ. In areas where oxygen concentration increases were observed in the subsurface, microbial populations increased by orders of magnitude, and temperatures increased from 18°C to as high as 27°C. In these areas, up to 99% reductions were observed in specific VOC and SVOC concentrations after 3 months of operation. Based on system monitoring, the remediation of soil contaminants was approximately 90% attributable to in situ biodegradation and 10% attributable to volatilization.

INTRODUCTION

The use of VE and bioventing was approved by the state regulatory agency to remediate an inactive landfill, comprised of a complex mixture of pharmaceutical intermediates, finished pharmaceutical products, research wastes, filter cakes, still bottoms, and oils. A VE system was used to extract vapors from a trench and to deliver oxygen to the subsurface. The constituents of concern with the highest concentrations relative to the site-specific regulatory cleanup goals were benzene (0.756 mg/kg goal), phenol (0.33 mg/kg goal), and 4-methyl phenol (1.8 mg/kg goal). Other constituents of concern included chlorinated VOCs and polycyclic aromatic hydrocarbons. The total organic carbon (TOC) concentration in the soils ranged from 2 to 5%. In soils at greater than 1.8 m below ground surface (bgs), where the process was monitored, 75 to 98% of the TOC was solvent extractable, which indicates that the source of TOC for the microbes was primarily landfill contamination. Both landfill materials (fill) and the underlying silt soils were addressed by the process; however, the fill is the primary focus of this paper. The silt is submerged by seasonally high groundwater for approximately 3 months per year. This paper addresses findings from pilot study operations from September 1993 through March 1994. VE and bioventing were selected to remediate VOCs and SVOCs in the landfill. The findings presented herein provided the design basis for a full-scale VE/bioventing system which is currently operational at the site.

PROCEDURES

A rotary lobe blower was operated at approximately 250 cfm (7 m^3/min), 8 to 12 h per day typically, extracting from a trench to evaluate the use of VE in the fill and silt soils, and to deliver oxygen to the subsurface to evaluate the use of bioventing. Operations began September 22, 1993, and after 2.5 months, system operation was discontinued for one month during December/January due to high groundwater conditions and mounding of the groundwater in the vicinity of the extraction trench. Operations restarted in the latter half of January 1994. Figure 1 illustrates the process and the monitoring points.

Two parallel trenches were similarly constructed and located approximately 18 m apart. The trenches are approximately 15 m long and extend into the silt, which underlies the more permeable fill. Liner and geotextile layers were installed to provide vapor seals to prevent air from migrating from the surface through the trench itself, i.e., short-circuiting. One trench was used as an extraction trench and the other as an air inlet trench.

Vapor monitoring probes were installed at 3 depths (using separate boreholes for each depth) and at 11 locations to monitor induced vacuum, oxygen concentrations, oxygen uptake rate, and carbon dioxide production rate. Induced vacuum was monitored at all of the probes on 10 different days during system operations to evaluate the area of influence of the VE system. Oxygen concentrations were monitored at all of the probes approximately weekly to evaluate the distribution of oxygen in the subsurface as a result of bioventing operations.

Oxygen uptake and carbon dioxide production measurements were performed on November 4, 1993 at each vapor monitoring probe. After the VE unit operated for an extended period of time to saturate the subsurface with oxygen, the unit was turned off, and oxygen and carbon dioxide concentrations were monitored periodically during a 4.5-hour (or greater) time period. The oxygen concentrations for each probe were plotted versus time to determine the rate of change in oxygen during the monitoring period. The oxygen uptake rate was calculated for each probe location by determining the slope of the line for oxygen concentrations greater than 5%. This rate is considered indicative of the overall rate of microbial activity, since microbial activity generally decreases significantly or ceases below 5% oxygen concentration (Kittel et al. 1993).

Temperature probes were installed at 2 depths (using separate boreholes for each depth) and at 10 locations to monitor subsurface temperatures. Temperatures

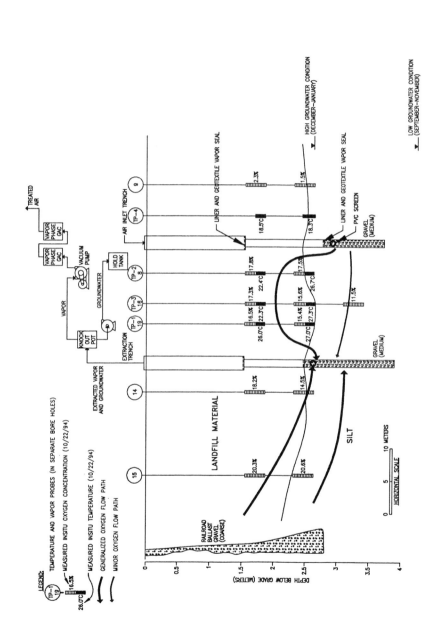

FIGURE 1. Cross section of extraction trench, air inlet locations, and system monitoring probes. Representative oxygen concentrations and temperatures in the subsurface are indicated.

were measured 2 to 3 times per week during system operations, and was used as an indicator of microbial activity.

Soil samples were collected before system startup, and 5 times thereafter. The samples were collected from 2 locations between the trenches to evaluate the area which was provided the most oxygen. At each location, samples were collected from the fill at 1.8-m depth bgs and from the silt at 3-m depth bgs. Samples were analyzed for VOCs by EPA Method SW846, SVOCs by EPA Method 8270, microbes, nutrients, and pH. Total heterotrophic microbes and VOC- and phenol-degrading microbes were analyzed using standard methods for microbial enumerations (ReTec 1991).

VE/bioventing system flowrates, pressures, temperatures, and vapor concentrations were monitored 2 to 3 times per week. These data were used to estimate mass flowrates, and to determine the need for carbon changeouts. Benzene concentrations in the vapor were measured on site using a gas chromatograph.

PROCESS MONITORING RESULTS

The system extracted approximately 900 kg of VOCs during 1,072 hours of extraction over 6 months, with 90% of the VOCs extracted during the first week of operation. The VOCs consisted primarily of benzene; toluene, 3-methyl thiophene, ethyl ether, methane, and mercury were also detected in the extracted vapor. In addition, the system extracted approximately 30,000 kg of carbon dioxide over 6 months at a relatively consistent rate during system operation.

The VE area of influence of the trench was evaluated by measuring induced vacuums at the probes at an applied vacuum of 84 mm Hg. The area of influence was extrapolated to be approximately 3,500 m^2, based on a minimum induced vacuum of 13 mm of water at the probes. Oxygen concentrations at the probes indicated that the effective oxygen delivery area of influence was approximately 1,500 square meters, based on a minimum oxygen concentration of 5% at the probes. Subsurface oxygen concentrations were highest between the extraction trench and the air inlet locations, as Figure 1 shows.

Temperatures in the oxygen area of influence increased significantly during operations, which is indicative of microbial activity (U.S. EPA 1979). Figure 2 illustrates temperatures measured over time at a probe between the trenches and at a probe outside the oxygen area of influence. The outlying temperature probe was installed in an area that had low oxygen concentrations, but was within the VE area of influence of the extraction trench. Subsurface temperatures measured using this probe remained relatively constant at approximately 18°C. Conversely, the probes within the oxygen delivery area of influence exhibited increases in temperature, up to approximately 27°C within the first month of operation, as shown in Figures 1 and 2. Temperatures remained elevated until system operation was interrupted due to high groundwater. The decreases in soil temperatures are partially attributable to decreases in ambient temperatures, but microbial activity may have begun to decrease due to decreased operating times (reduced oxygen delivery).

SOIL SAMPLE RESULTS
AND MICROBIAL POPULATIONS

Overall, VOC and SVOC concentrations decreased significantly in the study area; however, fluctuations in the results due to high detection limits, matrix interferences, and sampling variability hindered the use of soil sampling as a means of process monitoring. At one fill sample location between the trenches after 6 months, concentrations were reduced by 99.9% for benzene (from 140 to 0.081 mg/kg), 89% for phenol (from 7.3 to 0.77 mg/kg), and 90% for 4-methyl phenol (from 75 to 7.5 mg/kg), achieving the cleanup goal for benzene, and approaching the cleanup goals for phenol and 4-methyl phenol. At the other fill sample location between the trenches, however, the benzene concentration remained constant at approximately 80 mg/kg, and phenol and 4-methyl phenol reductions could not be evaluated since their initial concentrations were not detected (<3.7 mg/kg).

Indigenous microbial populations within the oxygen area of influence increased significantly and consistently. As shown in Figure 3, from September 1993 to April 1994, phenol-degrader and VOC-degrader populations increased by approximately 3 orders of magnitude at a sample location between the trenches. Microbial populations at both sample locations between the trenches increased similarly. The concentration of biphenyl, which is considered to be a site-specific representative compound, decreased during this time period as

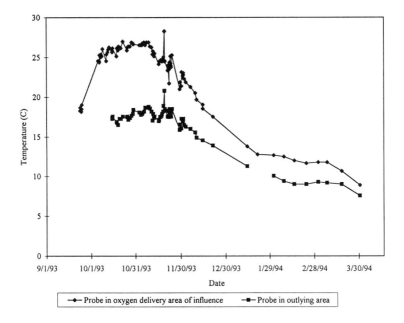

FIGURE 2. Temperatures in the subsurface versus time at probes within and outside the oxygen delivery area of influence.

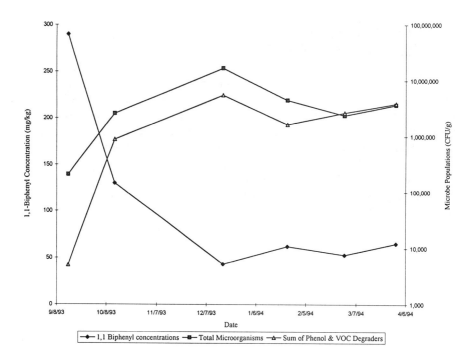

FIGURE 3. **Microbe populations and biphenyl concentrations versus time at a sample location between the trenches.**

shown on Figure 3. Although it is not a constituent of concern, biphenyl is prevalent in the landfill and is believed to be representative of the biodegradable constituents in the landfill, as it is in the mid-range of the molecular weights and sizes of the constituents.

Soil samples in each sampling round were analyzed for pH, nitrogen, and phosphorus. The pH ranged from 6 to 8, which is acceptable for bioremediation. Nitrate and nitrite concentrations were less than 1 mg/kg in all soil samples. Ammonia nitrogen concentrations ranged from 9.8 to 113 mg/kg. Total kjeldahl nitrogen (TKN) concentrations ranged from 344 to 4,800 mg/kg. Phosphate concentrations ranged from 23 to 7,700 mg/kg. The nutrient concentrations varied depending on the sample location, but were considered sufficient for biodegradation to occur using the indigenous microbes (Morgan and Watkinson 1992).

OXYGEN UPTAKE AND BIODEGRADATION RATE CONSTANTS

Oxygen uptake measurements were used to estimate oxygen uptake rates and biodegradation rate constants (Kittel et al. 1993). The relationship between oxygen concentration and time was modeled linearly to estimate oxygen uptake rates. Biodegradation rate constants were calculated as a function of these rates and the mass ratio of biphenyl to oxygen. Oxygen uptake rates at the probes in the oxygen area of influence ranged from 1.0 to 3.5%/h, and biodegradation rate constants in this area ranged from 22 to 79 mg/kg·day of organics as biphenyl. At a probe outside the oxygen delivery area of influence, but within the VE area of influence, the oxygen uptake rate was 0.28%/h, and the bio-degradation rate constant was 6.4 mg/kg·day.

CONTAMINANT BIODEGRADATION VERSUS EXTRACTION

During system operation, contaminated, oxygen-depleted soil vapor was removed from the subsurface through the extraction trench, and oxygen-rich air was drawn into the subsurface through the air inlet trench. In the oxygen-depleted, extracted soil vapor, carbon dioxide concentrations were elevated compared to air, typically at concentrations of 3 to 4%, due to microbial respiration. To evaluate the mass of organics degraded in situ, the total carbon dioxide produced was assumed to be due to the complete mineralization of biphenyl:

$$C_{12}H_{10} + 14.5 \ O_2 \rightarrow 12 \ CO_2 + 5 \ H_2O$$

Based on this stoichiometry, the 30,000 kg of carbon dioxide recovered in the extracted vapor corresponds to 8,750 kg of organics as biphenyl biodegraded in situ. An additional 900 kg of organics were extracted, thus the remediation of the total of 9,650 kg of landfill constituents was accomplished 90% by bio-degradation and 10% by volatilization.

Using these results to estimate a biodegradation rate constant, 2,500 kg of organics degraded from approximately 6.8 million kg of soil in 135 days (September 22, 1994 through March 18, 1995, omitting system downtime due to high groundwater) corresponds to 9.5 mg/kg·day. This is significantly lower than the rates calculated based on oxygen uptake rates at the probes. This lower rate is expected for carbon dioxide-based estimates based on previous studies (Hinchee and Ong 1992, Newman and Martinson 1992, Rasiah et al. 1992). In addition, some of the carbon which resulted from the biodegradation of contaminants would have been immobilized in the subsurface as microbial biomass (Rasiah et al. 1992).

Many assumptions were used in calculating these values, and there are inherent uncertainties in soil sample results. This analysis, however, combined with the microbial population increases, solvent-extractable TOC results, relatively high oxygen uptake rates, carbon dioxide increases, and temperature increases in the subsurface, indicates that biodegradation is occurring and is a prime contributor to contaminant reduction in the fill. Reductions in VOCs in the soil can be attributed to removal by VE and to in situ biodegradation by bioventing. Reductions in SVOCs, however, are almost solely attributable to in situ bio-degradation because of their lower volatility.

BIODEGRADATION OF
CONTAMINANTS IN THE SILT

Benzene in the silt was reduced by over 99% (from 3,000 to 20 mg/kg) at the two sample locations between trenches. The 4-methyl phenol concentration in the silt was reduced by approximately 73% (from 37 to <20 mg/kg) at one location between the trenches. Other reductions in phenol or 4-methyl phenol concentrations could not be quantified due to high detection limits (<38 mg/kg in the initial sampling event to <20 mg/kg in the final sampling event). The biphenyl concentrations in the silt decreased by approximately 93% at both sample locations between the trenches (from approximately 7,000 to 500 mg/kg). Initially, microbial populations in the silt were approximately 3 orders of magnitude less than those in the fill (100 colony forming units/gram [CFU/g] in the silt compared to 200,000 CFU/g in the fill). However, by March 1994, microbial populations comparable to those observed in the fill were achieved in the silt between the trenches (approximately 2,000,000 CFU/g in the fill and the silt).

At a fill probe between the trenches, the oxygen uptake rate was 1%/h, compared to that of an adjacent probe in the silt, which was significantly lower at 0.33%/h. The biodegradation rate constant at this location in the silt was 7.4 mg/kg·day based on the oxygen uptake rate. These lower rates indicate that less microbial activity is occurring in the silt than in the fill soils. Based on a comparison of the fill and soil types, the permeability of the silt is approximately 3 orders of magnitude lower than the fill. Because of its lower permeability, less oxygen is delivered to the silt, and it is expected that a longer time period will be required to achieve the same contaminant reductions as in the fill.

CONCLUSIONS

The findings presented herein provided the design basis for full-scale VE/bioventing of the landfill soils and the underlying silt. The full-scale system is currently operational. Oxygen, carbon dioxide, and temperatures in the subsurface soils are used to monitor microbial activity in the subsurface. Use of these indicator parameters minimizes analytical costs and provides realtime process monitoring data that can be used routinely to control system operations. Therefore, trends in the concentrations of contaminants and indigenous microbial populations are used less frequently to monitor the progress of the remedy. By constructing and operating the system as a bioventing system, the extracted VOC concentrations are significantly decreased, since the VOCs are degraded in situ. This significantly reduces the costs associated with vapor treatment.

Constructed air inlet locations are required to effectively deliver oxygen to the subsurface. To implement bioventing using a VE system to deliver oxygen to the subsurface, the permeability and stratigraphy of the soil must be evaluated to ensure that sufficient oxygen will be provide to the subsurface at depth. The success of the in situ bioventing process is dependent on its ability to deliver oxygen to the subsurface. Airflow must be induced by creating a vacuum in the subsurface and by providing constructed air inlet locations to direct the air to the contaminated soils in the subsurface. If air inlet locations at depth are not available, airflow will enter the soil from the surface, and the oxygen in the air may be consumed by microbes in the shallow soils. In this situation, the airflow to deeper soils may still provide a medium for extraction of volatiles from the soils, but will not deliver oxygen to the deeper soils to enhance biodegradation of contaminants using the indigenous microbial population.

REFERENCES

Hinchee, R. E., and S. K. Ong. 1992. "A Rapid In-Situ Respiration Test for Measuring Aerobic Biodegradation Rates of Hydrocarbons in Soil." *Journal of Air and Waste Management Association* 42: 1305-1312.

Kittel, J. A., R. E. Hinchee, R. Miller, C. Vogel, and R. Hoeppel. 1993. "In-Situ Respiration Testing: A Field Treatability Test for Bioventing." In *Proceedings of the 1993 Petroleum Hydrocarbons and Organic Chemicals in Groundwater: Prevention, Detection, and Restoration,* pp. 351-366. Houston, TX.

Morgan, P., and R. J. Watkinson. 1992. "Factors Limiting the Supply and Efficiency of Nutrient and Oxygen Supplements for the In-Situ Biotreatment of Contaminated Soil and Groundwater." *Water Resources* 26(1): 73-78.

Newman, W. A., and M. M. Martinson. 1992. "Let Biodegradation Promote In-Situ Soil Venting." *Remediation* Summer, pp. 277-291.

Rasiah, V., R. P. Voroney, and R. G. Kachanoski. 1992. "Biodegradation of an Oily Waste as Influenced by Nitrogen Forms and Sources." *Water, Air, and Soil Pollution* 65: 143-151.

Remediation Technologies Incorporated (ReTec). 1991. "Standard Method for Microbial Enumerations." January, pp. 1-11. Chapel Hill, NC.

U.S. Environmental Protection Agency (U.S. EPA). 1979. "Composting." *Process Design Manual: Sludge Treatment and Disposal,* p. 13. Municipal Environmental Research Laboratory, Cincinnati, OH.

Nitrogen Fate Model for Gas-Phase Ammonia-Enhanced In Situ Bioventing

Timothy R. Marshall

ABSTRACT

Subsurface bioremediation of contaminants is sometimes limited by the availability of nitrogen. Introduction of gaseous ammonia to the subsurface is a feasible and economical approach to enhance biodegradation in some environments. A gaseous nutrient source may be a practical option for sites where surface application of liquid nutrients is not possible, such as sites with shallow groundwater or sites with surface operations. A conceptual nitrogen fate model was developed to provide remediation scientists and engineers with some practical guidelines in the use of ammonia-enhanced bioventing. Ammonia supplied to the subsurface dissolves readily in soil moisture and sorbs strongly to soil particles. The ammonium ion is the preferred nutrient form of many microorganisms. Some of the ammonia will be converted to nitrate by ammonia-oxidizing organisms. Field monitoring data from an operating ammonia-enhanced bioventing remediation site for diesel fuel contamination are presented. Conservative additions of ammonia promoted appreciable increases in evolved carbon dioxide and rate of oxygen utilization. An overabundance of added ammonia promoted formation of methane from likely anaerobic hydrocarbon degradation in the presence of nitrate as the electron acceptor.

OVERVIEW

Nitrogen, an integral component of a variety of importance biological compounds, is used by microorganisms for growth, respiration, cell maintenance, and other metabolic functions (Brock 1979). For some environments where contaminant releases have occurred, sufficient nitrogen may be bound in soil organic matter or be found in the form of nitrogen salts. Additionally, biogeochemical cycling of available nitrogen supplies may be effective. For these sites, nutrient additions during remediation may not be necessary or may even cause further environmental impairment. However, biodegradation rates are reduced in some soil environments where natural nitrogen levels in soil may be low.

Oxygen transport by air flow is a more efficient mass transfer method than O_2- or air-saturated water (Dupont et al. 1991). Airflow is also a more uniform method of providing O_2 and gaseous nutrients to contaminated subsurface areas. Constraints at some bioremediation sites, particularly where in situ bioventing technology is used, preclude the use of solid or liquid nitrogen sources. Liquid nitrogen sources require special handling, storage, transportation, and spill contingency planning. Sites located in downtown urban areas or at active industrial facilities may be completely paved, and the use of a surface-applied liquid source is not possible. Additionally, applying liquid nutrients at sites where shallow groundwater is present may produce excess NO_3^- and may not be allowed by regulatory agencies.

Evaluation of the available nutrient status of contaminated aquifer and vadose zone systems is routinely conducted for biological remediation. Various forms of nitrogen are used by remediation engineers and scientists to augment the natural supply, including solid forms such as ammonium sulfate, ammonium nitrate, urea, and others. Liquid anhydrous ammonia (NH_3) is used extensively in agricultural and wastewater treatment applications. The anhydrous NH_3 is typically converted to NH_3 gas and introduced into wastestreams.

Gaseous NH_3 is a form of nitrogen that can be used simply and effectively to augment rates of biodegradation and mitigate low soil nitrogen levels in bioventing systems. NH_3 becomes available to microorganisms by dissolving readily in soil pore moisture. The ammonium ion (NH_4^+) is considered a fully available form of nitrogen and is actually preferred for many microorganisms, although nitrate (NO_3^-) is also utilized. The NH_4^+ is strongly adsorbing to cationic soil particles, and thus will not leach to groundwater as easily. Adsorption will also limit NH_3 transport by airflow. Table 1 is a summary of some properties of NH_3 relevant to its use in remediation strategies.

Cylinders of NH_3 in air mixtures (usually available from 1 to 10% by volume) or cylinders of liquid anhydrous ammonia can be integrated into existing remediation equipment. The gaseous NH_3 can be introduced into perimeter vapor

TABLE 1. Properties of ammonia gas.

1 ppm NH_3 = 0.71 mg NH_3/m^3 colorless, can be liquefied by compression	
molecular weight[a]	17.03
vapor pressure[a]	8.7 atm at 20°C
specific gravity[a]	0.817 at 79°C
solubility[a]	531,000 mg/L at 20°C
Henry's law constant[b] $K_H = [NH_{3(aq)}/P_{NH_3}]$	56.23

(a) Verschueren (1983).
(b) Stumm and Morgan (1981).

wells and pulled through the zone of contamination under negative pressure. Alternatively, the NH_3/air mixture can be injected into vapor wells in selected areas of a site including "hot spots." The method that maximizes the probability that NH_3 contacts the majority of the mass of contaminated soil is chosen.

Provisions for providing gaseous NH_3 to the subsurface are built into the reme-diation system. Required equipment includes cylinders of gaseous NH_3/air mix-tures, flowmeters, wellhead connections, and pressure gauges. Standard 2,000-psi cylinders normally contain approximately 120 ft^3 (3.4 m^3) of air. If the mixture is 10% NH_3/air, then the cylinder contains approximately 14 moles of NH_3. Liquid anhydrous NH_3 can provide up to 95% NH_3 under pressure, but must be diluted with air before injection. The information provided in Table 1 can be used to calculate theoretical quantities of NH_3 needed for a site-specific carbon load.

CONCEPTUAL FATE MODEL

The following discussion describes the conceptual fate of gaseous NH_3 and the ramifications on soil biochemical cycles in a contaminated soil system under-going active in situ bioventing. Figure 1 is a summary of the various conceptual processes. O_2 utilization, as calculated by controlled field testing, indicates that performance of the bioventing system is adequate, but is not optimum. Ground-water beneath the site is relatively shallow and is not impacted from the diesel fuel release. It is desired that O_2 utilization be enhanced.

Gaseous NH_3 introduced into the vadose zone dissolves in soil moisture read-ily and partitions into the water phase by the following reactions:

$$NH_{3(aqueous)} + H^+ = NH_4^+$$

$$NH_3 + H_2O = NH_4^+ + OH^-$$

A value for the dimensionless distribution coefficient for aqueous-gas equilibria for NH_3 defined as $H = C_{(gas)}/C_{(aqueous)}$ is listed by Stumm and Morgan (1981) as 0.00071, indicating that the gas will dissolve readily. Additionally, following establishment of equilibrium, diffusion of NH_3 will be controlled by gas-phase resistance.

Ammonia-oxidizing organisms may convert some of the NH_4^+ into nitrite (NO_2^-), NO_3^- and nitrogen oxides (NH_2OH) by the nitrification process (Brock 1979):

$$NH_3 + O_2 + AH_2 = NH_2OH + H_2O + A$$

where AH_2 is a source of reductant (Bedard and Knowles 1989).

$$NH_2OH \rightarrow NO_2^- \quad \text{(genus \textit{Nitrosomonas})}$$

$$NO_2^- \rightarrow NO_3^- \quad \text{(genus \textit{Nitrobacter})}$$

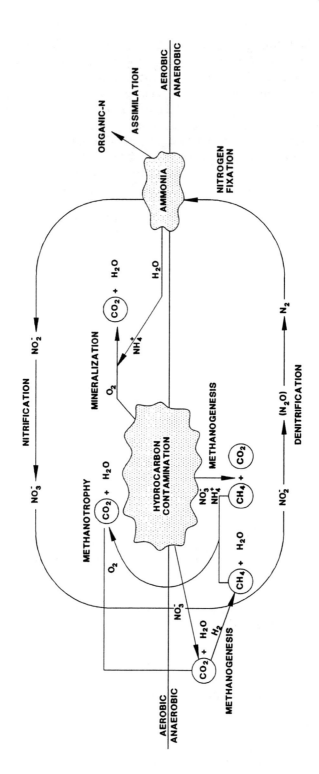

FIGURE 1. Conceptual nitrogen fate model.

Ammonia oxidation is an aerobic process, catalyzed by NH_3 oxygenase and hydroxylamine reductase. Additionally, in some environments, methanotrophic organisms can also oxidize NH_4^+ to NO_2^- in the presence of methane (Bedard and Knowles 1989).

Dissolved NO_3^- and NH_4^+ will subsequently be used by microorganisms as contaminants are biodegraded. The available nitrogen creates an extremely favorable environment for biodegradation of hydrocarbons. Aerobic biodegradation of contaminants, as well as nitrification processes, removes O_2 from the system rapidly. In the absence of O_2, certain groups of microorganisms will use the now-abundant available NO_3^- as an alternative electron acceptor and will continue to degrade the contaminants. However, methane (CH_4) may be formed because of the abundance of carbon dioxide (CO_2) formed, the availability of NO_3^- and reduced carbon, and the anaerobic conditions:

$$C_xH_y + NO_3^- = CH_4 + H_2O$$

where NO_3^- is the electron acceptor

$$4H_2 + CO_2 = CH_4 + 2H_2O$$

The production of CH_4 will cease as O_2 supplies are replenished. If the CH_4 concentrations are not removed from the system, utilization of the CH_4 by methanotrophic microorganisms may compete with aerobic mineralization for available O_2 (Large 1983):

$$CH_4 + O_2 = CO_2 + H_2O$$

In addition to assimilation during substrate degradation, NO_3^- may be lost from the system by denitrification under anaerobic conditions.

CASE STUDY

Subsurface investigations conducted at a facility detected diesel fuel-impacted soil at an approximate depth of 15 ft (4.6 m) below grade at concentrations to 57,000 mg/kg. The impacted soil underlies portions of the facility's parking structure, driveway, and fuel dispensing area. Excavation and off-site disposal of the impacted soil is not possible because of the presence of structures and extensive underground utility lines. Bioventing of the diesel fuel-impacted soil was chosen as the most feasible remedial technology.

Bench- and Field-Scale Testing

Bench- and field-scale testing was conducted at the facility to provide data for design of the bioventing system. Two vadose zone wells, designated as MW-1 (in noncontaminated soil) and MW-2 (in contaminated soil), were installed to a depth of approximately 25 ft (7.6 m) below grade. The zone of impacted soil is approximately 12 to 18 ft (3.6 to 5.5 m) below ground surface (Figure 2).

A limited bench-scale study was conducted using intact soil cores obtained during installation of the wells. The study evaluated the effects of nutrient and moisture additions on the rate of diesel fuel biodegradation and measured the reduction of diesel fuel in five treatment columns under the influence of simulated venting. The results indicated that biodegradation of diesel fuel can be enhanced in the laboratory soil cores by aeration and by providing supplemental nutrients.

Chemical and microbiological properties of the soil were evaluated for the bench-scale study. Native soil nitrogen values were found to be 1.73 mg/kg NH_3-N and 2.88 mg/kg NO_3^--N. Microbial populations (total heterotrophic organisms and hydrocarbon-oxidizing organisms) were estimated by enumeration on nutrient agar at 41 million colony-forming units per gram of dry soil (CFU/g) and 220,000 organisms per gram of dry soil measured as most probable number (mpn), respectively. The hydrocarbon-oxidizing population represents approximately 22% of the total population. These numbers indicate that the resident microbial populations are potentially adequate to support bioremediation at the site.

Field respiration testing of the bioventing system was conducted (details not reported here), as well as a limited NH_3 response testing. The concentration of gases (O_2, CO_2, NH_3, CH_4, and volatile organic compounds) in extracted air from Wells MW-1 and MW-2 were measured using a GA-90 Gas Analyzer (Landtec). Oxygen was also measured using a Beckman D2 paramagnetic oxygen meter. The instrument was calibrated using both atmospheric O_2 and a standard containing 17% O_2. Carbon dioxide was also measured using a Miran II wavelength-specific infrared analyzer. The instrument was calibrated in the laboratory using a standard containing 3.5% CO_2 in air. Ammonia was measured using Draeger colorimetric tubes (detection limit of 1 ppmv).

Table 2 is a summary of the concentrations of extracted gases from the vapor wells measured over the course of an NH_3 response test. Measurements were conducted in the field using an air sampling pump and the field instruments described above. The levels of O_2 and CO_2 detected during the test are similar to levels detected in previous testing at this site. Measurements taken on the first day of the field test show that O_2 readings in the extracted air are substantial (approximately 12% by volume in air from Well MW-2), indicating that O_2 utilization is limited. The CO_2 concentration was approximately 7% by volume on the beginning of testing (0.5% CO_2 was measured in extracted gas from Well MW-1 in a noncontaminated area). Oxygen concentrations in the extracted air measured on subsequent days remained at 17% to 18%, indicating limited consumption by microorganisms during the measurement period. Into both vapor wells 60 ft^3 (1.7 m^3) of 10% gaseous NH_3/air was injected to evaluate the effect of increased available nitrogen on O_2 utilization rates. Oxygen concentrations after 30 days (static conditions) decreased dramatically to approximately 3%, whereas historically the levels of O_2 have not declined below 10%. A slight increase in the amount of CO_2 was measured, and CH_4 levels increased to detectable levels. Ammonia

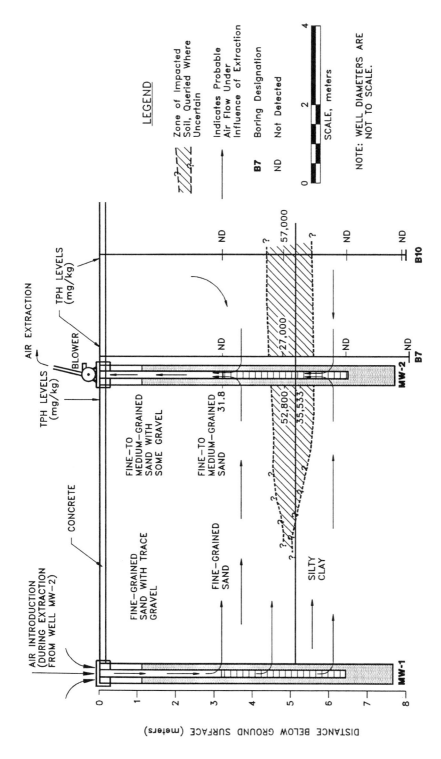

FIGURE 2. Schematic of subsurface conditions.

TABLE 2. Results of gas sampling.[a]

	Well MW-2 (Contaminated Conditions)				Well MW-1 (Noncontaminated Conditions)			
	O_2	CO_2	CH_4	NH_3	O_2	CO_2	CH_4	NH_3
Day 1 (static system)	12%	7%	<0.1%	—	19%	0.5%	<0.1%	—
Day 2 (after 8 hours of extraction)	17%	4%	<0.1%	—	19%	0.5%	<0.1%	—
Day 3 (after 48 hours of static system)	15%	4%	<0.1%	10	19%	0.5%	<0.1%	10
Day 4 (30 days following ammonia injection)	3%	6%	1-5%	none detected	19%	0.5%	<0.1%	2

(a) Results expressed in percent by volume except NH_3, which is expressed in parts per million by volume.

was not detectable in extracted air from Well MW-2 after 30 days. Methane was not detected either prior to or following NH_3 injection into Well MW-1.

CONCLUSIONS

The increase in O_2 utilization in Well MW-2 was most likely the result of the increase in available nitrogen. The produced CO_2 may have been used to some extent by methanogens.

Gaseous NH_3 is a relatively inexpensive and easy way to handle sources of nitrogen for bioremediation. The environmental dynamics are such that the nitrogen becomes usable immediately to microorganisms. Because it is easier to control in the gaseous state than as a liquid, gaseous NH_3 poses a greatly reduced potential for further environmental impairment. However, as shown above in the conceptual model and in data presented in the case study, judicious use of gaseous NH_3, coupled with an understanding of site biogeochemistry, is important.

Introduction of gaseous NH_3 may cause localized sterilization around well casings because of its relatively high solubility. It may be preferable at small sites to use clean vapor wells or perimeter wells as introduction points and move the gaseous NH_3 to more heavily contaminated subsurface areas under induced vacuum. At sites with widespread contamination or localized highly contaminated soil, it may be necessary to inject gaseous NH_3 into well casings in the most contaminated zones.

Methane can form if subsurface O_2 supplies become temporarily depleted, particularly if available nitrogen exceeds demand. Methane formation should be avoided at sites in areas where populations may be at risk. At some sites and for certain contaminants, however, it may be advantageous to design an alternating aerobic/anaerobic bioventing system. Further evaluation of the effects of increased nitrogen supplies for bioventing is warranted.

REFERENCES

Bedard, C., and R. Knowles. 1989. "Physiology, Biochemistry, and Specific Inhibitors of CH_4, NH_4^+, and CO Oxidation by Methanotrophs and Nitrifiers." *Microbiological Reviews*, 53(1):68-84.

Brock, T. D. 1979. *The Biology of Microorganisms*. Prentice-Hall, Inc., Englewood Cliffs, NJ.

Dupont, R. R., W. J. Doucette, and R. E. Hinchee. 1991. "Assessment of In Situ Bioremediation Potential and the Application of Bioventing at a Fuel-Contaminated Site." In R. E. Hinchee and R. F. Olfenbuttel (Eds.), *In Situ Bioreclamation: Applications and Investigations for Hydrocarbon and Contaminated Site Remediation*, pp. 262-282. Butterworth-Heinemann, Stoneham, MA.

Large, P. J. 1983. *Methylotrophy and Methanogenesis. Aspects of Microbiology*, Vol. 8. American Society for Microbiology, Washington, DC.

Stumm, W., and J. J. Morgan. 1981. *Aquatic Chemistry*. John Wiley and Sons, New York, NY.

Verschueren, K. 1983. *Handbook of Environmental Data on Organic Chemicals*. Van Nostrand Reinhold Company, New York, NY.

Determination of the Rate-Limiting Process for Bioventing

César Gómez-Lahoz, José Miguel Rodríguez-Maroto, and David J. Wilson

ABSTRACT

Vadose zone remediation by bioventing may be rate limited by biological activity or mass transfer processes affecting the stripping of the contaminant and the supply of oxygen from the gaseous to the aqueous phase. Knowledge of the rate coefficients for both processes is required for sound design and operation of bioventing systems. The rapid in situ respiration test presented by Hinchee and Ong (1992), together with the model presented here, can be used for the estimation of both kinetic parameters. These results indicate that oxygen supply to the aqueous phase may be, in some cases, the rate-limiting step for biodegradation. Equivalent aqueous diffusion lengths calculated from the mass transfer coefficients obtained are relatively small, in the range of few millimeters. The model can be used for decision making for bioventing optimization.

INTRODUCTION

Mass-transfer kinetic limitations frequently are responsible for the very low success rate observed in remediation technologies based on groundwater pump and treat. These limitations are usually related to the very low diffusivities of the contaminants in the aqueous phase, typically four orders of magnitude smaller than diffusivities of the same substances in air. One immediate consequence of this situation is the much higher success rate of soil vapor extraction (SVE) compared to groundwater pump and treat. Nevertheless, mass-transfer kinetic limitations have also been observed occasionally for SVE (see, for instance Wilson and Clarke, 1994), and therefore, should also be expected to occur in bioventing systems. Thus, understanding these processes is necessary for sound design monitoring and operation of bioventing as much as for SVE. This requires relatively complicated models which must include the description of the biological and the mass transfer processes. It is hoped that this model and its future refinements will prove useful in extracting from preliminary tests and pilot studies the parameters needed to model the expected behavior of full-scale operations under various conditions of airflow, moisture content, nutrient amendment, etc. This should prove useful in feasibility studies (what airflow must be delivered to all of the contaminated domain, for instance), and in design of optimal systems and operating conditions. For instance, the results of the fast in situ respiration tests, such as those described by Hinchee and Ong (1992), are used this paper for the determination of both the rate of the biological activity and the rate of mass transfer of oxygen from the gaseous to the aqueous phase.

MODEL DESCRIPTION

In the present model hydrocarbons and biodegradable solvents spilled in the vadose zone are considered to be basically in three phases: gaseous, aqueous, and nonaqueous phase liquid (NAPL). For soils with significant natural organic matter content sorption onto solids should also be included with the additional thermodynamic and kinetic parameters. A previous version of this model is reported by Gómez-Lahoz et al. (1994). Adsorption of organics to the soil is not explicitly included in the present model. If the adsorption isotherm for this is linear, adsorption should have effects on the behavior of the system similar to reductions in the contaminant Henry's constant and aqueous solubility. It is assumed in the model that the NAPL phase, if present, is separated from the vapor phase by an aqueous film, so that the air-water and water-NAPL phases may be approximated as equal. We anticipate that, as more and better data become available, the model will require further elaboration, certainly including adsorption of contaminant on soil and probably including a more precise description of the distribution of pollutants, water, and biomass in the soil pores.

The rate of change of the concentration in the aqueous phase due to the transport from the NAPL or gas phases is considered to be proportional to a driving force given by the actual bulk concentration of the component in one phase and the concentration that would be in equilibrium with the bulk concentration of the other phase. The different mass transfer coefficients, λ, are defined by equations 1 through 3.

$$\left(\frac{\partial O^s}{\partial t}\right)_{\text{phase exchange}} = \lambda_o \left[\frac{O^v}{K_{ho}}\right] - O^s \tag{1}$$

$$\left(\frac{\partial C^s}{\partial t}\right)_{\text{phase exchange}} = \lambda_o \left[\frac{C^v}{K_{hc}} - C^s\right] + \lambda_c' [S - C^s] \tag{2}$$

$$\left(\frac{\partial C^v}{\partial t}\right)_{\text{phase exchange}} = -\lambda_c \frac{\omega}{v}\left[\frac{C^v}{K_{hc}} - C^s\right] + \lambda_c'' \left[\frac{M_w P_v}{RT} - C^v\right] \tag{3}$$

where C^i and O^i are the contaminant and oxygen concentrations (mg/L) for the aqueous ($i = s$) and the gaseous ($i = v$) phase and M_w and P_v are the molar weight and vapor pressure of the contaminant. Other notation is defined in Table 1.

TABLE 1. Default values for the parameters.

Parameter	Default Value
Void fraction associated with the mobile phase (υ)	0.2
Volumetric moisture content of the soil (ω)	0.2
Initial contaminant concentration	1,500 mg cont./L soil
Contaminant aqueous solubility (S)	1,750 mg/L
Henry's constant of contaminant (K_{hc})	$1 \cdot 10^{-3}$
Henry's constant of oxygen (K_{ho})	30
Biomass yield coefficient (n)	0.5 g biomass/g substrate
Stoichiometric coefficient for oxygen (n_o)	3.5 g oxygen/g substrate
Stoichiometric coefficient for endogenous respiration (n_o)	0 g oxygen/g biomass
Maximum velocity constant (K_{max})	$1.54 \cdot 10^{-4}$ to $2 \cdot 10^{-3}$ s^{-1}
Half-saturation constant of substrate (K_c)	0.1 mg/L
Half-saturation constant of oxygen (K_o)	0.1 mg/L
Die-off coefficient of biomass (K_B)	10^{-6} s^{-1}

The main resistance for the mass transfer of oxygen between the gaseous phase and aqueous phase will be the diffusion through the aqueous phase given the difference between the diffusivity values for each phase. This is also true for contaminants with Henry's constants of 10^{-3} or more, for which the amount stripped with air could be significant for the remediation.

No mass transfer resistance between the NAPL and the other two phases could be on the NAPL side, since the NAPL is considered here to be pure and no diffusion is required for the contaminant to reach the interface. Thus the ratio λ_c'/λ_c'' will probably be similar (or even smaller under advecting conditions) to the ratio between the diffusivities in the aqueous and gaseous phases; this is about 10^{-4}. Thus, if mass transfer kinetic limitations occur, the portion of NAPL with gas/NAPL interface will be stripped very early during the remediation process, leaving behind that NAPL which requires diffusion through the aqueous phase to be removed. On the other hand, if the mass transfer coefficients are large enough, the gaseous concentration will be that given by the contaminant vapor pressure, no matter what transport processes are taking place. Therefore, direct transport between the NAPL and gas phase has not been included in the model (the second term on the right-hand side of equation 3 is omitted), because it is not significant for the design and operation of bioventing. This could yield some discrepancies between the model and field results, but only during the first stages of the remediation process.

The biological processes are described by Monod kinetics with an inhibition factor similar to that used by Kindred and Celia (1989) (I = 1 + B/B*), without which the model would impose no limit on the microorganism population. This inhibition factor is a simple mathematical tool to force an upper limit for the biomass concentration, and represents several of the natural mechanisms that will actually limit the growth of the microorganisms. Included among these mechanisms are:

1. nutrient (N, P, K, ...) limitations, with biomass reaching a steady population at that point where nutrient uptake by the living microorganisms equals nutrient return by mineralization, or
2. biofilm diffusion limitations; the model assumes fully-penetrated biofilms, but when large biomass concentrations occur this assumption is no longer valid, resulting in some of the microorganisms having lower available concentrations of the various substances necessary for biological activity.

Therefore no terms are included in the model to explicitly describe the possible nutrient limitations; the equations for the substances present in the aqueous phase include the biological terms and the transport from the gas phase (for oxygen and the contaminant) and from the NAPL for the contaminant:

$$\frac{\partial B}{\partial t} = K_{max} \frac{n\,B}{I} \frac{C^s}{K_c + C^s} \frac{O^s}{K_o + O^s} - K_B\, B \tag{4}$$

$$\frac{\partial C^s}{\partial t} = -K_{max} \frac{B}{I} \frac{C^s}{K_c + C^s} \frac{O^s}{K_o + O^s} + \lambda_c \left[\frac{C^v}{K_{hc}} - C^s \right] + \lambda_c' \left[S - C^s \right] \tag{5}$$

$$\frac{\partial O^s}{\partial t} = -n_o\, K_{max} \frac{B}{I} \frac{C^s}{K_c + C^s} \frac{O^s}{K_o + O^s} - n_o'\, K_B\, B + \lambda_o \left[\frac{O^v}{K_{ho}} - O^s \right] \tag{6}$$

The model is completed with the equations corresponding to the rate of change of oxygen and the contaminant concentrations in the aqueous phase, which include the advection terms and the rate of change of NAPL concentration (C^L; mg/L of soil) in the soil:

$$\frac{\partial O^v}{\partial t} = -\lambda_o \frac{\omega}{v} \left[\frac{O^v}{K_{ho}} - O^s \right] - \frac{\partial\,(v O^v)}{\partial x} \tag{7}$$

$$\frac{\partial C^v}{\partial t} = \lambda_c \frac{\omega}{v} \left[\frac{C^v}{K_{hc}} - C^s \right] - \frac{\partial\,(v C^v)}{\partial x} \tag{8}$$

$$\frac{\partial C^L}{\partial t} = \lambda_c'\, \omega\, \left[S - C^s \right] \tag{9}$$

MODEL RESULTS

Equations 4 through 9 are integrated forward in time using a predictor-corrector algorithm to simulate the fast in situ respiration tests presented by Hinchee and Ong (1992). Once the blower is shut down the advection terms are set equal to zero ($v = 0$). Results for these respiration tests are independent of most of the parameter values used (default values in Table 1), as long as, at the blower shutdown, the vapor phase oxygen concentration is close to atmospheric concentration, and the contaminant concentration is not limiting the biological activity ($C^s \gg K_c$). Therefore the values of these parameters, not relevant to this paper, are not necessarily those of the field cases studied. The in situ monitoring tests are modeled assuming a steady biomass population, so equation 4 is set equal to 0. This yields, for $O^s \gg K_o$ and $C^s \gg K_c$:

$$B = (K_{max} \, n - K_B)B* \tag{10}$$

where we use the same value for $B*$ (0.1 mg/L) as Kindred and Celia (1989). Other assumptions for these runs are that the ratio between the aqueous/gaseous mass transfer coefficients for oxygen and the contaminant (λ_o/λ_c) is equal to the ratio between the corresponding aqueous diffusivities, approximately 2, and that the contaminant mass transfer coefficients, λ_c and λ'_c, are equal since both are controlled by diffusion through the aqueous phase.

For the in situ respirometric tests, when oxygen uptake is controlled by the biological activity, linear plots are observed down to oxygen concentrations in the gaseous phase in equilibrium with an aqueous-phase concentration close to the half-saturation constant for oxygen. On the other hand, for oxygen uptake limited by the mass transfer from the gaseous to the aqueous phase, logarithmic curves are obtained. This can be observed in Figure 1, where results for the Patuxent Naval Air Station site, together with the model results are presented. The biological parameter was calculated by linear regression of the experimental data, as $K_{max} = 1.54 \cdot 10^{-4} \, s^{-1}$. Several values for λ_o have been tested, indicating that for the lower λ_o values the process would be rate limited by mass transport. The experimental values of oxygen concentration do not approach a logarithmic pattern down to the lowest values reported, so we can only estimate a minimum value for λ_o, about $4 \cdot 10^{-4} \, s^{-1}$.

The mass transport is most probably controlled by diffusion in the aqueous phase, so the diffusion length (Dx) may be estimated, assuming that diffusion is taking place from a flat surface, as:

$$V\frac{dC}{dt} = D_{aq} \, A\frac{C^g/K_{hc} - C^s}{\Delta x} = V \, \lambda_o \, (C^g/K_{hc} - C^s); \, \Delta x = \left(\frac{D_{aq}}{\lambda_o}\right)^{1/2} \tag{11}$$

This gives a maximum value for the diffusion length for oxygen in the aqueous phase of 2.3 mm.

In a similar fashion, minimum values of the mass transfer coefficients have been estimated for the experimental values presented by Hinchee and Ong for

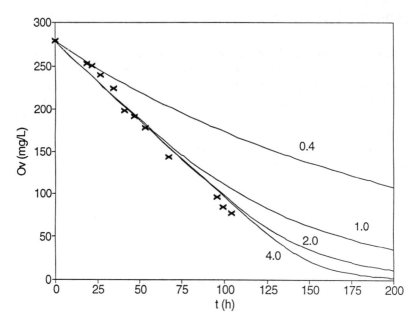

FIGURE 1. Patuxent Naval Air Station results (×) and curves obtained from the model, with values of λ_o of 0.4; 1; 2 and $4 \cdot 10^{-4} s^{-1}$. For all runs $K_{max} = 1.54 \cdot 10^{-4} s^{-1}$.

Tyndall (Figure 2) and Fallon AFBs (Figure 3). The experimental values for Tyndall were linear down to low values of gaseous-phase oxygen concentration while those for Fallon departed from linearity at relatively high values. The minimum values for λ_o are $2 \cdot 10^{-3} s^{-1}$ for Tyndall and $4 \cdot 10^{-4} s^{-1}$ for Fallon, which correspond to values for the diffusion length of 1.0 and 2.3 mm, respectively.

Figure 4 presents the experimental values reported for Eielson AFB with some of the results obtained with our model. Here the mass transfer coefficient for oxygen, λ_o, is the same for the three runs ($3.5 \cdot 10^{-4} s^{-1}$), and the maximum rate parameter, K_{max}, is changed from $8.9 \cdot 10^{-4}$ to $2 \cdot 10^{-3} s^{-1}$. As can be seen, good agreement is obtained between the model results and the experimental values down to relatively low values of the oxygen concentration. We understand that the lower experimental values are less reliable, and could be affected by several mechanisms, such as oxygen diffusion from the soil surface (the monitoring wells at Eielson are quite shallow), the sampling procedure (which requires purging three or four well volumes) or advective transport induced by oxygen uptake, which may happen if CO_2 does not evolve at the same rate as O_2 is consumed.

This kind of information can be very useful for decision making even for those sites already in operation. For instance, as long as the biological processes are controlling the rate of biodegradation one can decrease the airflow rate down to that value for which the gaseous-phase oxygen concentration in the soil is enough to maintain the same rate of biodegradation. On the other hand, for

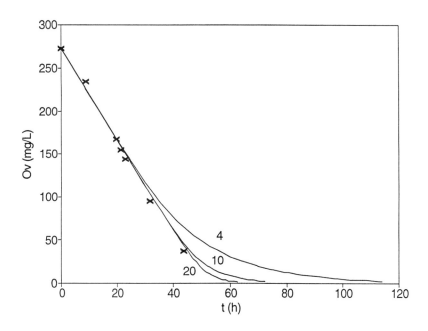

FIGURE 2. Tyndall AFB results (×) and curves obtained from the model, with values of λ_o of 4; 10 and $20 \cdot 10^{-4} \text{s}^{-1}$. For all runs $K_{max} = 4.5 \cdot 10^{-4} \text{s}^{-1}$.

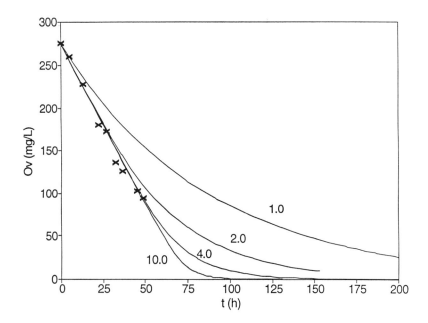

FIGURE 3. Fallon AFB results (×) and curves obtained from the model, with values of λ_o of 1; 2; 4 and $10 \cdot 10^{-4} \text{s}^{-1}$. For all runs $K_{max} = 3.16 \cdot 10^{-4} \text{s}^{-1}$.

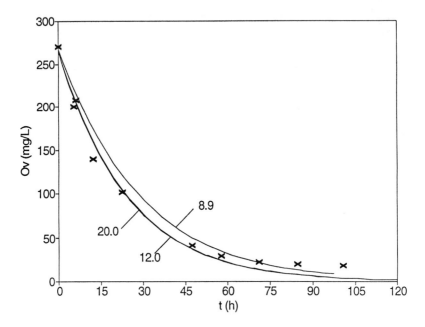

FIGURE 4. Eielson AFB results (x) and curves obtained from the model, with values of K_{max} of 8.9, 12 and $20 \cdot 10^{-4} s^{-1}$. For all runs $\lambda_o = 3.5 \cdot 10^{-4} s^{-1}$.

those sites where biodegradation is controlled by mass transfer kinetics, efforts to increase the biological activity such as nutrient addition to the soil, will be useless. In any case, rate parameter estimation would require that the fast in situ respirometric tests are carried out down to values of gaseous-phase oxygen concentration as low as possible within reliable values.

REFERENCES

Gómez-Lahoz, C., J. M. Rodríguez-Maroto, and D. J. Wilson. 1994. "Biodegradation phenomena during soil vapor extraction: A high-speed nonequilibrium model." *Sep. Sci. and Technol.* 29(4): 429-463.

Hinchee, R. E., and S. K. Ong. 1992. "A rapid in situ respiration test for measuring aerobic biodegradation rates of hydrocarbons in soil." *J. of the Air & Waste Management Association* 42(10): 1305-1312.

Kindred, J. S. and M. A. Celia. 1989. "Contaminant transport and biodegradation. 2. Conceptual model and test simulations." *Water Resources Research* 25(6): 1149-1159.

Wilson, D. J., and A. N. Clarke. 1994. *Hazardous Waste Site Soil Remediation, Theory and Application of Innovative Technologies.* Marcel Dekker, Inc., New York, NY.

Passive Bioventing Driven by Natural Air Exchange

Dean C. Foor, Thomas C. Zwick, Robert E. Hinchee,
Ron E. Hoeppel, Chris Kyburg, and Leon Bowling

ABSTRACT

Bioventing wells installed in the vadose zone of petroleum-contaminated sites at the Marine Corps Air Ground Combat Center (MCAGCC) in Twentynine Palms, California, naturally inhale and exhale air. This natural air exchange appears to be driven primarily by barometric pressure changes. The natural air exchange was utilized to engineer a passive bioventing system in which a valve allows only air injection and prevents soil gas extraction. The system is effective in aerating petroleum-contaminated, oxygen-limited subsurface soils. This aeration resulted in enhanced biological activity and site remediation. The bioventing wells (vent wells) were fitted with a passive valve mechanism that opens when the atmospheric pressure overcomes the internal vent well pressure. When the valve is open it permits atmospheric air to enter the vent well and infiltrate into the soil, thereby stimulating bioremediation. When the vent well pressure overcomes atmospheric pressure, the valve is closed and inhibits soil gas extraction. The vent wells are installed in a coarse sand where the depth to groundwater is approximately 220 ft (67 m). Generally, deeper vent wells produce greater flowrates. Passive airflow rates of up to 7 cfm (12 m^3/h) have been achieved at the bioventing wells.

PASSIVE BIOVENTING DRIVEN BY NATURAL AIR EXCHANGES

Bioventing is the process of aerating subsurface soils to stimulate in situ biological activity and promote bioremediation. Bioventing differs from soil venting in remedial approach. Soil venting is designed and operated to maximize the volatilization of low-molecular-weight compounds, with some biodegradation occurring. In contrast, bioventing is designed to maximize biodegradation of aerobically biodegradable compounds, regardless of their molecular weight, with some volatilization occurring. Bioventing is gaining wide acceptance as a remediation alternative at petroleum-contaminated sites (Kittel et al. 1993).

During routine bioventing investigation of a JP-5 jet fuel-contaminated site at the Expeditionary Air Field at the MCAGCC in Twentynine Palms, California, it was observed that bioventing wells installed in the unsaturated soils "breathed," or inhaled and exhaled air. During initial investigation of the breathing cycles, manual sampling of critical environmental parameters was conducted. Due to the need for intensive sampling to successfully map the breathing patterns, manual data gathering was replaced with an automated data acquisition system (DAS). The DAS was developed to record readings from many sensors at frequent intervals over long durations of time on a remote site. The DAS gathered the necessary data to gain an understanding of the breathing cycles. The DAS also was used after passive bioventing had begun to monitor system performance. Similar breathing cycles were observed during environmental investigating at the Hanford and Savannah River Sites. The breathing cycles were utilized to design a passive vapor extraction system (Rohay et al. 1993). The purpose of this paper is to describe the research performed to explain natural air exchanges and to describe the preliminary design of a valve for passive bioventing.

METHODS

Once a breathing cycle had been observed it was necessary to attempt to understand the pattern of the cycle and the factors that control the cycle. Initial data gathering was performed manually. Long-term data gathering was performed with electronic sensors and coupled to the DAS.

Data Acquisition System Development

Data Acquisition System. The DAS was designed to ensure rapid and complete data collection to enable data collection from electronic sensors over an extended period of time. The Fluke Hydra Data Bucket was the system utilized.

Electronic Barometer. An electronic barometer (Omega model PX960) was used to monitor the local barometric pressure. The barometer produces a voltage output that correlates to the actual barometric pressure. The barometer was factory-calibrated and has an accuracy of 0.01 in. Hg (0.02 mbar). Voltage output from the barometer and barometric pressure information for the same 2-day period were compared. From the comparison, a correlation factor to translate the voltage output to barometric pressure was determined.

Differential Pressure Sensors. Differential pressure sensors (Dwyer Photohelic series 3000MR) were used to monitor soil gas pressures relative to barometric pressure. The sensors integrate a traditional pressure gauge with a corresponding amperage output. Each of 12 sensors was factory-calibrated and laboratory-tested. The sensors had an accuracy of approximately 0.01 in. H_2O (0.02 mbar).

Groundwater Pressure Transducer. A groundwater pressure transducer (In Situ Inc. model PXD-260) was used to monitor small fluctuations in the ground-water elevation. The transducer was factory-calibrated and laboratory-tested. The pressure range for the transducer is 10 ft of water (0.3 bar). The transducer has an accuracy of approximately 0.01 ft of water (0.3 mbar).

Air Velocity Transducer. An air velocity transducer (TSI Inc. model 8470) was used to monitor the velocity of air moving through the vent wells being sampled. The transducer was factory-calibrated and laboratory-tested. The trans-ducer had a monitoring range of 20 to 2,000 ft/min (6 to 610 m/min) and an accuracy of 10 ft/min (3 m/min). This allowed for measurements of flow in a 2-in. (5-cm)-diameter well of up to ~40 cfm (~68 m^3/h).

Thermocouples. Standard type J thermocouples were used to measure atmo-spheric temperatures and the temperatures within the vent wells. The thermo-couples were laboratory-tested against ice and boiling water.

All sensor output was recorded by the DAS onto a portable, nonvolatile PCMCIA memory card for transfer to a Hewlett Packard 200LX palmtop compu-ter and then to a laptop computer for analysis. Data analysis and graphs were produced in Microsoft Excel 5.0.

The first sampling period using the DAS covered approximately 200 h. During this sampling period the following data were collected every 15 min: airflow from one 2-in. (5-cm)-diameter SCH 40 polyvinyl chloride (PVC) vent well screened from 10 to 60 ft (3 to 18 m); soil gas pressure from 12 monitoring points at various depths and three different distances from the vent well; baro-metric pressure; temperature at three locations within the vent well and one atmospheric location; and groundwater elevation at one monitoring well. Addi-tional sampling was performed at a location with a different depth to the ground-water table. Sampling was also performed at a deeper vent well screened from 20 to 190 ft (6 to 58 m).

RESULTS AND DISCUSSION

Data were gathered to determine the capabilities of the breathing cycles to promote passive bioventing and to obtain an estimate of the radius of influence of a passive bioventing well. Information obtained during the initial manual sampling events was used in the design of valves for the vent wells. Data also were gathered to determine the magnitude of oxygen increase that could be obtained in the soil gas.

Airflow

Data obtained from the DAS provided the necessary information to explain the breathing cycles of the vent wells. Figure 1 shows the barometric pressure change (in. Hg) and vent well flowrate (cfm) of one 2-in. (5-cm)-diameter vent

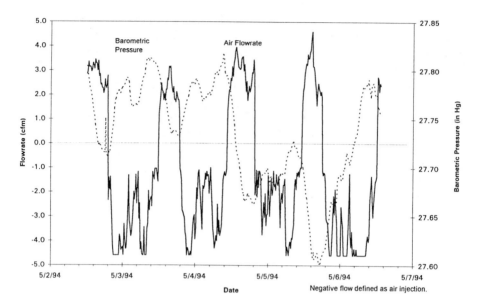

FIGURE 1.   Air flowrate and barometric pressure vs. time at 17A-VW4
(17A-VW4 screened 10 to 60 ft).

well screened from 10 to 60 ft (3 to 18 m) vs. elapsed time. The figure shows
that, during one summer day, the barometric pressure rose until early evening
and then began to fall until the following morning. The figure also shows that
due to the barometric pressure changing, the airflow from the vent well inhaled
for approximately 16 h and exhaled for approximately 8 h. The average inhale
airflow rate was approximately 2.6 cfm (4.4 m³/h) with maximum airflow rates
greater than 5 cfm (8.5 m³/h).

The most current data sampling shows that airflow rates of up to 15 cfm
(25 m³/h) have been observed in a deeper vent well, screened from 20 to 190 ft
(6 to 58 m). However, vent well airflow rates greater than 5 cfm (8.5 m³/h)
generally last for only short periods of time.

It should be noted that above summary is for data that were collected during
summer months when the weather patterns are relatively consistent. Observations of vent well airflow and barometric pressure made during the winter
months follow a less consistent pattern due to frequent changes in the weather.

Estimated Radius of Influence

Soil gas pressures were monitored at three monitoring points located 17, 80,
and 181 ft (5, 24, and 55 m) from the 2-in. (5-cm)-diameter vent well screened
from 10 to 60 ft (3 to 18 m). Each monitoring point, was screened at several
depths. The soil gas pressure was measured at the monitoring points for more
than 24 h both when the vent well was closed and when it was breathing. A

comparison between the maximum soil gas pressures reached while the vent well was closed and when it was open was made to estimate the radius of influence. Utilizing the steady-state method for radius of influence calculation (Johnson et al. 1990) and empirical data from other bioventing sites, an estimate of 20 ft (6 m) was made for the radius of influence. Testing at other vent wells produced similar results.

It appears that the radius of influence based on oxygen increase may be greater. Subsurface soil gas oxygen sensors were installed to collect data pertaining to the increase in oxygen caused by passive bioventing.

Mechanical and Passive Valve Designs

Interpretation of the soil gas pressure data and airflow rate data indicated that it might be possible to increase soil gas oxygen levels if a valve could be designed to allow air injection but prevent air extraction. A passive valve was designed to provide the necessary valving of the vent wells. A schematic of this passive valve is shown in Figure 2. A sample of the results from using the

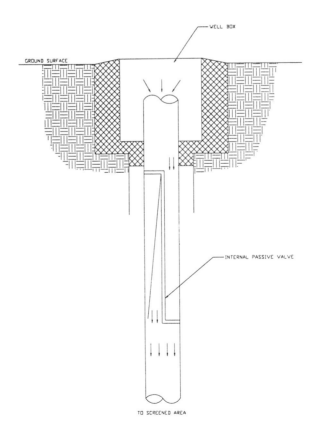

FIGURE 2. Passive valve design.

passive valve is provided in Figure 3. On the figure, negative flow is defined as air injection. The valve opens when the atmospheric pressure overcomes well pressure, at which time air begins to enter the soil. The valve closes when well pressure becomes greater than the atmospheric pressure and soil gas would normally begin to exhale from the well.

Soil Gas Oxygen Increase

An important factor was to determine if the soil gas oxygen concentrations could be increased as a result of this air injection. The passive valve was attached to the wellhead of a 1.5-in. (3.8-cm)-diameter vent well screened from 10 to 40 ft (3 to 12 m). Soil gas oxygen concentrations in monitoring points 9 ft (2.7 m) from the vent well were monitored several weeks prior to air injection and then once a day after passive air injection had begun. The soil gas readings taken during this testing period are shown in Figure 4. The results from this testing demonstrated that the oxygen concentrations could be increased with passive air injection.

CONCLUSIONS

Although the concept of passive bioventing is fairly new, bioventing is an established remediation technology for hydrocarbon-contaminated soils. Passive

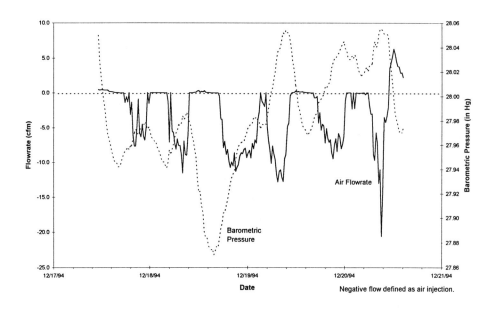

FIGURE 3. Flowrate and barometric pressure vs. time at 17A-VW4 (17A-VW4 screened 10 to 65 ft [3 to 20 m]).

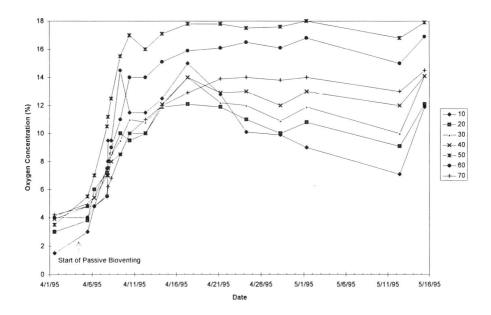

FIGURE 4. Oxygen levels during passive BV at 17A-MPH.

bioventing as described in this paper appears to be an approach that could reduce costs at many sites. It may be an especially attractive alternative for remote locations.

REFERENCES

Johnson, P. C., M. W. Kemblowski, and J. D. Colthart. 1990. "Quantitative Analysis for the Cleanup of Hydrocarbon-Contaminated Soils by In-Situ Soil Venting." *Ground Water 28*(3).

Kittel, J. A., R. E. Hinchee, R. N. Miller, C. Vogel, and R. Hoeppel. 1993. "In Situ Respiration Testing: A Field Treatability Test for Bioventing." *Proceedings of NGWA Petroleum Hydrocarbons Conference*, Houston, TX.

Rohay, V., J. Rossabi, B. Looney, R. Cameron, and B. Peters. 1993. "Well Venting and Application of Passive Soil Vapor Extraction at Hanford and Savannah River." *Proceedings ER'93 Environmental Remediation Conference*, Augusta, GA.

Measurement of Toluene Bioconversion During Ventilation in a Bench-Scale Soil Column

Grzegorz Malina, Tim Grotenhuis,
Chiel Cuypers, and Wim Rulkens

ABSTRACT

The ratio between ventilation and biodegradation of toluene in the vadose zone during bioventing was studied by bench-scale soil column experiments, using gas chromatography headspace analysis. Biodegradation batch tests showed that toluene vapor concentrations above 75% of the saturation concentration completely retarded the bioconversion rate. To determine the role of bioconversion and physical removal of toluene from soil, CO_2-free air and N_2 were used, respectively, as flushing gases, with a flowrate of 1.0 L/h or 39.5 $cm^3/(cm^2 \cdot h)$. In a column with ca. 4 kg of sandy soil, at a water content of 15% w/w, i.e., 75% of field capacity, and temperature 20°C, the initial concentration of toluene, 4,000 mg/kg, was reduced within 11 days to between 0.5 and 0.2 mg/kg during bioventing, and to between 60 and 70 mg/kg when bioconversion was not involved. Soil extraction after 24 days of venting showed a residual toluene concentration of 1.4 mg/kg. Mass balance analysis of toluene and CO_2 indicated that about 90% of toluene was evaporated and 10% was biodegraded. Time constants for volatilization and bioconversion were comparable at the flowrate applied. These results enable determination of the optimum airflow for venting and oxygen supply required for toluene biodegradation, and design of an optimum bioventing strategy for toluene removal.

INTRODUCTION

The use of airflow to remove volatile organic contaminants from the vadose zone and the biodegradation of contaminants by indigenous microorganisms are two attractive alternatives for in situ remediation of contaminated sites. When evaporation is minimized this process is referred to as bioventing. Evaporation especially occurs of the highly volatile constituents of the hydrocarbon mixture. Biodegradation can address both the less-volatile compounds and the volatile organics not evaporated during initial venting. Integrating these two processes allows a more diverse range of oil products to be remediated biologically in situ. Biodegradability of oil constituents has been extensively studied (Alvarez et al. 1991, Atlas 1981, Gibson 1984). Lab microcosm tests and both unsaturated and saturated soil columns have been used to investigate biodegradation and/or volatilization of organic compounds including oil mixtures (Baehr et al. 1989, Hinchee et al. 1994, Johnson 1993, van der Meer at al. 1992, Sims et al. 1993). This study was aimed to design short-term lab tests to find an optimum in the airflow for ventilation and the oxygen consumption rate needed for bioconversion to reduce the remediation costs for hydrocarbon-contaminated soil. The bioventing process was simulated in a bench-scale unsaturated soil column. The experimental setup allows semicontinuous monitoring of vented and biodegraded toluene, and consequently the application of this method for optimization and modeling of the bioventing process (de Wit et al. 1995).

MATERIALS AND METHODS

Laboratory Experiments

Sandy soil collected from an uncontaminated location at the Agricultural Test Station Kielekamp in Wageningen, The Netherlands, was air-dried and stored at 4°C prior to use. Toluene of 99.5% purity was purchased from Janssen Chimica.

Experimental Setup for Soil Bioventing. A scheme of the installation for soil bioventing is shown in Figure 1. Glass columns with a volume of ca. 4 L (60 cm × 9.6 cm i.d.) were used. Soil of 3.85 kg dry matter, after water adjustment to 75% of its field capacity (150 g H_2O/kg soil), was homogenized and packed to the height of 45 cm. Then 17.5 g of toluene was added to the column via sampling port 1. Nitrogen (ventilation), and CO_2-free air (bioventing) were applied at the bottom of the column, at constant flowrate of 39.5 $cm^3/(cm^2 \cdot h)$ with a total ε_{air} = (0.5 to 0.15), leading to mean gas residence time in the soil column of about 1 hour. Soil vapors in ports 2 and 3 and headspace were sampled for toluene at least once per day. CO_2 production and O_2 uptake were monitored with the same frequency only in the headspace (outlet gas). CO_2 was captured in 0.5M NaOH solution. A column without toluene was used as a control for indigenous CO_2 production. Prior to release, the outlet gas passed the columns containing activated carbon to determine the total evaporation of toluene with flushing gas. Wet gas meters were used to determine the volume of flushing gas that passed through the column. All pipe connections were either from glass or Teflon™, and Viton™ septa were used for sampling ports. At the end of the experiment, columns were dismantled for analysis of the residual concentration of toluene in soil, water content, and pH of the soil.

Batch Microcosms. The microcosms for biodegradation tests were 0.5-L glass bottles containing 75 g of soil with the moisture of 15% w/w, at 75% of

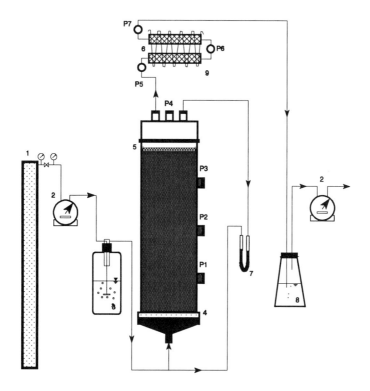

FIGURE 1. Lab installation for soil bioventing. 1 — N_2/CO_2-free air; 2 — wet gas meters; 3 — gas washer; 4 — glass filter, 5 — soil column (glass); 6 — activated carbon columns; 7 — manometer; 8 — CO_2-absorption chamber; 9 — heating wires; P1 — sampling port.

soil field capacity. Viton™ caps minimized hydrocarbon adsorption. The remaining headspace maintained aerobic conditions throughout the experiments. All tests were prepared in triplicate. The microcosms could be sampled repeatedly through Viton™ septa without significant toluene loss. Toluene was added to the initial concentrations of 210, 275, and 485 mg/L. Adsorption of toluene on soil led to 75% and 100% saturation, and to calculated oversaturation of 150% in the gas phase, respectively. Concentrations of toluene in headspace were monitored over time at intervals depending on the change in concentrations. O_2 uptake and CO_2 production also were monitored.

Analytical Methods. All samples of soil vapors and headspace were transferred by 100-µL gastight syringes and analyzed for toluene immediately after collection by HP GC 5890 Series II with flame ionization detection (FID). Headspace samples were analyzed for CO_2 and O_2 on GC 8000 Series (Fisons Instruments) by thermal conductivity detection (TCD). The activity of specific toluene degraders during bioventing experiments was estimated by comparing CO_2 production with a control column (no toluene). Residual concentrations of toluene in soil were determined by extraction of 25 g of soil with 50 mL of acetone. Because the extraction of activated carbon with acetone (ratio: 1:4) gave 41% toluene recovery, the solvent in this case was changed for CS_2 (ratio: 1:4) with the recovery of 98 to 100%. CO_2 produced during the bioventing experiment was absorbed by 0.5M NaOH solution and then determined by titration with a 0.1-M HCl solution.

RESULTS AND DISCUSSION

A rapid decrease of toluene in the headspace was observed at about 170 h for the bench-scale columns during bioventing and venting, respectively (Figure 2). However, in the bioventing column the concentration of 0.5 mg toluene/kg was reached after 264 hours. At that time still 60 mg toluene/kg was still in the vented column. A residual toluene concentration of 1.4 mg/kg was found for the venting experiment after 576 h based on soil extraction. This study shows that bioventing compared to venting may reduce the remediation time by half if the residual toluene concentration of 0.5 mg/kg has to be reached. The total amount of volatilized toluene determined by extraction from activated carbon was comparable to the calculations based on headspace measurements, enabling us to use headspace measurements to determine the kinetics of toluene removal from soil during bioventing. After a short lag phase the CO_2 content in the outlet gas increased from 0.5% to 2.2% (Figure 3). As soon as concentrations of toluene

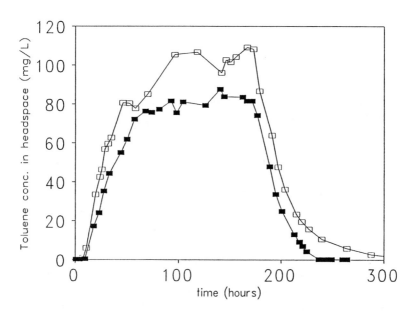

FIGURE 2. Toluene concentration in headspace with time (venting [□] and bioventing [■]).

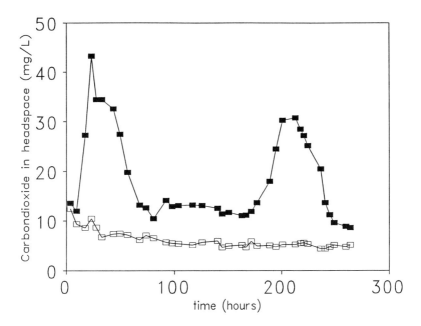

FIGURE 3. CO_2 concentration in headspace with time (bioventing [■] and control without toluene [□]).

in soil vapors and headspace approached the saturation concentration (after ca. 40 h), microbial activity decreased dramatically until most of the toluene was volatilized (ca. 170 h). About 1,600 mL of CO_2 was produced.

CO_2 production during biodegradation in batch tests indicated that equilibrium concentrations of toluene in gas phase above ca. 75% of the saturation concentrations inhibited the bioconversion of toluene (results not shown). This may explain the collapse of CO_2 production observed during bioventing (Figure 3). Similar behavior was found by monitoring the O_2 content in outlet gas (results not shown). A higher airflow at the beginning of the experiment may reduce the time interval at which inhibition of biological conversion occurs. This suggests a strategy of varying the air flowrate during soil bioventing. The constant air flowrate applied in the experiment resulted in a ratio of 9:1 for evaporated to biodegraded toluene (Table 1). Reduction of this flowrate after 75% of the saturation concentration in the soil vapors is reached may lower this ratio of 9:1, resulting in an optimum bioventing strategy. This strategy will reduce pumping costs and lower the cleanup costs of vapors extracted from soil.

ACKNOWLEDGMENT

This research was financially supported by the Netherlands Integrated Soil Research Programme.

TABLE 1. Volatilization-to-biodegradation ratio of toluene during bioventing experiment.

Toluene		Method of Determination
Volatilized (%)	Biodegraded (%)	
80	20	Headspace measurements of toluene
90	10	Extraction of soil and activated carbon
89	11	Stoichiometric reaction of toluene mineralization and CO_2 produced (measured in headspace)[a]
92	8	Stoichiometric reaction of toluene mineralization and CO_2 produced (determined by titration)[a]

(a) Assumed 50% yield of mineralization reaction (Geerdink 1995):
$$CH_{1,14} + 0.76\ O_2 + 0.1\ NH_3 \rightarrow 0.5\ CO_2 + 0.27\ H_2O + 0.5\ CH_{1,8}O_{0,5}N_{0,2}$$

REFERENCES

Alvarez, P. J. J., P. J. Anid, and T. M. Vogel. 1991. "Kinetics of aerobic biodegradation of benzene and toluene in sandy aquifer material." *Biodegradation 2*: 43-51. Kluwer Academic Publishers.

Atlas, R. M. 1981. "Microbial Degradation of Petroleum Hydrocarbons: An Environmental Perspective." *Microbiol. Rev. 45*(1): 180-209.

Baehr, A. L., G. E. Hoag, and M. C. Marley. 1989. "Removing volatile contaminants from the unsaturated zone by inducing advective air-phase transport." *J. Contam. Hydrol. 4*: 1-26. Elsevier Science Publishers B.V.

de Wit, J.C.M., L.G.C.M. Urlings, and P. A. Alphenaar. 1995. "Application of Mechanistic Models for Bioventing." In R. E. Hinchee, R. N. Miller, and P. C. Johnson (Eds.), *In Situ Aeration: Air Sparging, Bioventing, and Related Remediation Processes*. Battelle Press, Columbus, OH. pp. 450-458.

Geerdink, M. J. 1995. "Kinetics of the Microbial Degradation of Oil in Soil Slurry Reactors." Thesis, Delft University of Technology, Delft, The Netherlands.

Gibson, D. T. (Ed.). 1984. *Microbial Degradation of Organic Compounds*. Microbiol. Ser., Marcel Dekker Inc., NY.

Hinchee, R. E., B. C. Alleman, R. E. Hoeppel, and R. N. Miller (Eds.). 1994. *Hydrocarbon Bioremediation*. CRC Press, Inc., Lewis Publishers, Boca Raton, FL.

Johnson, Jr. S. W. 1993. "Laboratory examination of soil venting for the recovery of volatile organic contaminants from unsaturated soil." PhD dissertation, U.M.I Dissertation Information Service. A Bell & Howell Information Co., Ann Arbor, MI.

Sims, J. L., R. C. Sims, R. R. Dupont, J. E. Matthews, and H. H. Russell. 1993. *In Situ Bioremediation of Contaminated Unsaturated Subsurface Soils*. U.S. Environmental Protection Agency Technical Report, EPA/540/5-93/501, Utah State University, Logan, UT.

van der Meer, J. R., T.N.P. Bosma, W. P. de Bruin, H. Harms, C. Holliger, H.H.M. Rijnaarts, M. E. Tros, G. Schraa, and A.J.B. Zehnder. 1992. "Versatility of soil columns experiments to study biodegradation of halogenated compounds under environmental conditions." *Biodegradation 3*: 265-284. Kluwer Academic Publishers.

In Situ Bioventing:
Results of Three Pilot Tests
Performed in Hawaii

John W. Ratz, Greg D. Pierson,
K. Kyle Caskey, and William L. Barry

ABSTRACT

Three pilot-scale bioventing tests were performed to examine the potential for petroleum hydrocarbon biodegradation in volcanic and marine soils between 1.4 and 50 m below ground surface (bgs) on the island of Oahu, Hawaii. Aerobic petroleum hydrocarbon biodegradation was shown to be occurring at all three sites by comparing oxygen and carbon dioxide concentrations in soil gas from zones containing petroleum residuals to those in soil gas from unimpacted zones. In situ respiration testing demonstrated that petroleum hydrocarbons could be biodegraded at estimated rates ranging from 110 to 5,000 mg of fuel per kg of soil per y. Formation permeability testing demonstrated that oxygen could be uniformly delivered through a variety of lithologic types, including saprolite and volcanic tuff. Radii of influence for these single-well systems ranged from 8 to 12 m. The pilot-scale systems installed at each site were operated continuously for a 12-month extended testing phase to determine the long-term influences of bioventing. Order-of-magnitude decreases in soil and soil gas concentrations of benzene, toluene, ethylbenzene, and xylenes (BTEX) were documented over the extended testing phase, indicating that bioventing is a suitable technology for full-scale remediation of petroleum in soils at these sites.

INTRODUCTION

The use of air injection or soil gas extraction has become a widely accepted, cost-effective method to stimulate aerobic biodegradation of petroleum hydrocarbons in unsaturated soils. This process, known as in situ bioventing, is mechanically similar to standard soil vapor extraction, but uses lower flowrates to minimize the volatilization of soil contaminants. Because the physical, chemical, and biological characteristics of soil vary widely between sites, a pilot test normally is recommended to determine the feasibility of bioventing at a given site.

In April 1992, Parsons Engineering Science, Inc. (Parsons ES) was retained by the Air Force Center for Environmental Excellence (AFCEE) to conduct bioventing pilot tests at over 110 petroleum-contaminated sites on Air Force bases throughout the United States. Two of these sites, Area H and Area K, are located at Hickam Air Force Base (AFB), and a third site, Site 2, is located at the Waikakalaua Fuel Storage Annex, bordering the Wheeler Army Airfield on the Schofield Plateau (Figure 1). These three sites are unique to the overall project due to the tropical climate and the predominance of volcanic and marine soils at the sites. A bioventing pilot test was performed at each site between April 1993 and June 1994 (Engineering-Science, Inc. 1993a and 1993b) using procedures described by Hinchee et al. (1992).

SITE CONDITIONS

At Area H, the geology generally consists of volcanic tuff with some apparent fracture zones. The site contaminant is aviation gas, present in a thin "smear zone" just above the groundwater table at 5.5 to 6 m bgs. At Area K, soils consist

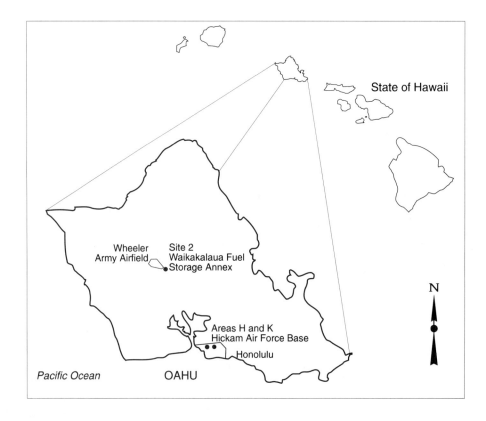

FIGURE 1. Site locations.

of coralline rubblestone and sand, and groundwater was present at 2.7 m bgs. Soils containing JP-4 jet fuel residuals were encountered in a "smear zone" at Area K extending from 1.4 m bgs to groundwater. Free product was present at both Hickam AFB sites, and average total BTEX concentrations were 21.1 and 42.1 mg/kg in soils at Area H and Area K, respectively. Soil temperatures ranged from 26.1 to 32°C.

At Site 2 on the Waikakalaua Fuel Storage Annex, soil generally consists of fine silt and clay from the surface to 6 m bgs. Below this surface layer, saprolite (weathered basalt) approximately 25-m thick was encountered. The saprolite is underlain by its parent material, basalt, which occurs at depths below 30 m bgs. Perched water was encountered at approximately 5 m bgs in one area and at approximately 15 m bgs throughout the site. At depths below 6 m bgs, the saprolite contained waste petroleum hydrocarbon residuals from an open-bottomed disposal basin. Total recoverable petroleum hydrocarbon (TRPH) concentrations in soils at Site 2 ranged from 550 to 3,600 mg/kg. Soil temperatures ranged from 22.4 to 26.4°C.

INITIAL PILOT TESTING

The objectives of the initial pilot testing phase were to assess the potential for supplying oxygen throughout soil zones, to determine if indigenous populations of soil microorganisms were capable of biodegrading petroleum hydrocarbon residuals and, if so, to quantify the rates at which hydrocarbons could be biodegraded under enhanced oxygen conditions.

A vent well (VW), for injecting air into the subsurface, and three multiple-depth vapor monitoring points (MPs), for soil gas sampling, were installed in soils containing petroleum residuals at each site. Additionally, a background MP was installed in unimpacted soils at Hickam AFB and at Site 2 to determine parameters in petroleum-free soil gas. Each VW consisted of 4-in (10.2-cm) diameter Schedule 40 polyvinyl chloride (PVC) casing that was screened in soils containing petroleum residuals. The MP screens consisted of 15-cm sections of 1-in. (2.5-cm)-diameter PVC slotted screen.

Degradation of petroleum due to biological activity was shown to be occurring at all three sites. Initial oxygen levels were depleted (less than 2%), and carbon dioxide concentrations were elevated (5 to 14%) in soil gas from petroleum-contaminated soils. In contrast, soil gas from unimpacted soil near each site was oxygen-rich (18.9% at Hickam AFB and 11.5% at Site 2) and contained low concentrations of carbon dioxide, demonstrating that oxygen depletion and carbon dioxide accumulation in soil containing petroleum residuals was due to the degradation of the petroleum rather than naturally occurring soil organic matter or due to abiotic processes. Background soil gas at Site 2 was slightly oxygen depleted, perhaps due to iron oxidation, as the saprolite contained elevated concentrations of iron ranging from 86,000 to 119,000 mg/kg. The soil gas survey confirmed that contaminated soils at these sites would benefit from oxygen addition and the accelerated biodegradation rates afforded by aerobic conditions.

Formation permeability tests were conducted to determine if oxygen could be delivered throughout the subject soil formations. At each site, air was injected into the formation through the VW, while changes in pressure and soil gas composition were observed at surrounding MPs. Oxygen was easily delivered throughout soils in the pilot test zone at Area K. Although the tuff at Area H was highly impermeable to soil gas at first, oxygen and pressure influences were established in the fracture zones, where injected air was capable of migrating through the formation. Permeability of the tuff increased over time and, after the system had operated for 6 months, oxygen had become uniformly distributed throughout the tuff. The increase in formation permeability can be attributed to the displacement of soil moisture and fine-grained soil particles within the soil matrix caused by long-term air injection. Oxygen influence was also observed at Site 2 in unsaturated zones, although the presence of the perched water zones interfered with the distribution of oxygen in saturated intervals. Steady-state, radial flow equations described by Johnson et al. (1990) were used to estimate soil gas permeabilities of 5.3 darcy units at Area K and 4.2 darcy units in unsaturated, intermediate-depth soils (5 to 15 m bgs) at Site 2. These permeability values are typical of fine- to medium-grained sands. A soil gas permeability value could not be calculated for Area H due to the channeled airflow caused by the fractured nature of the media.

In situ respiration testing was performed at each site to quantify the rates of aerobic petroleum hydrocarbon degradation. Air and approximately 1% helium (an inert nonbiodegradable tracer gas) were injected into contaminated soils, and the rates of oxygen consumption, carbon dioxide production, and helium diffusion were monitored after injection ceased. Respiration data from MPB at Area K are illustrated in Figure 2. Oxygen was consumed at rates of up to 1.2% per hr, while helium levels remained unchanged, demonstrating that oxygen loss was due to biological consumption rather than diffusion. Background oxygen levels remained constant, indicating that oxygen in contaminated soils was being used specifically for petroleum hydrocarbon biodegradation. Carbon dioxide concentrations increased with time, indicating that the petroleum hydrocarbons were being mineralized. Using observed oxygen consumption rates, estimated air-filled porosities, and a conservative ratio of 3.5 mg of oxygen consumed for every mg of fuel biodegraded, estimated petroleum biodegradation rates ranged from 110 to 210 mg/kg/y at Area H, 1,800 to 5,000 mg/kg/y at Area K, and 350 to 1,100 mg/kg/y at Site 2.

EXTENDED TESTING PHASE

The pilot-scale bioventing systems installed at each site were operated continuously for a 12-month extended testing phase to determine the long-term influences of bioventing. The systems installed at Areas H and K were 1.5-horsepower (HP) rotary-vane blowers that injected air into the subsurface at a rate of 0.6 m³/min and average pressures of 300 mm Hg and 125 mm Hg, respectively.

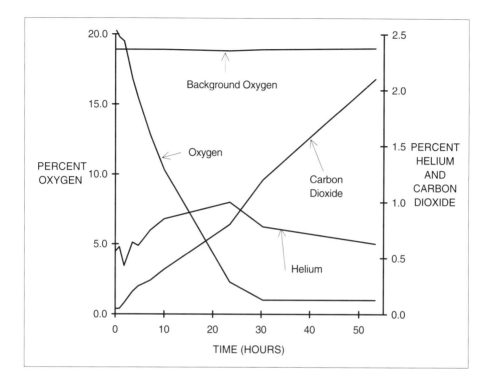

FIGURE 2. Respiration test results at Area K.

A 2.5-HP regenerative blower was installed at Site 2. Initially, the Site 2 blower injected air at 0.6 m³/min due to the high injection pressures caused by the elevated soil moisture content. After 6 days of operation, the average air injection flow rate had increased to 2.2 m³/min at an injection pressure of approximately 90 mm Hg.

Respiration tests were performed at the sites after 6 months of pilot system operation. After 12 months of operation, final respiration tests were performed, and soil and soil gas samples were collected and analyzed to determine the degree of cleanup that had been achieved. Respiration rates remained relatively constant at Area K and Site 2, but decreased significantly at Area H, probably due to the unavailability of petroleum substrate during later stages of the extended testing phase. Table 1 summarizes the impact of in situ bioventing on the petroleum hydrocarbon concentrations at the three testing sites. Benzene and ethylbenzene concentrations in soil at Site 2 did not decrease due to the interference with oxygen delivery caused by the saturated conditions in the perched water regions. Order-of-magnitude decreases in all other soil and soil gas concentrations of BTEX were documented over the extended testing phase, indicating that bioventing is a viable technology for full-scale remediation of these petroleum-impacted sites.

TABLE 1. Reductions in average contaminant concentrations observed after 12 months of bioventing.

Analyte (Units)[a]	Pilot Test Site					
	Area H		Area K		Site 2	
	Initial[b]	12-Month[b]	Initial[b]	12-Month[b]	Initial[b]	12-Month[b]
Soil Gas Hydrocarbons (ppmv)						
TVH	237,000	72	26,000	16,000	14,000	6,400
Benzene	ND[c]	ND	85	ND	15	ND
Toluene	ND	ND	ND	ND	29	ND
Ethylbenzene	28	ND	22	2.0	12	7.4
Xylenes	22	ND	48	5.3	40	18
Soil Hydrocarbons (mg/kg)						
Benzene	2.8	.08	1.1	ND	.66	.95
Toluene	5.3	.01	12	ND	11	3.5
Ethylbenzene	5.5	.005	10	ND	7.4	11
Xylenes	7.5	.005	19	ND	38	12

(a) TVH = total volatile hydrocarbons; ppmv = parts per million, volume per volume; mg/kg = milligrams per kilogram.
(b) Average of three samples per site.
(c) ND = Not detected.

DISCUSSION

These pilot testing efforts clearly showed the potential for full-scale remediation in volcanic and marine soils using in situ bioventing. During one year of pilot-scale bioventing, the total volumes of petroleum hydrocarbons destroyed at Area H, Area K, and Site 2 were estimated at 0.2 m^3, 4.4 m^3, and 2.7 m^3, respectively. Although the time required to remediate sites using in situ bioventing will be longer than various ex situ remediation methods, the cost of in situ remediation is expected to be very competitive. The total cost for the bioventing pilot tests at Areas H and K and Site 2 was $180,000, or approximately $20 for every m^3 of soil oxygenated by the pilot-scale systems. Long-term operation and maintenance costs are minimal, ranging from $1 to $3 per m^3/y. In situ bioventing offers a very simple and cost-competitive means of remediating most sites with petroleum-contaminated soils. The diversity of environments where bioventing has been successful, including the sites discussed herein, indicates the broad applicability of bioventing as a remedial measure.

REFERENCES

Engineering-Science, Inc. 1993a. *Bioventing Pilot Test Work Plan for Areas H and K, and Site 2, Hickam AFB, Hawaii.* Denver, CO.
Engineering-Science, Inc. 1993b. *Draft Interim Pilot Test Results Report for Areas H and K, and Site 2, Hickam AFB, Hawaii.* Denver, CO.
Hinchee, R. E., S. K. Ong, R. N. Miller, D. C. Downey, and R. Frandt. 1992. *Test Plan and Technical Protocol for a Field Treatability Test for Bioventing.* Brooks AFB, TX.
Johnson, P. C., M. W. Kemblowski, and J. D. Colhart. 1990. "Quantitative Analysis for the Cleanup of Hydrocarbon Contaminated Soils by In Situ Soil Venting." *Ground Water* 28(3): 413-429.

Nutrient Demand in Bioventing of Fuel Oil Pollution

Gijs D. Breedveld, Gunnar Olstad,
Tormod Briseid, and Audun Hauge

ABSTRACT

The effect of nutrient addition on bioventing of fuel oil pollution in an artificially polluted sandy soil has been studied at different experimental scales to assess the predictive value of laboratory treatability studies. The results of batch studies (5-g samples), laboratory column studies (6-kg samples), and pilot-scale field tests (10 tons of soil) were compared. The qualitative response to nutrient addition was comparable in all experiments. Without nutrient addition, a minimal respiration rate was observed. With nutrient addition, respiration rates increased almost instantaneously. The highest rates were observed in the batch studies. The column study and pilot-scale field test indicated similar respiration rates, at approximately one sixth the respiration rates in the batch study. Respiration rates in the pilot-scale field study decreased during the winter season. Analysis of the residual oil composition in soil samples showed a relation between the degree of weathering, measured as the n-C_{17}/pristane and n-C_{18}/phytane ratio, and nutrient addition. Lower n-C_{17}/pristane ratios were observed at higher total nitrogen content. After 1 year of bioventing with nutrient addition, a 66% reduction in TPH content was observed. Without nutrient addition, the residual oil still closely resembled the original fuel oil product, with only minor removal of the light-end compounds.

INTRODUCTION

Sufficient supply of nitrogen and phosphorous is essential for the successful biodegradation of organic pollutants such as petroleum hydrocarbons and poly-cyclic aromatic hydrocarbons (PAHs). Although many subsoils contain nitrogen and phosphorous sources, laboratory degradation studies often show a positive response on nitrogen and phosphorous amendment (Harder et al. 1991, Lindhardt et al. 1991). It has been reported that this response to nutrient addition is not observed in field-scale bioventing (Miller 1990, Miller et al. 1991). The lack of response is attributed to naturally available nitrogen and phosphorous which were adequate for the observed biodegradation (Miller 1990). Other environmental factors such as oxygen supply, moisture content, and soil temperature are believed to be often rate limiting under field conditions (Ong et al. 1994). This limits the predictive value of laboratory treatability studies. To assess this problem, nutrient demand in relation to test scale has been investigated in laboratory-scale batch and column studies and pilot-scale field tests.

MATERIALS AND METHODS

Soil samples from the glaciofluvial sand deposit at Trandum military base were used in all experiments. The soil can be characterized as medium to coarse sand and gravel, with a low organic carbon content (0.22%). The soil has a total nitrogen content of 300 mg/kg and a total phosphorous content of 450 mg/kg. For the batch and column studies, soil material was passed through a 4-mm sieve, homogenized, and stored at 4°C. Soil samples were artificially polluted with fuel oil no. 1 (Statoil) to approximately 10 g/kg. This oil contains hydrocarbons with a boiling point range between n-C_{10} and n-C_{22}, and has a BTEX content below 1%. For the pilot study, soil material was used without pretreatment.

Batch degradation experiments were carried out in a Sapromat respirometer (Voith, Heidenheim), which measures oxygen uptake. Dissolved nutrients (800 mg NH_4NO_3-N/kg and 240 mg PO_4-P/kg) or equal amounts of moisture were added to soil samples (5 g) as a single dose.

For the column study, glass columns (10 cm diam. × 50 cm) were packed with 6 kg polluted soil. The columns were subjected to downward forced aeration (3 pore volumes per day) and downward percolation with a nutrient solution (1 L/d, 200 mg NH_4-N/L and 50 mg PO_4-P/L) or equal amounts of moisture. This resulted in a mean water content of 14% by weight. CO_2 production in the gas phase was measured using a CO_2 trap (NaOH).

Pilot-scale field experiments were carried out in steel containers of 6 m³ packed with unpolluted soil (approx. 10 tons). Soil was polluted by surface application of 100 L fuel oil to each container, resulting in a mean oil content of 8 g/kg. The containers were subjected to downward forced aeration (2 pore volumes per day) and downward percolation with a nutrient solution (100 L/week, 1 g NH_4-N/L and 0.3 g PO_4-P/L) or equal amounts of moisture in addition to natural rainwater. CO_2 production and O_2 consumption in the gas phase were measured using a field-portable CO_2/O_2 analyzer. The three different experiments are summarized in Table 1 (Hauge et al. 1992).

After 1 year of bioventing, soil samples were taken from the pilot-scale containers at 4 sites and 4 depths. The samples were analyzed for total petroleum hydrocarbons (TPH) using gas chromatography with flame ionization detector (GC/FID) after dichloromethane extraction. From the chromatograms the n-C_{17}/pristane and n-C_{18}/phytane ratios were determined (Olstad 1994). Total nitrogen and total phosphorous were determined photometrically after Se-H_2SO_4 extraction (Houba et al. 1989).

TABLE 1. Experimental conditions for batch, column, and pilot-scale studies.

Parameter		Batch	Column	Pilot
Soil mass (kg)		0.005	6	10,000
Nutrients:	method	single dose	continuous	weekly batch
	total amount N g/kg	0.8	4.7 (1.2)[a]	0.15
	total amount P g/kg	0.24	1.2 (0.3)[a]	0.05
Aeration (pore volume/day)		—	3	2
Respiration measurement		O_2	CO_2	O_2/CO_2
Temperature (°C)		15	10	0-17

(a) Number within parentheses () is amount added until breakthrough was observed.

RESULTS AND DISCUSSION

To compare the respiration rates from the batch, column, and field experiments, O_2 consumption from the batch experiments was converted to CO_2 production rates using a respiration coefficient ($RQ = \%CO_2/\Delta\%O_2$) of 0.69 (Olstad 1994). The cumulative CO_2 production in the three experiments shows clearly that respiration is very low with the addition of water only (Figure 1). Addition

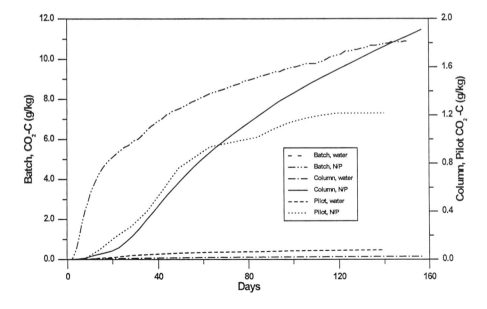

FIGURE 1. Cumulative CO_2 production in batch, column, and pilot-scale experiments with water (water) and nutrient (N/P) addition.

of a nitrogen and phosphorous source resulted in a rapid increase in respiration in all experiments. The strongest response was observed in the batch experiment, whereas a more gradual increase in respiration rate was observed in the column and pilot study. After 150 days, the cumulative respiration was approximately a factor 6 higher in the batch experiment compared to the column and pilot-scale experiments. This is presumably a result of the phase ratio (gas/fluid/solid), which is not representative for in situ soil conditions. The column and pilot study showed very similar respiration rates through the first 100 days; in the next 50 days of the study, the respiration rates in the pilot study dropped to low levels. This is probably caused by a decrease in soil temperature in the pilot-scale field test during the autumn (from 17°C to 1°C). The following spring respiration rates returned to high values without additional nutrient addition (Olstad 1994).

TPH analyses results from the pilot study show a large variation both in horizontal and vertical extent (Table 2). This is a result of the surface application of the oil resulting in local variation in oil penetration. The mean TPH content after 1 year of bioventing was reduced by 66% with the addition of nutrients, compared to an initial mean concentration of 8 g/kg TPH (calculated). The decrease in oil concentration is greatest in the uppermost 1 m of the container. Below 1 m there is strong local variation in TPH content. Without nutrient addition an increase in TPH content with depth is observed (Table 2). This is probably a result of the downward forced aeration resulting in a redistribution of the applied oil compared to the reference container. Typical gas chromatograms of the residual oil in the soil samples show that, without nutrient addition, the oil resembles the original fuel oil, whereas the residual oil in the nutrient addition treatment is strongly degraded (Figure 2). Straight-chained alkanes are degraded, leaving highly branched hydrocarbons. This is illustrated by the n-C_{17}/pristane ratio, which is strongly reduced, in the upper 1.5 m, with nutrient addition (Table 3). At the bottom of the container, at 1.5 to 2 m depth, the oil still resembles the original fuel oil. Similar results are obtained for the n-C_{18}/phytane ratio (Olstad 1994).

TABLE 2. Mean TPH levels ± standard deviation (g/kg) in soil samples from the pilot study after 1 year without bioventing (reference), with bioventing and water addition (water), and with bioventing and nutrient addition (N/P).

Treatment	Sampling Depth				
	0 – 0.5 m	0.5 – 1 m	1 – 1.5 m	1.5 – 2 m	mean
Reference	6.1±2.8	5.1±1.0	4.1±0.9	3.6±0.01	4.9±1.8
Water	4.6±1.0	6.4±0.9	8.9±2.3	9.0	6.4±2.1
N/P	1.9±0.3	2.2±0.6	3.5±2.1	4.0±0.8	2.7±1.4

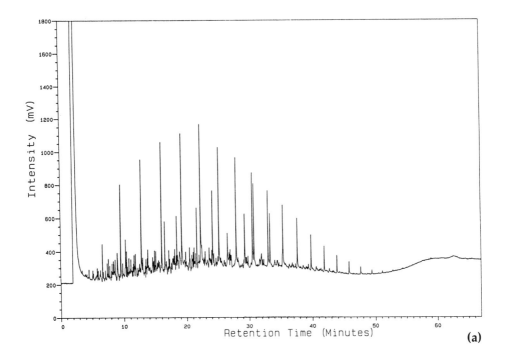

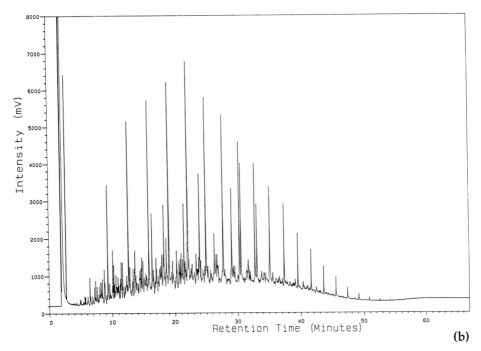

FIGURE 2. Gas chromatograms of fuel oil no. 1 (a) and fuel oil polluted soil from the pilot study (0.5 to 1 m depth) after 1 year without bioventing (b).

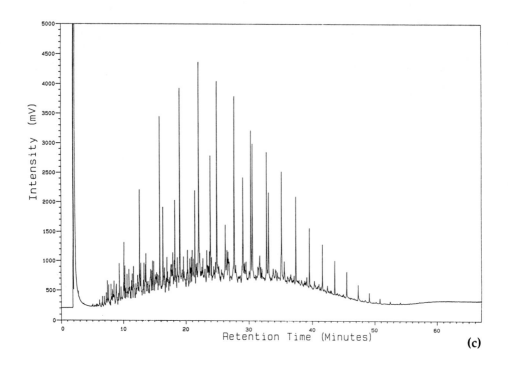

(c)

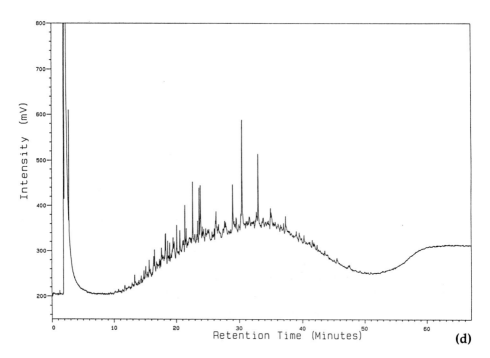

(d)

FIGURE 2 (continued). Gas chromatograms of fuel oil no. 1 with bioventing and water addition (c), and with bioventing and nutrient addition (d).

TABLE 3. Mean n-C_{17}/pristane ratios ± standard deviation in soil samples from the pilot study after 1 year without bioventing (reference), with bioventing and water addition (water), and with bioventing and nutrient addition (N/P).

	Sampling Depth			
Treatment	0 – 0.5 m	0.5 – 1 m	1 – 1.5 m	1.5 – 2 m
Reference	1.04±0.05	1.14±0.03	1.10±0.04	1.05±0.10
Water	0.68±0.28	1.02±0.10	1.14±0.04	1.25
N/P	0.37±0.17	0.26±0.15	0.46±0.43	1.05±0.16

The relation between total nitrogen content and n-C_{17}/pristane ratio shows clearly that samples from the reference container and some samples from the bioventing container have a higher n-C_{17}/pristane ratio at lower total nitrogen values (Figure 3). Samples from the bioventing and nutrient addition container

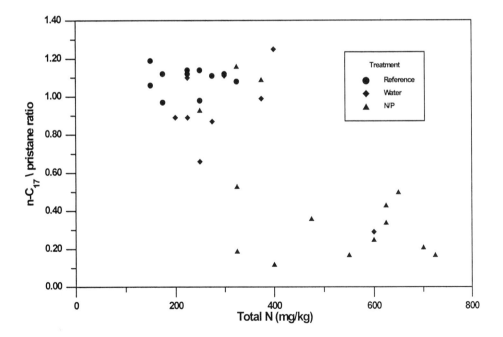

FIGURE 3. Relation between n-C_{17}/pristane ratio and total nitrogen content (mg/kg) in soil samples from the pilot-scale study, without bioventing (reference), with bioventing and water addition (water), and with bioventing and nutrient addition (N/P).

show low n-C_{17}/pristane ratios at higher total nitrogen content. Samples from the bottom of the nutrient addition container (1.5 to 2 m depth) show that high n-C_{17}/pristane ratios are related to a lower total nitrogen content, indicating that the nutrients have not reached the bottom of the container in the course of the experiments. There is a large variation in the results, which can be caused by limited availability of different soil nitrogen fractions for microorganisms as well as soil matrix variation in this highly inhomogeneous sand deposit.

CONCLUSIONS

Batch, column, and pilot-scale experiments clearly show that nutrient addition is necessary to stimulate biodegradation of artificial oil pollution in soil material from the Trandum deposit. All three experimental tests show comparable qualitative results. Quantitatively, the batch study overestimates respiration rates by a factor of 6. Laboratory column studies closely resemble the observations in the pilot-scale field study.

Besides CO_2 production and O_2 consumption, n-C_{17}/pristane and n-C_{18}/phytane ratios are useful parameters to evaluate the progress of in situ biodegradation processes. TPH content shows strong local variation based on pollution history and soil matrix and is therefore of limited value to assess bioremediation effectiveness under field conditions.

ACKNOWLEDGMENTS

This project was funded by the State Pollution Control Authorities (SFT), the Norwegian Defence Construction Service (NODCS), and Norsk Hydro. The authors would especially like to thank Per Kolstad and Hege Jonassen for establishing the pilot-scale field site. Dag Karlsen at the Department of Geology, the University of Oslo, helped in developing the soil analyses methods.

REFERENCES

Harder, H., B. Kürzel-Seidel, and T. Höpner. 1991. "Hydrocarbon biodegradation in sediments and soils. A systematic examination of physical and chemical conditions — Part IV. Special aspects of nutrient demand." *Erdöl und Kohle — Erdgas — Petrochemie.* 44(2): 59-62.

Hauge, A., G. D. Breedveld, H. M. Jonassen, and T. Briseid. 1992. *In situ biological cleaning of oil polluted soil — results of experiments (in Norwegian).* NGI report no. 537002-4, Norwegian Geotechnical Institute, Oslo, Norway.

Houba, V.J.G., J. J van der Lee, and I. Novozamsky. 1989. *Soil and Plant Analysis, Part 5 Soil Analysis Procedures.* Department of Soil Science and Plant Nutrition, Wageningen Agricultural University, Wageningen, the Netherlands.

Lindhardt, B., J. Jacobsen, and E. Andersen. 1991. "Degradation of diesel oil in the unsaturated zone (in Danish)." *Vand og Miljø.* 8(5): 257-261.

Miller, R. N. 1990. "A field scale investigation of enhanced petroleum hydrocarbon biodegradation in the vadose zone combining soil venting as an oxygen source with moisture and nutrient addition." PhD. thesis, Department of Civil and Environmental Engineering, Utah State University, Logan, UT.

Miller, R. N., C. C. Vogel, and R. E. Hinchee. 1991. "A field scale investigation of petroleum hydrocarbon biodegradation in the vadose zone enhanced by soil venting at Tyndall AFB, Florida." In R. E. Hinchee and R. F. Olfenbuttel (Eds.), *In Situ Bioreclamation: Applications and Investigations for Hydrocarbon and Contaminated Site Remediation*, pp. 283-302. Butterworth-Heinemann, Stoneham, MA.

Olstad, G. 1994. "In situ biological cleanup of oil polluted soil — pilot test (in Norwegian)." MSc. thesis, Department of Geology, University of Oslo, Oslo, Norway.

Ong, S. K., A. Leeson, R. E. Hinchee, J. Kittel, C. M. Vogel, G. D. Sayles, and R. N. Miller. 1994. "Cold climate applications of bioventing." In R. E. Hinchee, B. C. Alleman, R. E. Hoeppel, and R. N. Miller (Eds.), *Hydrocarbon Bioremediation*, pp. 444-453. Lewis Publishers, Boca Raton, FL.

Application and Performance of Remote Bioventing Systems Powered by Wind

Duane Graves, Thomas Dillon, Jr., Keith Hague, Jerry Klein, John McLaughlin, Bill Wilson, and Gus Olson

ABSTRACT ━━━━━━━━━━━━━━━━━━━━━━━━━━━━━━━━━━━

Bioventing is a simple in situ treatment alternative for soil containing biodegradable contaminants; however, site accessibility and power are usually required elements for bioventing. Wind-powered bioventing systems were designed to operate at remote locations in the absence of electrical power. Laboratory measurements of soil respiration under bioventing conditions indicated the biodegradation of up to 25 mg of weathered diesel per kg of site soil per day. Further testing demonstrated the potential for harnessing wind-power to stimulate air movement through vadose zone soil. A 12-in. (30.5-cm) attic turbine in a 10-mph (16.1-km/h) wind (the prevailing wind speed on site) was found to generate 0.025 in. (0.064 cm) of water vacuum with an airflow of approximately 2.5 ft^3 (0.07 m^3) per min. The flowrate generated by the turbine could replace the soil gas in a treatment area 50 ft by 50 ft by 4 ft deep (15.2 m by 15.2 m by 1.2 m deep) in 24 hours, thus exceeding the biological oxygen demand of the contaminated soil. Two wind-powered bioventing systems were installed near Nome, Alaska. In situ respiration tests and soil gas composition measurements indicated that the systems were capable of aerating the soil. Measurements of diesel-range organics (DRO) taken during installation (early June) and at the end of the treatment season (early September) show concentration reductions of 29 and 87% at the two sites. The results demonstrate the effectiveness of wind-powered biovents. The low cost, low maintenance, and simplicity of the biovents make them a very attractive treatment option for windy, remote sites with unsaturated soil impacted by biodegradable contaminants.

INTRODUCTION

During World War II, the U.S. Army constructed several diesel-fueled communications outposts near Nome and in remote locations on the Seward Peninsula.

Due to the remoteness and the difficulty of transporting larger containers of fuel, diesel was delivered in 55-gal (208-L) drums. At the end of World War II, the outposts were abandoned and unused fuel was left behind. Over the years, some drums have leaked fuel and contaminated the soil. Bioventing systems powered by wind were installed at several of these sites to remediate fuel-contaminated soil.

Three distinct types of soil conditions exist at potential bioventing sites. Undisturbed soil has permafrost occurring a few inches from the surface. The first few inches are composed of decaying moss and other plant material. The underlying soil is a highly plastic gray clay. The soil is often water saturated from the surface to the permafrost. These "wet tundra" conditions along with keen regulatory interest in maintaining permafrost prevent the application of bioventing at such sites. In contrast, much of the soil near Nome has been disturbed by gold mining operations resulting in disruption of the natural permafrost. Mined soil and tailings are very porous, well drained with deep permafrost, and acceptable for bioventing. The third type of soil is characterized as moist tundra. It typically overlies deeper permafrost and is thus suitable for bioventing because the unsaturated soil is usually 3 to 5 ft (1 to 1.5 m) deep.

Bioventing was successfully applied to sites with appropriate air permeability and permafrost depth. Bioventing offered a simple-to-install and operate treatment strategy (Dupont 1993). The lack of electrical power at all sites led to the design of wind-powered bioventing systems. Contaminant characterization and laboratory biodegradation studies supported the installation and operation of wind-powered bioventing systems at selected sites. The preliminary evaluation of sites treated for 3 months indicates significant reduction in DRO within the bioventing treatment area.

CONTAMINANT CHARACTERIZATION

The original petroleum fuel was diesel; however, once the fuel was released, local conditions resulted in severe weathering of the oil. A comparative analysis of site contaminants with fresh diesel and motor oil revealed that the residual petroleum was mostly composed of hydrocarbons that were equivalent to or heavier than motor oil. Most sites were to be remediated based on a DRO standard, even though the hydrocarbon contamination contained only a small fraction of oil components that were within the range of diesel constituents.

LABORATORY STUDIES FOR PROOF-OF-CONCEPT AND FIELD DESIGN

A series of laboratory studies were conducted to evaluate the performance of bioventing in the subject soil, to determine the utility of adding nutrients to the soil, and to provide a functional design for the wind-powered bioventing system. Two distinct soil types representing soils potentially subject to bioventing were examined for physical, chemical, and microbiological characteristics that can affect the performance of bioremediation. Table 1 summarizes the results.

Laboratory Soil Respiration Testing

Bioventing was evaluated in 3-ft (91-m)-tall by 2-in. (5-cm)-wide soil columns. Air was passed through the columns at a rate of 2 mL/min. Soil respiration was measured by trapping the evolved carbon dioxide in 1N NaOH connected to the effluent gas line. The oxygen consumption rate was determined by stopping the airflow to each column, sealing both ends of the columns, and measuring, over time, the change in the gaseous oxygen content in the soil gas. The respiration rates calculated from oxygen and carbon dioxide results are summarized in Table 2. Hydrocarbon biodegradation rates were estimated from the oxygen consumption rates using a ratio of 3.5 parts oxygen per part of hydrocarbon biodegraded.

The residual contamination appeared to be subject to biodegradation based on laboratory evaluation of microbial respiration in aerated soil. The oxygen-based degradation rate correlated to the biodegradation of 2,400 mg of petroleum per kg of soil per treatment season (4 months).

Effect of Nutrient Addition

Because of the low nutrient concentration observed in the original soil samples, a nutrient solution was applied to the top surface of one soil column of each soil type and allowed to trickle through the soil. The other two soil columns

TABLE 1. Characteristics of soil used for treatability testing.

Parameter	Soil Type 1	Soil Type 2
Ammonia	<4 mg/kg	<4 mg/kg
Orthophosphate	<2.5 mg/kg	<2.5 mg/kg
pH	6.6	6.1
Soil Moisture	7.3%	12%
Heterotrophs	6.9×10^6 CFU/g[a]	3.8×10^7 CFU/g
Hydrocarbon Degraders[b]	5.8×10^6 CFU/g	1.9×10^7 CFU/g
Soil Type	Mine tailings (sand and gravel)	Moist tundra (organic soil)
Air Permeability	3 cm/s	0.49 cm/s

(a) CFU/g, colony-forming units per gram of dry soil.
(b) Hydrocarbon-degrading bacteria were grown on a carbon-free mineral salts agar with organic carbon supplied as diesel vapors.

TABLE 2. Laboratory respiration and biodegradation rates calculated from oxygen and carbon dioxide.

Sample	Oxygen Consumption Rate (mg/kg·h)	Hydrocarbon Biodegradation Rate[a] (mg/kg·day)	Carbon Dioxide Production Rate (mg/kg·h)
Site 1 with water only	1.7	11.5	0.08
Site 1 with nutrients	3.5	24.2	0.2
Site 2 with water only	3.9	26.8	0.1
Site 2 with nutrients	4.0	27.7	0.4

(a) The hydrocarbon biodegradation rate was calculated from the oxygen consumption rate assuming 3.5 parts oxygen per part hydrocarbon biodegraded.

were treated with the same volume of water without dissolved nutrients in order to maintain comparable levels of water saturation for each soil type.

The effectiveness of nutrient distribution was determined by analyzing soil samples collected from various depths in the columns. Results indicated that nutrients were distributed throughout the treated soil columns. Ammonium distribution was fairly uniform in the columns, but phosphate distribution was retarded resulting in a concentration gradient from top to bottom. Trickling a solution of nutrients from the surface was recommended for field applications to eliminate the need to mix the soil to distribute nutrients.

As indicated in Table 2, nutrients nearly doubled the oxygen consumption rate in the mineral soil sample (mine tailings) but had no effect on the other. In contrast, the organic soil contained a large amount of decaying plant matter that presumably supplied adequate levels of organic nitrogen and phosphorus. Although the oxygen consumption rate was not increased by the addition of nutrients, the apparent carbon dioxide production rate more than tripled in the organic soil (Table 2, Site 2).

The increase in carbon dioxide production was hypothesized to be due to a change in the carbonate to carbon dioxide equilibrium resulting from the addition of nutrients; however, this was not investigated. Poor recovery of carbon dioxide from soil due to the formation of carbonate usually precludes the use of carbon dioxide respiration data as a quantitative indicator of microbial respiration in soil. Low carbon dioxide production rates, relative to the amount of oxygen consumed, and the variability between treatments with nearly the same oxygen consumption rate relegate carbon dioxide production to a qualitative indicator of microbial respiration in soil.

Design of Bioventing Equipment

A system was needed that could facilitate sufficient air movement in the soil to meet the biological oxygen demand without electricity. Meteorology data show that prevailing winds average 10 mph (16.1 km/h) throughout the year in and around Nome. Simple attic type turbines of various sizes were tested in a 10-mph (16.1-km/h) wind to establish airflow and vacuum generated. Wind-powered turbines were coupled directly to the bioventing wells.

The effectiveness of this concept was tested in the laboratory and by computer modeling. Attic turbines, 4-, 6-, and 12-in.-diameter (10.2-, 15.2-, and 30.5-cm-diameter, respectively), were tested for airflow and vacuum in a 10 mph wind (Table 3). The performance of the 4-in. turbine was clearly unsatisfactory. Both the 6- and 12-in. turbines provided appreciable airflow and measurable vacuum. Although the 12-in. turbine was not twice as effective as the 6-in. model, the performance improvement was substantial. Larger turbines could provide ever greater performance; however, their size and weight could make them impractical for field installation on a 4-in. pipe.

Airflow through the soil using a 12-in. turbine in a 10-mph wind placed on a 4-in. pipe in the center of a covered 50-ft by 50-ft area was modeled using Air3D (API), a three-dimensional airflow model. Using the measured air conductivity of 3 cm/s, a soil porosity of 0.3, and 0.025 in. (0.064 cm) of water vacuum, Air3D calculated that a single bioventing system would remove 2.5 ft^3 (0.07 m^3) of air per minute. This flowrate is adequate to replace the soil gas in a 50-ft by 50-ft by 4-ft-deep (15.2-m by 15.2-m by 1.2-m-deep) treatment area in less than 24 h. The oxygen consumption rates observed during laboratory respiration tests indicated that this flowrate should match or exceed the oxygen demand exerted by the soil.

INSTALLATION AND OPERATION OF WIND-POWERED BIOVENTING SYSTEMS

Sites subject to treatment were sampled, nutrient-amended, and covered with dark polyvinyl chloride (PVC) sheets. The dark PVC was chosen to facilitate snow melt in the early spring. Although clear plastic increases the soil temperature by a few degrees (U.S. EPA 1994), extending the treatment season by aiding snow melt and retaining heat in the fall was judged to be more important than a slight temperature increase during the summer. Bioventing systems were

TABLE 3. Turbine performance results in a 10-mph wind.

Turbine Diameter (in.)	Air Flow		Static Vacuum (in. of water)
	(ft/min)	(ft^3/min)	
4	<200	<17	not detected
6	300	26	0.015
12	400	35	0.025

installed through the PVC cover. The design of the bioventing wells was very simple and easy to install by hand. Figure 1 shows the components of the bio-venting system. Although the wells proved to be no match for curious bears, replacement or repair was simple and could be quickly accomplished in the field.

At one site accessible from Nome, nutrients were mixed into the soil using a backhoe. Immediately after installation of the bioventing well, the soil gas oxygen concentration was 15.5% and the carbon dioxide concentration was 0.8%. After 72 hours of operation, the oxygen concentration was 18% with 1.5% carbon dioxide, suggesting that the biovent was able to aerate the soil at a rate that exceeded the biological oxygen demand. The soil gas oxygen and carbon dioxide in nearby petroleum-free soil was 20.5% and 0.55%, respectively. The difference observed within the contaminated area reflects microbial respiration associated with petroleum biodegradation.

In situ respiration tests (Hinchee and Ong 1992) conducted at five bioventing sites just before winter indicated oxygen consumption rates ranging from 0.92 to

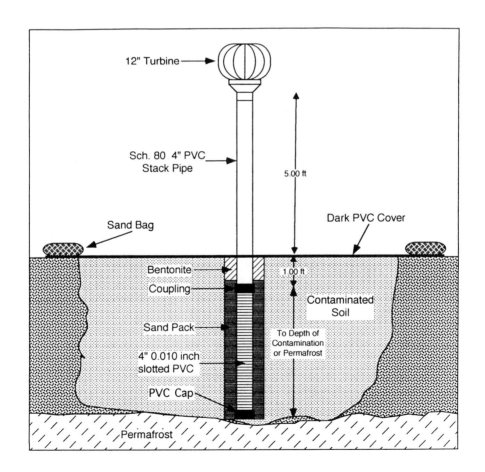

FIGURE 1. Wind-powered bioventing system design.

TABLE 4. Treatment of DRO in soil at wind-powered bioventing sites.

Site	Soil Characteristics	Depth to Permafrost (ft)	Mean DRO (mg/kg)		DRO Reduction (%)	Degradation Rate (day^{-1})
			Jun	Sep		
A	Mine Tailings	>5	9,520	6,800	29	−0.0036
B	Moist Tundra	3 to 4	13,650	1,650	88	−0.023

5.54 mg of oxygen per kg of soil per day. Calculated hydrocarbon biodegradation rates ranged from 0.3 to 1.6 mg of petroleum per kg of soil per day. The in situ respiration rate measured at one bioventing site in the early summer indicated a degradation rate of 2 mg of petroleum per kg of soil per day. Table 4 shows the DRO content of two sites before and after one season (3 months) of bioventing using the wind-powered systems. Using a t-test to compare means with unequal variance, the difference between initial (June) and end of season (September) results for Site A were significant at the 85% confidence level ($P = 0.15$). The difference in mean DRO concentrations before and after one season of treatment at Site B was significant at the 99% confidence level ($P = 0.01$).

CONCLUSIONS

Very low maintenance, simple design, inexpensive components, and no need for electricity made the application of wind-powered bioventing systems feasible. Laboratory results suggested that bioventing would stimulate biodegradation of highly weathered petroleum and that nutrient addition could be beneficial at some sites. Preliminary field data suggest that biodegradation was stimulated by the wind-powered units. Although limited data have been collected during the first season of operation, the available results indicate successful reduction in DRO within bioventing treatment areas. The next season of operation will focus on the performance of the units. Attention will be given to accurate measurements of in situ respiration, nutrient utilization, soil temperature, air flow, and the effect of the PVC cover for extending the treatment season.

REFERENCES

Dupont, R. R. 1993. "Fundamentals of Bioventing Applied to Fuel Contaminated Sites." *Environmental Progress* 12(1): 45-53.

Hinchee, R. E., and S. K. Ong. 1992. "A Rapid In Situ Respiration Test for Measuring Aerobic Biodegradation Rates of Hydrocarbons in Soil." *Journal of the Air and Waste Management Association* 43: 1305-1312.

U.S. EPA. 1994. *Bioremediation in the Field.* "Soil Warming Found to Enhance Effectiveness of Bioventing at Eielson Air Force Base." EPA/540/N-94/500. U.S. Environmental Protection Agency.

Monitoring Bioventing of Soil Contaminated with Mineral Oil

Jaap J. van der Waarde, Edwin J. Dijkhuis,
Sander K. Heijs, Maurice J. C. Henssen,
and Sytze Keuning

ABSTRACT

Preceding in situ bioventing of a sandy aquifer contaminated with mineral oil, preinvestigation studies were performed. Biodegradation was monitored by contaminant analysis, CO_2 and O_2 measurements, bacterial numbers, and enzyme activities. Batch experiments showed the feasibility of the biodegradation process in a sandy soil, but not in a peat-like soil from the same site. Addition of inorganic nutrients enhanced CO_2 production. Bioventing in undisturbed column studies resulted in a 55 to 60% removal of mineral oil in 7 weeks, from which 11 to 13% was removed by biodegradation. The rate of biodegradation that was determined with O_2 consumption and CO_2 production was 2 mg mineral oil/kg dry weight (dw)/day (d). Dehydrogenase activity correlated well with mineralization in batch culture and soil slurries, and to a lesser extent in undisturbed soil columns. Specific bacterial numbers in soil were higher in the contaminated columns than in the reference columns. No good correlation was found between FDA hydrolysis and actual biodegradation in these studies. Based on these studies it is concluded that, in addition to contaminant levels, measurement of O_2 consumption and dehydrogenase activity can be used for monitoring biodegradation.

INTRODUCTION

In situ bioremediation of a hydrocarbon-contaminated site in The Netherlands will be performed using soil vapor extraction for the vadose zone and groundwater circulation and air injection for the saturated zone. Biodegradation studies in batch incubations were performed to determine nutrient demand and maximal biodegradation rates. Simulation of full-scale bioremediation, was performed using undisturbed soil columns from the site. The biodegradation process in the preinvestigation studies was monitored by measuring contaminant levels,

O_2, CO_2, bacterial numbers, dehydrogenase activity and fluorescein diacetate (FDA) hydrolysis.

Dehydrogenases are involved in the respiration process and can be used as a measure of biological activity in soil (Thalmann 1968). FDA is hydrolyzed by a number of different enzymes, such as proteases, lipases, and esterases. Therefore FDA hydrolysis can be used as a measure of total microbial activity in soil (Schnürer & Rosswall 1982).

MATERIALS AND METHODS

Site Description

The site is an oil production plant located in the northeast of Holland. The soil consists of medium-grained sand or peat and is contaminated to a depth of 3 m. The contamination consists mainly of diesel fuel; contamination levels are between 1,000 and 10,000 mg hydrocarbon/kg dry weight (dw).

Batch Studies

Closed batch studies were performed at 20°C in slurries (45% dw) of soil samples from both contaminated and noncontaminated parts of a sandy aquifer and a peat-like soil, with and without the addition of inorganic nutrients (KNO_3, Na_2HPO_4, and KH_2PO_4) in a relative concentration of C:N:P = 250:10:5. C was equal to the mineral oil concentration (mg/kg dw). Phosphates were added in equal amounts. CO_2 concentrations were determined with alkali entrapment. A mixed bacterial culture was grown on mineral medium MMY (Janssen et al. 1985) supplemented with diesel fuel (500 μL/L), at 30°C under rotary shaking.

Column Studies

Column studies were performed with undisturbed soil cores (approximately 10 kg) from the sandy aquifer from the site. Two contaminated (1,400 to 2,900 mg mineral oil/kg dw) columns were taken in the vadose and the saturated zone in the center of the contamination. Two noncontaminated columns were taken in the vadose and the saturated zone, 20 m upstream from the contaminated hot spot, in an area of comparable geochemistry in which no contamination had been detected in previous sampling. Columns were continuously flushed upflow (saturated) and downflow (nonsaturated) with air (4 mL/min) and tapwater (2 mL/min) at 20°C. Nutrients (KNO_3 (0.26 g/L), $Na_2KPO_4*12H_2O$ (0.12 g/L), KH_2PO_4 (0.05 g/L)) were added to the influent water, but no recirculation of effluent water or air was applied. CO_2 concentrations were measured after alkali entrapment (water phase), and with infrared detection (gas phase, Dräger), 1 to 5 times per week. O_2 concentrations were determined with a Clark type electrode (water phase), and with an electrochemical cell (gas phase, Dräger), 1 to 5 times per week.

Analyses

Total viable cell numbers and viable numbers of mineral oil-degrading bacteria were weekly determined with the most probable number (MPN) assay, using respectively R2A medium or mineral oil as the growth substrate. Dehydrogenase activity was weekly determined using a modified spectrophotometric method according to Thalmann (1968), and expressed as µg triphenylformazan (TPF) produced per g dw or mL. FDA hydrolysis was weekly determined according to a modified procedure of Schnürer & Rosswall (1982), and expressed as µg fluorescein (F) produced per g dw or mL.

Pilot Study

Water was extracted (3.3 m^3/d) to remove the surplus of rainfall in the shallow zone (2 to 5 m) and maintain a vadose zone in a 1,100-m^2 pilot. In deeper layers (6.5 to 9 m), water was removed at a speed of 14 m^3/d. Air was injected into the soil at 60 m^3/d. After 180 days of operation the treatment was stopped due to technical problems.

RESULTS

Batch Study

No satisfying removal of mineral oil in the peat (from 350 to 290 mg/kg dw in 28 days) could be obtained under optimized conditions in batch studies. Lack of biodegradation could be caused by low pH (3.8) which was difficult to buffer, or by decreased bioavailability due to sorption of the contaminants to the humus. Complete removal of the mineral oil was achieved in the sandy soil from the same site (from 1,400 to <25 mg/kg dw in 28 days), resulting in a mean rate of biodegradation of 50 mg/kg dw/day. Complete contaminant removal was also achieved in the absence of added nutrients, but nutrient amendment resulted in a five-fold increase in CO_2 production (Figure 1). A low CO_2 production was found in the noncontaminated soil without nutrient amendment. CO_2 production was a factor 2 to 3 higher than could be expected on the basis of mineral oil removal, presumably due to solubilization of calcareous compounds. A peak in dehydrogenase activity coincided with a sharp increase in CO_2 production, followed by a mutual decline. FDA hydrolysis increased during the course of the experiment. Based on these results it was concluded that bioremediation of the sandy aquifer was feasible, and column studies were performed with material from the sandy aquifer. Bioremediation of the peat-like soil was rejected.

Column Studies

Mineral Oil. Minor concentrations of contamination were present in the reference columns at the start of the bioremediation. After 7 weeks of operation the mineral oil concentration in the contaminated columns had decreased by

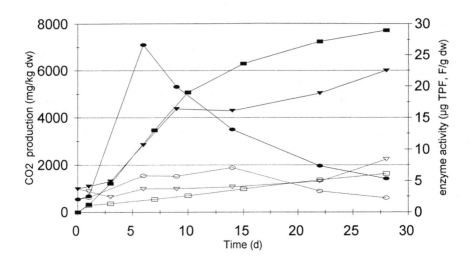

FIGURE 1. Biodegradation of mineral oil in batches with contaminated sand. □ CO₂ production; O dehydrogenase activity (µg TPF/g dw); ∇ FDA hydrolysis (µg F/g dw). Closed symbols = with nutrients; open symbols = without nutrients.

55% (saturated column) and 60% (nonsaturated column), resulting in overall removal rates of 33 and 17 mg mineral oil/kg dw/day, respectively (Table 1).

Mineralization. The cumulative O_2 consumption, as measured in the gas phase plus the water phase, in the contaminated columns remained fairly constant, and reached a total amount of 3 to 4 times the O_2 consumption in the reference columns during the 9 weeks of operation (Figure 2). The CO_2 production was maximal during the first three weeks of operation. After correction for O_2 consumption in the reference columns, and assuming a growth yield of 0.5, it could be calculated that after 7 weeks, biodegradation corresponded with 11% (169 mg mineral oil/kg dw) and 13% (105 mg mineral oil/kg dw) mineral oil removal, for the saturated and nonsaturated columns, respectively. After 3 weeks of operation, biodegradation rates on the basis of both CO_2 production and O_2 consumption in both contaminated columns stabilized towards a value of 2 mg mineral oil/kg dw/d.

Enzyme Activities. Dehydrogenase activity in the contaminated soil was always higher than in the noncontaminated columns during the 9 weeks of measurement (Figure 3). Dehydrogenase activity in the effluent water decreased to levels near or below the detection limit within 2 weeks for all columns.

FDA hydrolysis in the soil of the nonsaturated contaminated column was higher than in the other columns, but no increase or decrease in FDA hydrolysis was observed in any column during the biodegradation process. FDA hydrolysis in the effluent water was stable and low in all columns.

TABLE 1. Bioventing of undisturbed sand columns.

	Contaminated Saturated		Contaminated Nonsaturated		Noncontaminated Saturated		Noncontaminated Nonsaturated	
	t = 0[a]	t = 64	t = 0	t = 64	t = 0	t = 64	t = 0	t = 64
mineral oil (mg/kg dw)	2,900	1,300	1,400	570	70	n.d.	130	n.d.
N_k effl. (mg/L)	1.2	1.3	<1.0	1.1	<1.0	<1.0	<1.0	<1.0
PO_4 effl. (mg/L)	0.3	3.1	<0.2	5.2	0.5	12	<0.2	7.7
O_2 cons. (mg/kg dw)		595		472		134		186
CO_2 prod. (mg/kg dw)		775		675		183		135
org. cont. soil (mg/kg dw)	5,400	24,400[b]	14,800	12,200[b]	4,100	2,100[b]	5,100	1,800[b]
pH soil	5.8	6.8[b]	5.5	7.8[b]	6.7	7.5[b]	8.2	8.0[b]
pH effl.	7.0	6.8[b]	6.5	7.3[b]	6.9	7.5[b]	7.0	7.7[b]
MPN total soil	$1.9*10^8$	$4.0*10^6$	$2.0*10^8$	$4.8*10^7$	$1.7*10^7$	$3.3*10^4$	$2.6*10^6$	$2.6*10^6$
MPN min. oil soil	$1.1*10^6$	$7.9*10^6$	$4.4*10^5$	$1.7*10^7$	$1.2*10^6$	$2.5*10^5$	$1.7*10^5$	$2.4*10^6$
MPN total effl.	$3.9*10^6$	$1.1*10^5$	$1.4*10^7$	$1.1*10^5$	$1.1*10^6$	$1.0*10^4$	$6.2*10^5$	$1.0*10^4$
MPN min. oil effl.	$3.6*10^5$	$6.0*10^4$	$1.6*10^5$	$1.0*10^4$	$3.0*10^4$	$1.1*10^4$	$2.3*10^4$	$3.6*10^3$
dehydrog. soil (µg TPF/g dw)	5.4	4.8[b]	1.3	0.7[b]	1.7	<0.1[b]	0.1	0.2[b]
dehydrog. effl. (µg TPF/mL)	0.71	<0.01[b]	<0.01	<0.01[b]	0.47	<0.01[b]	0.10	<0.01[b]
FDA hydr. soil (µg F/g dw)	19	27[b]	30	39[b]	21	4[b]	15	5[b]
FDA hydr. effl. (µg F/mL)	0.84	1.05[b]	1.19	0.81	0.67	0.93	0.53	0.86[b]

(a) Time (days).   (b) After 49 days.   effl: effluent; n.d.: not determined.

Bacterial Numbers. Total viable bacterial numbers were higher in soil from contaminated columns than in reference columns, and remained at a constant level during the experiment. The mineral oil-degrading population was increased in the contaminated columns by a factor 10 during the experiment, but remained constant in the reference columns (Figure 4). Effluent bacterial numbers were low in all columns and decreased during the experiment.

pH and Nutrients. The initial pH in the contaminated soil columns was lower than in the reference columns. The effluent pH values in the contaminated columns remained significantly lower in the contaminated columns during the course of the experiment. The organic content was heterogeneously distributed through the columns due to patches of peat. Orthophosphate increased in all columns, but remained below the influent concentration of 66 mg PO_4/L.

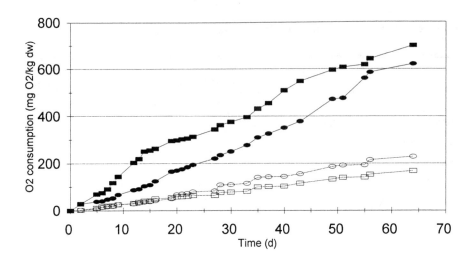

FIGURE 2. O₂ consumption in undisturbed sand columns. ■ saturated contaminated; ● nonsaturated contaminated; ▢ saturated noncontaminated; O nonsaturated noncontaminated.

Mixed Bacterial Culture

A bacterial consortium was isolated from the contaminated columns, and CO_2 production and enzyme assays were correlated during growth on mineral oil. A good correlation existed between CO_2 production and dehydrogenase

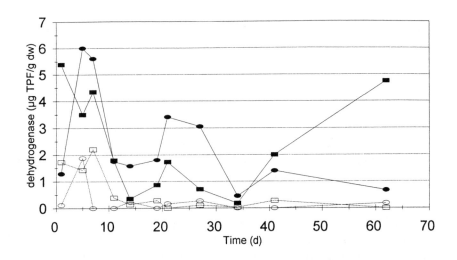

FIGURE 3. Dehydrogenase activity in undisturbed sand columns. ■ saturated contaminated; ● nonsaturated contaminated; ▢ saturated noncontaminated; O nonsaturated noncontaminated.

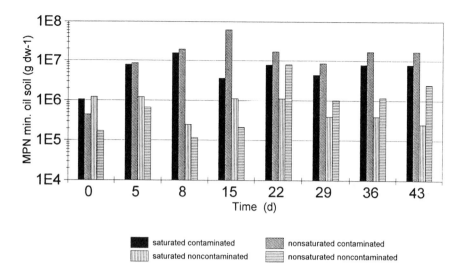

FIGURE 4. Numbers of mineral oil-degrading bacteria in undisturbed sand columns.

activity (Figure 5). FDA hydrolysis correlated with these parameters during an increase of the biodegradation process, but after growth and biodegradation had stopped, FDA hydrolysis decreased only slowly.

Pilot Study

Bioremediation in the field pilot was started with extraction of groundwater and soil vapor, and air injection. Due to an extremely high water level, technical problems occurred during the first months of the treatment, and no vadose zone could be maintained. No data are available on enzyme activities nor soil vapor composition. After a restart of the bioremediation in spring 1995, contaminant levels, soil vapor CO_2 and O_2 data, enzyme activities and bacterial numbers will be monitored during the pilot study, and used to validate the column studies.

DISCUSSION

Bioventing of saturated and nonsaturated undisturbed sand columns resulted in a total removal of 55-60% of mineral oil after 7 weeks of operation, equalling an overall removal rate of 17 to 33 mg mineral oil/kg dw/d. This is a factor 2 to 3 slower than in slurry incubations from the same site, indicating the stimulating effect of mixing. The rate of biodegradation in the saturated and nonsaturated columns was 2 mg mineral oil/kg dw/d, which is within the range that is found for in situ bioventing (Hoeppel et al 1991; Hinchee & Ong 1992). Data on venting are not available, but venting has most likely removed a larger part of the contamination. Biodegradation of hydrocarbons was not affected by the presence of a saturating amount of water.

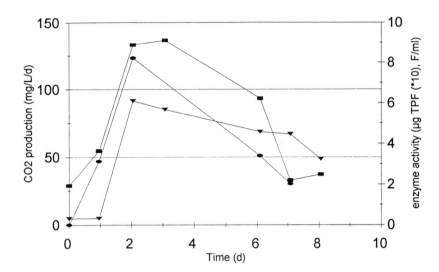

FIGURE 5. **Biodegradation of mineral oil by a mixed microbial population.** ■ **CO$_2$ production;** ● **dehydrogenase activity (μg TPF/g dw);** ▼ **FDA hydrolysis (μg F/g dw).**

Dehydrogenase activity correlated well with the overall biodegradation in mixed microbial culture and soil slurry incubations, and, to a lesser extent, in undisturbed soil columns. Dehydrogenase levels were in a lower range as compared to other studies (Thalmann 1968, Casida 1977, Smith & Pugh 1979, Tiberg et al. 1992). This difference can be caused by the omission of additional substrate in the assay, to permit the determination of the actual dehydrogenase activity as opposed to a potential enzyme activity. Dehydrogenase levels did not represent a quantitative measure of mineral oil degradation, but were indicative of enhanced biological activity.

FDA hydrolysis did not correlate with biodegradation in columns studies and failed to detect a decline in activity in batch studies and therefore may not represent a good indicator of actual biological activity. The sensitivity of the measured biological parameters (MPN, dehydrogenase, FDA hydrolysis) was higher in soil samples than in water samples.

Because no information was available on the actual biodegradation rates in the pilot study, no verification of these methods could be made. It was concluded from the lab studies that, in addition to contaminant levels, soil vapor O$_2$ data and dehydrogenase activity in soil appear to be suitable tools for monitoring biological activity.

REFERENCES

Casida, L. E. 1977. "Microbial Metabolic Activity in Soil as Measured by Dehydrogenase Determinations." *Appl. Environ. Microbiol.* 34:630-636.

Hinchee, R. E., and S. K. Ong. 1992. "A Rapid In Situ Respiration Test for Measuring Aerobic Biodegradation Rates of Hydrocarbons in Soil." *J. Air Waste Manage. Assoc.* 42:1305-1312.

Hoeppel, R. E., R. E. Hinchee, and M. F. Arthur. 1991. "Bioventing Soils Contaminated With Petroleum Hydrocarbons." *J. Ind. Microbiol.* 8:141-146.

Janssen, D. B., A. Scheper, L. Dijkhuizen, and B. Witholt. 1985. "Degradation of Halogenated Aliphatic Compounds by *Xanthobacter autotrophicus* GJ10." *Appl. Environ. Microbiol.* 49:673-677.

Schnürer, J., and Th. Rosswall. 1982. "Fluorescein Diacetate Hydrolyses as a Measure of Total Microbial Activity in Soil and Litter." *Appl. Environ. Microbiol.* 43:1256-1261.

Smith, S. N., and G.J.F. Pugh. 1979. "Evaluation of Dehydrogenase as a Suitable Indicator of Soil Microflora Activity." *Enzyme Microb. Technol.* 1:279-281.

Thalmann, A. 1968. "Zur Methodik der Bestimmung der Dehydrogenaseaktivität im Bodem Mittels Triphenyltetrazoliumchlorid (TTC)." *Landwirtschaftliche Forschung.* 21:249-258.

Tiberg, E., R. Adam, W. Fischer, H. Knoblauch, U. Genz, and E. Kaun. 1992. "Laboruntersuchungen zur Mikrobiellen Abbaubarkeit Verschiedener Mineralölkontaminerter Böden." In DECHEMA, *Bewertung und Sanierung Mineralöl-Kontaminierter Böden.* pp. 442-448. Frankfurt am Main, Germany.

Field Application and Results of an Engineered Bioventing Process

Richard M. Raetz and Davis L. Scharff

ABSTRACT

Mechanical and bioprocess engineering design methods have been employed to control subsurface soil gas flow and amendment feed systems using soil gas recirculation, liquid nutrient injection, and groundwater containment processes. A 15,000-ft^3 (425-m^3) soil mass contained approximately 7,000 lb (3,175 kg) of hydrocarbon (HC) defined by benzene, toluene, ethylbenzene, and xylenes (BTEX) and the alkane chain HCs (C_1 to C_{10}) prior to implementing source area bioremediation in September 1993. After ten months of analyzing various operating modes (pulse, continuous, and vapor recycle) for the Gas Research Institute, approximately 923 lb (419 kg) of HC remained. In July 1994 the field research was completed and a mode of soil gas recirculation and continuous liquid-phase nutrient injection was implemented for Union Pacific Resources Company. The bioventing and biosparging systems were amended with sodium nitrate, triethyl phosphate, pure oxygen, and inoculate grown from on-site groundwater. Inoculate (200 L) containing 650,000 colony-forming units (CFU)/mL of toluene degraders and 5,200,000 CFU/mL hexadecane degraders was injected into the subsurface aquifer. Respirometry test results demonstrated that the biodegradation rate increased from 0.28 mg HC/kg soil-day to 4.28 mg HC/kg soil-day in the bioventing system's primary bioactive zone 90 days after inoculation. The biodegradation rate then decreased to 2.43 mg HC/kg soil-day 180 days after inoculation. Analytical test results indicate that approximately 82% of the remaining HCs have been removed over the last 6 months by bioremediation and groundwater recovery, leaving 162 lb (73 kg) to remediate before site closure.

INTRODUCTION

A full-scale in situ bioremediation cleanup effort is being performed at a former natural gas production well site near Traverse City, Michigan. In situ bioremediation goals have been set to (1) promote bioventing efficiency by increasing HC mass loading rates in the unsaturated portion of the aquifer, thereby eliminating potential carbon limitations for HC-degrading microbes; (2) increase biosparging efficiency by creating a greater dissolved oxygen radius of influence (ROI) using higher air sparge rates and mixing pure oxygen into the sparge air; (3) evenly distribute nutrients throughout the primary bioactive zone of the aquifer; (4) boost the in situ population of HC-degrading microorganisms by using liquid-phase nutrients and bioaugmentation; and (5) recirculate a portion of the soil gas containing volatile organic compounds (VOCs) through an established primary bioactive zone, thereby increasing vapor retention time in the system.

This paper discusses the site hydrogeology, engineering design, field operations, and test results of the in situ bioventing and biosparging remediation processes as it relates to activates performed on site over the past 6 months (July 1994 to February 1995). A discussion of the previous 10 months (September 1993 to June 1994) can be found in Lawrence et al. (1994).

SITE HYDROGEOLOGY

The site aquifer makes up a portion of the glacial outwash plain and contains a soil matrix of medium grain sand with an occasional fine gravel layer. Parameters of the aquifer are as follows: (1) unconfined, (2) approximately 25 ft (7.6 m) in saturated thickness, (3) depth to water equal to 25 ft (7.6 m), (4) aquifer transmissivity equal to 29,000 gpd/ft (3.6×10^5 L/day-m), (5) hydraulic gradient equal to 3.5 ft/1,000 ft (3.5 m/1,000 m), and (6) hydraulic conductivity ranges between 50 to 150 ft/day (15.2 to 45.7 m/day).

ENGINEERING DESIGN

Contaminant Mass and Distribution

Contamination was created by condensing liquids from a glycol reboiler that were lost to the subsurface. The liquid consisted of water and more than 7,000 lb (3,175 kg) of petroleum HC as VOCs (BTEX and C_1 to C_{10}). Site investigations revealed that the HC was interstitially trapped as residual free- and sorbed-phase product in the capillary fringe and in the first 10 ft (3 m) of the groundwater.

After 3 years of mechanical pumping and 10 months of bioventing and biosparging, 922 lb (418 kg) of VOCs remained in the source area. The remaining contaminant was distributed in an area 66 ft (20.1 m) in width by 90 ft (27.4 m) in length (Figure 1; Items 4 and 5). The subsurface position is shown in Figure 2 and is labeled as Primary Bioactive and Contaminant Zone.

Well Placement and Vertical Distribution

Five bioremediation wells were placed in a star pattern at a spacing of 21 ft (6.4 m). A sixth well was placed in the center of the star and a seventh well

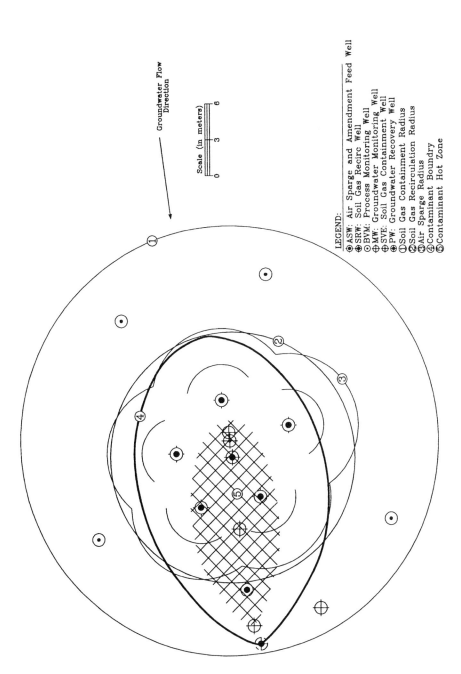

FIGURE 1. Bioremediation plan map.

downgradient of the contaminant's center (Figure 1). This pattern was used to optimize sparge radius enveloping in the subsurface.

Two pilot sparge tests were performed to select optimum flow rates necessary for biosparging relative to well spacing. One test employed the use of helium as a tracer gas. Results demonstrated that a 20-ft (6-m) dissolved oxygen ROI could be obtained while operating at a sparge rate of 1.25 ft³/min (35.4 L/min).

Bioremediation well construction included 7 air sparge wells placed 10 ft (3 m) into the saturated portion of the aquifer, 6 nutrient injection wells intersecting the capillary fringe, 1 soil vapor recirculation well, and 1 soil vapor containment well (Figures 1 and 2). Finally, one recovery well maintains a hydraulically closed-loop system while performing in situ bioremediation.

Process Mixing — Soil Gas

In situ bioremediation of HC in the subsurface is enhanced when conditions for bioactivity are optimized. Optimization techniques for this site included selecting a specific region of the most highly contaminated source area as a biofilter, inoculation of the biofilter, and supplying the microorganism population with sufficient oxygen, nutrients, and HCs. Figure 2 presents the conceptual soil gas flow profile and primary bioactive zone used for process mixing.

Pore volume exchange rates were calculated for the bioactive zone to determine sample frequencies at startup and soil gas retention times. Dissolved oxygen

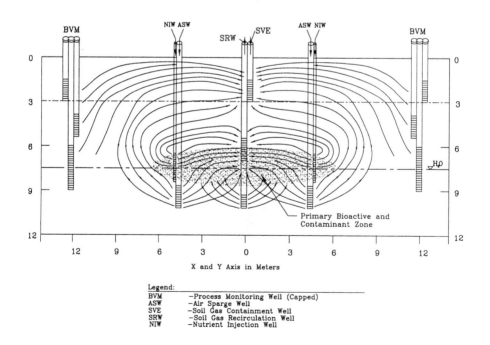

FIGURE 2. Conceptual soil gas flow and bioactive zone profile.

concentrations at various flowrates and radial distances from an air sparge well were used to estimate the dissolved oxygen ROI values shown in Table 1.

A pore volume exchange rate of 6 to 29 hours was calculated for the soil gas containment zone based on the flowrates and dissolved oxygen ROI values presented. Calculations shown in Table 1 consider a parabola both above and below the water-table surface. From these calculations, it can be determined that the soil volume included as part of the bioactive zone was as large as 15,000 ft³ (425 m³). The primary bioactive and contaminant zone that received metered quantities of amendment and inoculate is shown in Figure 2 and contains a soil volume of 9,675 ft³ (274 m³).

Process Mixing — Amendments

Biodegradation rates measured from field data were used to calculate required amendment injection quantities to the subsurface bioventing and biosparging zones. For this bioactive system, a rate of 1.5 mg HC/kg soil-day was initially used to formulate the nutrient mix. This biodegradation rate was selected based on a review of averages throughout the country. In November 1994, 90 days after operation, a biodegradation rate of 4.25 mg HC/kg soil-day was determined during respirometry testing. This value was used to calculate new amendment injection quantities.

Using the biodegradation rate of 4.25 mg HC/kg soil-day and 394,416 kg of soil in the targeted primary bioactive zone, it was calculated that 1.68 kg of HC mass can be consumed daily. Bioactivity required 5.87 kg of oxygen based on a ratio of 3.5 kg of oxygen per kg of HC. Using a carbon:nitrogen:phosphorus ratio of 100:10:2, it was calculated that 0.17 kg of nitrogen and 0.05 kg of phosphorus are required daily.

Inoculation

The following outlines the general procedure for inoculation production. Source area groundwater containing 52 mg/L total BTEX and contaminated soil were added to a shaker flask with minimal salts medium, general nutrients, trace metals, and deionized water, and then placed on a shaker table for 4 days. Next, 20 mL of the water was removed and added to 80 mL of deionized water, minimal salts medium, and toluene (concentration = 30 mg/L) for an additional 4 days. Eventually 2 L of this inoculate was shipped from the laboratory to the field site.

The 2 L of inoculate was transferred to a 55-gal (208 L) drum, and the process of adding contaminated groundwater containing 50 mg/L BTEX, balanced nutrients, and pure oxygen was carried out over 5 days until 200 L of the batch mix existed. Dextrose was then added at a concentration of 250 mg/L for 2 additional days. The final result was a concentrated batch of inoculate containing 650,000 CFU/mL of toluene degraders and 5,200,000 CFU/mL of hexadecane degraders. The entire batch was injected into the unsaturated zone approximately 7 ft (2 m) above the water-table surface and into the capillary fringe at 7 discrete locations in the bioactive zone in August 1994. For further reading on bioaugmentation methods see Leavitt & Brown (1993).

TABLE 1. Pore volume exchange calculations.

Fixed Parameters

Number of ASWs	Saturated H$_2$O Depth (m)	Air in H$_2$O (%)	Capillary Fringe Thickness (m)	Unsaturated Depth (m)	Soil Porosity (%)
1	2.13	0.02	0.46	4.11	0.3

Variable Parameters

SVE (typical)

Flowrate (L/min)	Groundwater ROI (m)	Flowrate (L/min)	Unsaturated H$_2$O (m)	ROI Envelope (ratio)	Total Volume H$_2$O (m^3)
14.16	4.57	28.32	1.52	1.00	21.02
28.32	6.10	56.63	3.05	1.00	37.36
42.47	7.62	84.95	4.57	1.00	58.38
56.77	9.14	113.26	6.10	1.00	84.07
70.97	10.67	141.58	7.62	1.00	114.42

Flowrate (L/min)	Air Void Volume in H$_2$O (m^3)	Saturated PVER (min)	Total Unsaturated Soil Volume (m^3)	Air Void Volumes (m^3)	Unsaturated PVER (h)	Total (h)
14.16	0.42	29.69	16.68	5.00	5.89	6.39
28.32	0.75	26.39	66.72	20.02	11.78	12.22
42.47	1.17	27.49	150.12	45.04	17.67	18.13
56.77	1.68	29.62	266.88	80.06	23.50	24.00
70.97	2.29	32.25	417.00	125.10	29.38	29.92

ASW = air sparge well; SVE = soil vapor extraction; ROI = radius of influence; PVER = pore volume exchange rate.

FIELD OPERATIONS

Soil Gas Flow

The bioventing and biosparging system operated at 0.25 to 0.5 ft^3/min (7 to 14 L/min) into each of the 7 sparge wells for one month prior to inoculation in August 1994. Flowrates were then increased to 1 ft^3/min (28 L/min) during inoculation, 1.5 ft^3/min (42.5 L/min) 30 days after inoculation, and 2 ft^3/min (56.6 L/min) 90 days after inoculation. This system operated for a total of 180 days after inoculation. Pure oxygen was added as part of the total flow at an average rate of 0.16 ft^3/min (4.5 L/min).

A portion of the sparged soil gas (50 to 60%) was collected in a deep recirculation well placed 7 ft (2 m) above the water-table surface and in the primary bioactive zone (Figure 2; labeled as SRW). This soil gas was diluted with atmospheric air, amended with pure oxygen, and reinjected as sparge air. A shallow vent well operated above the primary bioactive zone at 12 to 14 ft^3/min (340 to 400 L/min) to maintain a soil gas collection cap over the bioventing system.

Nutrient Injection

Nutrients were added to reinjection water flowing at 1 gpm (3.8 L/min) into each of 6 wells screened through the capillary fringe of the aquifer (Figure 2; labeled as NIW). A groundwater recovery well operated at 15 gpm (53.2 L/min) to maintain a hydraulically closed-loop system. Nutrients were, in general, added at rates of 1.75 kg/day sodium nitrate and 0.35 kg/day triethyl phosphate (TEP). Nutrients were also added in batch mode to the SRW.

HYDRAULIC CONTAINMENT

The source area biosparging system was hydraulically controlled by 2 pumping wells placed on the central axis of the plume. Figure 3 shows the location of the biosparging in the contaminant zone relative to groundwater flow direction and pumping well drawdown cones. The biosparging zone was 66 ft (20 m) in width while the contaminant capture zone was greater than 132 ft (40 m) in width, with all wells in operation. Flowrates were generally maintained at 15 gpm (56.8 L/min) for each recovery well and 1.5 ft^3/min (42.5 L/m) for each sparge well during data collection.

RESPIROMETRY AND ANALYTIC TEST RESULTS

Bioventing Zone — Biodegradation Rates

Bioventing respirometry tests were performed 60 days prior to, 90 days after, and 180 days after inoculation. Soil gas respirometry test results 60 days prior to inoculation showed that the biodegradation rate of the bioventing zone was

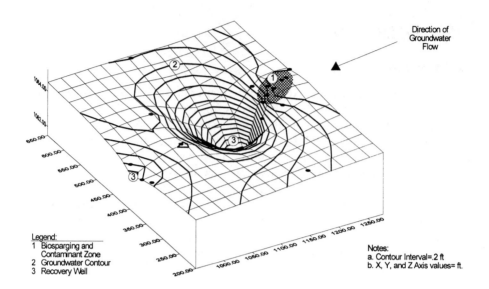

FIGURE 3. Hydraulic containment plan.

at a high of 0.28 mg HC/kg soil-day, indicating that the system was nutrient-limited or microbial population-limited (Figure 5; June 1994).

The biodegradation rate for the primary bioactive zone increased to a high of 4.28 mg HC/kg soil-day 90 days after inoculation and dropped to a high of 2.43 mg HC/kg soil-day, 180 days after inoculation (Figure 4 and Figure 5; November 1994 and February 1995, respectively). The average biodegradation rates for the 90- and 180-day postinoculation periods were 2.49 and 1.55 mg HC/kg soil-day respectively. The above biodegradation rates were calculated by using equations developed by Hinchee et al. (1992).

An average of the post inoculation biodegradation rate (calculated from the 90- and 180-day rates) of 2.0 mg HC/kg soil-day indicated that the addition of liquid nutrients and inoculate increased bioactivity 7-fold since June 1994. February 1995 respirometry test data showed that the biodegradation rate dropped proportionately to the remaining HC concentration. These data suggest that the decrease may be due to the beginning stages of an HC-limiting condition.

Bioventing Zone — Data Analysis

Biodegradation rates, microbial populations in situ, nutrients, and soil gas HC concentrations in the primary bioactive zone have been cross-correlated for September 1, 1993; December 14, 1993; June 28, 1994; November 7, 1994; and February 1995 (Figure 5). A discussion of this analysis follows.

A biodegradation rate of 3.65 mg HC/kg soil-day was obtained during start-up of the bioventing and biosparging system in September 1993 in the absence of amendments. The Figure 5 data reveal that nitrogen was present in the soil at the time of testing. In December 1993 a biodegradation rate of 0.19 mg HC/kg

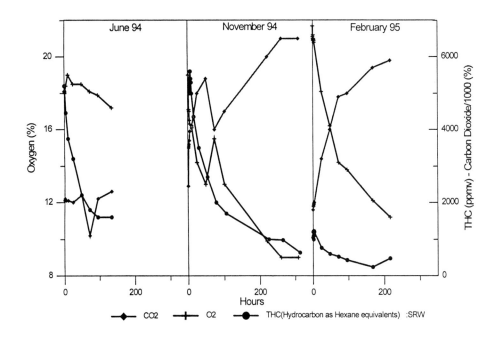

FIGURE 4. Bioventing zone respirometry test results.

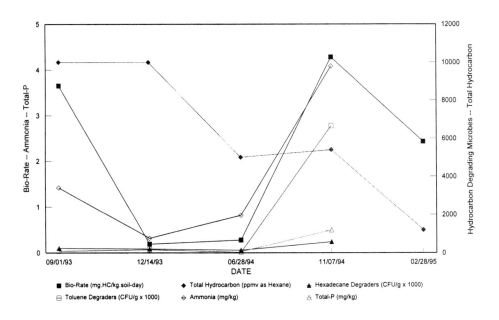

FIGURE 5. A comparison of biodegradation rate vs. microbial populations, nutrients, and gaseous HC in the bioventing zone.

soil-day was obtained and nitrogen was no longer detected in soils; providing a indication that the system became nutrient-limited. Gaseous-phase nutrients (nitrous oxide and heated TEP) were then added to the system prior to June 1994 respirometry testing. However, bioactivity remained low due to an apparent precipitation of the TEP about the well screen and nonbioavailability of the nitrous oxide.

In November 1994 bioactivity increased to 4.28 mg HC/kg soil-day as a result of the August 1994 inoculation and continual liquid-phase nutrient (sodium nitrate and TEP) addition. This relatively high biodegradation rate may be partially due to additional biological oxygen demand on the system as a result of inoculation. A more representative biodegradation rate, resulting from inoculation, is the 90-day and 180-day postinoculation average of 2.0 mg HC/kg soil-day.

Biosparging Zone — CO_2, pH, Dissolved Oxygen

The biosparging system was also analyzed 60 days prior to, 90 days after, and 180 days after inoculation. Source area carbon dioxide increased from 20 mg/L to 70 mg/L and the pH varied between 6.8 and 7.2. The dissolved oxygen concentration in the primary bioactive zone ranged between 0.1 and 2.8 mg/L throughout the 6-month test period.

Biosparging Zone — BTEX

A plot of total BTEX concentrations in groundwater of the biosparging zone revealed that total BTEX dropped from 88,000 µg/L to 55,000 µg/L during 28 months (1.36 mg/L-month) of groundwater recovery (Figure 6). Biosparging was initiated with the groundwater recovery process, and total BTEX dropped from 55,000 µg/L to 37,000 µg/L during the next 10 months (1.3 mg/L-month). Finally, the source area was inoculated and biosparging, liquid-phase nutrient addition, and groundwater recovery continued, resulting in a total BTEX drop from 37,000 µg/L to 6,000 µg/L during the last 6 months (5.2 mg/L-month) of operation.

Biosparging Zone — Microbes

Inoculation resulted in a source area HC-degrading microbe (toluene and hexadecane degraders) population increase of 600,000 CFU/mL in groundwater (Figure 7). The microbe populations over the 180-day period then dropped to less than 100,000 CFU/mL while the total BTEX concentration dropped from 38,000 µg/L to less than 6,000 µg/L. Data are not available to determine whether HC-degrading microbe populations would have sustained their initial average in the presence of a higher BTEX concentration.

Biosparging Zone — Nutrients

Biodegradation rates, HC-degrading microbe populations in groundwater, and nutrient concentrations in the primary bioactive zone have been cross-correlated

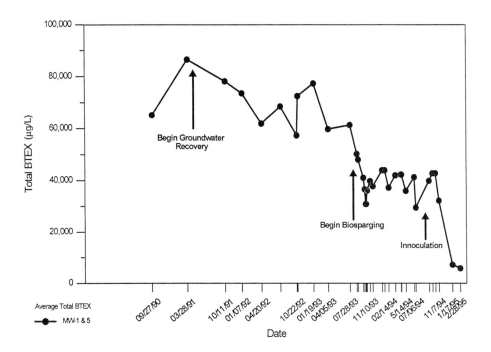

FIGURE 6. Stages of remediation vs. BTEX removal.

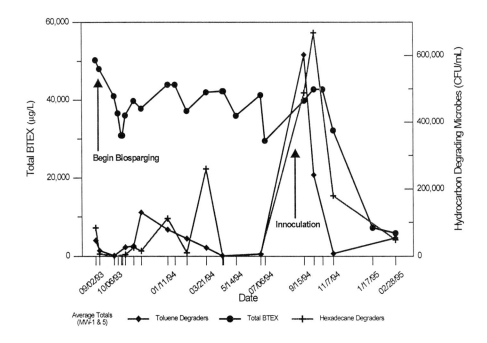

FIGURE 7. BTEX removal vs. microbe populations.

for select respirometry test events between September 1993 and February 1995 (Figure 8). During this time period total BTEX concentrations in groundwater decreased from 50 mg/L to less than 6 mg/L. Cross plots reveal that the bio-degradation rate was highest 90 days after inoculation (November 1994). This event correlated with the highest population of HC-degrading microbes. Nitrogen and phosphorus levels were trace to nondetect throughout the project life even though the metered quantities, discussed earlier, were continually added to the system. In addition, dissolved oxygen concentrations generally remained below 1 mg/L in the primary bioactive and contaminant zone even though pure oxygen was mixed with the sparge air.

MASS BALANCE

The source area contained approximately 922 lb (418.5 kg) of HC prior to inoculation in August 1994. After 180 days, the HC remaining in the system was 162 lb (73.7 kg). The initial HC mass was determined by split barrel sampling soil at 12 discrete locations in the source area. These results were then compared to the contaminant concentration in groundwater and sorbed to soils. The sorbed-phase mass was calculated using octanol/water partitioning coefficients. The initial mass determined from soil sampling agreed within 1% of the mass determined with partitioning coefficients. Soil sampling data was not obtained at the end of the 6 month test period, therefore, a final system mass was calculated using the partitioning coefficients and the contaminant concentration in

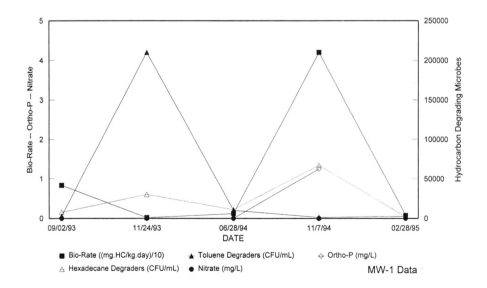

FIGURE 8. A comparison of biodegradation rate vs. microbial populations and nutrients in the biosparging zone.

groundwater. The initial and final in-place soil mass was then correlated with contaminant recovered by pumping and soil gas collected by the extraction well to determine the mass biodegraded using the following equation:

$$\text{Mass Biodegraded (235.7 lb [106.9 kg])} =$$
$$\text{Mass Initial (922.7 lb [418.5 kg])} - \text{Mass Final (162.5 lb [73.7 kg])} -$$
$$\text{Mass Pumped (226.6 lb [102.8 kg])} - \text{Mass Collected (297.9 lb [135.1 kg])}$$

The above results demonstrate that over the 180 days of operation, an average of 4.2 lb (1.9 kg) of HC was removed daily. Of the 4.2 lb (1.9 kg), 30% was removed by the on-site groundwater recovery system, 39% was captured in the soil gas containment well responsible for maintaining the hydraulic gas cap over the system, and the remaining 31% was biodegraded.

A correlation of the daily HC mass biodegraded was made between mass balance calculations and respirometry test data. Using a primary bioactive zone soil mass of 394,560 kg and the daily HC mass biodegraded of 1.3 lb/day (0.59 kg/day) a biodegradation rate of 1.5 mg HC/kg soil-day was calculated. This agrees well with the 6-month postinoculation average of 2 mg HC/kg soil-day.

CONCLUSIONS

1. Soil gas recirculation increases retention time and allows for the flexibility of selecting a primary bioactive zone into which biovented soil gas is recirculated.
2. Inoculation of the primary bioactive zone with HC degrading microorganisms from on-site groundwater and the addition of liquid-phase nutrients successfully increased HC biodegradation rates 7-fold.
3. In the absence of liquid-phase nutrient addition and inoculation, the biodegradation rate was 0.28 mg HC/kg soil-day. After implementing liquid-phase nutrient addition and inoculating, the biodegradation rate averaged 2 mg HC/kg soil-day over the 6-month test period.
4. Inoculation resulted in a source area HC degrading microbe population increase of 600,000 CFU/mL in groundwater. Microbe populations decreased to less than 100,000 CFU/mL over the 6-month test period while the total BTEX concentration dropped from 38,000 µg/L to less than 6,000 µg/L.
5. The source area total BTEX concentration in groundwater dropped an average of 1.3 mg/L-month while biosparging and performing groundwater recovery. After inoculation, the source area total BTEX concentration dropped an average of 5.2 mg/L-month while biosparging and performing groundwater recovery.
6. An average of 4.2 lb (1.9 kg) of HC was removed daily over the 6-month test period. Of these 4.2 lb (1.9 kg), 30% was removed by the on-site groundwater recovery system, 39% of the HC was captured by the soil gas containment well responsible for maintaining the hydraulic gas cap, and the remaining 31% of HC was biodegraded.

ACKNOWLEDGMENTS

Global Remediation Technologies, Inc. wishes to thank Davis Scharff of Union Pacific Resources Company for his technical input and funding of the remediation. We also wish to thank Jeff Miller, Remediation Technologies, Inc., and Tom Hayes, Gas Research Institute, for their insights and participation in the project.

REFERENCES

Hinchee, R. E., S. K. Ong, R. N. Miller, D. C. Downey, and R. Frandt. 1992. *Test Plan and Technical Protocol for a Field Treatability Test for Bioventing*, for U.S. Air Force Center for Environmental Excellence, Brooks Air Force Base, TX.
Lawrence, A. W., D. L. Miller, J. A. Miller, R. L. Weightman, R. M. Raetz, and T. D. Hayes. 1994. "In Situ Bioventing for Environmental Remediation of a Natural Gas Dehydration Site: A Field Demonstration." SPE Paper 28351 Presented at the 1994 SPE Annual Technical Conference and Exhibition, New Orleans, LA.
Leavitt, M. E., and K. L. Brown. 1993. "Biostimulation versus Bioaugmentation — 3 Case Studies." In R. E. Hinchee, B. C. Alleman, R. E. Hoeppel, and R. N. Miller (Eds.), *Hydrocarbon Bioremediation*. Lewis Publishers, Ann Arbor, MI. pp. 72-79.

Hydrocarbon Biodegradation Kinetics in an Intact Unsaturated Zone Soil Core

Ellen E. Moyer, David W. Ostendorf,
Robin J. Richards, and Steve Goodwin

ABSTRACT

Aerobic biodegradation of vapor-phase petroleum hydrocarbons was evaluated in an intact soil core from the site of an aviation gasoline release. A mid-depth unsaturated zone soil core was subjected to a flow of nitrogen gas, oxygen, water vapor, and vapor-phase hydrocarbons in a configuration analogous to a biofilter or an in situ bioventing or sparging situation. The vertical profiles of vapor-phase hydrocarbon concentration in the soil core were determined by gas chromatography of vapor samples. Steady-state concentrations were input to a simple analytical model balancing advection and first-order biodegradation of hydrocarbons. First-order rate constants for each major hydrocarbon compound were used to calibrate the model to the concentration profiles. Compounds with lower molecular weights, fewer methyl groups, and no quaternary carbons tended to have higher rate constants. The first-order rate constants were consistent with kinetic parameters determined from microcosm studies at the same field site, suggesting that both estimation methods were effective.

INTRODUCTION

Aerobic biodegradation of vapor-phase petroleum hydrocarbons was evaluated in an intact soil core from the site of an aviation gasoline release to determine biodegradation kinetic parameters under environmentally realistic conditions. A mid-depth unsaturated zone soil core was subjected to a flow of nitrogen, oxygen, water vapor, and vapor-phase hydrocarbons. The vertical profiles of vapor-phase hydrocarbon concentration in the soil core were determined by gas chromatography (GC) of vapor samples. Steady-state concentrations were input to a simple analytical model balancing advection and first-order biodegradation of hydrocarbons. First-order rate constants for each major hydrocarbon compound were used to calibrate the model to the concentration profiles. The results were then compared with results of microcosm studies. The utility of determining biodegradation kinetic parameters is that the values can be used in saturated zone site models which predict contaminant concentrations as a function of space and/or time during bioventing (e.g., Ostendorf and Kampbell 1990) or under ambient conditions (e.g., Ostendorf and Kampbell 1991).

SAMPLING AND ANALYSIS METHODS

The field site was at the U.S. Coast Guard Air Station in Traverse City, Michigan. This site was chosen for its geologic simplicity, well-acclimated microbial community, and extensive characterization in previous studies. A 1969 subsurface release of an estimated 100,000 kg of aviation gasoline has since migrated along a fluctuating water table downgradient from its original source (Ostendorf 1990). Residual light nonaqueous phase liquid (LNAPL) is present in the vicinity of the water table, and the 5-m-thick unsaturated zone is contaminated with vapor-phase petroleum hydrocarbons rising from the residual source (Ostendorf and Kampbell 1991). Soil throughout the vertical profile at the site is uniform fine-grained beach sand of low natural organic carbon content. Primary constituents of the weathered LNAPL are di-, tri-, and tetramethyl pentanes and hexanes, toluene, and dimethylbutane (Ostendorf et al. 1989).

A drilling rig and crew collected vertical intact soil cores at the field site using drilling techniques described by Leach et al. (1988) and Ostendorf et al. (1991; 1993b). Intact cores were obtained from the residually contaminated interval just above the capillary fringe and from mid-depth in the unsaturated zone at a location designated as 50CL. Two soil cores were connected in series, the deeper core containing residual LNAPL simply serving as a source of vapor-phase hydrocarbons for the mid-depth core. The deeper core had previously been used in advective stripping experiments, which had depleted some of the residual LNAPL. A mixture of 79% nitrogen gas and 21% oxygen flowed at 3 mL/min through a water saturator for humidification, then upward through the deeper soil core containing residual LNAPL and upward through the mid-depth soil core. The temperatures in both soil cores were maintained at 12°C. Biodegradation was measured in the mid-depth core by GC analysis of hydrocarbon vapor samples from ports installed at 3-cm intervals. Details on soil core hardware and GC analysis are published in Ostendorf et al. (1993b) and Richards et al. (1992). The mid-depth core concentration profiles were analyzed periodically until the profile of total hydrocarbon concentration was replicated, indicating quasi-steady state of biodegradation rates.

RESULTS

The GC results for the quasi-steady concentration profiles of the seven most predominant weathered aviation gasoline compounds in the 50CL source core are summarized in Figure 1. Concentrations are normalized to influent concentrations, which ranged from 7.3×10^{-6} to 1.4×10^{-4} kg/m³ (0.4 to 8 ppm). The extent of biodegradation is reflected in hydrocarbon concentration decreases with elevation in the soil core. Under steady conditions in the absence of biodegradation,

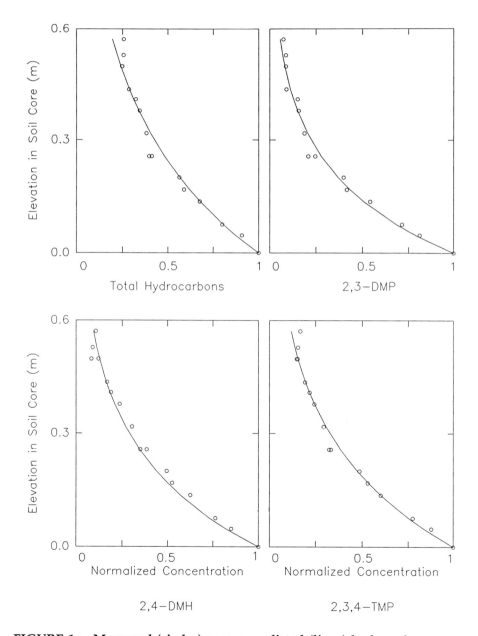

FIGURE 1a. Measured (circles) versus predicted (lines) hydrocarbon vapor concentrations in a 2.1- to 2.7-m-deep soil core.

adsorption is not a factor, and uniform concentrations equal to influent concentrations occur at all elevations (Ostendorf et al. 1993a).

Influent concentrations of all the detected standard compounds were reduced by 50% or more by the time the air had flowed through the 0.6-m-long soil column.

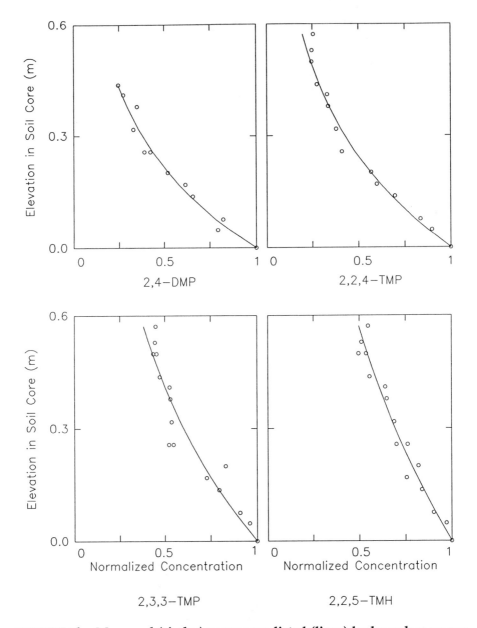

FIGURE 1b. Measured (circles) versus predicted (lines) hydrocarbon vapor concentrations in a 2.1- to 2.7-m-deep soil core.

Several related trends are apparent in the data. The extent of biodegradation tended to decrease with increasing molecular weight and increasing number of methyl groups. The concentration of one of the two lowest-molecular-weight compounds, 2,3-dimethylpentane, was reduced to the greatest extent, with an exit concentration equal to 7.5% of the influent concentration. The heaviest compound, 2,2,5-trimethylhexane, was the least biodegraded, and its exit concentration was 55% of the influent concentration; 2,4-dimethylpentane deviated from this trend.

Greater reductions were observed in the four compounds with no quaternary carbons (i.e., carbon atoms bonded to four other carbon atoms) than in the 3 compounds with 1 quaternary carbon and 2 tertiary carbons. This is well illustrated by the three trimethylpentane compounds. Of these compounds, 2,3,4-trimethylpentane, with three tertiary carbons, was biodegraded to the greatest extent; 2,2,4-trimethylpentane, with a quaternary carbon and a tertiary carbon separated by a secondary carbon, was intermediate; and 2,3,3-trimethylpentane, with a quaternary carbon bonded directly to a tertiary carbon, was the least biodegraded.

The experiment was analytically modeled as a steady balance of biodegradation and advection. Substrate-limited biodegradation reaction rate, R, is often quantified using a hyperbolic expression relating substrate (hydrocarbon) concentration, H (mass of hydrocarbon per unit volume of air, e.g. kg/m^3), and two kinetic parameters, maximum reaction rate, V (maximum rate of disappearance of H, e.g. kg/m^3-s), and half-saturation constant, K (the H value at which the rate of disappearance of H is at half of its maximum value, V)

$$R = -\frac{VH}{K+H} \tag{1}$$

At low substrate concentrations, the expression reduces to a first-order reaction; at high substrate concentrations, the reaction is zero order (Grady and Lim 1980).

Applying conservation of mass to a control volume yielded the following governing differential equation

$$w\frac{dH}{dz} = -\theta\frac{VH}{K+H} \tag{2}$$

with air-filled porosity, θ, air specific discharge, w (the flux rate of air through the column, e.g. m/s), and elevation in the soil core, z. Known influent ($z = 0$) hydrocarbon concentration H_0 is the boundary condition.

In the soil core experiment, the estimated influent concentration of total hydrocarbons (4.7×10^{-4} kg/m^3) was below published values for K (8.0×10^{-4} and 8.5×10^{-4} kg/m^3) at nearby locations at the field site (Ostendorf and Kampbell 1991; 1990), and the biodegradation reaction term in equation 2 was approximated as first order. Upon integration, the solution is

$$H = H_0\exp\left[-\frac{V}{K}\frac{\theta z}{w}\right] \qquad (H<<K) \tag{3}$$

The air specific discharge was 1.05×10^{-5} m/s, and a site measured value of 0.274 was adopted for air-filled porosity (Ostendorf and Kampbell 1991). The experimental results for each detected standard compound were calibrated to equation 3 using V/K as a first-order rate constant in a single-parameter Fibonacci search (Beveridge and Schechter 1970). The results of the calibration are shown in Table 1 and Figure 1. The first-order rate constants for individual compounds ranged from 4.7×10^{-5} to 1.9×10^{-4} L/s, yielding error standard deviations between 5 to 16% and mean errors of 0.2% or less.

To compare the results with literature values for total hydrocarbon V and K, soil core total hydrocarbon concentrations were also modeled. Standard calibration curves of total GC peak area versus total concentration of nine standard compounds were used. The estimated total hydrocarbon first-order rate constant was 1.1×10^{-5} L/s.

In a companion study, the disappearance of hydrocarbons was tracked in microcosms sampled from one of the 50CL replicate borings (Richards et al. 1992). Unsaturated zone samples were dosed with a gaseous mixture of weathered aviation gasoline compounds and incubated at 15°C. The headspace of the microcosms was periodically sampled and analyzed by GC using the method described previously. The total hydrocarbon concentration data were fit to the unsteady model of Ostendorf and Kampbell (1990) by calibration of acclimation time and V. A value of 0.001 kg/m³ for K was adopted from previous studies. Calibrated lag times ranged from 8 to 439 h, and V ranged from 1.2×10^{-9} to 3.5×10^{-8} kg/m³-s.

The database for the two microcosms from 2.3 m below the ground surface and the two microcosms from 2.5 m in that study is further presented here on an individual compound basis for comparison with the results for the 50CL soil core (from 2.1 to 2.7 m below the ground surface). Initial hydrocarbon concentrations were higher than the influent concentrations for the soil core experiment; therefore, biodegradation was not approximated as first order, and V and K values were optimized individually.

TABLE 1. Soil core and microcosm first-order rate constants.

Compound	V/K (L/s)	
	Soil Core	Microcosm Average
2,3-Dimethylpentane	1.9×10^{-4}	1.6×10^{-4}
2,4-Dimethylhexane	1.6×10^{-4}	4.4×10^{-5}
2,3,4-Trimethylpentane	1.4×10^{-4}	2.4×10^{-4}
2,4-Dimethylpentane	1.2×10^{-4}	3.6×10^{-4}
2,2,4-Trimethylpentane	1.1×10^{-4}	3.5×10^{-4}
2,3,3-Trimethylpentane	6.4×10^{-5}	3.1×10^{-4}
2,2,5-Trimethylhexane	4.7×10^{-5}	6.6×10^{-5}
Total Hydrocarbons	1.1×10^{-4}	1.5×10^{-4}

Resulting first-order rate constants from the microcosm and soil core data agreed well, as summarized in Table 1. For all compounds, the average microcosm V/K and the soil core V/K differed by less than a factor of 5. The range of V/K (4.4×10^{-5} to 3.6×10^{-4} L/s) in the microcosm calibrations was very similar to that of the soil core calibrations (4.7×10^{-5} to 1.9×10^{-4} L/s). The order of the compounds with increasing V/K was different than for the soil core results.

V/K for total hydrocarbons for the microcosms (1.5×10^{-4} L/s) also agreed well with the soil core V/K (1.1×10^{-4} L/s). A somewhat higher V/K for the microcosms is logical because incubation temperature was slightly higher than the soil core temperature, and lighter compounds were more prevalent in the hydrocarbon blend in the microcosms.

CONCLUSIONS

Biodegradation reduced low influent hydrocarbon concentrations by 45 to 92% over a 0.6-m interval of an intact soil core. The estimated total hydrocarbon concentration was reduced by 75% from 26 to 7 ppm. Soil core first-order rate constants for 7 individual hydrocarbon compounds varied by a factor of 4. Compounds with lower molecular weights, fewer methyl groups, and no quaternary carbons tended to have higher first-order rate constants.

Model calibrations yielded first-order rate constants that were consistent with kinetic parameters determined from companion microcosm studies at the field site. There was strong agreement in spite of the fact that different models; hydrocarbon blends; and time, length, and concentration scales were involved. The study findings suggest that both methods of estimating kinetic parameters were effective at this site. Once kinetic parameters are estimated, an expression for biodegradation (Equation 1) can be included as a term in unsaturated zone models, balancing other mechanisms such as diffusion, advection, and/or storage change, to predict concentrations of contaminants undergoing biodegradation.

ACKNOWLEDGMENTS

This research was supported as U.S. Environmental Protection Agency (EPA) Contract CR 816821 with the University of Massachusetts at Amherst, administered through the R.S. Kerr Environmental Research Laboratory in Ada, Oklahoma. The paper has not been subjected to EPA review however, and accordingly does not necessarily reflect the views of the EPA, so no official endorsement should be inferred.

REFERENCES

Beveridge, G.S.G., and R. S. Schechter. 1970. *Optimization: Theory and Practice.* McGraw-Hill, New York, NY.

Grady, C.P.L., Jr. and H. C. Lim. 1980. *Biological Wastewater Treatment Theory and Applications.* Marcel Dekker, Inc., New York, NY.

Leach, L. E., F. P. Beck, J. T. Wilson, and D. H. Kampbell. 1988. "Aseptic subsurface sampling techniques for hollow-stem auger drilling." *Proceedings: Petroleum Hydrocarbons and Organic Chemicals in Ground Water,* pp. 31-51. NWWA/API, Dublin, OH.

Ostendorf, D. W. 1990. "Long term fate and transport of immiscible aviation gasoline in the subsurface environment." *Water Science and Technology* 22(6):37-44.

Ostendorf, D. W. and D. H. Kampbell. 1990. "Bioremediated soil venting of light hydrocarbons." *Hazardous Waste and Hazardous Materials* 7(4):319-334.

Ostendorf, D. W. and D. H. Kampbell. 1991. "Biodegradation of hydrocarbon vapors in the unsaturated zone." *Water Resources Research* 27(4):453-462.

Ostendorf, D. W., D. H. Kampbell, J. T. Wilson, and J. H. Sammons. 1989. "Mobilization of aviation gasoline from a residual phase." *Research Journal of the Water Pollution Control Federation* 61(11/12):1684-1690.

Ostendorf, D. W., L. E. Leach, E. S. Hinlein, and Y. Xie. 1991. "Field sampling of residual aviation gasoline in sandy soil." *Ground Water Monitoring Review* 11(2):107-120.

Ostendorf, D. W., E. E. Moyer, and E. S. Hinlein. 1993a. "Petroleum hydrocarbon sparging from intact core sleeve samples." *Proceedings: Petroleum Hydrocarbons and Organic Chemicals in Groundwater,* pp. 415-427. NGWA/API, Dublin, OH.

Ostendorf, D. W., E. E. Moyer, Y. Xie, and R. V. Rajan. 1993b. "Hydrocarbon vapor diffusion in intact core sleeves." *Ground Water Monitoring and Remediation* 13(1):139-150.

Richards, R. J., D. W. Ostendorf, and M. S. Switzenbaum. 1992. "Aerobic soil microcosms for long-term biodegradation of hydrocarbon vapors." *Hazardous Waste and Hazardous Materials* 9(4):397-410.

In Situ Diesel Fuel Bioremediation:
A Case History

Derek K. Rhodes, George K. Burke,
Nancy Smith, and David Clark

ABSTRACT ━━━━━━━━━━━━━━━━━━━━━━━━━━━━━━━━━━

As a result of a ruptured fuel line, the study site had diesel fuel soil contamination and free product more than 2 ft (0.75 m) thick on the groundwater surface. Diesel fuel, which is composed of a high percentage of nonvolatile compounds, has proven difficult to remediate using conventional extraction remediation techniques. A number of remedial alternatives were reviewed, and the patented in situ biodegradation BioSparge[SM] technology was selected for the site and performed under license by a specialty contractor. BioSparge[SM] is a field-proven closed-loop (no vapor emissions) system that supplies a continuous, steady supply of oxygen, moisture, and additional heat to enhance microorganism activity. The system injects an enriched airstream beneath the groundwater surface elevation and/or within the contaminant plume and removes residual vapors from vadose zone soil within and above the contaminant plume. The technology has no air discharge, which is critical in areas where strict air discharge regulations apply. The focus of this paper is the viability of in situ biodegradation as an effective remediation alternative for reducing nonvolatile petroleum products.

INTRODUCTION

The BioSparge[SM] system is a closed-loop in situ remediation technology that uses a designed system of gas injection sparge/purge wells combined with surrounding vapor extraction wells. A mobile surface treatment system provides injection, capture, and treatment without gas venting and emissions (Figure 1).

The technology has been applied to a select number of petroleum hydrocarbon sites in the southwestern United States and in Wisconsin. The site presented is a unique and difficult in situ remediation problem which demonstrates the effectiveness of biosparging technology to remediate nonvolatile, free product compounds.

SITE BACKGROUND

The site is at a truck refueling terminal located in New Mexico, and consists of a maintenance building, a pump island with an overhead canopy, and a 15,000-gal (56,775-L) aboveground storage tank (AST) located approximately 110 ft (33 m) from the pump island. The entire property is paved with 3-in.-thick (8-cm-thick) asphalt.

In 1987, the 3-in. (8-cm) fiberglass product line was ruptured, and approximately 4,000 gal (15,140 L) of #2 diesel fuel was released into the underlying soils. A consulting firm was contracted to characterize the subsurface conditions and determine the potential impact to the site. The firm installed fifteen 2-in.-diameter (5-cm-diameter) monitoring wells. Based on the information obtained from the wells, the consulting firm completed a site characterization study.

Borings indicated that the site stratigraphy consists of low plasticity clay for the upper 4 to 6 ft (1.2 to 1.8 m), which is underlain by 20 to 25 ft (6 to 7.6 m) of poorly graded sand. Beneath the sand is a medium plasticity, cohesive clay that acts as an aquiclude. Groundwater typically is 21 to 23 ft (6.4 to 7 m) below the surface. Slug tests were performed and an average transmissivity for the site of 12,800 gpd/ft was calculated, with maximum horizontal product migration of 90 ft (28 m) in 6 years. The released fuel migrated through the soils and pooled at the groundwater surface, with a maximum thickness exceeding 2 ft (0.6 m). Based on groundwater samples, it was determined that no substantial dissolved-phase contamination existed within the groundwater. As a result of this study, the firm installed a free product recovery system which consisted of two recovery pumps placed in the wells with the thickest product.

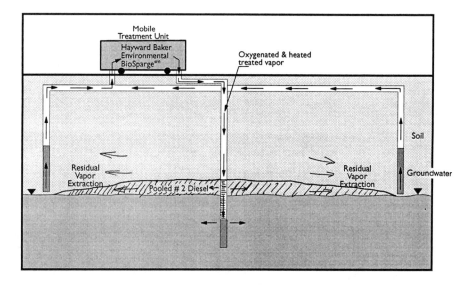

FIGURE 1. Truck refueling terminal BioSparge^{SM} system.

The pumps recovered a few hundred gallons of free product; however, production dramatically decreased after 1 to 2 years. It was theorized that this decrease was due to the fact that the free product was trapped in the capillary fringe and therefore had minimal horizontal migration to the wells. The consultant prepared a preliminary free product contour based on the well data and characterized the plume as being approximately 100 ft by 130 ft (30 m by 40 m). Given an average thickness of capillary fringe contamination by diesel fuel of 1 ft, the consultant calculated a total contaminated soil volume of 480 yd^3 (370 m^3) which contained at least 1,020 gal (4,075 L) of #2 diesel, at the start of remediation.

REMEDIATION SYSTEM

The owner, wanting to move the site to closure, felt additional remediation efforts would be required to remove the product still residing in the soils. Another consulting firm was selected to install two additional monitoring/recovery wells and prepare a remediation bid package outlining the site conditions. The bid package allowed potential contractors to submit a bid based on the technology of their choice. A number of firms submitted soil vacuum extraction systems and excavation/disposal alternatives.

Soil vacuum extraction is ineffective on nonvolatile products such as diesel fuel and excavation/disposal is costly and would require the closure and removal of the refueling terminal. Alternative bioremediation methods were proposed, but these were based on groundwater injection/extraction, which would not benefit degradation of product in the capillary fringe where the majority of contamination resided.

From these bids, the biosparging alternative was selected based on cost, probability of success and minimal disruption to the site operations and facilities. Another key factor in selecting the biosparging technology was a unique negotiated contract that provided for payment based on the remediation percentage achieved at the site — a type of contract widely used in the construction industry but seldom used for contaminant remediation.

The infrastructure designed for the site consisted of sixteen 4-in.-diameter (10-cm-diameter) vapor extraction wells and nine 4-in.-diameter (10-cm-diameter) vapor injection wells. The vapor extraction wells were screened at an average depth of 15 to 25 ft (4.5 to 7.6 m) below the ground surface and the injection wells were screened at intervals of 18 to 28 ft (5.5 to 8.5 m) below the ground surface. The extraction wells were designed to ring the area of contamination and were connected by a common manifold. These wells were connected by a second separate manifold (Figure 2). All wells were individually valved from the main trunk line, and pressure meters were attached to each well. Free product recovery pumps were installed in four of the nine injection wells; however, each of the nine wellheads was designed to allow movement of the pumps to the wells with the thickest product.

The BioSparge^{SM} treatment unit was constructed in a container selected for ease of transport, security, rigidity, and vibration dampening characteristics. The

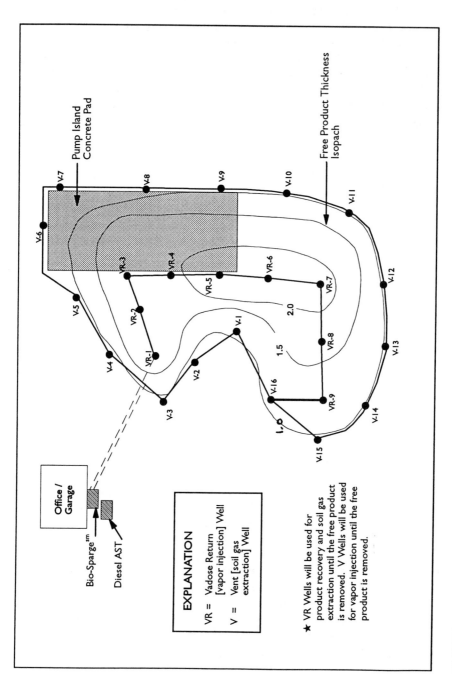

FIGURE 2. Infrastructure design.

treatment system included a positive displacement blower for low-flow extraction/injection of the soil vapors. An oxygen generator was installed to feed the absorption tank and the site wells, and a vapor heating system was installed to provide heat to the wells to increase microbial activity and decrease product viscosity. A peristaltic injection system was also added to allow low-flow continuous injection of surfactants into the pressure flow (injection wells) side of the system. The free product recovery pump control and air supply system was also installed in the unit for ease of control. A strict regimen of bionutrients was continuously metered into the treatment system (Figure 3).

The entire treatment system required only 18 kW electrical power to operate. No other power or energy source is required. Because the system is closed-loop by design, no air treatment is required and, thus, no carbon or thermal systems are used.

The infrastructure was installed in April 1994, and the treatment system was started in May 1994. To promote the efficiency of the four free product recovery pumps, the initial airflow was reversed from that shown in Figure 1, with vapor extraction from the middle wells and injection in the perimeter wells. This would serve to accelerate the free product recovery and improve the conditions for in situ biodegradation. The wells were screened in poorly graded sands,

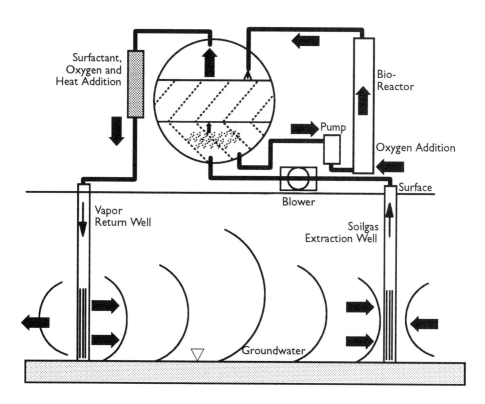

FIGURE 3. BioSparge/BioPurge^{SM} schematic.

and injection pressures remained below 3 psi (20,700 N/m^2). The blower was regeared from 50 cfm (0.024 m^3/s) to a maximum of 65 cfm (0.03 m^3/s).

Coincident with these activities, two independent microbial laboratories performed separate treatability studies on soil samples collected from the site. Both microbial laboratories determined that site soils were deficient of most microbial nutrients, especially nitrogen and phosphorous sources. From these data, an injection profile was developed that consisted of surfactant-producing enzymatic bacteria supplemented by nutrients (MicroBac 1994). The results of the tests and a breakdown of the components were forwarded to the New Mexico Environmental Department (NMED) for approval. The NMED determined that a discharge permit would be required since the product contained a regulated nitrogen source even though the concentration was below the regulated limit. After 6 months of negotiations with the state, it was decided to inject the products without the regulated nitrogen source.

RESULTS

For the year before the biosparging unit was activated, the two recovery pumps had removed approximately one 55-gal (208-L) drum of product from the site. After operating for 7 months, the biosparging remediation system had removed more than 350 gal (1,325 L) of free product without the aid of the injected surfactant-producing enzymatic bacteria. An undetermined volume of product has been degraded within the subsoils, and out of the 25 injection/extraction wells, the original up to 2 ft of free product in 9 wells has been reduced to a sheen in three of the on-site wells after a 48-hour shutdown period. Injection of the enzymatic bacteria was started at the end of November 1994, and borings for soil sampling and testing are expected to be completed in April 1995. The BioSparge^{SM} system is now operating as designed and indicated in Figure 1, working on Phase 2 of the site remediation to reduce soil contamination to less than 100 ppm TPH. Total site remediation is to be completed by the end of 1995.

REFERENCES

Michael M. Hobby, LTD. 1994. *Microbial Treatability Test Results*. Las Vegas, NV.
MicroBac International, Inc. 1994. *Microbial Treatability Test Results*. Austin, TX.
Souder, Miller & Associates. 1993. *Request for Proposals to Perform Bioremediation Services*. Santa Fe, NM.

Multiphase, Multicomponent Numerical Model of Bioventing with Nonequilibrium Mass Exchange

John R. Lang, Klaus M. Rathfelder, and Linda M. Abriola

ABSTRACT

A numerical model is presented that has been specifically designed to simulate the combined processes of soil vapor extraction and enhanced bioremediation known as bioventing. In this model, equations describing multiphase flow, multicomponent advective diffusive transport, and biodegradation are coupled. An entrapped organic residual, mobile gas and aqueous phases, and a reactive biophase are modeled. Components include n organic contaminants, oxygen, nitrogen, and water. Rate-limited mass exchange between the phases is simulated using linear driving force expressions. These expressions model volatilization and dissolution of the entrapped organic residual, rate-limited transport between the gas and aqueous phases, and rate-limited transport to the biophase. Monod-type kinetic expressions are employed to describe biophase utilization of substrates, the electron acceptor, and a limiting nutrient, as well as the growth of the microbial population. The coupled nonlinear governing equations are solved using a set iterative finite element method. Numerical simulations are presented for one-dimensional bench-scale column studies. These simulations illustrate the potential importance of biological degradation in the remediation of systems that are subject to mass transfer limitations.

INTRODUCTION

Soil vapor extraction (SVE) and bioventing (BV) technologies are established and widely used remediation technologies for removal of volatile organic contaminants from unsaturated soils (Rathfelder et al. 1994). These methods are often selected for their effectiveness and cost efficiency. The complex interplay of spatially dependent physical, chemical, and biological processes, however makes the assessment of SVE/BV performance particularly difficult. Consequently the design and operation of these systems has been largely based on empiricism, i.e., on practical experience or simple design equations (Johnson et al. 1990).

Increasing use of SVE and BV has led to a clearer recognition of the applicability of these technologies and has focused attention on improving the understanding of processes that limit their effectiveness. Laboratory and field evidence suggest that a primary factor constraining efficiency relates to limitations on mass transfer between liquid/solid and liquid/gas phases (Cho and Jaffe 1990; Berndtson and Bunge 1991; McClellan and Gilham 1992). Numerical models have also been developed as tools for studying the interaction of physical, chemical, and biological processes, and for assisting in the design and evaluation of SVE/BV systems (Forsyth and Shao 1991; Rathfelder et al. 1991; Chen et al. 1992; Sleep and Sykes 1991). Bioremediation models developed to date cannot fully account for nonequilibrium mass transfer processes among constituent phases. This paper presents preliminary work on the development of a numerical model for SVE/BV processes designed to incorporate nonequilibrium mass transfer among the gas, aqueous, organic, and biophases.

CONCEPTUAL MODEL AND MATHEMATICAL FORMULATION

Formulation of a mathematical description of the bioventing process requires a conceptualization of the soil-fluid-microbial system. In this work, the subsurface formation is assumed to be spatially heterogeneous in permeability and porosity. Three fluid phases may occupy the soil pores: an immobile residual organic liquid, a mobile gas phase, and a mobile aqueous phase. The gas and aqueous phases can flow simultaneously in response to applied stresses at extraction/injection wells, and/or to density gradients arising from spatial variation in phase composition. The movement of these phases is described by standard macroscopically averaged flow equations (Abriola 1989):

$$\frac{\partial}{\partial t}(\phi \rho_\alpha^* S_\alpha) - \nabla \cdot \left[\rho_\alpha^* \frac{\mathbf{k} k_{\alpha r}}{\mu_\alpha}(\nabla P_\alpha - \rho_\alpha^* g \nabla z)\right] = \phi \sum_i E_{\alpha \beta i}^* \qquad (1)$$

where $\alpha = g, a$ denotes the gas and aqueous phases, ϕ is porosity, ρ_α^* is phase mass density, S_α is phase saturation, $\mathbf{k}$ is the intrinsic permeability tensor, $k_{r\alpha}$ is phase relative permeability, μ_α is phase dynamic viscosity, P_α is phase pressure, g is gravitational acceleration, z is the positive downward vertical direction, and $E_{\alpha \beta}^*$ is the net rate of interphase mass transfer of component i to the α-phase from all contiguous phases, β. Both the gas and aqueous phases are in contact with each other and with the organic phase. The aqueous phase is also in contact with the attached biophase. Because the organic liquid is assumed to be immobile, changes in organic liquid saturation result solely from interphase mass transfer; e.g., the organic liquid mass balance is:

$$\frac{\partial}{\partial t}(\phi \rho_o^* S_o) = \phi \sum_i E_{o \beta i}^* \qquad (2)$$

The composition of the fluid phases is subject to the following assumptions. The organic liquid is considered to be a mixture of an unrestricted number of organic components. The gas phase is assumed to be comprised of nitrogen and oxygen (i.e., the two major components of air), water vapor, volatile components of the organic liquid, and a limiting nutrient. The aqueous phase is limited to components of the organic liquid, water, oxygen, and a limiting nutrient.

The migration of individual phase components is represented by a general macroscopically averaged transport equation (Abriola 1989):

$$\frac{\partial}{\partial t}(\phi S_\alpha \rho_\alpha x_{\alpha i}) + \nabla \cdot \phi S_\alpha (\rho_\alpha x_{\alpha i} V_\alpha - \rho_\alpha D_{\alpha i}^h \nabla x_{\alpha i}) = \phi E_{\alpha \beta i} \qquad (3)$$

where ρ_α is phase molar density, $x_{\alpha i}$ is the mole fraction of component i in phase α, V_α is the average phase velocity, $D_{\alpha i}^h$ is the phase hydrodynamic dispersion tensor of component i, and $E_{\alpha \beta i}$ is the net rate of moles of component i transferred to the α-phase from all contiguous phases β. Nonequilibrium interphase partitioning is represented with a linear driving force expression (Welty et al. 1984):

$$E_{\alpha \beta i} = \rho_\alpha K_{\alpha \beta i} S_\alpha (x_{\alpha i} - x_{\alpha i}^e) \qquad (4)$$

where α is the controlling phase, $K_{\alpha \beta i}$ is the overall α-β mass transfer coefficient, and $x_{\alpha i}^e$ is the α phase mole fraction of component i in equilibrium with the mole fraction of i in the β phase. Equation (4) is used to model volatilization and dissolution of entrapped organic liquids, gas/aqueous interchange of organic components and oxygen, and rate-limited transport to the biophase. The mass transfer resistance is assumed to occur in the aqueous phase for organic dissolution and gas/aqueous partitioning and in the gas phase for organic liquid volatilization.

Quantification of the biotransformation processes follows the conceptual approach of Chen et al. (1992). Biodegradation is assumed to occur only within the aqueous phase by an indigenous, spatially heterogeneous, mixed microbial population that is present as attached microcolonies. It is assumed that biomass growth does not affect soil permeability and there is no biomass transport. Monod-type kinetic expressions are employed to describe biophase utilization of substrates, the electron acceptor, and a limiting nutrient:

$$E_{bai} = \rho_b S_b K_{bai}(x_{bi} - x_{bi}^e) =$$
$$-S_b F_{il} k_l X \left(\frac{\rho_a x_{bl}}{k_{s_l} + \rho_a x_{bl}} \right) \left(\frac{\rho_a x_{bO_2}}{k_{s_{O_2}} + \rho_a x_{bO_2}} \right) \left(\frac{\rho_a x_{bN}}{k_{s_N} + \rho_a x_{bN}} \right) \qquad (5)$$

where K_{bai} is the overall biophase/aqueous mass exchange coefficient for component i, x_{bi} is the mole fraction of component i in the biophase, x_{ai} is the mole fraction of component i in the aqueous phase, F_{il} is the use coefficient of component i with substrate l degradation ($F_{il} = 1$ for i = l), k_l is the maximum specific substrate utilization rate of substrate l, X is the active biomass concentration,

K_{sl} is the half-saturation coefficient of component I, O_2 is the electron acceptor, and N denotes the nutrient. When i is O_2 or N, Equation (5) is summed over all the substrates l. Growth of the microbial population is represented by:

$$\frac{dX}{dt} = \left[\sum_l Y_l k_l \left(\frac{\rho_a x_{bl}}{k_{s_l} + \rho_a x_{bl}} \right) \left(\frac{\rho_a x_{bO_2}}{k_{s_{O_2}} + \rho_a x_{bO_2}} \right) \left(\frac{\rho_a x_{bN}}{k_{s_N} + \rho_a x_{bN}} \right) \left(1 - \frac{X}{X_m} \right) - K_d \right] X \quad (6)$$

where Y_l is the yield coefficient for the metabolism of substrate l, X_m is the maximum permitted biomass, and K_d is the decay coefficient of the microorganisms. The detachment or sloughing of the attached biofilm is not considered in this equation. Furthermore, biomass is not permitted to fall below a minimum concentration reflecting the indigenous population present in uncontaminated subsurface environments.

NUMERICAL SOLUTION APPROACH

The flow and transport equations are solved in two space dimensions using a standard Galerkin finite element approach with linear triangular elements. The coupled nonlinear equations are solved using a set iterative finite element method. In this approach, the sets of flow, transport, and biodegradation equations are decoupled within the simulator and solved separately to reduce computational requirements. Decoupling is accomplished by lagging, either by one iteration or one time step, the coupling terms which are the phase density and interphase mass transfer. Picard iteration is used to account for nonlinearities. Iteration between each equation set is performed to ensure solution accuracy.

EXAMPLE SIMULATION

A hypothetical laboratory column bioventing experiment is simulated. The column is 30 cm in length and is filled with a sandy soil (porosity 0.39) containing an aqueous phase at 15% saturation and liquid benzene at 1% saturation. Both liquid phases are at residual and therefore immobile. The gas phase is composed of benzene (B), nitrogen, and oxygen (when biodegradation is considered). The aqueous phase constituents are water, benzene, and oxygen (when biodegradation is considered). Benzene is initially distributed between the gas and aqueous phases at equilibrium concentrations. Gas flow is then initiated at a darcy velocity of 0.001019 m/s. Because the velocity field is constant for this simulation, the flow simulator is not used. A mass transfer coefficient of 1,000/day is used for interactions between the organic residual and both the gas and aqueous phases, and for interactions between the aqueous phase and biophase. This value approximates the equilibrium partitioning for volatilization and dissolution of entrapped organic liquids observed in bench-scale column studies (Berndtson and Bunge 1991; Bloes et al. 1992). A mass transfer coefficient of 1/day is used for nonequilibrium interactions between the gas and aqueous phases, once the organic residual has been removed. In Figure 1, the total mass of benzene remaining in the column is plotted on a log scale along with the mass of benzene remaining in each phase for a simulation run without biodegradation. Benzene mass is normalized with the initial total benzene mass in the column. Although volatilization is effective in removing the organic residual substantial tailing would be observed in effluent gas concentrations due to rate-limited aqueous/gas mass exchange. Figure 2 illustrates that the inclusion of biodegradation results in a significantly higher remediation rate of the dissolved benzene. Here the fraction of the initial total benzene remaining in the aqueous phase is compared with and without biodegradation. The biological parameters used in this simulation are from Chen et al. 1992, and include F_{il} 2.15 gm O_2 per gm B (calculated), k_l 9.9/day O_2 and 8.3/day B (measured), K_{si} 0.0001 gm/L O_2 (literature) and 0.0122 gm/L B (measured), Y_l 0.5 gm cell per gm B (measured); X_m 0.100 gm/L, and K_d 0.1/day (literature). The measured values were obtained from sandy aquifer material underlying a Kalkaska gasoline plant. In Figure 2, volatilization alone removed only 20% of the aqueous phase contamination after 40 hours. When biodegradation was included, the fraction of initial total benzene remaining in the aqueous phase was reduced nearly three orders of magnitude in the same time period.

CONCLUSIONS

A conceptual model of SVE/BV systems that incorporates the complex compositional and biological processes representative of field-scale settings was

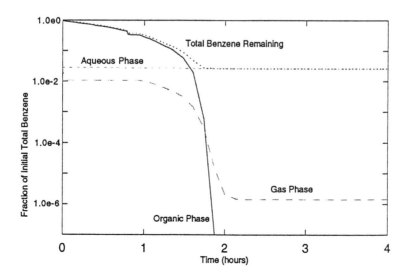

FIGURE 1. Phase distribution of benzene during simulated one-dimensional soil vapor extraction.

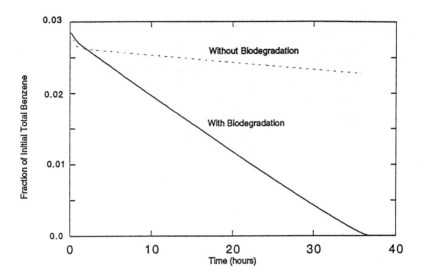

FIGURE 2. Phase distribution of benzene during simulated one-dimensional bioventing.

presented. This conceptual model was implemented in a two-dimensional Galerkin finite element simulator employing a set iterative solution scheme. Preliminary results are presented that demonstrate the potential importance of biological degradation for remediation of sites where mass transfer limitations are operative.

ACKNOWLEDGMENT

This work was supported by the U.S. Environmental Protection Agency R.S. Kerr Environmental Research Laboratory under grant RFA-93-B3. This research has not been subjected to Agency review and therefore does not necessarily reflect the view of the Agency and no official endorsement should be inferred.

REFERENCES

Abriola, L. M. 1989. "Modeling multiphase migration of organic chemicals in groundwater systems — A review and assessment." *Environmental Health Perspectives* 83: 117-143.

Berndtson, M. J., and A. L. Bunge. 1991. "A mechanistic study of forced aeration for in-place remediation of vadose zone soils." In *Proceedings: Petroleum Hydrocarbons and Organic Chemicals in Ground Water*, pp. 249-263. Houston, TX.

Bloes, M. B., K. M. Rathfelder, and D. M. Mackay. 1992. "Laboratory studies of vapor extraction for remediation of contaminated soil." In K. U. Weyer (Ed.), *Subsurface Contamination by Immiscible Fluids*, pp. 255-262. A. A. Bakema, Rotterdam, Holland.

Chen, Y-M., L. M. Abriola, P.J.J. Alvarez, P. J. Anid, and T. M. Vogel. 1992. "Modeling transport and biodegradation of benzene and toluene in sandy aquifer material: Comparisons with experimental measurements." *Water Resources Research* 28(7): 1833-1847.

Cho, H. J., and P. R. Jaffe. 1990. "The volatilization of organic compounds in unsaturated porous media during infiltration." *Journal of Contaminant Hydrology* 6: 387-410.

Forsyth, P. A., and B. Y. Shao. 1991. *Numerical Simulation of Gas Venting for NAPL Site Remediation*. University of Waterloo Report, Waterloo, Canada.

Johnson, P. C., C. C. Stanley, M. W. Kemblowski, D. L. Byers, and J. D. Colthart. 1990. "A practical approach to the design, operation and monitoring of in situ soil-venting systems." *Groundwater Monitoring Review* 10(2): 159-178.

McClellan, R. D., and R. W. Gilham. 1992. "Vapour extraction of trichloroethylene under controlled conditions at the Borden site." In K. U. Weyer (Ed.), *Subsurface Contamination by Immiscible Fluids*, pp. 89-96. A. A. Bakema, Rotterdam, Holland.

Rathfelder, K. M., W. W-G. Yeh, and D. Mackay. 1991. "Mathematical simulation of soil vapor extraction systems: Model development and numerical examples." *Journal of Contaminant Hydrology* 8: 263-297.

Rathfelder, K. M., J. R. Lang, and L. M. Abriola. accepted November 1994. "Soil vapor extraction and bioventing: Applications, limitations, and future research directions." *Reviews of Geophysics IUGG Quadrennial Report*, in press.

Sleep, B. E., and J. F. Sykes. 1991. "Biodegradation of volatile organic compounds in porous media with natural and forced gas-phase advection." In R. E. Hinchee and R. F. Olfenbuttel (Eds.), *In Situ Bioreclamation: Applications and Investigations for Hydrocarbon and Contaminated Site Remediation*, pp. 245-261. Butterworth-Heinemann, Stoneham, MA.

Welty, J. R., C. E. Wicks, and R. E. Wilson. 1969. *Fundamentals of Momentum, Heat, and Mass Transfer*. John Wiley & Sons. New York, NY.

Soil Vapor Extraction Pilot Study at a Piedmont UST Site

Mark A. Widdowson, C. Marjorie Aelion,
Richard P. Ray, and Howard W. Reeves

ABSTRACT

A pilot study of soil vapor extraction (SVE) at a gasoline-contaminated site in the Piedmont physiographic region of South Carolina is presented. The objective of the pilot study is to determine the efficacy of SVE in remediating petroleum-contaminated Piedmont sites. Soil of the Piedmont region is characterized by fine-grained materials that exhibit a stratified, anisotropic structure, often dominated by zones of low permeability. The pilot remediation project consists of a multiple-well SVE and air sparging system located in the contaminant source area. Hourly measurement of mass extraction rates show elevated hydrocarbon (HC) concentrations during the first hour of operation and a rapid decline to asymptotic values. Time-averaged hydrocarbon mass extraction rates range from 22 to 68 kg HC per day for eight SVE wells operating 6 to 8 h per day. Elevated levels of CO_2 in extracted soil vapors indicate microbial activity contributing to bioremediation at the site.

INTRODUCTION

The applicability of SVE at an underground storage tank (UST) site depends to a large extent on the air-phase permeability (k_{air}) of contaminated soil strata. Technical overviews of SVE and air sparging by Johnson et al. (1990) and Loden (1992), respectively, place limiting k_{air} and hydraulic conductivity (K) values at 10^{-9} to 10^{-8} cm^2 and 10^{-3} cm/s for the respective remediation processes. However, several case studies support the notion that large-scale heterogeneity (e.g., lenses and thin strata of coarse-grained material) and fractures in soil comprised of primarily low-permeability, fine-grained material may result in acceptable mass extraction rates and higher than anticipated k_{air}. For example, Gibson et al. (1993) report a single-well mass extraction of 1.40 kg/d and k_{air} in the range of 10^{-7} cm^2 at a paint thinner-contaminated site underlain by fractured glacial deposits.

Near-surface Piedmont soil is often dominated by clay-rich, fine-grained materials interbedded with laminae of fine- to coarse-grained sand, thin gravel layers, quartz veins, and fractures (Heath 1989). Soil strata of Piedmont saprolite, literally decomposing rock, tend to reflect the structure of the parent rock formation resulting in a stratified, anisotropic structure. Although a saprolitic vadose zone is viewed as a relatively low-permeability environment, permeable planes and fractures can potentially serve as conduits for airflow, resulting in favorable conditions for SVE-based remediation.

The extent to which this complex soil structure will influence vacuum-induced vapor flow, and therefore SVE, air sparging, and bioventing operations, at Piedmont UST sites is unknown. Also unknown are the presence and activity level of endogenous, potentially hydrocarbon-degrading microorganisms (Landmeyer et al. 1994) and the extent to which microbial processes contribute to remediation of Piedmont soils using these systems. To address these issues, a pilot study of SVE and air sparging was undertaken at a gasoline-contaminated site in the Piedmont. This note will present the results from the initial stage of the pilot study in which SVE is implemented without air sparging.

SITE DESCRIPTION

The study site is a leaking UST site in Columbia, South Carolina. The site is located in a transition zone between the Upper Atlantic Coastal Plain and Piedmont physiographic regions known as the Carolina Slate Belt. Initial abatement, including tank removal, and preliminary environmental site assessments were completed by June 1992. In conjunction with this study, an expanded site assessment was initiated to determine the baseline level of hydrocarbon contamination and to design an SVE/air sparging system.

The expanded site assessment, completed in January 1994, consisted of a variety of tasks concentrated in the known contaminant source area including monitoring of groundwater quality, laboratory evaluation of physical properties and contaminant levels of multilevel soil samples, laboratory incubation studies of endogenous respiration, short-duration SVE and k_{air} testing, and installation and sampling of multilevel soil gas monitoring probes. Methods and materials and results of this phase of the investigation are provided in Widdowson et al. (1995).

The site is underlain by soil strata typical of saprolite in the Carolina Slate Belt; a saprolite developed from phyllites and shales in an area of moderate regional metamorphism (Landmeyer et al. 1994). Generally the soils are combinations of sands, silts, and clays with localized seams of angular gravels and 2.5- to 5-cm-thick quartz veins. The vadose zone varies in thickness from 6.1 to 7.6 m, depending on seasonal conditions. Near-surface stratigraphy consists of three strata: an upper zone (0 to 4.6 m) of soil dominated by clay and silt fractions, a transition zone (4.6 to 7.0 m) with an increasing sand fraction with depth, and a lower zone (depth > 7.0 m) of poorly sorted materials including gravels. Laboratory evaluation of soil samples from 6.1 to 11 m show permeability (K) varies from 6.23×10^{-7} to 3.37×10^{-4} cm/s. Total porosity ranged from 0.35 to 0.52.

Particle size distribution of soil samples varies with location and depth. Soil samples show a significant portion of fine-grained materials (d <0.075 mm), ranging from 19 to 42 (% passing by weight). Sand and gravel fractions ranged from 56 to 80 (% retained by weight) and 0.23 to 14%, respectively (Widdowson et al. 1995).

Groundwater and Soil Contamination

Groundwater samples collected prior to the pilot study exhibit benzene, toluene, ethylbenzene, and total xylenes (BTEX) concentrations ranging from 18.2 to 150 mg/L in source area water-table wells. Total petroleum hydrocarbons (TPH) range from 48 to 420 ppm, and methyl tertiary butyl ether (MTBE) ranges from 2.40 to 155 mg/L in the same wells. BTEX concentrations in multilevel groundwater wells in the source area range from 48.9 to 234 mg/L. Analysis of multilevel soil samples in the source area indicates that TPH concentrations range from not detected (ND) to 7,400 mg/kg. BTEX and MTBE range from ND to 793 mg/kg and ND to 24 mg/kg, respectively. Soil samples obtained in the vicinity of the water table (depths between 7.0 to 7.6 m or 23 to 25 ft) show higher levels of TPH and BTEX.

Initial Assessment of Natural Bioattenuation

Soil gas samples collected in the contaminated source area prior to the start of SVE operations indicate elevated levels of CO_2 ($\leq 16\%$) and somewhat depleted levels of O_2 ($\geq 10\%$), but total depletion of O_2 in the soil gas was not found (Aelion et al. 1995). Reduced levels of dissolved oxygen in groundwater (<1.0 mg/L) within the contaminant plume relative to downgradient wells (1.0 to 2.0 mg/L) and a deeper monitoring well (7.3 mg/L) also indicate the presence of aerobic microbial activity. In addition, aerobic incubation studies using soil samples collected in the source area show oxygen consumption and CO_2 production (Widdowson et al. 1995); however, other data indicate that aerobic bacteria populations may be spatially variable or inactive in some locations and that the level of activity may be inhibited by environmental factors. Although experimental evidence is inconclusive as to the extent of natural bioattenuation, a measurable level of bioremediation was present prior to the start of the pilot study (Aelion et al. 1995).

SYSTEM DESIGN

Pneumatic testing was conducted in each stratum of the vadose zone to determine volatile organic compound (VOC) mass extraction rates and k_{air} in each zone. Analysis of pressure versus time data collected at observation probes in the upper stratum shows k_{air} in the range of 10^{-9} to 10^{-8} cm^2 and $1 \times 10^{-7} \leq k_{air} \leq 1$ to 3×10^{-7} cm^2 at the interface between middle and lower strata (Widdowson et al. 1995). Data collected from a short-duration SVE test in the more-permeable zone indicate a VOC mass extraction rate of 1.8 kg/d at a volumetric flowrate of 0.65 m^3/min per m of screen. Although these data give a preliminary indication that SVE is a feasible remediation option at this site, these rates are achieved only under low-flow, high-vacuum (0.5 to 0.6 atm) conditions at extraction wells screened in the permeable interface. In addition, pneumatic tests indicate that isolated SVE wells will impact only a limited area defined by a 3- to 6-m radius of influence.

The design of the pilot remediation system reflects these constraints and is directed primarily at the known contaminant source area. The pilot system consists of 12 SVE wells and six air sparging wells. To create adequate areal coverage, SVE wells are spaced at equal intervals (3 m) in two parallel lines. The lines of SVE wells (six wells per line) are spaced 3 m apart. Air sparging wells are nested in combination with SVE wells along one of the two lines. SVE wells are screened over a 1.5-m interval to a depth of 6.4 m. Extracted soil vapor from each line of wells is conveyed through a manifold piping system, constructed below grade, to a vacuum pump and discharged to the atmosphere through a stack.

RESULTS AND DISCUSSION

Initial tests of the SVE system indicated that only eight of the 12 SVE wells were producing significant airflow due to locally perched groundwater. The combined airflow from all contributing wells varied from 0.65 to 1.7 m^3/min over a wellhead vacuum varying between 152 to 305 mm Hg. Two 6-h tests conducted at a 200-mm Hg vacuum showed an average hydrocarbon mass extraction rate of 39 kg per test. Results of the initial SVE tests indicated that, after 10 to 12 tests per month, each lasting 6 h, the hydrocarbon emission rate permitted by the state (500 kg per month) will be exceeded. Rather than incorporating an off-gas treatment system, a schedule of three 6- to 8-h tests per week was implemented during the initial period of the pilot test as a means to establish a trend in the data. Second, this schedule served as a means to "pulse" the source area, which may enable vapor-phase contaminants trapped in immobile pockets of the vadose zone to diffuse into permeable regions during shutdown of the system.

A total of 13 tests were conducted during the month of June 1994. Hourly samples of off-gas were analyzed on site for %O$_2$, %CO$_2$, and total hydrocarbons using a portable meter. Samples also were collected for analysis of VOC concentrations by gas chromatography. Figure 1 is a plot of the total mass of hydrocarbon extracted for each test. Each test was conducted under approximately identical operating conditions and lasted a total of 6 to 8 h. Notable exceptions are tests #9 and #11 (1-h duration) and test #13 (24-h). Extraction rates varied from 7.7 to 19 kg/h for tests #1 through #12. An extraction rate of 98 kg/d was measured for the 24-h test. The cumulative hydrocarbon mass extracted during the month was 486 kg. This trend continued during the next several months.

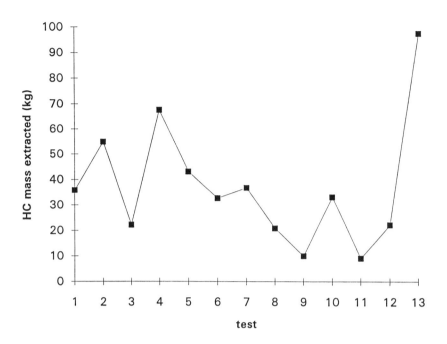

FIGURE 1. Hydrocarbon mass extracted (total per test) for each test conducted during the first month of the pilot study using 8 of 12 SVE wells. Mean test duration is 6 h. Tests #9 and #11 are short duration tests (1 h), and test #13 is a 24-h test.

Figure 2 shows a plot of $\%CO_2$, BTEX in ppm, and total hydrocarbons in ppm $\times 10^{-3}$ for the 24-h test. Asymptotic values of hydrocarbon and BTEX concentrations measured in gas samples are noted following a rapid decline from initial elevated levels. Concentrations of total hydrocarbons ranged from 18,400 to 2,700 ppm and 11.5 to 3.13 ppm for BTEX. Total hydrocarbons show a steeper decline following the elevated levels in early-time samples. Levels of CO_2 were elevated above background levels in soil gas and samples of the local atmosphere (0.05%). Percent CO_2 ranged from 3.8% in the initial reading to 1.1% in diluted off-gas samples taken near the end of the test. Percent O_2 in diluted off-gas samples increased from an initial reading of 17.4% to background levels 6 to 7 h into the 24-h test.

CONCLUSIONS

These results indicate that satisfactory levels of VOC mass extraction in petroleum-contaminated Piedmont soil can be achieved using SVE provided the system is designed for closely spaced wells operating under a high vacuum.

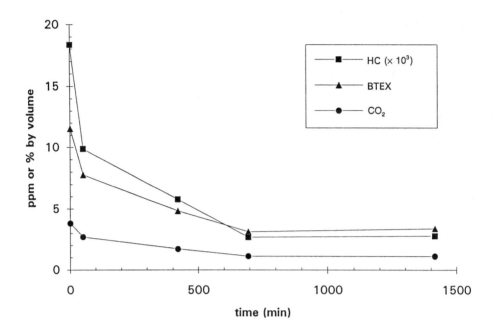

FIGURE 2. Hydrocarbon and BTEX concentration (ppm) and %CO$_2$ (% by volume) of off-gas samples versus time during the 24-h test (#13).

However, BTEX and TPH concentrations of groundwater samples collected from source area monitoring wells showed no dramatic decrease or a discernible downward trend with time during the first several months of the pilot test indicating that hydrocarbon extraction may be limited to the vadose zone. Analysis of the off-gas samples (CO$_2$% and O$_2$%) indicates that a measurable component of remediation can be attributed to microbial processes. This finding points to the potential use of bioventing as a remediation option in petroleum-contaminated Piedmont sites. However, data are insufficient to demonstrate an increased level of bioremediation due to bioventing. These results point to the difficulty and uncertainty of implementing SVE-based in Piedmont soils and the extent to which bioattenuation processes are active and can be elevated through bioventing. Monitoring of long-term trends in soil gas, off-gas, and groundwater composition continues as air sparging is implemented.

REFERENCES

Aelion, C. M., M. A. Widdowson, R. P. Ray, H. W. Reeves, and J. N. Shaw. 1995. "Biodegradation, Vapor Extraction, and Air Sparging in Low-Permeability Soils." In R. E. Hinchee, R. N. Miller, and P. C. Johnson (Eds.), *In Situ Aeration: Air Sparging, Bioventing, and Related Remediation Processes*. Battelle Press, Columbus, OH. pp. 127-134.

Gibson, T. L., A. S. Abdul, W. A. Glasson, C. C. Ang, and D. W. Gatlin. 1993. "Vapor Extraction of Volatile Organic Compounds from Clay Soil: A Long-Term Field Pilot Study." *Ground Water* 31(4): 616-626.

Heath, R. C. 1989. "The Piedmont Ground-Water System." In C. C. Daniel, R. K. White, and P. A. Stone (Eds.), *Proceedings of a Conference on Ground Water in the Piedmont of the Eastern United States*, pp. 1-13. Clemson University, Clemson, SC.

Johnson, P. C., C. C. Stanley, M. W. Kemblowski, D. L., Byers, and J. D. Colthart. 1990. "A Practical Approach to the Design, Operation, and Monitoring of In Situ Soil-Venting Systems." *Ground Water Monitoring Review* 10(2): 159-178.

Landmeyer, J. E., F. H. Chapelle, P. M. Bradley, and P. A. Stone. 1994. "Microbial Activity in Saprolite Aquifers Overlying Two Different Types of Metamorphic Bedrock, South Carolina, USA." In *Proceedings of the Second International Conference on Ground-Water Ecology*, pp. 137-142.

Loden, M. E. 1992. *A Technology Assessment of Soil Vapor Extraction and Air Sparging*. EPA/600/R-92/173. U.S. Environmental Protection Agency, Office of Research and Development, Washington, DC.

Widdowson, M. A., R. P. Ray, H. W. Reeves, and C. M. Aelion. 1995. "Integrated Site Characterization for Soil Vapor Extraction Design." In Y. B. Acar and D. E. Daniel (Eds.), *Proceedings of The Geoenvironmental 2000*, vol. 2, pp. 1291-1305. American Society of Civil Engineers, New York, NY.

Application of Mechanistic Models for Bioventing

Johannes C.M. de Wit, Leon G.C.M. Urlings,
and P. Arne Alphenaar

ABSTRACT

During many full-scale, in situ bioremediations the remediation process stagnates. Slow, diffusion-controlled release of the contaminants is the most important factor that causes this stagnation. Most likely, this slow release is caused by stagnant phases in the soil where convective flow is absent. For sound design and operation of in situ soil bioremediations, these nonequilibrium phenomena have to be considered explicitly. To do this, tools and models are needed that are applicable in the practical field, a field where time, budget, and data are always limited. In this paper, we have tried to use such a model for the prediction of the bioremediation of a toluene-contaminated site. The site has a sandy soil with, locally, a high clay and organic matter content. The calculations show that, to optimize biodegradation, soil vapor extraction with a low average extraction rate obtained, for example, by an intermittent extraction, should be favored over extraction with a high flowrate.

INTRODUCTION

For several years now, it has been believed that in situ (bio)remediation should play an important role in the cleanup of contaminated sites in the Netherlands, but the application of these techniques is still very limited. The main reasons are the strict Dutch policy and the image of in situ bioremediation techniques: the techniques are not reliable and their duration is unpredictable.

The unpredictability of full-scale in situ (bio)remediations is not just a function of the complexity of the soil system. Practical constraints, such as limited time and budget for data collection, are important. In the practical field, knowledge of relevant processes often is not sufficient, and, only rough estimates of the duration of the remediation can be made. These estimates, based on average properties, chemical equilibrium, and 0th or 1st-order decay, are too optimistic (e.g., Figure 1).

In a joint research project conducted by the Departments of Environmental Technology and Soil Science and Plant Nutrition of Wageningen Agricultural

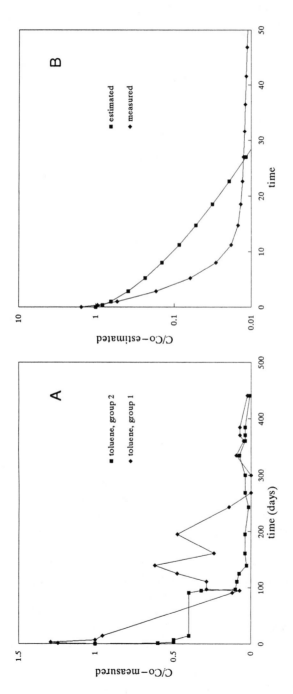

FIGURE 1. (A) Observed gas-phase concentration in time for a full-scale in situ bioventing remediation. (B) Schematic representation of the concentration decrease estimated with "simple" models and (average) concentration decrease observed in many full-scale remediations; $c_{o-measured}$ is the measured initial concentration; $c_{o-estimated}$ is the estimated concentration.

University and Tauw Milieu b.v., we have tried to improve the predictions. Our goal was to investigate the applicability of simplified, but mechanistic models in the practice of soil remediation. As an example of a mechanistic model we used the ECOSAT model, a modified chemical equilibrium model (Keizer & Van Riemsdijk 1994). In the research project, we calibrated ECOSAT for the bioventing process with laboratory experiments (batch and column experiments) with artificially contaminated soil (Malina et al. 1995 a,b; Mous et al. 1995), and with core soil samples (Tauw Milieu b.v. 1995). As expected, benzene, toluene, ethylbenzene, and xylene (BTEX) compounds and light hydrocarbons showed linear sorption behavior. Although sorption was rather rapid, sorption kinetics had to be included to describe the results from the column experiments.

In this paper, we briefly discuss the results of an evaluation of an array of full-scale remediations. In this evaluation we used the ECOSAT model to analyze the nature of the observed stagnation of the in situ remediation process. Further, we will discuss the effect of continuous extraction and intermittent extraction on (1) duration of the bioremediation, and (2) the contribution of biodegradation. This discussion is based on calculations for a toluene-contaminated sandy site, with locally high clay and organic matter content. The parameters used in the calculations are based on the characteristics of the contaminated site, on the experiments used to calibrate ECOSAT, and on the parameters used to describe the stagnation of the full-scale remediations.

EVALUATION OF FULL-SCALE IN SITU REMEDIATIONS

Although in the Netherlands the application of full-scale in situ (bio)reme-diation techniques has been limited to "ideal" sites with sandy soils, good bio-degradable compounds, and no nonaqueous-phase liquids (NAPLs) present, many in situ bioremediations stagnate (see Figure 1). That is, after a fairly rapid concentration decrease, the rate of the remediation process diminishes. Stagnation suggests that a significant fraction of the contaminants are not readily available for leaching, volatilization, or biodegradation. The reduced availability of the contaminants may be due to (1) nonlinear sorption, (2) heterogeneity or spatial variability of site characteristics, and/or (3) nonequilibrium phenomena.

The concentration decrease, observed in the full-scale remediations, could be described by assuming: (1) strong nonlinear desorption, (2) an unrealistic spatial variability of sorption parameters (e.g., organic matter content), or (3) a slow release of a part of the hydrocarbons. For BTEX compounds and light hydrocar-bons, a very strong nonlinearity of the desorption isotherm seems not very realistic. Therefore, nonequilibrium seems to be the most important factor causing the stag-nation of the remediation process. Increasing concentrations in the gas phase, observed at many sites during interruptions of vapor extraction, support this idea.

Except for desorption kinetics, most nonequilibrium phenomena are due to diffusion-controlled mass transfer from areas of the soil where convective flow is absent. The size of these stagnant phases depends on intrinsic soil properties (variations in permeability) and on the induced convective flow during the remediation. To describe the stagnation, we had to assume that the slow release was a factor of 50 to 2,000 slower than observed in the column experiments with artificially contaminated soil. This very slow release suggests diffusion from stagnant phases being more important than sorption kinetics. The fraction of the contamination that was slowly released varied from 5 to 50%.

SCENARIO CALCULATIONS

Model Description

As a first-order approach, we considered the soil system as a single mixed cell in which the gas phase can be flushed (Johnson et al. 1990). Chromatography, caused by multidimensional flow, is ignored for the moment. The estimated residence time of the soil vapor during flushing follows from the design of the installation (extraction rate, number of soil vapor extraction filters) and from the site characteristics (soil type, volume of soil to be treated).

All mass transfers are described by kinetic expressions. Toluene is sorbed to two sorption site types. One site type represents the good available fraction; the other is the slow-release sorption site type. This site type represents the part of the toluene that is not readily available. Note that, in soil science, the slow release of this fraction often is mathematically described as rate-limited *sorption* (Boekhold 1992). However, the nature of the slow release may be caused by other phenomena, such as diffusion-controlled release from the stagnant phases.

For the contaminated site considered, a sandy soil with locally increased organic matter and clay content, we have assumed that 70% of the toluene is available and 30% will be slowly released. The rate constants for the available sorption sites correspond to those observed in the column experiments (Malina et al. 1995a,b; Tauw Milieu b.v. 1995). The rate constant for mass transfer to the slow-release sites is estimated to be a factor 250 lower. Biodegradation is described with an oxygen- and toluene-dependent expression. The biodegradation constants and all other rate constants also are based on the column experiments. Nutrient concentrations were not limiting for biodegradation. An overview of the equations and parameters used in the model is given in Table 1 and Figure 2.

Calculations and Discussion

We have predicted the concentration decrease in time for two different cases: continuous soil vapor extraction and intermittent extraction. In the intermittent case, the soil vapor is extracted only 1 day out of 10 days. The results of the calculations are summarized in Figure 3.

Continuous extraction results in a rapid concentration decrease in gas phase, water phase and of the good available fraction. The reduction of the slow release

TABLE 1. Parameters and variables used in the calculations.

Parameters and Variables		Value
$k_{tol,w/g}$	rate constant for mass transfer of toluene from water phase → gas phase (L/d)	4
$k_{tol,g/w}$	rate constant for mass transfer of toluene from gas phase → water phase (L/d)	1.71
$k_{O,w/g}$	rate constant for mass transfer of oxygen from water phase → gas phase (L/d)	4
$k_{O,g/w}$	rate constant for mass transfer of oxygen from gas phase → water phase (L/d)	0.06
$k_{fast,w/s}$	rate constant for mass transfer of toluene from water phase → good available sorption sites (L/d)	50
$k_{fast,s/w}$	rate constant for mass transfer of toluene from good available sorption sites → water phase (L/d)	4.7
$k_{slow,w/s}$	rate constant for mas transfer of toluene from water phase → slow release sorption sites (L/d)	0.2
$k_{slow,s/w}$	rate constant for mass transfer of toluene from slow release sorption sites → water phase (L/d)	0.02
$c_{tol,in}$	concentration of toluene in the air used to flush the system (mg/L)	0
$c_{O,in}$	concentration of oxygen in the air used to flush the system (mg/L)	275
t_{res}	residence time in the gas phase during flushing (d)	0.065
r_{tol}	mg toluene consumed for degradation of 1 mg toluene (dummy parameter)	1
r_O	mg oxygen consumed for degradation of 1 mg toluene	3
k_{tol}	biodegradation constant (mg/L)	3.16
k_O	biodegradation constant (mg/L)	0.32
k_{afb}	biodegradation rate constant (mg/L/d)	100
ρ	dry bulk density of the soil (kg/L)	1.6
θ_w	water-filled porosity	0.15
θ_g	gas-filled porosity	0.35
Initial Conditions		
$q_{tol,fast}$	toluene sorbed at the good available sorption sites (mg/kg)	696
$q_{tol,slow}$	toluene sorbed at the slow release sorption sites (mg/kg)	298
$c_{tol,w}$	toluene concentration in the water phase (mg/L-soil water)	40
$c_{O,w}$	oxygen concentration in the water phase (mg/L-soil water)	0
$c_{tol,g}$	toluene concentration in the gas phase (mg/L-soil gas)	8.7
$c_{tol,g}$	toluene concentration in the gas phase (mg/L-soil gas)	275

Sorption of dissolved toluene to the good available sorption sites (j=fast) and the slow release sorption sites (j=slow) is described by the following mass transfer functions:

$$\frac{dc_{tol,w}}{dt} = -k_{j,w/s}c_{tol,w} + k_{j,s/w}\frac{\rho}{\theta_w}q_{j,tol} \tag{1}$$

$$\frac{dq_{j,tol}}{dt} = k_{j,w/s}\frac{\theta_w}{\rho}c_{tol,w} - k_{j,s/w}q_{j,tol} \tag{2}$$

The rate constants are related to the linear sorption constants $K_{j,d}$ ($\equiv f_{j,oc}.K_{oc}$; the organic carbon fraction times the sorption constant for the soil organic matter):

$$k_{j,s/w} = \frac{1}{K_{j,d}}\frac{\theta_w}{\rho}k_{j,w/s} \tag{3}$$

Volatilization of toluene (i=tol) or oxygen (i=O) to the gas phase is described by:

$$\frac{dc_{i,g}}{dt} = -k_{i,g/w}c_{i,g} + k_{i,w/g}\frac{\theta_w}{\theta_g}c_{i,w} \tag{4}$$

$$\frac{dc_{i,w}}{dt} = \frac{\theta_g}{\theta_w}k_{i,g/w}c_{i,g} - k_{i,w/g}c_{i,w} \tag{5}$$

with the rate constants related to the Henry coefficients for toluene (i=tol) and oxygen (i=O):

$$H_i = \frac{c_{i,g}}{c_{i,w}} = \frac{k_{i,w/g}}{k_{i,g/w}}\frac{\theta_w}{\theta_g} \tag{6}$$

Biodegradation is described by:

$$\frac{dc_{i,w}}{dt} = -k_{afb}r_i\frac{c_{tol,w}}{k_{tol}+c_{tol,w}} \times \frac{c_{O,w}}{k_O+c_{O,w}} \tag{7}$$

Flushing of the gas phase is given by:

$$\frac{dc_{i,g}}{dt} = \frac{1}{t_{res}}(c_{i,in}-c_{i,g}) \tag{8}$$

FIGURE 2. Overview of the equations used in the model description.

fraction in time is much smaller, consequently, the remediation process starts to stagnate after approximately 200 days.

In the first 200 days, the contribution of biodegradation to the removal is much smaller than the contribution of volatilization (Figure 3g). In this period, the oxygen concentration in the aqueous phase is very low and is the limiting factor for biodegradation. Note that higher gas flowrates will not result in increased dissolved oxygen concentrations. The oxygen concentration in the gas phase equals the input value (Figure 3b). Mass transfer from the gas phase to the water phase is the limiting factor.

After 200 days, the available fraction is removed. The toluene concentration in the aqueous phase strongly decreases and becomes the limiting factor for biodegradation. From this moment on the oxygen concentration increases, and the conditions are such that the slowly released toluene is almost fully biodegraded. The contribution of volatilization to the removal has become negligible.

The concentration decrease in the intermittent extraction regime strongly differs from that observed with the continuous extraction. In the gas phase, the

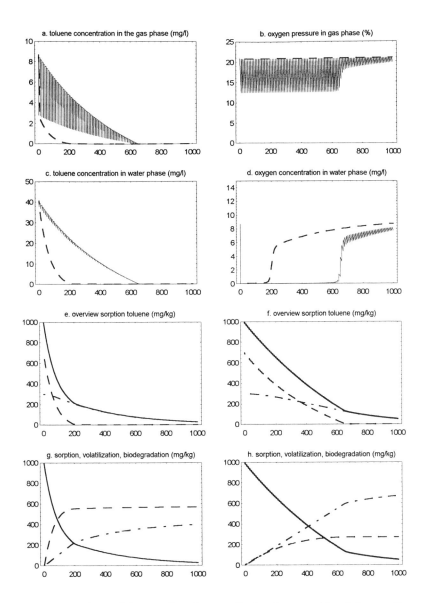

FIGURE 3. Overview of the predicted remediation in time (days) for continuous extraction and intermittent extraction (1 day out of 10 days) of the gas phase. Figures a-d: concentration decrease in time (days); the dashed line is continuous extraction; the solid line is intermittent extraction. Figures e-f: overview of sorption for continuous extraction (e) and intermittent extraction; solid line is overall sorption; the dashed line is the available fraction; the dot-dash line is the slow release fraction. Figures g-h: overview of sorption, volatilization, and biodegradation for continuous extraction (g) and intermittent extraction (h); the solid line is overall sorption; the dashed line is volatilization; the dot-dash line is biodegradation.

concentration decrease during the 1 day of extraction is partly refilled during the other 9 days (Figure 3a). In the aqueous phase this "sawtooth" is less pronounced (Figure 3b). An opposite "sawtooth" is observed in the oxygen concentration (Figures 3b and 3d). The concentration increases during extraction and is subsequently consumed by the biodegradation of toluene.

The (average) concentration decrease in the intermittent case is more gradual than in the continuous case. The time to remove the available fraction has increased from approximately 200 days to 700 days. However, how long it takes for full remediation to natural reference values is approximately equal for both cases because the time is determined mainly by the slow-release sorption sites. In the intermittent case, volatilization is smaller and the consumption of the oxygen concentration is more efficient. Consequently, the contribution of biodegradation to the overall removal has strongly increased (Figure 3h). Note that the effect of intermittent extraction is somewhat similar to continuous pumping with smaller flowrates. However, a disadvantage of a smaller flowrate is the smaller radius of influence, which may result in reduced ventilation of some parts of the soil.

In the simplified model, the parameters for the slow-release sorption sites are the most unreliable parameters. When their contribution to sorption is smaller or the release is faster, the stagnation observed in the continuous extraction is less pronounced. The duration of full remediation will become significantly smaller than for the intermittent extraction regime. When their contribution is larger or the release is slower, the opposite holds.

The preference for the continuous or the intermittent regime depends on costs and on the objectives of the remediation. Continuous pumping consumes more energy but has the advantage of a rapid risk reduction due to the rapid concentration decrease in the gas and water phases. The total amount of toluene to be treated in extracted air is larger, but the period during which off-gas treatment is needed is shorter, because the concentrations in the extracted air are negligible after 200 days. For the toluene-contaminated site, one may consider combining both regimes, i.e., continuous extraction until the concentrations in the gas phase are strongly reduced and then shifting to intermittent extraction.

CONCLUDING REMARKS

During many full-scale in situ bioremediations, the remediation process stagnates. Slow, diffusion-controlled release of the contaminants is the most important factor causing this stagnation. Most likely, this slow release is caused by stagnant phases in the soil where convective flow is absent.

At contaminated sites, where a significant fraction of the contamination is slowly released from the soil matrix, rather small, (average) extraction rates suffice for complete remediation to natural reference values. Small average extraction rates enhance *bio*remediation, whereas at high flowrates most of the volatile contaminants are removed by volatilization.

At least partly, the size of the stagnant phases where convective transport is absent depends on the induced convective flow during the remediation and, thus, on the actual design and operation of the in situ bioremediation. Consequently, a priori predictions of the remediation process will always be rough estimates. In the practical field, we have to learn how to handle nonequilibrium phenomena and to optimize the full-scale remediation during its operation. This involves a continuous feedback between monitoring, data interpretation, and process control, and, if necessary, the installation of additional extraction filters. Currently in the Netherlands, the bulk of the soil investigation budget is spent on the preliminary work, such as site characterization. In our opinion, for successful application of in situ (bio)remediation techniques, the emphasis in the investigation should shift from the preliminary work to design and optimization of the in situ remediation in operation.

ACKNOWLEDGMENT

This work was partially funded by the Netherlands Integrated Soil Research Programme under Project Number 5029.

REFERENCES

Boekhold, A. E. 1992. "Field Scale Behaviour of Cadmium in Soil." Ph.D Thesis, Wageningen Agricultural University, The Netherlands.

Johnson, P. C., M. W. Kemblowski, and J. D. Colthart. 1990. *Ground Water 28*: 413-429.

Keizer, M. G., and W. H. Van Riemsdijk. 1994. *ECOSAT, Version 3.5*. Department of Soil Science and Plant Nutrition, Wageningen Agricultural University, The Netherlands.

Malina, G., T. Grotenhuis, C. Cuypers, and W. Rulkens. 1995a. "Measurement of Toluene Bioconversion During Ventilation in a Bench-Scale Soil Column." In R. E. Hinchee, R. N. Miller, and P. C. Johnson (Eds.), *In Situ Aeration: Air Sparging, Bioventing, and Related Remediation Processes*. Battelle Press, Columbus, OH. pp. 377-382.

Malina, G., T. Grotenhuis, S. Mous, and J.C.M. de Wit. 1995b. "Laboratory Experiments for Optimization and Modeling of In Situ Soil Bioventing" (to be submitted).

Mous, S.L.J., M. G. Keizer, G. Malina, and J.C.M. de Wit. 1995. "Optimum Experimental Design of a Column Experiment for Estimating Model Parameters of a Bioventing Model" (to be submitted).

Tauw Milieu b.v. 1995. Report number 2410131.T01/JCI (in Dutch). Tauw Milieu b.v., Deventer, The Netherlands.

Bioventing PAH Contamination at the Reilly Tar Site

Bruce C. Alleman, Robert E. Hinchee,
Richard C. Brenner, and Paul T. McCauley

ABSTRACT

A pilot-scale bioventing demonstration has been in progress since November 1992 to determine if bioventing is an effective remediation treatment for polycyclic aromatic hydrocarbons (PAHs). The goal of the project is to achieve 10% greater PAH removal over background degradation for each year of the 3-year study. Respiration measurements were made to estimate PAH biodegradation as a means of monitoring the progress of the technology. These measurements indicated that 13.4% and 17.3% degradation of the total PAH was possible during the first year and second year, respectively. Although not all of the respiration can be attributed conclusively to PAH metabolism, strong correlations were found between the PAH concentration and biodegradation rates.

INTRODUCTION

PAH contamination is widespread as a result of numerous industrial processes including fossil fuel refining, wood preserving, and coke processing. Certain PAH compounds are known to be toxic, mutagenic, and/or carcinogenic, and the U.S. Environmental Protection Agency (U.S. EPA) has listed 16 specific PAHs as priority pollutants (Heitkamp et al. 1987; Mihelcic and Luthy 1988). Because PAH contamination is so widespread, there is a high potential for human exposure and threat to the environment. To reduce this threat, efforts are under way to develop effective and cost-efficient technologies for remediation of PAH-contaminated sites.

Bioventing is one of the technologies being studied to determine its feasibility for PAH remediation. Typically, soils contaminated with compounds that can serve as growth substrates for indigenous microorganisms, such as certain PAHs, are depleted of oxygen so that biodegradation becomes oxygen limited. Bioventing is designed to provide oxygen to indigenous soil microorganisms in anoxic soils, to support aerobic biodegradation of targeted contaminants. Oxygen delivery is achieved through induced airflow by injection or extraction of atmospheric air using a blower and vent system. The oxygen supply usually is sufficient to support maximum biodegradation rates for petroleum hydrocarbon contaminants; however, under certain circumstances, biodegradation may be enhanced by adding moisture and/or nutrients. The need for such additions is site specific and must be determined on a case-by-case basis.

This paper describes a 3-year pilot-scale study examining the feasibility of using conventional bioventing to remediate polycyclic aromatic hydrocarbon (PAH) contamination. Results from the initial site characterization and the first 2 years of operation are presented, and the implications of these results are discussed.

OBJECTIVE

The objective of this study is to determine the feasibility of using bioventing to remediate PAH-contaminated soils. The goal is to achieve 10% greater reduction per year in the sum total concentration of the 16 PAH compounds listed in Table 1 in the treatment plot over the no-treatment control plot, over a 3-year period. This translates into a total reduction of greater than 27.1% in the initial

TABLE 1. List of the 16 PAH compounds of interest and their averaged initial concentration in the treatment plot at the Reilly Tar Site.

Compound	Concentration (mg/kg)	Percentage of Total PAH
Naphthalene	321.4	12.3
Acenaphthalene	11.2	0.4
Acenaphthene	335.1	12.8
Fluorene	198.4	7.6
Phenanthrene	421.1	16.1
Anthracene	139.4	5.3
Fluoranthene	326.3	12.5
Pyrene	283.4	10.8
Benzo(a)anthracene	83.5	3.2
Chrysene	101.6	3.9
Benzo(b)fluoranthene	79.6	3.0
Benzo(k)fluoranthene	76.1	2.9
Benzo(a)pyrene	73.3	2.8
Indeno(123-cd)pyrene	64.4	2.5
Dibenzo(ah)anthracene	27.4	1.1
Benzo(ghi)perylene	74.4	2.8
Total PAH	2,616.60	100

PAH concentration between the plots over the 3 years of the study. This goal was established as the criterion for this bioventing demonstration as a measure of success for the Superfund Innovative Technology Evaluation (SITE) Program's evaluation.

SITE DESCRIPTION

The Reilly Tar and Chemical Corporation site in St. Louis Park, Minnesota, was selected for this demonstration. The location is the site of a former coal tar refinery and wood-preserving facility at which creosote in mineral oil served as the primary preservative. The facility was operated from 1917 until 1979, at which time it was demolished and the site was converted into a city park and residential housing development.

The test system is located in the park section of the site. The test plot is covered by grass. Approximately 2 ft (0.6 m) of topsoil overlies a 1-ft (0.3-m)-thick layer of an asphaltic-type material. Below the asphaltic layer is coarse brown sand extending to approximately 15 ft (4.6 m) below ground surface (bgs) where there is a nonuniform layer of peat. Groundwater at the site varies between 9 and 10 ft (2.7 and 3.0 m) bgs.

SYSTEM DESIGN, INSTALLATION, AND OPERATION

A pilot-scale bioventing system consisting of a single vent well (2-in.-diameter, sch. 40 polyvinylchloride [PVC]) and 12 trilevel soil gas monitoring points was designed and installed in November, 1992. The vent well was placed in the center of a 50-ft by 50-ft (15.2-m by 15.2-m) plot that was delineated based on depressed O_2 concentrations as measured during an initial soil gas survey. The vent well was screened from 5 to 15 ft (1.5 to 4.6 m) bgs as shown in Figure 1. The soil gas monitoring points were placed radially outward from the vent well in four arms extending towards the corners of the plot at 10, 20, and 30 ft (3, 6, and 9 m) from the vent well. The points were completed so that the probes were set at 4, 6, and 8 ft (1.2, 1.8, and 2.4 m) bgs. A Type K thermocouple was installed in conjunction with each soil gas probe, and the wire was fed to a 40-channel data logger housed in the site trailer. A 2-hp regenerative air blower was placed in the trailer and plumbed to the vent well through a PVC manifold pipe (2-in.-diameter, sch. 80).

The no-treatment control plot was established approximately 150 ft (46 m) to the northwest of the treatment plot. The plot is not being aerated but contains soil gas monitoring points in each of the four corners. The plot is routinely monitored to ensure that it remains anoxic. The PAH data from initial and final sets of soil samples collected from this plot will be used to establish the background PAH removal.

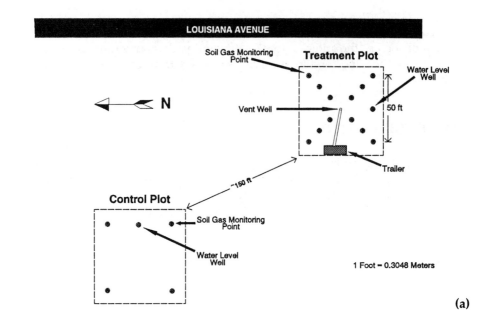

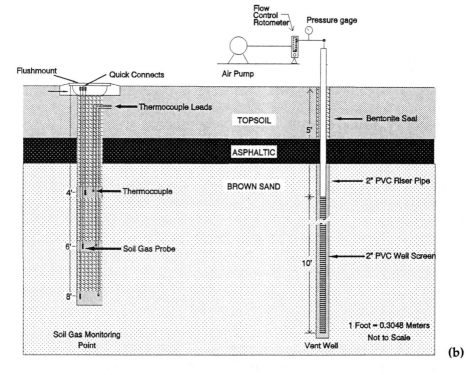

FIGURE 1. Pilot-scale bioventing system design. (a) Plan view showing placement of vent well and 12 soil gas monitoring points. (b) Cross section
showing the completion of the vent well and soil gas monitoring points.

SOIL SAMPLING AND ANALYSIS

A set of 120 soil samples was collected from both the treatment and no-treatment control plots prior to venting. The samples were collected using a split-spoon technique by driving the spoons ahead of hollow-stem augers. The interval between 3 to 8 ft (0.9 to 2.4 m) bgs was collected and homogenized, and aliquots were pulled into glass containers for analysis. U.S. EPA SW-846 Method 3550/8270 was used to quantify the PAH concentrations in each of the soil samples.

IN SITU RESPIRATION TESTS

In situ respiration tests were conducted every 3 months to measure O_2 utilization rates to calculate biodegradation rates (Hinchee et al. 1992). The tests consisted of taking initial O_2 and carbon dioxide (CO_2) readings, then turning the blower off and monitoring the O_2 and CO_2 concentrations over a 2-week period. The O_2 data are used to determine the O_2 utilization rate, and the CO_2 data are used to verify biodegradation. O_2 utilization rates were determined for each soil gas probe by regressing the zero-order portion of the oxygen vs. time curve for that probe. O_2 utilization rates are used to calculate a theoretical biodegradation rate using the method described by Hinchee with the stoichiometric oxidation of phenanthrene shown in equation 1 being substituted in place of hexane.

$$C_{14}H_{10} + 16.5O_2 \rightarrow 14CO_2 + 5H_2O \tag{1}$$

Based on the O_2 utilization rates (change of oxygen (%) per day), the biodegradation rate in terms of milligrams of phenanthrene-equivalent per kilogram of soil per year was calculated using equation 2.

$$K_B = 365(K_O A D_O C / 100) \tag{2}$$

Where K_B = biodegradation rate (mg/kg/year)
$\quad K_O$ = oxygen utilization rate (percent per day)
$\quad A$ = volume of air/kg of soil (L/kg)
$\quad D_O$ = density of oxygen gas (mg/L)
$\quad C$ = mass ratio of phenanthrene to oxygen required for mineralization.

Substituting a porosity value of 0.3, a soil bulk density of 1,440 kg/m^3, an oxygen density of 1,330 mg/L, and a phenanthrene-to-oxygen mass ratio of 1/2.97 determined from equation 1 into equation 2 yields equation 3.

$$K_B = -365(K_O)(0.21)(1,330)(1/2.97)/100 = 343.1K_O \tag{3}$$

RESULTS AND DISCUSSION

Soil PAH Analysis

The data from the PAH analysis indicated that the total PAH concentration in the treatment plot ranged from less than 1,000 mg PAH/kg soil to more than 19,000 mg PAH/kg soil. Figure 2 shows the concentration contours based on the data from the 120 samples. In general, the PAH concentrations increase from east to west with the northwest corner having the highest concentrations. Although the area was delineated based on depleted oxygen concentrations in the soil gas, the plot appears to straddle the edge of the PAH contamination. The fact that the areas characterized by low PAH concentration were oxygen limited suggested that the asphaltic layer was effective at preventing oxygen diffusion from the surface into the contaminated sand layer.

The data for the 120 samples were averaged to provide an indication of the distribution of the 16 PAH compounds of interest and to determine their

FIGURE 2. **Contour map of the initial PAH concentrations in the treatment plot at the Reilly Tar Site.**

percentage of the total PAHs. The averaged data are presented in Table 1. On average, PAH compounds with three or fewer rings accounted for 54.5%, four-ring compounds accounted for 30.4%, and five or more rings accounted for 15.1% of the total PAHs, respectively. The lower-molecular-weight PAH compounds (two and three rings) are the more biodegradable, and their relative percentages may be indicative of the overall biodegradability of the total PAH.

Respiration Tests

Averaged O_2 utilization rates were determined for each of the eight respiration tests as the slope of the linear part of the oxygen vs. time curve. The averaged results for each test for each year are plotted in Figure 3. The trends in O_2 utilization rates were consistent over the 2 years with the higher rates being observed during the warmer months and the lower rates in the winter. The rates were slightly higher in the second year indicating increased microbial activity. This is commonly observed at sites characterized by low oxygen levels and where populations of aerobic microorganisms have been in a stressed state. Following air injection, oxygen is no longer limited and the microbial community takes time to adjust and develop to the maximum numbers that the environment will support. It appeared that this was the case in the treatment plot.

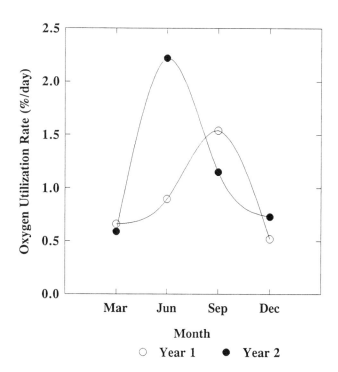

FIGURE 3. Averaged O_2 utilization rates measured in the treatment plot at the Reilly Tar Site during the first 2 years of system operation.

Calculated Biodegradation Rates

Averaged biodegradation rates were calculated for each of the 12 soil gas monitoring point locations using the O_2 utilization rates determined from the data collected during each respiration test. The rates were determined by averaging the O_2 utilization data from the three probes at each sampling point location, then averaging the data from the four tests for each year. Figures 4 and 5 are plots showing the biodegradation rate profiles across the treatment plot for the first year and second year, respectively.

The rate profile shown in Figure 4 shows that the biodegradation rates are lowest on the east side of the plot and consistently increase towards the west side of the plot. The northwest corner showed the highest level of biodegradation activity with rates up to 1,220 mg PAH/kg/year. Comparing the profiles in Figures 2 and 4 shows that, in general, the biodegradation rate profile during the first year of operation correlated fairly well with the PAH distribution.

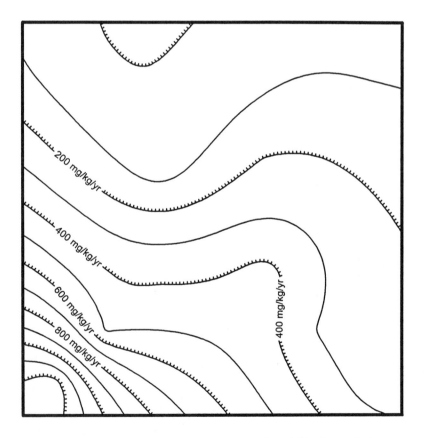

FIGURE 4. Contour map of the averaged calculated biodegradation rates in the treatment plot at the Reilly Tar Site during the first year of system operation.

FIGURE 5. Contour map of the averaged calculated biodegradation rates in the treatment plot at the Reilly Tar Site during the second year of system operation.

During the second year, the biodegradation rate profile became more established. Comparing Figure 5 with the PAH distribution given in Figure 2 shows that a stronger correlation existed between the degradation rates and PAH concentrations during the second year than during the first. The maximum rate showed a moderate increase to 1,300 mg PAH/kg/year in the northwest corner and the areas characterized by higher PAH concentrations generally showed increased biodegradation rates.

An overall biodegradation rate was calculated to approximate the amount of PAH that would have been degraded if the O_2 utilization was due to the oxidation of PAH. As previously mentioned, the goal of this study is to determine if bioventing increases biodegradation of PAH by 10% per year over background degradation over the 3 years of the study. The averaged biodegradation rates were 350 mg PAH/kg/year and 391 mg PAH/kg/year for the first year and second year, respectively. Using 2,617 mg PAH/kg of soil as the initial PAH concentration (Table 1), 13.4% of the PAH was degraded during the first year. Subtracting the 350 mg PAH degraded during the first year indicated that 2,267 mg PAH/kg soil remained after the first year. Using this remaining concentration, 17.3% of the PAH was degraded during the second year. These results suggest that the 10% PAH degradation/year criterion is being achieved.

The data from the first 2 years of operation are promising. The way the data are presented above would indicate that bioventing is working well for PAH remediation. However, the data must be evaluated with caution. Although respiration rates have been used successfully to monitor degradation at sites where petroleum hydrocarbons are the main source of carbon, the 16 PAH compounds listed in Table 1 comprise a small fraction (approximately 4%) of the total organic content in the soil at the Reilly Tar Site. It is unknown what fraction of the O_2 utilization is actually from PAH biodegradation. It is quite possible that organic constituents remaining from the carrier oil, as well as other constituents of the creosote mixture, could be exerting a significant portion of the O_2 utilization.

Although it cannot be verified that PAH has been degraded as calculated above, it is clear that the implementation of bioventing has increased the microbial activity in the treatment plot and that the increased activity correlates well with the PAH concentration. In situations where there are compounds ranging from those that are easily biodegraded, such as naphthalene, to the very recalcitrant compounds, such as the five- and six-ring PAHs, it is quite probable that there will be sequential degradation. If the organic matter in the soils at the Reilly Tar Site is resistant to microbial attack and if there is sequential degradation of the PAH compounds, the distribution found in the soil samples (see Table 1) would favor a successful study.

The actual percentage of PAH that has been degraded will not be known until the final set of soil samples is collected and analyzed after completion of the third year of operation. At that time it will be possible to better correlate the O_2 utilization with the degradation of PAH as well as the degradation of other organic matter.

REFERENCES

Heitkamp, M. A., J. P. Freeman, and C. E. Cerniglia. 1987. "Naphthalene Biodegradation in Environmental Microcosms: Estimates of Degradation Rates and Characterization of Metabolites." *Appl. Environ. Microbiol.* 53(1): 129-136.

Hinchee, R. E., S. K. Ong, R. N. Miller, D. C. Downey, and R. Frandt. 1992. *Test Plan and Technical Protocol for a Field Treatability Test for Bioventing.* Prepared for the U.S. Air Force, Center for Environmental Excellence.

Mihelcic, J. R., and R. G. Luthy. 1988. "Degradation of Polycyclic Aromatic Hydrocarbon Compounds under Various Redox Conditions in Soil-Water Systems." *Appl. Environ. Microbiol.* 54(5): 1182-1187.

Vertical Circulation Flows for Vadose and Groundwater Zone In Situ (Bio-)Remediation

Juergen Stamm

ABSTRACT

Vertical circulation flows have been established under in situ remediation techniques. Their hydraulic flow field permits physical and biological remediation of the saturated, as well as the unsaturated subsoil. A special advantage is that these techniques can be combined with any appropriate in-well or on-site technique. Even addition of nutrients and/or electron acceptors for stimulating biological degradation processes are possible. This paper discusses the different remediation techniques and the numerical results associated with the influence of hydrogeologic conditions on the system's radius of influence and time behavior.

INTRODUCTION

Because of the risk of groundwater and soil contaminants to humans and the environment, a strong effort has been made over the last decade to find innovative in situ remediation techniques and to improve existing methods to remove the contaminants. In situ techniques are less threatening to the environment and can be cost-effective systems. Furthermore, alternatives to pump-and-treat techniques, which have been proven inadequate in many cases, are needed (U.S. EPA 1989a, 1989b). Various existing methods are convenient for handling saturated or unsaturated soil. In the unsaturated zone, soil air is used as a solvent and transport medium for contaminants, and analogous free groundwater is used in the saturated zone. Whereas some treatment methods are based only on physical cleaning, others are supported by biological degradation processes (Hinchee 1994).

Vertical circulation flows around wells with at least two screen sections are universally applicable remediation tools. They are employed in several techniques, e.g., the groundwater circulation wells (German: Grundwasser-Zirkulations-Brunnen [GZB]), the vacuum vaporizer well (Unterdruck-Verdampfer-Brunnen [UVB]), and the groundwater flushing circulation well (SZB). Within the well, the groundwater moves vertically. The contaminated groundwater enters the well at the bottom, and stripped or treated water leaves at the top or vice versa. In the vicinity of the well, an area of vertical flow circulation is created. One well should be used to remediate only one aquifer (confined or phreatic) and should not connect different aquifers.

VERTICAL CIRCULATION FLOWS
FOR PHYSICAL IN SITU REMEDIATION

At numerous sites in Germany and more recently in the United States, the UVB technique has been used for in situ groundwater remediation where the underground is contaminated by strippable substances such as the volatile chlorinated hydrocarbons benzene, toluene, ethylbenzene, and xylenes (BTEX). As an alternative to conventional hydraulic redevelopment measures (pumping, off-site cleaning, and reinfiltration), the contaminated groundwater is stripped by air in a below-atmospheric pressure field in the UVB. In the case of contamination heavier than water (DNAPL) an upward operating UVB (Figure 1) is used, whereas for lighter compounds (LNAPL) the well works downward. Often the well is used for vapor extraction at the same time to support the remediation of the vadose zone as demonstrated in Figure 1. The contaminated air is cleaned by using activated carbon or, in the case of suitable contaminants, by using biofilters.

Through this technique, groundwater is pumped/injected along one screen in a well and withdrawn at another screen at another location in the same well to induce circulation. No water comes out of the soil, thus reducing the risk of further pollution. The well casing is divided by a separating plate into a lower and an upper part. A pump transports the water from the lower section to the stripping area (Figure 1). This causes a potential gradient between the two screen sections, which induces the circulation flow in the aquifer. Additionally, soil air is drawn from the surrounding contaminated unsaturated zone at many sites. Stripped air and soil air are transported through the ventilator and across activated carbon, onto which the contamination is adsorbed. Thus, only clean air escapes into the atmosphere. The cleaning effect of the well is based on (1) the high concentration gradient between water and clean air; (2) the considerable surface area of the air bubbles as a result of the air intermixing; and (3) the reduced pressure, which reinforces the escape of volatile contamination out of the water.

The cleaned groundwater leaves the well casing through the upper screen section in the reach of the groundwater surface, which is lifted in a phreatic aquifer by the previously explained pump processes and the below-atmospheric pressure (Figure 1). The groundwater then returns in an extensive circulation to the well bottom or the upper screen, respectively. In this way, the aquifer material surrounding the well also is remediated. The artificial groundwater circulation determines the sphere of influence of a well and overlaps the natural groundwater flow.

VERTICAL CIRCULATION FLOWS
FOR IN SITU BIORESTORATION

When the groundwater is contaminated by other than strippable substances, which are suitable for bioreclamation, the extensive circulation flow around the UVB can be used to bring nutrients and/or electron acceptors to all places within the circulation cell, where they are needed. Any appropriate gaseous or liquid substance that is soluble in water can be added in measured quantities while the groundwater passes the well casing. In this case the aquifer itself is used as a bioreactor. For in situ bioremediation of many contaminants, oxygen is essentially needed. The in situ stripping process with air of a UVB provides oxygen saturation. While the quantity of groundwater captured by a well remains

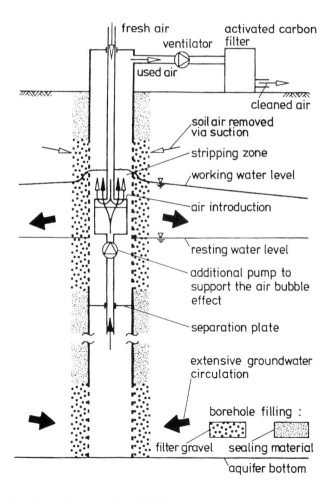

FIGURE 1. In situ stripping by a UVB operating upward for DNAPL (e.g., PCE, TCE).

relatively constant, the quantity of circulating water around the UVB can be extremely enhanced by a stronger pump in the well casing which results in a faster rotation velocity of the circulation flow. Thus, the amount of oxygen supplied for in situ bioremediation can be considerably increased. Carbon dioxide as a by-product is removed from the groundwater by the same stripping process, so new problems don't arise due to a drop in pH value. The contaminated air is cleaned by using activated carbon or biofilters. A UVB technique that combines vapor extraction with the stripping process is generally used for those sites. It supplies oxygen to the vapor zone and capillary fringe for biodegrading processes.

On the other hand, a special bioreactor has been installed within the well casing between the lower and upper screen in the case of a triazine contamination (Buermann et al. 1992). The vertical circulation delivers the hydraulic flow field which transports the contamination from the surrounding aquifer into the well. Here the pesticide is adsorbed within the in-well bioreactor and, after reaching the bioavailable concentration, is biodegraded.

An analogous treatment of groundwater contaminated by nitrate is possible. The use of in-well containers, in which a catalytic reduction of nitrate to N_2 by immobilized enzymes occurs, enabling the elimination of nitrate from the groundwater. The dissolved N_2 is finally removed via in situ stripping using the UVB technique. The technique has been developed at the laboratory scale and is being prepared for field applications (Mellor et al. 1992).

GROUNDWATER FLUSHING IN THE UNSATURATED ZONE

In the unsaturated zone, bioremediation is influenced by the soil moisture content. For most biological degradation processes, the optimal water content is in a range between 50% and 80%. When the vadose zone is contaminated with light, nonaqueous-phase liquids (LNAPLs; e.g., diesel, BTEX, mineral oil), the groundwater flushing circulation well (SZB) makes it possible to establish an adjustable, vertical, unsaturated multiphase flow in the contaminated region (see Figure 2). The flushing water is pumped from the upper saturated groundwater zone and/or the capillary fringe to a reactor situated at the upper end of the well casing near the ground surface. The water enters the otherwise closed casing through a local screen at that height. At the reactor, the water is (optionally) stripped with air in a vacuum. Before stripping, nutrients can be added for bioremediation processes or tensides for an enhanced flushing process. The stripping with air leads to oxygen saturation of the water.

Before the water leaves the reactor zone, it flows through a zone with a special granulated material separating the LNAPL from the water; LNAPL remains on top of the granulated material and can be recovered as free product from time to time. The vacuum in the reactor leads to a vacuum pressure distribution under the filter material, which dictates the unsaturated inflow conditions. Therefore, a vertical, circular, unsaturated multiphase flow occurs. A "dynamic

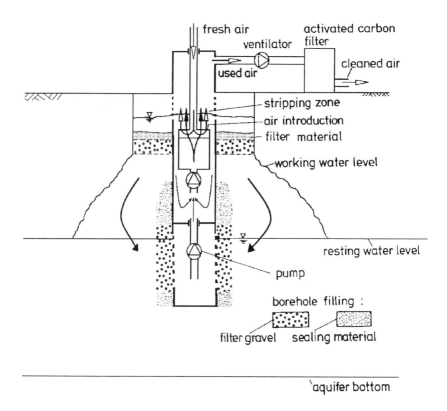

FIGURE 2. Groundwater flushing circulation well (SZB) for remediation of the vadose zone and capillary fringe. Various circulation flow patterns are possible.

water mound" with adjustable flushing water saturation is produced around the well, and leads to the uniform distribution of nutrients and oxygen within its sphere of influence.

Table 1 shows an overview of possible applications of vertical circulation flows in the vadose and groundwater zone for different contaminants. It does not claim completeness. All UVB and GZB systems can be employed for source as well as for plume restoration. The SZB-technique focuses on point-source treatment in the vadose zone and the capillary fringe.

NUMERICAL INVESTIGATIONS

In this paper, only flow for confined aquifer conditions is demonstrated. In the computations the local below-atmospheric-pressure field (in case of a UVB) was neglected. Further, density effects were ignored; only steady-state conditions were taken into account, and, to estimate the capture zone, only convective

TABLE 1. Overview of vertical circulation flow applications.

Contaminants	Technique	Method	Special Features	Zone of Applicability
VOCs				
DNAPLs (e.g., PCE, TCE, VC)	upward operating UVB[a]	physical in situ stripping plus aeration/biodegradation	vapor extraction soil-air treatment	groundwater and vadose zone
LNAPLs (e.g., BTEX, kerosene, phenol)	downward operating UVB	physical in situ stripping plus aeration/biodegradation	vapor extraction soil-air treatment	groundwater and vadose zone
Nonvolatiles				
NAPLs	UVB/GZB[b]	aeration/biodegradation	addition of nutrients (gaseous or liquid)	support of biological degradation within the aquifer
DNAPLs (e.g., creosote, PCP)	UVB/GZB	biodegradation with in situ bioreactor	second pump system	free product recovery
Other biodegradable substances	SZB[c]	air-water flushing in the vadose zone	addition of nutrients	biostimulation and degradation of residual contaminants
	SZB		combination with UVB possible	treatment of water-saturated zone
Pesticides, nitrate	UVB/GZB	bioreactor (e.g., activated carbon, enzymatic biodegradation)	in-well bioreactors	water-saturated zone anaerobic degradation

(a) UVB: vacuum vaporizer well.
(b) GZB: groundwater circulation well.
(c) SZB: groundwater flushing circulation well.

transport was considered. All necessary diagrams for sizing a vertical circulation flow system, even for partial extraction or infiltration, are published by (Herrling & Stamm 1992).

The general character of vertical circulation flow is shown in Figure 3. In a vertical longitudinal section parallel to natural groundwater flow, streamlines and isopotential lines mark the flow around one (Figure 3a) and two (Figure 3b) upward-pumping UVBs or GZBs, which are separated by the distance S between the stagnation point and the well axis. The shape of the isopotentials (dashed lines in Figure 3a) indicates the reach of hydraulic influence of the circulation system. In a distance of approximately 4H (H = aquifer thickness), the isopotential lines are rather vertical, i.e., they are unaffected by the well. The strong vertical circulation flow, which is extremely beneficial in a highly polluted area near the contamination source, is evident even between the two wells (Figure 3b). Two wells aligned in the flow direction can be used to generate an anaerobic biodegradation zone around the first circulation well (GZB without air stripping, but with carbon source added within the well casing) and an aerobic zone with an UVB around the second well. Figure 3c demonstrates the flow pattern in a stratified aquifer with three layers, where the anisotropy K_H/K_V of each layer is equal to five (ratio between horizontal and vertical permeability) and the middle layer is ten times less permeable than the upper and lower one. It is obvious that stratification enlarges the circulation flow zone.

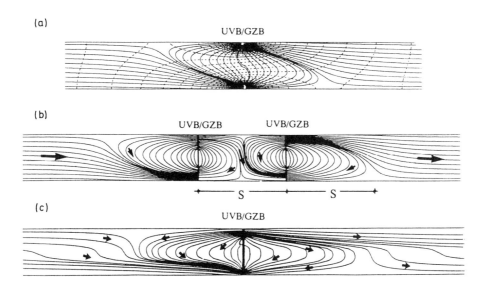

FIGURE 3. Streamlines and isopotential lines around (a) one UVB or GZB and (b) two UVBs or GZBs in a homogeneous aquifer, and (c) in a layered aquifer, shown in a vertical longitudinal section parallel to the natural groundwater flow.

INFLUENCE OF HYDROGEOLOGY

In a simulated test aquifer with seven equidistant horizontal layers, the influence of layering was investigated. Each layer has a thickness, d, and has a realistic anisotropy of $K_H/K_V = 5$ (Figure 4). The model was used to determine the influence of a single layer in various positions and with various permeabilities. The parameter α is introduced to define the decadal logarithmic ratio between the hydraulic permeability of the layer and of the entire aquifer ($\alpha = 1$ means the permeability of the layer is ten times higher than the permeability of the aquifer).

Figure 5 demonstrates the effect of layer position and ratio of permeability, α, on the effective anisotropy of the whole system. In the absence of natural groundwater flow, for example, the sphere of influence of a GZB with a central layer ($d = H/7$) that is 100 times less permeable than the ambient aquifer ($\alpha = -2$) is identical to the radius of influence in a homogeneous aquifer with an anisotropy of $K_H/K_V = 140$ and the same overall thickness H (Figure 5). As the anisotropy increases, the radius of influence of a GZB also increases. The case $\alpha < 0$ leads to a rapid increase in effective anisotropy, whereas for $\alpha > 0$ the changes are negligible. Furthermore, it is obvious that the closer the layer is to the middle of the aquifer (pos. 0), the higher its influence on the circulation flow regime.

One consequence of increasing effective anisotropy, accompanied by enlarging circulation cell diameters, is a decrease in circulation velocity. Figure 6a shows, in a dimensionless form, the dependence of the effective anisotropy (K_H/K_V) on the relative circulation quantity (Q_{Tzirk}/Q) within a certain travel time T_{Zirk}. This diagram permits determining the percentage of circulating water Q_{Tzirk} within a definite time from the total well discharge Q. Qualitatively with increasing anisotropy the quota Q_{Tzirk}/Q decreases for a fixed time.

The knowledge of Q_{Tzirk}/Q, or in a more common form Q_r/Q (defines the portion of Q that circulates within a radius r around the well), allows a determination of corresponding radius r (see Figure 6b), over which this percentage of Q circulates during the time T_{Zirk}. From these data it is possible to determine the supply of nutrients over time and location. For the case where natural groundwater flow is present, several diagrams are available.

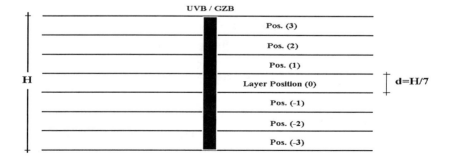

FIGURE 4. Test aquifer for numerical simulations with seven layers.

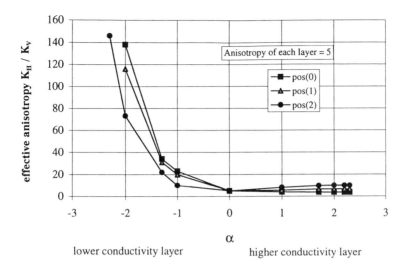

FIGURE 5. Effective anisotropy of an aquifer as a function of the position and permeability ratio of an intermediate layer vs. overall homogeneous medium.

CONCLUSION

The broad applicability of vertical circulation flow systems around groundwater circulation wells (GZB) has been summarized for various in situ and remediation techniques. The modular concept of the presented technique allows many system variations and their respective adaptations to specific site requirements. By means of numerical computations, diagrams based upon dimensionless parameters have been created that enable the sizing of vertical circulation flow remediation measures in a layered aquifer. It has been shown that the effect of a layer is equivalent to an increasing effective anisotropy for a homogeneous medium.

ACKNOWLEDGMENTS

The work presented originated from a long-standing collaboration with Dr. Bruno Herrling, University of Karlsruhe, Germany. Dr. Herrling's death in October 1994 prevents me from passing on my gratitude to him for this period of collaboration. Grateful acknowledgment is extended to IEG mbH, D-72770 Reutlingen (Germany), for financially supporting these investigations, in particular B. Bernhardt, IEG mbH, D-72770 Reutlingen, inventor of the described technologies. All technologies described in this paper are patented by IEG mbH, D-72770 Reutlingen in the USA, Europe, and other countries. I also thank the firms that placed the systems and field data at our disposal, as well as my colleagues for many helpful discussions and contributions.

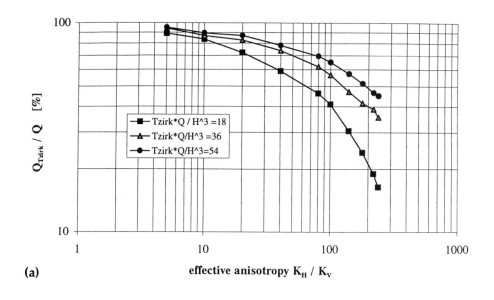

(a)

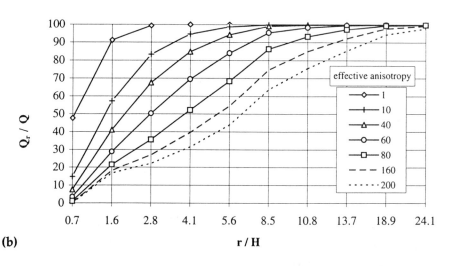

(b)

FIGURE 6. (a) Ratio of circulation quantity (Q_{Tzirk}) within a definite time to total well discharge (Q) vs. effective anisotropy (K_H/K_V). (b) Ratio of circulation quantity within a definite radius (Q_r) to total well discharge (Q) vs. relative well distance (r/H) for several effective anisotropies.

REFERENCES

Buermann, W., G. Bott-Breuning, and R. Krug. 1992. "Groundwater Remediation Using the Vacuum-Vaporizer-Well." In W. Pillmann (Ed.), *Industrial Waste Management (Proc. Envirotech Vienna 1992)*, pp. 723-732. A. Riegelnik Printers, Vienna, Austria.

Herrling, B., and J. Stamm. 1992. "Numerical Results of Calculated 3D Vertical Circulation Flows Around Wells with Two Screen Sections for In Situ Aquifer Remediation." In T. F. Russel et al. (Eds.), *Computational Methods in Water Resources IX, Vol.1: Numerical Methods in Water Resources*, pp. 483-492. Elsevier Applied Science, London.

Hinchee, R. E. 1994. "Air Sparging State of the Art." In R. E. Hinchee (Ed.), *Air Sparging for Site Remediation*, pp. 1-13. Lewis Publishers, Boca Raton, FL.

Mellor, R. B., J. Ronnenberg, W. H. Campbell, and S. Diekmann. 1992. "Reduction of Nitrate and Nitrite in Water by Immobilized Enzymes." *Nature 355:* 717-719.

U.S. EPA. 1989a. *Evaluation of Ground Water Extraction Remedies*, vol. 1. Summary Report EPA/540/2-89/054. Cincinnati, OH.

U.S. EPA. 1989b. *Evaluation of Ground Water Extraction Remedies*, vol. 2. Case Studies 1-19, EPA/540/2-89/054a. Cincinnati, OH.

Evaluation of Vertical Circulation Wells for Enhanced Bioremediation

Douglas R. McCaulou, Walter T. Weinig, and Gary R. Walter

ABSTRACT

A vertical circulation well (VCW) can be used to enhance bioremediation of a contaminated aquifer by introducing terminal electron acceptors (TEAs). Significant advantages of this approach are that no foreign water is injected and no water is produced at the surface requiring treatment and disposal. A simple mass-transport model is presented to predict the zone of the aquifer that will be effectively treated over time by a VCW. A retardation factor is derived for the relative movement of a TEA front through a contaminated zone compared to advection of recirculated water. When the hydrodynamic retardation factor of a contaminant is greater than the TEA retardation factor, biodegradation effectively reduces cleanup times. The aquifer volume in which active biodegradation is enhanced can be considerably smaller than the zone of physical groundwater circulation at a given time. In this case, spacing of VCWs depends on the rate of TEA delivery and the desired cleanup duration. When the biodegradation rate is limited by mass-transfer processes, the resulting cleanup times become more dependent on the rate-limiting step than on the TEA mass-delivery rate. In those cases, additional VCWs will not reduce cleanup times.

INTRODUCTION

Several investigators have used conservative particle-tracking models to illustrate the flow fields associated with VCWs in a variety of scenarios (Burns 1969; Herrling et al. 1991; Philip and Walter 1992). Using the analytical model of Philip and Walter (1992) and the aquifer parameters representative of a sandy aquifer listed in Table 1, a steady-state flow field for a single VCW was simulated. Ninety percent of the recirculation flow occurs within a 40-m radius of the well.

Figure 1 shows isochronal contours that illustrate the location of circulated water in the flow field with time. Using the Philip and Walter (1992) model, water circulates through 50%, 75%, and 100% of the cylindrical volume within the 40-m radius in 21, 90, and 250 days, respectively.

TABLE 1. Model and contaminant parameters.

Parameter	Value
Horizontal Hydraulic Conductivity (cm/s)	0.1
Vertical Hydraulic Conductivity (cm/s)	0.01
Porosity	0.3
Dry Bulk Density (g/cm³)	1.5
Fraction Organic Carbon (%)	1.0
Regional Flow Gradient	0
Pump Rate (m³/h)	20.16
Well Diameter (cm)	10.16
Top Screen Interval (m)	2
Bottom Screen Interval (m)	1
Initial Concentration of Benzene and Naphthalene (mg/kg)	20
Dissolved Oxygen Concentration of Recirculated Water (mg/L)	7
Distribution Coefficient for Benzene (K_d)	0.646
Distribution Coefficient for Naphthalene (K_d)	12.88

If the circulated water is augmented with a TEA or nutrient to induce in situ bioremediation of the aquifer, its consumption rate rather than the hydraulic circulation rate may determine the time required to remediate a given volume of aquifer. Design of these types of enhanced bioremediation systems requires consideration of the mass-transport and biodegradation properties, in addition to the hydrodynamics of the vertical-well flow field.

This paper focuses on inducing in situ bioremediation by delivering TEAs throughout the aquifer, although the rate of biodegradation may be affected by other factors. A simple mass-transfer model is used to provide a screening-level evaluation of VCW feasibility at a specific site. Assumptions of the model include a homogeneous and anisotropic aquifer, no abiotic reactions that consume the TEA, instantaneous degradation reactions between the TEA and substrate, and negligible dispersion effects. For more reliable estimates, more complex transport and biodegradation models should be used to formally design a VCW system.

VCW DESIGN CRITERIA

A system that is designed to remediate a contaminant plume may include several VCWs to assure that the local groundwater flow is captured for in-well treatment or to assure that the mass delivery rate of TEAs is sufficient to stimulate

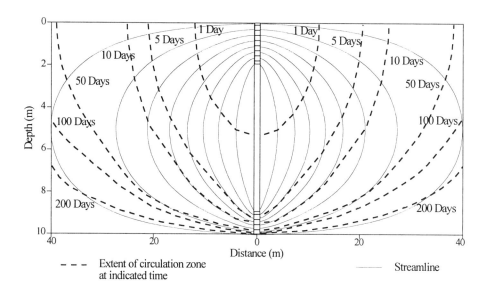

FIGURE 1. Hydraulic circulation flow lines with isochronal contours showing the distance along each flow line injected water would travel at given times.

biodegradation in the zones between and surrounding the VCWs. Additional wells, increased pumping rates, and closer spacing between VCWs can decrease the time required to introduce TEAs and hydraulically capture a contaminant plume. However, shorter hydraulic capture times may not translate into shorter cleanup times when aquifer conditions limit the rate of contaminant mass transfer or advective transport.

Several textbooks present the derivation of a hydrodynamic retardation factor to represent the relatively slower movement of a dissolved, reactive contaminant due to sorption compared to the groundwater velocity in an aquifer (e.g., Freeze and Cherry 1979). Assuming that the sorption/desorption process is fast compared to the groundwater velocity, completely reversible, and can be described by a linear adsorption isotherm, the hydrodynamic retardation factor typically is presented as:

$$R_h = \frac{v_w}{v_c} = 1 + \frac{\rho_b K_d}{\theta} \qquad (1)$$

where R_h is the hydrodynamic retardation factor [dimensionless ratio];
v_w is the average pore velocity of the water [L/t];
v_c is the apparent retarded pore velocity of the contaminant front [L/t];
ρ_b is the dry bulk soil density [M/L^3];
K_d is the water-solid distribution coefficient [L^3/M]; and
θ is the porosity of the medium [dimensionless].

The hydrodynamic retardation factor also describes the relative velocity of clean water recirculated by a VCW through a contaminated aquifer zone after in-well treatment. Assuming no biodegradation or dispersion effects and 100% efficiency of the in-well treatment system, the front of clean water (no remaining contaminant) is retarded compared to the velocity of the circulated water by a factor R_h calculated according to (1). If dispersion is considered, the hydrodynamic retardation factor describes the retardation of the center of mass of the clean-water front, with concentrations at the VCW inlet diminishing over time.

BIODEGRADATION KINETICS

Consumption of oxygen as a TEA and degradation of hydrocarbons has been modeled as an instantaneous reaction in a hydrocarbon plume where oxygen transport was rate limiting (Borden and Bedient 1986). In such a case, the biodegradation front between contaminated and remediated zones is very sharp because the utilization of oxygen and hydrocarbon is complete and nearly instantaneous. A simple TEA retardation factor can be derived to estimate the location of the active biodegradation front at a given time or to estimate the total time necessary for cleanup.

The following differential equation describes the mass balance of TEAs in an infinitesimal portion of a stream tube:

$$dM_o = q(s)A(s)C_o dt - \alpha dM_s \qquad (2)$$

where dM_o is the change in TEA mass within the volume A(s) ds [M];
$\quad dM_s$ is the mass of substrate in the infinitesimal volume [M];
$\quad \alpha$ is the ratio describing the mass of TEA consumed to a given mass of substrate;
$\quad q(s)$ is the water flux at distance s from the upstream end of the stream tube [L/t];
$\quad A(s)$ is the cross-sectional area of the stream tube at distance s [L^2];
$\quad C_o$ is the input TEA concentration [M/L^3]; and
$\quad t$ is the time [t].

Writing the mass terms of (2) in terms of concentration and rearranging gives:

$$\frac{ds}{dt} = v_{TEA} = \frac{\theta C_o}{\theta C_o + \alpha S_s \rho_B} v_w \qquad (3)$$

where v_{TEA} is the apparent pore velocity of the TEA front [L/t];
$\quad v_w$ is the pore velocity of the water, $q(s)/\theta$ [L/t]; and
$\quad S_s$ is the concentration of substrate on the medium [M/M].

The retardation factor, R_{TEA}, of the TEA front with respect to the water pore velocity is thus:

$$R_{TEA} = 1 + \frac{\alpha S_s \rho_B}{C_o \theta} = \frac{v_w}{v_{TEA}} \quad (4)$$

The TEA retardation factor is dependent on the initial concentration of contaminant in the aquifer and the concentration and types of TEAs in the injected water. The TEA retardation factor is based on a mass balance of TEA and substrate along a streamtube. Thus, inclusion of dispersion would not alter the model because it does not alter the mass of TEA needed to degrade a given mass of substrate.

DISCUSSION

When advective transport and in situ biodegradation are the major contaminant-fate mechanisms under consideration, two general cases illustrate the usefulness of this analysis. First, if the hydrodynamic retardation factor, R_h, is greater than the TEA retardation factor, R_{TEA}, enhanced in situ biodegradation may significantly reduce the time required to remediate the contaminated portion of an aquifer. Second, if R_{TEA} is much greater than R_h, biodegradation may only be a minor component of the overall remediation.

Consider an aquifer with the parameters listed in Table 1 contaminated with benzene at 20 mg/kg. The R_h of benzene in the model aquifer would be approximately 4.2 based on the K_d and equation (1). Using oxygen as the TEA at a concentration of 7 mg/L in the recirculated water, the R_{TEA} would be 47, using the stoichiometric 3:1 oxygen to benzene mass-consumption ratio. This suggests that enhanced in situ biodegradation would occur only at the interface between the contaminant-free recirculated water and the oxygen-depleted contaminated zone. The majority of the contaminant mass would be removed by advective transport and in-well treatment.

In the first case, the remediation of the circulation zone extending to 40 m from the well would take less than 3 years (y) (250 days [d] times 4.2) in the absence of biodegradation. Biodegradation would have little effect on the overall remediation because the majority of the benzene would desorb and be flushed out before sufficient mass of oxygen could be delivered to degrade the benzene. However, increasing the TEA concentration of the recirculated water to 40 mg/L by saturating it with pure oxygen would decrease the R_{TEA} to 9, a level at which in situ biodegradation could be more significant.

The same aquifer contaminated with naphthalene at 20 mg/kg concentration would have a calculated R_h of 65.4. Naphthalene also has a stoichiometric 3:1 TEA to substrate mass-consumption ratio. With an oxygen content of 7 mg/L in the recirculated water, the R_{TEA} would still be 47. In this case, advective transport of naphthalene would be sufficiently retarded so that oxygenated water could circulate through the contaminated zone before the contaminant was flushed out of the aquifer. This suggests that in situ biodegradation would be a significant factor in the overall remediation strategy.

In the second case, the aquifer volume which has been completely oxygenated at a given time would be smaller than the zone of groundwater circulation at that time by a factor equal to R_{TEA}. The time to completely perfuse the contaminated aquifer volume within a radius of 40 m of the VCW with the TEA would be 32 y (250 d times 47). This retardation is due to the consumption of the TEA as recirculated water travels along a streamline.

The simple analytical model presented above can be used to estimate the relative importance of advective transport and in-well treatment compared to enhanced in situ biodegradation for a given VCW system. The practical limitation of this model is the assumption that contaminants instantaneously degrade. Instantaneous consumption and degradation reaction kinetics result in an easily calculated retardation factor, but are too simplistic to represent systems in which mass transfer is limited by factors such as recalcitrant compounds, tight formations, coupled degradation reactions, or dissolution of nonaqueous-phase liquids.

The comparison of advective contaminant transport to biodegradation capacity can be applied to a site for a preliminary evaluation of the potential usefulness of VCW systems to enhance in situ biodegradation. For a given contaminant concentration, R_{TEA} can be reduced by increasing the concentration of TEAs in the circulating water and/or decreasing the ratio of the mass TEAs consumed to a given mass of substrate, perhaps by changing the TEA composition. For example, if R_{TEA} is greater than R_h for oxygen at normal atmospheric concentrations, injection of pure oxygen will yield a much lower R_{TEA}, thereby increasing the effectiveness of in situ bioremediation in the overall treatment system.

Use of an instantaneous model may be inappropriate to calculate cleanup times for compounds with slow biodegradation rates or when biodegradation is limited by mass transfer. However, if the mass-transfer steps are known and can be parameterized, this screening model may indicate when more complex transport and biodegradation models may be useful. A limitation of the more complex models is that it is very difficult to economically obtain parameter values that accurately describe field-scale dispersion and biodegradation. However, if the biodegradation rate or mass-transfer step can be modeled as a first-order decay reaction, the subsequent cleanup time can be estimated by adding the time to circulate the TEA throughout the system to the exponential decay time. The R_{TEA} for a specific site and hydrodynamic design parameters can be used to estimate the time required to circulate enough TEA to stimulate biodegradation throughout the aquifer.

When an aquifer and contaminant system is dominated by mass-transfer limitations or when biodegradation reactions are coupled, VCWs can be used to stimulate and maintain favorable conditions for biodegradation but the total cleanup time will be controlled by the rate-limiting step. In these situations, the time required to circulate a TEA or nutrient can be expected to be a relatively small component of the overall remediation time. Therefore, additional VCWs and other engineered designs that shorten circulation time will have little effect on the overall cleanup time. In extreme conditions where mass transfer is limited to diffusion-like rates, the actual rates of the biodegradation processes, regardless of the type of substrate, may only be a minor factor in the total cleanup time.

REFERENCES

Borden, R. C., and P. B. Bedient. 1986. "Transport of Dissolved Hydrocarbons Influenced by Oxygen-Limited Biodegradation, 1. Theoretical Development." *Water Resources Research* 22(13): 1973-1982.

Burns, W. A., Jr. 1969. "New Single-Well Test for Determining Vertical Permeability." *Journal of Petroleum Technology* July: 743-752.

Freeze, R. A., and J. A. Cherry. 1979. *Groundwater.* Prentice-Hall, Inc., Englewood Cliffs, NJ.

Herrling, B., J. Stamm, and W. Buermann. 1991. "Hydraulic Circulation System for In Situ Bioreclamation and/or In Situ Remediation of Strippable Contamination." In R. E. Hinchee and R. F. Olfenbuttel (Eds.), *On-Site Bioreclamation: Processes for Xenobiotic and Hydrocarbon Treatment.* Butterworth-Heinemann, Boston, MA. pp. 173-195.

Philip, R. D. and G. R. Walter. 1992. "Prediction of Flow and Hydraulic Head Fields for Vertical Circulation Wells." *Ground Water* 30(3).

Enhanced In Situ Bioremediation Using Foams and Oil Aphrons

Michael V. Enzien, Donald L. Michelsen, Robert W. Peters, Jacques X. Bouillard, and James R. Frank

ABSTRACT

The use of foams and oil-core aphrons (OCAs) to extract, mobilize, and disperse nonaqueous-phase liquid (NAPL) contaminants for increased bioavailability was investigated. Soil column experiments were used to evaluate foam and OCA flow characteristics in soils. Comparison of pressure drops in soil columns with water, surfactant solution, foams, and OCAs indicated that foams have the largest pressure drops. Pressure drops with water, surfactant solutions, and OCAs were all comparable. The scouring efficiency of NAPL pools with foams indicated >90% removal, while surfactant solutions removed <10%. OCAs were ineffective at removing contaminants from soils in our experiments. A flat plate visualization cell was used to observe foam flow patterns through porous media. Flow experiments with this cell indicated that (1) foams flow through porous media as a front, whereas surfactant solutions tend to channel; (2) foams can encapsulate low permeability lenses; and (3) foam front advancement increases when vacuum extraction is applied to the outlet. These observations have important implications for potential field-design scenarios.

INTRODUCTION

At many hazardous waste sites, in situ bioremediation is limited by contaminant bioavailability as a result of the physical and chemical nature of the porous media and contaminant interactions (Rittmann et al. 1994). Nonaqueous-phase liquids (NAPLs) create a problem for in situ bioremediation when concentrations reach levels toxic to microorganisms (Phelps et al. 1988). Foams or OCAs can be used to overcome these obstacles.

Foams are a dispersion of gas microbubbles, ranging in size from 50 to 70 μm, in a continuous liquid phase stabilized by small amounts of surfactants. OCAs are a dispersion of oil microbubbles, ranging in size from 1 to 40 μm (averaging

< 10 μm), stabilized by small amounts of surfactants. Microbubble foams have been used for many years in various industrial processes, especially in the areas of mineral, coal, and wastewater solids flotation; dust suppression; petroleum production; and fire fighting. Research and some pilot-plant activities have also demonstrated that microbubble foams can (1) deliver and retain oxygen and air microbubbles in various soil matrices and contaminated harbor sediments (Michelsen et al. 1984a; 1984b; 1985) and (2) biodegrade dissolved and dispersed organics in place or as they are injected to form microbubble-treatment barriers (Jenkins et al. 1993). The use of air or oxygen microbubbles to improve bioreactor performance has been demonstrated in the laboratory and resulted in marked improvement in oxygen mass transfer (as a result of surface area) (Kaster et al. 1989). Unlike surfactants, foams remove contaminants by scouring the contaminants, as well as through partial solubilization and emulsification by reducing surface tension. OCAs have shown to be effective at removing as high as 99% bitumen from tar sands (Riviello et al. 1991). OCAs have not previously been used for in situ remediation of NAPL-contaminated soils. The focus of this research was to investigate the feasibility of using either foams or OCAs (or a combination) for extraction and dispersion of NAPLs from sandy soils rendering residual soils amenable to in situ bioremediation.

MATERIALS AND METHODS

Small soil columns packed with clean quartz sands (Flint Shot 2.6, U.S. Silica) were used to test and compare the flow characteristics and extraction efficiencies of foams, OCAs, and surfactant solutions. Additional flow characteristics for different soil types can be found in Enzien et al. (1994). Foams were generated with a spinning-disc generator (Sebba 1985) and pumped through soils at flowrates of 3 to 10 mL/s. Similar flowrates were used for OCAs and surfactant solutions. OCAs were generated by using vegetable oil or dodecane as the oil phase and stabilized with oil and water-soluble surfactants (Enzien et al. 1994). A phase-volume ratio of 5 was produced for OCAs (i.e., 50 mL of oil to 10 mL of water). OCAs were diluted to 10 or 100 to 1 in water prior to extraction experiments. Surfactant solutions used for foam generation contained active ingredients of either a nonionic ethoxylated alcohol solution (Tergitol 15S12) or sodium dodecyl benzyl sulfonate (NaDBS, Biosoft D-40) at concentrations ranging from 500 to 2,000 mg/L. Pressure drops across soil column lengths and flowrates were measured for all experiments.

A flat parallel plate cell was used to observe and compare flow characteristics of foams, OCAs, and surfactant solutions, as well as NAPL extraction/dispersion mechanisms. The cell was packed with quartz sands containing several low-permeability lenses. Texaco Regal Oil 150 was injected into the test cell through a port in the middle of vessel to simulate a NAPL pool. Details of the test cell are described elsewhere (Enzien et al. 1994).

RESULTS

The flow characteristics for foams, OCAs, and surfactant solutions indicated that foams flow through test sands with greater pressure drops than do OCAs and surfactant solutions (Table 1). The results from our study (Enzien et al. 1994) and Longe (1989) for foam flow characteristics differ from those reported in previous work, which suggested that foams yield lower pressure drops than do surfactant flushing solutions (Roy et al. 1992).

Several types of contaminant removal experiments were conducted in soil columns; these experiments were designed to compare extraction efficiencies of surrogate NAPLs using foams, OCAs, and surfactant solutions. Concentrations were chosen in order to test the effectiveness of extraction over several orders of magnitude and were not meant to represent a specific site. Four pore volumes of water were flushed through columns prior to extraction tests. This was done in an attempt to redistribute the NAPL phase. Flushing experiments commenced immediately after NAPL spiking without any aging. For these experiments, removal efficiency was measured by visually inspecting sands after treatment and by volumetrically collecting the dyed oil phase in extraction solutions. Surfactant flushing solutions performed equally well as foams for NAPL removal (Table 2). The level of surfactant loading for foam and surfactant flushes was equivalent in all experiments. Thus, the actual volume of foams injected is 2.5 times greater than surfactant solutions because the foams are 60 to 65% gas by volume. Equivalent surfactant loadings translate into equivalent material costs for surfactants.

In extraction experiments with lower concentrations of mineral oil volumetric determinations of oil extracts could not be made because of the small volume of contaminant added and interferences attributable to surfactant compounds made gas chromatography difficult. Qualitative estimates were achieved by inspecting the soil column effluent streams and soils themselves (Table 2). Sands removed from these test columns appeared to have any remaining mineral oil uniformly dispersed throughout the soils. In the test with 5,000 mg/kg mineral oil, four separate depth profiles were removed from the column, placed in beakers, and mixed with water. Controls indicated that any remaining mineral

TABLE 1. Pressure drops for soil columns packed with quartz sands, permeability of 9.7×10^{-3} cm/s. Pressure ranges are for flowrates between 1 and 10 mL/s for all solutions.

Flushing Solution	Pressure (psi)
Oil core aphrons	1-4
Surfactant solutions	1-4
Foams	15-20

TABLE 2. Extraction efficiencies of mineral oil spiked quartz sands, permeability of 9.7×10^{-3} cm/s, packed in a 2-in. OD × 5.5 in. soil column.
Surfactants used to generate foams and flushing solutions were sodium
dodecylbenzene sulfonate and Tergitol 15S12 (500 to 2,000 mg/L) and the
table represents pooled results for different concentrations. Refer to
Enzien et al. (1994) for OCA formulations.

Extraction Solution	Mineral Oil Concentration (mg/kg)	Removal Efficiency
Oil-core aphrons	500	clear extracts[a]
	5,000	clear extracts[a]
	50,000	not detectable[b]
Surfactant solutions	500	turbid extracts[a]
	5,000	turbid extracts[a]
	50,000	≥90%[b]
Foams	500	turbid extracts[a]
	5,000	turbid extracts[a]
	50,000	≥90%[b]

(a) Removal efficiencies based on turbidity of column extract, turbidity indicating
removal of mineral oil.
(b) Removal efficiencies based on volume of mineral oil collected in extracts.

oil would easily be visible as a separate phase. No oil was detected in any of
the profiles following a 3-pore-volume foam post-flush.

Experiments with the flat plate visualization cell clearly demonstrated foam
flow patterns through porous media. Unlike surfactant solutions, which can
be clearly seen to channel through porous media, foams sweep through soils
as a front. Longe (1989) made this same observation where a two-phase front
develops when foam microbubbles are injected into porous media. With soil
permeabilities of 6.5×10^{-2} cm/s, the foam front was unable to advance farther
than two-thirds the length of the cell at 30 psi backpressure. When a vacuum
of 10 to 15 in. Hg was applied to the outlet, breakthrough of foam microbubbles
was achieved; however, the foam front did not advance. The vacuum caused
the foam microbubbles to channel through the sands instead of advancing as
a front. In effect, the vacuum creates conditions similar to air sparging, with
the foam front interface serving as the source of gas.

In experiments with low-permeability lenses, the foam front advancement
channeled around the low-permeability lenses and completely encapsulated them
instead of evenly penetrating them (Figure 1a). As the foam front advanced
farther and the pressures increased, the lenses were slowly penetrated by foams.
Eventually, the low-permeability lenses were completely penetrated by foams
(Figure 1b). In contrast, when dyed water and surfactant solutions were pumped
through the same soil matrix, channeling around low-permeability lenses was

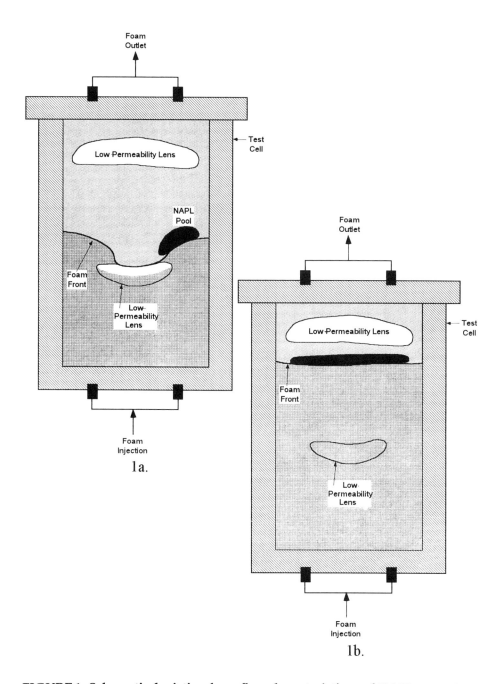

FIGURE 1. Schematic depicting foam flow characteristics and NAPL extraction mechanisms. 1a. Foam flows around a low-permeability lens, causing NAPL pool to laterally smear. 1b. With further advancement of the foam front, pressure differentials increase and low-permeability lenses are penetrated. NAPL pool continues to scour in direction of foam front movement.

clearly observed. Under these conditions, the low-permeability lenses were only slightly penetrated.

In experiments comparing NAPL extraction efficiencies between surfactant flushes and foams using the same heterogeneous matrices, clear differences were both visually and quantitatively apparent. With both types of surfactants, Tergitol 15S12 and NaDBS, foams were at least 10 times more efficient at removing the NAPL pools than were surfactant solutions for the same volume of total surfactant liquid. Foams recovered 90 to 100% of oils injected in the test cell, and surfactant solutions removed 1 to 10%. The scouring mechanisms of NAPLs appeared to be similar for foams made with either Tergitol 15S12 NaDBS. The heterogeneities of the soil matrix caused the initial scouring action of the NAPL pool to smear slightly laterally because of the foam flow effects created by low-permeability lenses (Figure 1a). Once the foam front advanced farther and the low-permeability lenses were either completely penetrated or encapsulated by foam flow, oil scouring continued vertically (Figure 1b).

DISCUSSION

On the basis of observations made during these experiments, we have shown that foams are effective at removing high concentrations of NAPL pools from fairly porous media and that they appear to be more efficient than surfactant solutions alone. At lower concentrations of NAPL contamination, we are less sure of foam extraction efficiencies; however we do suspect, at the very least, dispersion processes will be much more effective than surfactant solutions because foams do not tend to channel. This phenomenon becomes important when NAPL contamination consists of small ganglia trapped within pore throats of soil grains. Surfactant flushing solutions will tend to bypass these pore throats, whereas foams will tend to physically scour out these small ganglia. The fate of dispersed or immobilized NAPL contaminants still remains to be determined. On the basis of earlier preliminary studies, we do know that chemical association between contaminant and foam microbubbles provides for a bioavailable substrate (Michelsen et al. 1985). Initial work by the Virginia Polytechnic Institute and State University indicates that foams do in fact enhance biodegradation processes. The ability of foams to encapsulate low-permeability lenses may allow this technology to be coupled with other physical chemical treatments aimed at increasing bioavailability. In this case, foams could be used as barriers for contaminant containment as other methods (such as electrokinetics or in situ thermal desorption) are used to extract contaminants. Inherent in any of these remediation processes is the enhancement of oxygen mass transfer offered by microbubble foams.

Many scenarios can be envisioned coupling foam remediation with in situ bioremediation. As indicated by this study and other studies, one of the main geotechnical hurdles for foam remediation will be foam delivery strategies to the subsurface. Our experiments suggest that pressure drops may be overcome by applying a vacuum extraction system. With this scenario, foams would be injected into the subsurface to extract or disperse NAPLs by scouring, and then a vacuum extraction system is applied at the foam front interface to remove volatile organic compounds and surfactant-solubilized volatile and semivolatile compounds. Because the foams may not be able to advance great distances in the vertical direction because of pressure limitations, successive stages or blankets of foam injections could be attempted with sophisticated well designs. In situ bioremediation could then provide a "polishing" step in which residual contaminants and surfactants would be biodegraded.

ACKNOWLEDGMENT

Work supported by the U.S. Department of Energy, Assistant Secretary for Conservation and Renewable Energy, under Contract W-31-109-Eng-38.

REFERENCES

Enzien, M. V., J. X. Bouillard, D. L. Michelsen, R. W. Peters, J. R. Frank, R. E. Botto, and G. Cody. 1994. *Remediation of NAPL-Contaminated Soil/Groundwater by Using Foams.* DOE technical report, TTP NO. CH-2-4-10-93. Argonne National Laboratory, Argonne, IL.

Jenkins, K. B., D. L. Michelsen, and J. T. Novak. 1993. "Application of Oxygen Microbubbles for In Situ Biodegradation of *p*-Xylene-Contaminated Groundwater in a Soil Column." *Biotechnol. Prog. 9:* 394-400.

Kaster, J .A., D. L. Michelsen, and W. H. Velander. 1989. "Increased Oxygen Transfer in Yeast Fermenter Using a Microbubble Dispersion." *Appl. Biochem. & Biotechnol. 24/25:* 469-484.

Longe, T. A. 1989. "Application of Oxygen Microbubbles in Groundwater Oxygenation to Enhance Biodegradation of Hydrocarbons in Soil Systems." Ph.D. Thesis, Virginia Polytechnic Institute and State University, Blacksburg, VA.

Michelsen, D. L., D. A. Wallis, and F. Sebba. 1984a. "In Situ Biological Oxidation of Hazardous Organics." *Environ. Prog. 3(2):* 103-107.

Michelsen, D. L., D. A. Wallis, and F. Sebba. 1984b. "The Use of a Microdispersion of Air in Water for In Situ Treatment of Hazardous Organics." *Proc. Fifth National Conf. on Management of Uncontrolled Hazardous Waste Sites.* Washington, DC. pp. 398-403.

Michelsen, D. L., D. A. Wallis, and S. R. Lavinder. 1985. "In Situ Biodegradation of Dispersed Organics Using a Microdispersion of Air in Water." *Proc. Sixth National Conf. on Management of Uncontrolled Hazardous Waste Sites.* Washington, DC. pp. 291-299.

Phelps, T. J., D. Ringelberg, D. Hedrick, J. Davis, C. B. Fliermans, and D. C. White. 1988. "Microbial Biomass and Activities Associated with Subsurface Environments Contaminated with Chlorinated Hydrocarbons." *Geomicrobiology Journal 6:* 157-170.

Rittmann, B. E., E. Seagren, B. A. Wrenn, A. J. Valocchi, C. Ray, and L. Raskin. 1994. *In Situ Bioremediation,* 2nd. ed. Noyes Publications, Park Ridge, NJ.

Riviello, A. E., M. Lotfi, F. Sebba, and D. L. Michelsen. 1991. "Cold Separation of Bitumen from Tar Sands." In *Tar Sands and Oil Upgrading Technology, AIChE Symposium Series,* 87(282): 10-15.

Roy, C., K. T. Valsaraj, and A. Tamayo. 1992. "Comparison of Soil Washing Using Conventional Surfactant Solutions and Colloidal Gas Aphron Suspensions." *Separation Science and Technology 27(12):* 1555-1568.

Sebba, F. 1985. "An Improved Generator for Micron-Sized Bubbles." *Chemistry & Industry Feb. 4(3):* 91-92.

Use of Microbubble Dispersion for Soil Scouring

Timothy A. Longe, Jacques X. Bouillard,
and Donald L. Michelsen

ABSTRACT

Techniques for generating a microbubble dispersion (colloidal gas aphrons) have been developed. The microbubbles typically consist of 60 to 70% dispersion of 55-μ microbubbles in water, although dispersion up to 90 to 95% can be generated continuously. A number of laboratory soil column flow studies have been completed to define the potential of using these microbubbles to scour and release dispersed organics for subsequent pumping and removal or to enhance in situ degradation. The higher viscosity foams flow forward and fill up larger channels. The pressure drop builds up in the channel, resulting in foam flow into less accessible spill zones. In scouring hexadecane from columns containing 50- to 70-mesh sand, following a water preflush, up to 80% of the remaining organic could be flushed using a 70% CGA quality (70% air, 30% liquid). The technique was less effective at lower CGA quality. In general, a surfactant concentration of 1,000 to 5,000 ppm was needed to generate the microbubbles. Microbubble scouring can be 3 to 6 times more effective than surfactant flushing at the same surfactant concentration and flowrate. Channeling and poor sweep encountered with surfactant flushing are not expected to occur in microbubble scouring. But three-dimensional pilot and field testing is required for substantiation. However, the problem of pressure drop required to pump microbubbles into soil with low permeability could limit its application. Flow modeling has been initiated with the ultimate goal of determining the limits for field use.

INTRODUCTION

Attempts have been made to overcome the soil/organic bond by using surfactant solutions (Texas Research Institute 1982; Ellis et al. 1985; Nash 1987; Riviello et al. 1991; Peters et al. 1992). Although most of these attempts were relatively successful in the laboratory, in situ soil washing under field conditions was unsuccessful largely because of poor areal sweep efficiency. The surfactant solution would channel through the path of least resistance that probably contained the least contaminant.

The use of a microbubble dispersion offers a way of lowering the interfacial tension between the organic and reservoir water and contaminant while at the same time providing the viscous forces needed for efficient areal sweep.

The microbubble dispersion used in this work is a collection of spherical, micron-sized gas bubbles dispersed in an aqueous surfactant solution with a volumetric gas fraction (quality) of, at most, 0.74. The bubbles generally do not exceed 100 μ in diameter. Sebba proposed the name colloidal gas aphrons (CGAs) for this type of gas-liquid dispersion (Sebba and Barnett 1981). Microbubbles made from air and oxygen have been explored and tested, and have been shown to enhance flotation, mass transfer in bioreactors, and in situ biodegradation (O'Palko et al. 1992; Kaster et al. 1989; Michelsen and Lotfi 1990).

EXPERIMENTAL MATERIALS AND PROCEDURES

The experimental setup for the scouring studies is illustrated in Figure 1. It consists of a CGA generation system, a sand packed column and an effluent recovery system (Longe 1989).

CGAs are produced using the spinning disc generator, a mechanical gas-liquid contactor (Sebba 1985). The surfactant used was sodium dodecylbenzene sulfonate (NaDBS), an anionic surfactant with an average molecular weight of 348.

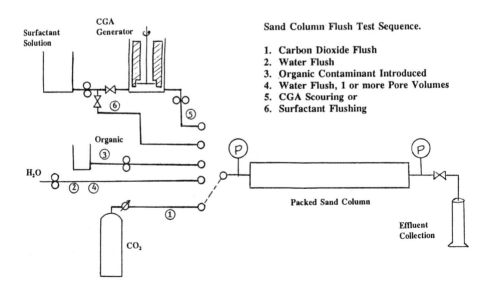

FIGURE 1. Setup for CGA flushing studies.

The CGA temperature was maintained at 28°C (82.4°F) for all tests, whereas the surfactant concentration, CGA quality, and flowrate were varied as necessary.

The sand-packed column consisted of Corning Pyrex™ glass column 30.8 cm long, with a 3.81 cm inside diameter (volume 351-cm³) and 0.44-cm-thick walls. End fittings were made from ¼-in. (0.6-cm) aluminum blocks. Two types of testing sand were used for this work; 20 to 30 mesh (841 to 595 µm) and 50 to 70 mesh (297 to 210 µm). Graduated tubes (25 mL) were used to collect the liquid effluents. A concentrated solution of aluminum sulfate was used as a de-emulsifier. Hexadecane, a diesel oil surrogate, and other organics were used for the parameter studies.

For a given test run, the saturated sand-packed column flushed to eliminate entrapped air was flooded with hexadecane to irreducible water content at a feed rate of 10 mL/min. Subsequently, the column was flooded with at least 1 pore volume of water at the rate of 2 mL/min. Less than 0.7 pore volume was needed to achieve water breakthrough. The amount of organic displaced was measured, and, hence, the residual organic in the column was determined.

CGAs of desired quality were generated and pumped into the column using a peristaltic pump. At least 6 pore volumes of CGAs were injected for each test. The effluent was collected in 25-mL graduated test tubes and the organic recovery was determined. In some instances an oil emulsion was formed, particularly when high surfactant concentrations were used. A drop or two of concentrated aluminum sulfate solution was used as the de-emulsifier. The variables examined were surfactant concentration, CGA quality, CGA feed rate, type of contaminant, and soil type. The surfactant concentration was varied between 10.0 g/L and 0.5 g/L. The CGA quality ranged from 0.7 to 0.4, and the CGA feed rate was between 0.1 cm³/s and 0.8 cm³/s.

RESULTS AND DISCUSSION

Table 1 shows a summary of the column scouring studies. Figure 2 is a typical good removal curve, i.e., percentage of residual organic (organic left after water flooding) that was removed versus pore volume of CGAs injected. The first set of CGA bubbles that entered the column readily coalesced on contact with the oil phase. The duration of this coalescent phase decreased with increase in surfactant concentration, CGA quality, and CGA flowrate. As the rate of bubble coalescence decreased, CGAs formed a displacement front that moved across the column rather uniformly, sweeping the organic phase along. The frontal advance was accompanied by a rise in overall pressure drop through the column.

In general, very little oil was removed with the first one to two pore volumes of CGAs. As the CGA front approached the end of the column, the total organic recovery rose up steadily and then leveled off as the combined foam/contaminant front existed the column. Usually, between 3 and 6 pore volumes of CGAs were needed to scour out the organic and reach the condition where further organic

TABLE 1. Hydrophobic organic displacement studies.

Test #	Soil Type[a]	Organic	ROIP[b] %PV[c]	Surfactant Conc. g/L	CGA Quality	CGA Feed Rate cm³/s	Removal %ROIP[b]
1	B	Hexadecane	20.1	10.0	0.5	0.40	43.2
2	B	"	23.5	10.0	0.6	0.40	50.3
3	B	"	30.9	10.0	0.7	0.40	79.5
4	B	"	30.9	5.0	0.7	0.40	75.5
5	B	"	30.1	2.5	0.7	0.40	66.1
6	B	"	27.6	1.0	0.7	0.40	5.9
7	B	"	23.6	0.5	0.7	0.40	5.0
8	B	"	33.1	2.5	0.7	0.10	4.8
9	B	"	31.6	2.5	0.7	0.20	36.0
10	B	"	31.6	2.5	0.7	0.60	66.0
11	B	"	30.1	2.5	0.7	0.80	61.2
12	B	"	31.6	2.5	0.0	0.40	18.8
13	A	"	35.8	2.5	0.0	0.40	10.2
14	A	"	30.9	10.0	0.7	0.40	78.7
15	A	"	31.7	2.5	0.7	0.40	67.7
16	A	"	32.5	2.5	0.7	0.20	44.8
17	A	"	32.5	2.5	0.7	0.10	8.5
18	A	"	31.7	2.5	0.7	0.60	87.7
19	A	Hexane	30.9	2.5	0.7	0.40	78.9
20	A	Decane	32.5	2.5	0.7	0.40	80.5
21	A	Tetradecane	35.0	2.5	0.7	0.40	88.8
22	A	Hexachloro-1,3-butadiene	27.6	2.5	0.7	0.40	83.2
23	A	Hexadecane	35.8	2.5	0.7	0.40	10.2

(a) Soil Type A is 20-30 mesh Ottawa testing sand. Soil Type B is 50-70 mesh Ottawa testing sand.
(b) ROIP is residual oil in place or oil left after water flooding.
(c) PV is pore volume, 136.3 cm³.

removal was minimized. This also corresponded to the complete breakthrough of the CGA-gas front. Such a high volume of CGAs was needed because of the problem of bubble coalescence. In some of the tests, up to 80% of the residual organic content (organic left in the column after flooding with water) was removed by scouring with CGAs.

Effect of Surfactant Concentration

The surfactant concentration has a significant effect on the organic removal efficiency from soil with CGAs. Using NaDBS, it was found that at concentrations less or equal to 1.0 g/L, the removal efficiency was about 5%. When the surfactant concentration was raised to 2.5 g/L, the removal efficiency rose to 66%. Further increase in surfactant concentration to 5.0 g/L and 10.0 g/L resulted in 76 and 80% removal efficiency, a slight improvement over the 2.5 g/L concentration. The high level of residual organic concentration in soil (about 30 mg organic per gram of soil) contributed significantly to CGA destabilization and reduced removal efficiency.

Effect of CGA Quality

Increasing CGA quality from 0.5 to 0.6 increased removal efficiency from 43 to 50% compared to an 80% removal efficiency for a CGA quality of 0.70. This trend corresponds to that observed on the effect of quality on the rheological properties of CGAs (Longe 1989). CGAs behave as a Bingham plastic fluid at quality below 0.6 and as a pseudoplastic fluid above this quality range. This result is a jump in CGA apparent viscosity at high quality. As CGAs become more viscous, the capillary number decreases. As a result, the removal efficiency increases.

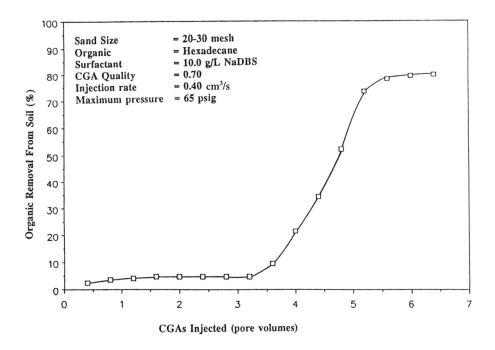

FIGURE 2. Hexadecane removal versus volume of CGAs injected.

Thus, at higher CGA quality, the CGA mobility decreases (higher viscosity) and these less mobile CGA bubbles increase the viscous action and scouring. In addition, at high CGA quality the improved scouring action results in a higher residual gas saturation in the treated soils (Longe 1989).

Effect of Feed Rate

Using a 20 to 30 mesh sand and hexadecane, organic removal was found to be linearly related to the feed rate of CGAs. At 0.10 cm^3/s, removal efficiency was found to be 8.5% compared to 88% removal efficiency at 0.60 cm^3/s. With a 50 to 70 mesh sand a similar linear performance was observed, except that removal efficiency soon leveled off at 0.40 cm^3/s with an efficiency of about 65%. The leveling off of removal efficiency for the less-permeable medium was due to the problem of maintaining the high flowrate at high pressure drop. The flowrate gradually decreased during the experiment as the pressure drop rose above the pump's design limit of about 35 psi.

Comparison with Surfactant Flushing

Runs 12 and 13 on Table 1 using 2.5 g/L of surfactant solution were compared to runs 5, 10, 11, and 15 using the same solution generated into a high quality CGA. CGA scouring (removal % ROIP on Table 1) was 3 to 6 times more effective in removing residual organic content than was surfactant flushing alone. Unlike with CGAs, removal occurred only with the first two pore volumes injected during surfactant flushing. In surfactant flushing, the capillary number is increased only by decreasing the interfacial tension and not by increasing the viscous forces of the displacing fluid. The surfactant solution cannot exert a sufficient driving force on the oil phase. Once breakthrough occurs, the surfactant solution would channel through, following the path of least resistance. CGA scouring both decreases interfacial tension but also increases viscous forces. It lowers the interfacial tension through the action of its surfactant molecules. In addition, the capillary number is further increased through an increase in effective viscosity of the displacing fluid. As a result, a higher displacement efficiency is possible.

To achieve a high removal efficiency with surfactant flushing, a much higher surfactant concentration than with CGA is required. According to studies at the Texas Research Institute (1982) and by Ellis and coworkers (1985), up to 40 g/L surfactant solution may be required. Because of such high levels of surfactant, emulsions are often formed in surfactant flushing making organic recovery more difficult.

Finally, a series of CGA flow tests using 65% CGA quality were conducted in a Plexiglas™ visualization cell containing a 15-in.-long by 10-in.-wide by 0.25-in.-deep (38-cm-long by 25-cm-wide by 0.6-cm-deep) sand bed. CGAs were introduced along the entire 10-in. (25-cm) edge with removal over the entire opposite 10-in. edge. Using a dyed surfactant solution for CGA flow characteristics, the leading water dye front trailed by the CGA front was followed. Good areal sweep efficiency with no channeling was observed. Upon breakthrough, the gas phase in the void volume was as high as 85 to 95%. The gaseous phase is held back because the gas/liquid relative permeability, which is in part a function of the microbubble size and soil characteristics. These data have now been modeled with the fronts correlated as a function of the overall pressure drop. This represents the first step toward a generated microbubble flow model.

SUMMARY

The effectiveness of CGAs as a scouring agent depends on the formation of a stable CGA front that is capable of mobilizing the trapped organic compounds in a porous media. CGA's scouring ability is favored by relatively high surfactant concentrations (above the critical micelle concentration [CMC] for ionic surfactants), high CGA flowrate, and high CGA quality. In general, a surfactant concentration of 1,000 to 5,000 ppm is needed to generate the microbubbles. Below these levels, CGA is destabilized by the relatively high organic content. With the lower level of organics found at most contaminated sites, it may be possible to lower the level of surfactant required for scouring.

Microbubble scouring can be 3 to 6 times more effective than surfactant flushing at the same surfactant concentration and flowrate. And unlike the latter, emulsification does not often occur with microbubble scouring. The problem of channeling and poor sweep often encountered with surfactant flushing is not expected to occur in microbubble scouring but field testing is necessary for substantiation. The problem of pressure drop required to pump microbubbles into soil with low permeability could be the challenge during a field pilot study.

Follow-up studies on the flow characteristics of microbubbles though various soil types have just been reported (Enzien et al. 1994). CGA pressure versus flowrate relationships were shown to be highly dependent on the soil matrix permeability and the surfactant type and concentration used for CGA generation and quality. The key is now to explore a three-dimensional model for CGA delivery and scouring based on results to date to include the impact of delivering smaller microbubbles, and, thereafter, conduct an actual pilot remediation or limited field injection/recovery study to verify the predictive model.

REFERENCES

Ellis, W. D., J. R. Payne, and G. D. McNabb. 1985. *Treatment of Contaminated Soils with Aqueous Surfactants.* EPA/600/2-85/129, 84 pp. [NTIS Order No. PB 86-122561/AS].

Enzien, M. V., J. X. Bouillard, D. L. Michelsen, R. W. Peters, J. R. Frank, R. E. Botto, and G. Cody. 1994. *Remediation of NAPL-Contaminated Soil/Groundwater by Using Foams.* DOE Technical Report TTP No CH-2-4-10-93, Argonne National Laboratory, Argonne, IL.

Kaster, J. A., D. L. Michelsen, and W. H. Velander. 1989. "Increased Oxygen Transfer in Yeast Fermenter Using a Microbubble Dispersion." *Applied Biochemistry & Biotechnology* 24/25: 469-484.

Longe, T. A. 1989. "Colloidal Gas Aphrons, Generation, Flow Characterization, and Application in Soil and Groundwater Decontamination." Ph.D. Dissertation, Virginia Tech, Blacksburg, VA.

Michelsen, D. L., and Lotfi. 1990. "Oxygen Microbubbles for In-Situ Bioremediation: Possible Field Scenario." In H. Freeman (Ed.), *Innovative Hazardous Waste Treatment Systems*, pp. 131-142. Technomic Publishing Company, Inc., Lancaster, PA.

Nash, J. A. 1987. *Field Studies of In Situ Soil Washing.* Report Performed for U.S. Environmental Protection Agency, EPA-600/2-87/110, NTIS PB88-146808.

O'Palko, B. A., S. D. West, D. L. Michelsen, David L. Michelsen, and K. Rodarte. 1992. "The Effects of a Microbubble Dispersion on the Performance of a POTW Dissolved Air Flotation System." *47th Annual Purdue University Industrial Waste Conference*, pp. 327-336.

Peters, R. W., C. D. Monternagno, L. Shern, and B. A. Lewis. 1992. "Surfactant Screening of Diesel-Contaminated Soil." *Hazardous Waste and Hazardous Material* 9(2): 113-116.

Riviello, A. E., M. Lotfi, F. Sebba and D. L. Michelsen. 1991. "Cold Bitumen from Tar Sands." *Tar Sands and Oil Upgrading Technology, AIChE Symposium Series 87*: 282, pp. 10-15.

Sebba, F. 1985. "An Improved Generator for Micron-Sized Bubbles." *Chemistry & Industry* Feb. 4(3):91-92.

Sebba, F., and Barnett. 1981. "Separations Using Colloidal Gas Aphrons." In *Proceedings of the Second World Congress of Chemical Engineering IV*:27.

Texas Research Institute. 1982. *Test Results of Surfactant Enhanced Gasoline Recovery in Large-Scale Model Aquifer.* Prepared for the American Petroleum Institute.

Integrated Dissolved Gas Management for Contaminated Aquifer In Situ Bioremediation

Charles J. Gantzer

ABSTRACT

Integrated management is the simultaneous management of a target gas concentration and the total gas pressure (the sum of the partial pressures of all dissolved gases) in an aqueous stream. A membrane-based integrated gas management system is presented that allows the aqueous delivery of elevated dissolved concentrations of gaseous microbial substrates (e.g., oxygen, methane, and hydrogen) to an aquifer with no potential for bubble formation. The delivery of gaseous microbial substrates can enhance the in situ bioremediation of a contaminated aquifer. Bubble formation in an aquifer is undesirable for three reasons: substrate is wasted, gases migrate off site, and the aquifer clogs with bubbles. Integrated gas management is a two-step process. The first step consists of the nonselective removal of dissolved gases to reduce the total gas pressure of the injection water. The second step consists of dissolving the desired gaseous substrate. The resulting water has an elevated concentration of the gaseous substrate and a total gas pressure less than the absolute hydrostatic pressure at the delivery point for the aquifer. A membrane-based integrated gas management system has operated for 9 months at a former manufactured gas plant site and delivers 5 gpm of oxygenated water (25 mg O_2/L) to a silt-clay aquifer at a total gas pressure of 1 atmosphere.

INTRODUCTION

The gaseous microbial substrates oxygen, methane, and hydrogen have several economic and operational advantages over alternative substrates in the in situ bioremediation of aquifers contaminated with petroleum hydrocarbons and chlorinated aliphatic hydrocarbons. For example, in the bioremediation of petroleum-contaminated aquifers, oxygen is $^1/_{40}$ the cost of hydrogen peroxide and $^1/_{10}$ the cost of nitrate per electron equivalent. Also, in the aerobic cometabolism of trichloroethene (TCE), methane is $^1/_{500}$ the cost of phenol, $^1/_{13}$ the cost of toluene, and ½ the cost of propane per electron equivalent.

However, the high Henry's law constants (atm/mole fraction) and the resulting low water solubilities of the gaseous substrates limit the amount of gas that can be dissolved into water. Because the biological demand for a gaseous substrate in an aquifer can exceed the water solubility of the gas, the mass flux of a gaseous substrate can determine the rate of aquifer bioreclamation. The mass flux of a gaseous substrate into an aquifer is the product of its water-phase concentration and the water flowrate. Because the amount of water that can be pumped through an aquifer is determined by hydrogeology and the number of injection and recovery wells that can economically be placed at a contaminated site, gas dissolution devices that generate high dissolved gas concentrations often are desirable.

Need for Gas Removal

In an effort to maximize dissolved gas concentrations, the total gas pressure of the water (i.e., the sum of the partial pressures of the dissolved gases) injected into an aquifer may exceed the ambient pressure and result in the formation of bubbles. For example, the total gas pressure (TGP) of injected water at the groundwater table must be less than 1 atmosphere to assure no bubble formation. The TGP of water delivered to an aquifer via an infiltration gallery must also be below 1 atm or bubbles will form. Bubble formation in an aquifer or an infiltration gallery is undesirable for several reasons. First, the migration of gaseous substrate bubbles from the aquifer to the vadose zone represents wastage of substrate. A second reason that bubbles are undesirable is that the bubbles of methane and hydrogen migrate into the vadose zone, and eventually to confined spaces where an explosive atmosphere can be created (e.g., sump pump wells and basements), which represents a safety and liability concern. Third, the formation of bubbles in "tight" aquifers (e.g., silty aquifers) can prevent water passage by filling the voids between particles. Clogging an aquifer in this manner can make the in situ bioremediation of an aquifer technically impossible.

Nitrogen gas can be removed from the water prior to dissolution of the gaseous substrate to assure maximum delivery of a gaseous substrate to an aquifer while maintaining a TGP less than the ambient pressure. For example, assume that the bubble-free delivery of 25 mg O_2/L at the water table is desired. As illustrated in Figure 1, water in equilibrium with the air has 0.79 atm N_2 (16.7 mg N_2/L at 15°C) and 0.21 atm O_2 (10.3 mg O_2/L at 15°C). If the oxygen concentration were increased to 25 mg O_2/L, then the partial pressure of oxygen would be 0.51 atm. The total gas pressure would be 1.3 atm because the partial pressure of nitrogen has not changed. The ambient pressure at the water table is 1 atm. Bubbles will form when the oxygenated water is released at the water table, because the total gas pressure is greater than the ambient pressure. The potential for bubble formation would be removed if the water prior to oxygen addition had been degassed, reducing the partial pressure of nitrogen from 0.79 atm to 0.49 atm (a 38% reduction in nitrogen partial pressure). The resulting

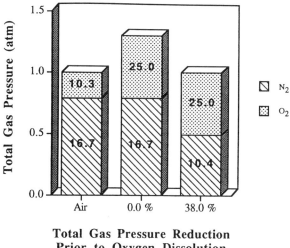

Total Gas Pressure Reduction
Prior to Oxygen Dissolution

FIGURE 1. Total gas pressure (TGP) for water in equilibrium with air at 15°C, for water with its oxygen concentration increased to 25 mg O_2/L without degassing, and for water that had a 38% reduction in total gas pressure prior to the oxygen concentration being increased to 25 mg O_2/L. The numbers on the graph's columns refer to the dissolved oxygen and nitrogen concentrations in mg/L.

total gas pressure after degassing and increasing the oxygen concentration to 25 mg O_2/L is 1 atm. Because the total gas pressure (1 atm) does not exceed the ambient pressure (1 atm), no bubbles will form.

Integrated Gas Management

Integrated gas management results in the delivery of a specified gaseous substrate concentration at a specified total gas pressure. Integrated gas management is a two-step process consisting of

- The nonselective removal of dissolved gases from water
- The dissolution of the desired gaseous substrate.

The goal of integrated gas management in the in situ bioremediation of contaminated aquifers is the guaranteed delivery of elevated gaseous substrate(s) concentrations. The delivery of elevated gaseous substrate concentrations only can be guaranteed when the total gas pressure is less than the ambient pressure in the aquifer, i.e., there is no potential for bubble formation. As illustrated in Figure 2, the partial reduction in the TGP obtained by degassing allows additional oxygen, methane, or a stoichiometric mixture of methane and oxygen (1 mole CH_4 to 1.6 moles O_2) to be added to the water without an increase in bubble formation potential. The elevated concentrations of gaseous substrates can accelerate the rate of aquifer bioremediation.

MEMBRANE-BASED
GAS-MANAGEMENT TECHNOLOGIES

The integrated gas management system installed at a former manufactured gas plant used membrane-based gas-transfer technologies in the reduction of total gas pressure and in the dissolution of oxygen. The membrane gas-dissolution and gas-removal technologies are described below.

Membran Corporation's gas-dissolution technology (U.S. Patent 5,034,164 with other patents pending) can generate high dissolved gas concentrations. The direct (bubbleless) dissolution of gases is accomplished in pipes (modules) containing thousands of sealed, hollow, gas-permeable fibers that are filled with pure gases under pressure. A schematic diagram of a Membran module is provided in Figure 3. The small diameter of the fibers (about 300 μ) means that a large surface area of membrane can be installed in a module. The sealed ends

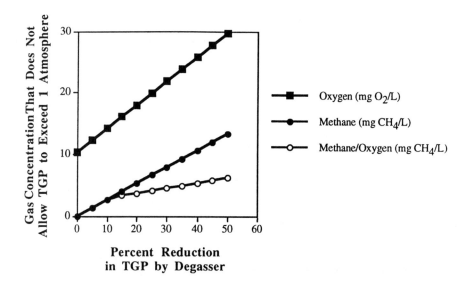

FIGURE 2. Gas concentrations that can be obtained without exceeding a TGP of 1 atmosphere when the TGP in influent line to a gas-dissolution device is reduced by the indicated percentage. The curves assume a water temperature of 15°C and that the initial water is in equilibrium with the atmosphere. The "Methane/Oxygen" line indicates the methane concentration that can be obtained assuming that 1.6 moles of O_2 must be simultaneously dissolved with each mole of CH_4 dissolved (the theoretical stoichiometric ratio for methanotroph growth).

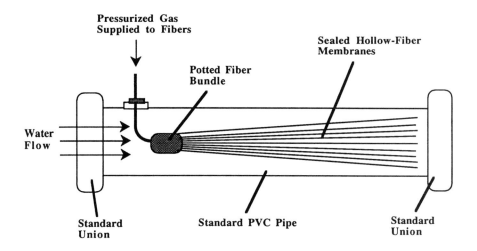

FIGURE 3. Schematic diagram of a Membran bubbleless gas-dissolution device.

of the fibers are not joined and are free to move independently in the turbulent water flow found inside the pipe. The gas diffuses across the fiber walls and dissolves directly into the water that flows over the outer surface of the fiber membrane. For a given fiber packing density and fiber length, gas-dissolution performance is controlled by changing the water flowrate (influences water-boundary-layer thickness) and the gas pressure (alters driving force for gas dissolution). The ability of a single membrane gas-dissolution module to dissolve oxygen, methane, and hydrogen is provided in Figure 4. Higher dissolved gas concentrations can be obtained by operating modules in series, because performance is almost additive. For example, one Membran BMA-31-2 module will increase the oxygen concentration by about 20 mg/L at a water flowrate of 35 gpm. Two modules in series will increase the oxygen concentration by about 39 mg/L. Three modules will increase the concentration by about 57 mg/L.

Membran Corporation's vacuum degassing technology (patents pending) uses sealed, microporous, hollow-fiber membranes. The degassing modules have the same components as the gas-dissolution module illustrated in Figure 3, except that the lumens of the fibers are exposed to a vacuum (absolute pressure near 50 torr) instead of being pressurized with gas.

DUBUQUE, IOWA, INSTALLATION

A membrane-based integrated gas-management system was installed at a former manufactured gas plant site in Dubuque, Iowa, to stimulate the bioremediation of a contaminated aquifer by adding oxygen to the injection water. The aquifer was contaminated with polycyclic aromatic hydrocarbons and was described as anaerobic prior to oxygen delivery (Nelson et al. 1995). The delivery of 25 mg O_2/L into an aquifer at a flowrate of 5 gpm at 15°C with no potential for off-gassing or bubble formation was specified. The gas-removal step consisted of a recirculating membrane-based vacuum-degassing system. The oxygen-dissolution step consisted of a recirculating membrane-based gas-dissolution system. A schematic diagram of the installed integrated gas-management system is provided in Figure 5.

Dissolved gases were removed by four membrane gas-removal modules operated in series and installed in a recycle loop around a 275-gallon tank. The modules consisted of 4-in.-diameter (10-cm-diameter) PVC pipe shells filled with 4,000 sealed-end hollow-fiber microporous membranes. With a feed flowrate of 5 gpm, a recycle flowrate of 70 gpm, a water temperature of 15°C, and a vacuum of 26 in. (66 cm) of mercury applied to the lumens of the sealed fibers, the gas-removal system was capable of reducing total gas pressures by at least 50%. This level of gas removal ensured that, when the oxygen concentration was increased to 25 mg/L in the second step of the process, the total gas pressure did not exceed 1 atmosphere (i.e., there was no potential for gas bubble formation in the oxygenated water).

The oxygen dissolution step was accomplished using a single membrane module installed in a recycle loop. The overflow from the gas-removal tank flowed by gravity into a second 275-gal (1,040-L) tank. A single 2-inch-diameter

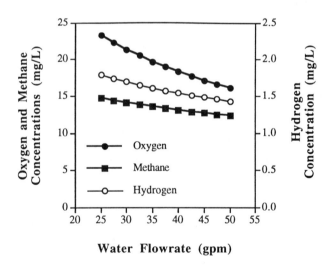

Water Flowrate (gpm)

FIGURE 4. Clean-water dissolved effluent gas concentrations obtained with a 2-in.-diameter (5-cm-diameter) module containing 3,100 composite hollow-fiber membranes that have a total fiber active length of 60 in. (152 cm). The above curves assume a water temperature of 15°C, influent gas concentrations of 0 (zero) mg/L, and a gas pressure of 75 psig applied to the fibers.

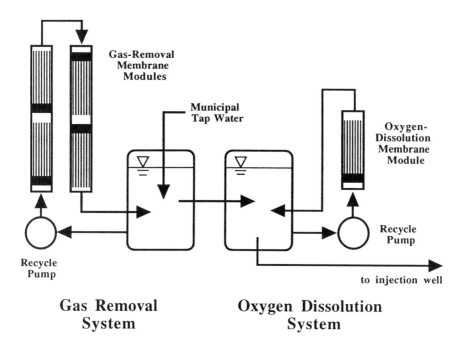

FIGURE 5. Schematic diagram of a membrane-based integrated gas-management system that delivers a 5-gpm water flow with 25 mg O_2/L at 15°C with a total gas pressure less than 1 atmosphere.

(5-cm-diameter) membrane gas-dissolution module containing of 3,100 sealed-end hollow-fiber composite membranes was installed in a 40-gpm recycle loop around the second 275-gal (1,040-L) tank. The lumens of the sealed fibers were pressurized with pure oxygen. Oxygen was supplied by gas oxygen cylinders, which were replaced every 2 weeks. The oxygen pressure applied to the fibers was adjusted such that the effluent from the gas-dissolution tank was 25 mg O_2/L. The overflow from the oxygen-dissolution tank flowed by gravity to the injection well.

The integrated gas management system has operated for 9 months. The dissolved oxygen plume has not reached a monitoring well located 25 ft (7.6 m) downgradient of the injection well (Nelson et al. 1995). This suggests a high oxygen demand, clogging of the aquifer with mineral or biological solids such that the oxygenated water will not reach the monitoring well, or both. However, water table mounding at the injection well has been minimal (Nelson et al. 1995), which suggests clogging is not a problem.

The system has consistently maintained a TGP of 1 atmosphere and a 25 mg/L oxygen concentration in the injection water, except for two mechanical problems. First, one of the degassing membrane modules started to draw water after a week of operation. The water caused the positive displacement vacuum pump to fail. Both the membrane module and vacuum pump were replaced.

Second, the long-term of passage of water vapor through the replacement vacuum pump resulted in corrosion of the piston seals and the pump's valves. The vacuum pump was replaced with a liquid-ring vacuum pump. The last 5 months of operation has been maintenance free, except for the replacement of the oxygen cylinder every 2 weeks. Membrane fouling or membrane fatigue has not been a problem.

The estimated daily operating cost for the membrane gas management system is $2.75, assuming electricity costs $0.05/kW·h and oxygen from gas cylinders costs $0.40/lb ($0.40/0.45 kg). Even with the over-sized pumps and the expensive source of oxygen, this cost is similar to the estimated chemical feed cost for supplying 25 mg O_2/L as hydrogen peroxide ($2.50/day). Improved pump sizing and the on-site generation of oxygen would substantially reduce operating costs per unit of contaminant biodegraded.

DISCUSSION

A membrane-based integrated gas management system has operated continuously at a former manufactured gas plant for 9 months with no apparent loss in performance due to membrane fouling or membrane fatigue. The gas management system consistently maintained a TGP of 1 atmosphere and an oxygen concentration of 25 mg/L in the municipal tap water being used as injection water. The successful pilot-scale demonstration of integrated gas management system at the Dubuque site suggests that the concept is valid for the management of methane for the aerobic cometabolism of trichloroethylene and hydrogen for the anaerobic reductive dehalogenation of chlorinated organic compounds.

REFERENCE

Nelson, G.L.S., B. Harrison, D. J. Fetter, and D. E. Richard. 1995. "In Situ Bioremediation: Confined Aquifer Contaminated with MGP Wastes." In R. E. Hinchee, J. A. Kittel, and H. J. Reisinger (Eds.), *Applied Bioremediation of Petroleum Hydrocarbons*. Battelle Press, Columbus, OH. pp. 165-173.

Alternative Systems for In Situ Bioremediation: Enhanced Control and Contact

George K. Burke and Derek K. Rhodes

ABSTRACT

Much of the past emphasis on biological degradation remediation has been placed on culturing or enhancing microbes to consume contaminants within a soil or water matrix, and site contaminant characterization. This emphasis has demonstrated that microbes are effective degraders for a variety of contaminants, and at most sites, contaminant-degrading microbes are present within the subsurface. For sites where microbes are present, they typically are inefficient for in situ remediation without the appropriate environmental conditions. In situ bioremediation tends to be governed by the ability to cost effectively and rapidly distribute oxygen, microbes, nutrients, and/or surfactants throughout the subsurface soils while simultaneously maintaining a controlled subsurface environment. Adapted equipment has been used to efficiently permeate or saturate the contaminated soils with a combination of oxygen source material, nutrients, surfactants and/or microbial cultures. These technologies, combined with oxygen delivery and control systems, enhance bioremediation as a viable alternative for in situ remediation. These same systems can deliver oxidation chemistry to pretreat the soils. The development and utilization of a number of in situ bioremediation technologies with a demonstrated ability to enhance *contact* and *control* within the contaminated subsoils are discussed, focusing on Bioventing, BioSparge[SM], and Deep Soil Fracture BioInjection[TM].

INTRODUCTION

Biological remediation has been used for a number of years to remediate ex situ soils contaminated by organic compounds, with minor emphasis on in situ applications. This work has demonstrated that bioremediation offers the advantages of being cost effective, environmentally safe, field operational, and technically effective. The majority of the research and site application has been focused on site contaminant characterization, bacteria cultures for bioaugmentation, or the application of inorganic nutrients and/or electron acceptors for biostimulation.

The site characterizations or phase investigations typically performed provide site background information, contaminant identifications and concentrations, groundwater elevations, geologic profiles, and occasionally a microbial treatability study. Rarely do these studies provide the engineering properties of the soil or geologic units, which are essential for the physical technology application. This lack of thorough engineering investigation is reflected in the minor emphasis that has been placed on the two key factors for success: contact and control.

The original in situ bioremediation efforts were a spinoff from the pump-and-treat technology. The groundwater was extracted, enhanced with microbes and/or nutrients and reinjected in upgradient wells in a method commonly referred to as the Raymond Method (Rittmann et al. 1993). This in situ bioremediation technology was limited by biofouling of the well screens and was dependent on groundwater flow paths and velocity. The treatment systems did little to supply an electron acceptor (oxygen source) for the microbes (except at the well screen) and left the vadose zone virtually untreated. Although valuable in situ biomechanic information was obtained from these systems, site applications were costly and relatively unsuccessful, demonstrating the need to improve the delivery system.

BIOVENTING

Soil vapor extraction was increasingly used in the late 1980s and early 1990s to remediate unsaturated soils that were untreatable by conventional groundwater pump and treat methods. Scientists and engineers realized that positive displacement blowers provided a relatively inexpensive and continuous supply of oxygen essential for aerobic degradation through the subsurface soils. Soil vapor extraction is based on the principle of reducing the vapor pressure within the subsoils, which increases volatilization of certain compounds in the subsoils. The volatilized gases are then extracted from the subsoils with the same applied vacuum. Unfortunately, kerosenes, diesel fuels and other hydrocarbons contain nonvolatile components that cannot be volatilized and extracted. By reducing the air extraction or injection rates, it was found that drying effects were dramatically reduced and biological degradation significantly increased; therefore, successful in situ contaminant degradation would occur even on nonvolatile components. Another form of bioventing, commonly referred to as air sparging, involves injecting a low flow air pressure into the subsurface to increase the subsurface oxygen with minimal dispersion of the contaminants.

Bioventing requires a very low capital investment, with most sites using a single blower (venting or sparging) or a compressor (sparging) and a few wells located in the source of the product. For bioventing in municipal areas, off-gas treatment is usually required, which can be costly with time. Bioventing has proven quite effective for low concentration products within the unsaturated soils, for a wide variety of petroleum hydrocarbons (including nonvolatile components as found in diesel fuels), and in subsurface conditions conducive to appropriate distribution. Unfortunately, bioventing-sparging offers little control as to flow direction, which is required by most regulatory agencies, whereas bioventing-extraction requires treatment and monitoring of the off-gas, as is typical of soil vapor extraction. Bioventing also is unable to apply other essential microbial nutrients or to compensate for soil moisture loss, which is critical in arid regions or during dry seasons. Like soil vapor extraction, the technology is typically ineffective in silts and clays where the porosity and transmissivity is low. Although little up-front capital investment is required for the technology, the client typically spends much more monitoring the site for regulatory compliance than with other technologies.

BIOPURGE[SM]/BIOSPARGE[SM]

To provide enhanced subsurface control and maintain a consistent soil moisture profile, the BioPurge[SM]/BioSparge[SM] technology was developed in the late 1980s. This system was based on low-volume airflow as developed for bioventing, but with the adaption of the closed-loop concept. Soil vapor is extracted from wells typically placed at the perimeter of the contaminated soil area. The extracted vapor passes through the ex situ treatment unit, where high concentration volatiles are absorbed and biologically degraded. The vapor is enriched with oxygen, nutrients, and heat while maintaining or increasing the vapor humidity. The enriched vapor stream is then reinjected near the source of the contaminated soil area (Figure 1). When the injection is above the groundwater level the system is called BioPurge[SM]. When the vapor injection is below the groundwater level the system is called BioSparge[SM]. The technology therefore has no off-gassing and assuming a control oriented manifold infrastructure is installed, the system can control subsurface vapor migration, and regulate soil moisture, nutrients and oxygen. The technology has a greater up-front capital investment but the cost may be recovered in reduced sampling and monitoring, decreased treatment time, and ease of regulatory acceptance (Hobby 1993). Like bioventing, this technology alone has limited success in silts and clays.

A remediation project is currently under way where a treatment until has been modified to include an ozone generator in order to oxidize pentachlorophenol (PCP). Once the chlorine compounds are chemically cleaved from the PCP compound, the by-products may be easily biologically degraded. This adaption of the technology greatly increases the range of contaminants that may be degraded.

DEEP SOIL FRACTURE BIOINJECTION™

The civil geotechnical construction industry has been using a variety of injection techniques to obtain intimate soil contact with stabilizing fluids, even in tight or fat clays. This same equipment has been modified for in situ bioremediation or chemical oxidation, depending upon the contaminant.

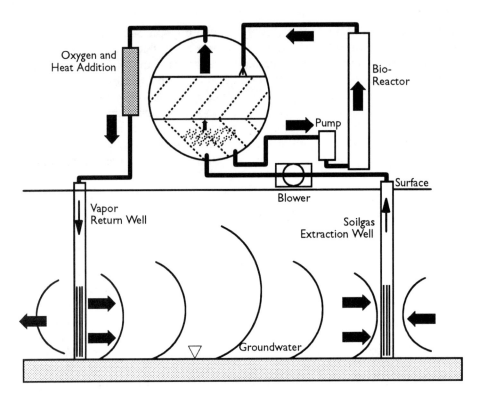

FIGURE 1. **BioSparge/BioPurge**^{SM} **schematic.**

The Deep Soil Fracture Bioinjection™ process achieves in situ bioremediation of hydrocarbons by the pressurized subsurface injection, in an overlapping grid pattern, of a slurry consisting of a predesigned mixture of controlled-release oxygen sources, controlled-release nutrient sources, and (if necessary) microbial cultures (Figure 2). This pattern assures complete coverage of the contaminated zone, increased permeability, and reduced time for diffusion. Successful in situ bioremediation relies on contacting sufficient nutrients, oxygen, and microbes with subsurface contaminated media.

Vapors moving through the soil in response to a vapor extraction system are preferentially transported through macropores, which constitute 0.0001% to 0.050% of the total soil volume (Morrison & McGowan 1993). Bioinjection allows in situ bioremediation to proceed independently of a formation's ability to transmit water or air by physically permeating the contaminated zone to access the macropores and micropores. The time required for remediation using Bioinjection™ is much shortened because the remedial time frame is driven by the microbial kinetics rather than diffusion and water/vapor transmissivity. To introduce these agents to the subsurface, hydraulic injection rigs are used. The injection rig consists of a rubber-tired, crawler-mounted or truck-mounted vehicle, with a hydraulically powered, vertical injection mast. One to four injection rods

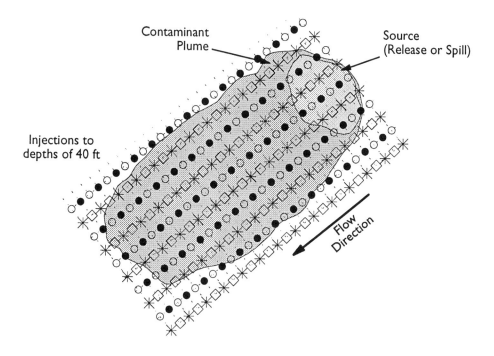

FIGURE 2. Injection pattern.

are mounted on the injection mast, spaced at 2 to 5 ft (0.6 to 1.5 m) centers (Figure 3). Existing injection equipment can treat soils to a depth of 40 ft (12 m). The 20% to 30% dry weight solids in slurry form is pumped under pressures of 50 to 300 psi (3.5 to 20.5 bar) during the downstroke stage of the injection mast. The slurry is continuously injected horizontally through each of the heads. A 2- to 2.5-ft (0.6- to 0.75-m) spacing is typically used to ensure complete permeation of the contaminated zone; therefore excellent transmittance of materials is achieved through even silt and clay soils.

As the design materials are injected into the soil mass, they will flow through the paths of least resistance. These generally will be desiccation cracks, fissures, sand lenses, and other geologic conditions that are predominant in most soil formations, i.e., the same pathways that the contaminants followed into the soil. Injection pressures ensure that materials are well distributed into the soil mass. This, coupled with a close grid spacing accomplished by making several injection passes over the site, ensures excellent distribution of the injected materials, especially along the pathways where contaminants are more concentrated. Also, because many of the injected materials are soluble, they will be further distributed into the soil mass through soil suction and diffusion mechanisms as the soil mass seeks to equilibrate the additional moisture that has been injected. The effectiveness of this system's ability to distribute the slurry is based on over 20 years of its use to treat expansive clays.

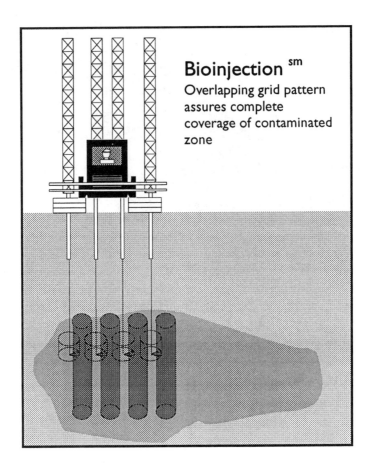

FIGURE 3. Injection equipment.

Bioinjection is an effective and economical remedial technology for the in situ treatment of hydrocarbon affected soils. The advantages of bioinjection are that the remedial time frame is much shorter than traditional in situ systems, no above-grade equipment is required after injection of materials, no operator attention is required after initial injection, remediation is somewhat independent of the formations ability to transmit water or air, biological agents will be deposited in the same cracks and fissures as the contaminants, remediation can occur in operating facilities and even below buildings, without interruption of activities, and there is reduced reliance on diffusion processes for contact.

SUMMARY

Biological degradation has been proven as an effective remediation tool in the laboratory and with ex situ remediation work. Only recently has more emphasis been placed on the two key factors required for in situ bioremediation, contact and control. The development of system technologies or utilization of existing equipment has demonstrated that bioremediation is a viable in situ alternative. A comparison follows (Table 1).

Bioventing demonstrated that successful contact bioremediation of the unsaturated permeable soils can be performed economically. The development of the BioSparge^{SM} technology has provided not only contact but control of bioremediation, both in the saturated and unsaturated permeable soils, which cost effectively meets the strict regulatory requirements. Bioinjection™, using proven equipment for a new application, is an example of a technology developed specifically to provide intimate contact and control in all soil types. The U.S. Department of Energy has recognized the necessity to develop a system that enhances contact and control and has initiated a research project to examine the effectiveness of the Bioinjection™ technology. Demonstrated field application has been completed, and the results will be available in late 1995.

TABLE 1. Technology comparisons.

	Bioventing	BioSparge^{SM} BioPurge^{SM}	Fracture Injection
Characteristics	Low-flow vapor extraction	Low-flow vapor extraction and reinjection	No vapor emissions
	Furnishes oxygen (in air)	No vapor emissions	Can furnish chemical oxygen
	Slight drying effect	Extracted vapor treated	Increases soil moisture
	Vapor treatment?	Injected vapor enriched	Increases permeability
	Above groundwater only	No soil drying	Increases transmissivity
		Flow controlled	Multiple injection likely
Target Contaminants	Light petroleum compounds	Light- to medium-weight petroleum compounds	Light- to medium-weight petroleum compounds
Target Soil Conditions	Porous sands and gravels	Sands, silty sands, gravels and some silts	All nonorganic soils: sands, silts, clays, and mixtures
			No gravels or cobbles
Approximate Cost	$15 to $30/cy	$20 to $50/cy	$20 to $50/cy

Further work is needed to refine these in situ bioremediation technologies or develop other systems for microbial degradation which provide contact and control in a variety of subsurface conditions. The first step in the development of the in situ bioremediation technologies is the need to examine both the engineering properties of remediation sites, and the ability to work within these boundaries. It is anticipated that a combination of these technologies will be utilized on many future sites.

REFERENCES

Hobby, M. M. 1993. "BioSparge^{SM} Kinetics," pp. 10-13. Las Vegas, NV.
Morrison, R., and E. McGowan. 1993. "Hydrocarbon Transport in Soils." *The National Environmental Journal*, (Sept./Oct.): 52-56.
Rittmann, B. E. (Chair, National Research Council). 1993. "In Situ Bioremediation — When Does It Work," pp. 50-59. National Academy Press, Washington, DC.

Pilot-Scale Feasibility of Petroleum Hydrocarbon-Contaminated Soil In Situ Bioremediation

Joseph F. Walker, Jr., and Angela B. Walker

ABSTRACT

An environmental project was conducted to evaluate in situ bioremediation of petroleum hydrocarbon-contaminated soils on Kwajalein Island, a U.S. Army Kwajalein Atoll base in the Republic of the Marshall Islands. Results of laboratory column studies determined that nutrient loadings stimulated biodegradation rates and that bioremediation of hydrocarbon-contaminated soils at Kwajalein was possible using indigenous microbes. The column studies were followed by an ~10-month on-site demonstration at Kwajalein to further evaluate in situ bioremediation and to determine design and operating conditions necessary to optimize the process. The demonstration site contained low levels of total petroleum hydrocarbons (diesel fuel) in the soil near the ground surface, with concentrations increasing to ~10,000 mg/kg in the soil near the groundwater. The demonstration utilized 12 in situ plots to evaluate the effects of various combinations of water, air, and nutrient additions on both the microbial population and the hydrocarbon concentration within the treatment plots as a function of depth from the ground surface.

INTRODUCTION

The U.S. Army Kwajalein Atoll (USAKA) base is located within the Republic of the Marshall Islands in the west-central Pacific Ocean. The Kwajalein Atoll consists of ~100 small islands and forms the largest enclosed lagoon in the world. Kwajalein Island, with a land surface area of ~1.2 mi² (3.1 km²), is the largest island within the atoll. It is located ~2,100 mi (~3,380 km) southwest of Honolulu, Hawaii, and 700 mi (1,127 km) north of the equator.

USAKA has significant petroleum hydrocarbon contamination resulting from years of military activities. Given the remoteness of the site, the lack of sophisticated on-site remediation or waste disposal facilities, and the amenability of petroleum hydrocarbons to biodegradation, USAKA requested, through the

Hazardous Waste Remedial Actions Program, that a project be initiated to evaluate the feasibility of using bioremediation for environmental restoration of contaminated sites within the atoll. In January 1991, a team of scientists and engineers from Oak Ridge National Laboratory, Oak Ridge Associated Universities, and The University of Tennessee was commissioned to conduct the project.

The first phase of the project was to conduct preliminary on-site characterization and biotreatability studies. The second phase was to determine the area of contamination, to determine soil and groundwater characteristics that could affect in situ bioremediation, and to collect and transport soil columns to the United States for laboratory studies. The third phase was to conduct biotreatability studies on the 25 soil columns, each 7.6 cm in diameter by 91 cm tall, which had been shipped to the United States. The results of these three phases of the project indicated that (1) indigenous microorganisms on Kwajalein were capable of degrading certain fractions of hydrocarbons, (2) bioremediation appeared to be a viable alternative for environmental restoration at Kwajalein, (3) the addition of air and nutrients would be required to increase the number of microorganisms in the areas of contamination and to enhance bioremediation, (4) high concentrations of weathered diesel fuel might be difficult to biodegrade, and (5) an on-site demonstration was required to further evaluate bioremediation for environmental restoration at Kwajalein, as well as to determine the design and operating conditions to optimize the process (Siegrist et al. 1991, Adler et. al 1992, Phelps & Siegrist 1993).

ON-SITE DEMONSTRATION

Twelve in situ plots, each 8 ft square, were distributed across the demonstration area. These plots were separated by a distance of at least 8 ft on all sides. A schematic diagram showing the design of the individual treatment plots is presented in Figure 1. As can be seen, the vadose zone was located in the first 3 ft (0.91 m) of soil, the capillary fringe was in the area from ~3 to 7 ft (0.91 to 2.13 m) below ground surface, and the saturated zone was below ~7 ft (2.13 m). The mean ground level was ~7 ft (2.13 m) below ground surface and the tidal fluctuation varied from ~1 to 2 ft (0.30 to 0.61 m). Each plot contained a centrally located sparge well for air delivery, a monitoring well for groundwater sampling, and vapor implants for soil gas collection. In addition, 15 monitoring wells were placed around the demonstration area for collection of groundwater samples.

The in situ plots were supplied different combinations of water, air, and nutrients, and samples were periodically taken and analyzed to determine the extent of biodegradation. The treatment regimens used during the demonstration were as follows: (1) plots 1 and 9 received periodic additions of air and water; (2) plots 2, 4, and 8 received periodic additions of air, water, and nutrients; (3) plots 3 and 7 received periodic additions of water; (4) plots 6, 10, and 12 received periodic additions of water and nutrients; and (5) plots 5 and 11 were control plots and received no additions. Plots receiving water and nutrients were fed every 6 h, and plots receiving air were fed in 4-h increments between

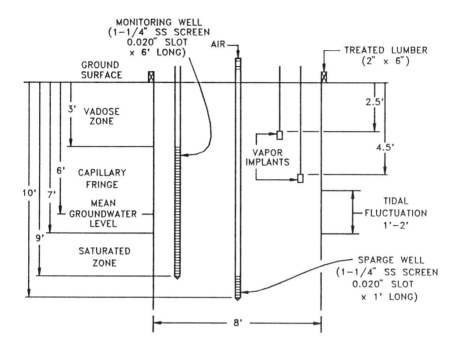

FIGURE 1. Cross section of an in situ test plot.

nutrient feedings. The analyses conducted during the demonstration, along with the frequency of the analyses, are presented in Table 1. Details of the design and the analytical methods have been provided in a previously issued report (Walker & Walker 1994).

Microbial abundance for each plot was assessed by plate count methods prior to startup (sample period 1) and for eight additional sampling periods (sample periods 2 through 9) thereafter at 4- to 6-week intervals. Results of these analyses indicated that the addition of nutrients alone did not increase the microbial population density above that of the control plots. However, the addition of air, with or without nutrient addition, resulted in a marked increase in the number of cell forming units (CFU). The number of CFU in the plots receiving air or air and nutrients increased by more than an order of magnitude over pre-startup concentrations, indicating the importance of supplying oxygen to the subsurface to develop and maintain microbial growth in the contaminated soils at Kwajalein. A plot of the mean CFU over the entire demonstration period for plots receiving water, air, and nutrients is presented in Figure 2 (Walker & Walker 1994).

Information regarding the microbial populations on Kwajalein was also determined by utilizing ester-linked phospholipid fatty acid (PLFA) analysis of the in situ soils. The mean cell population, as determined by PLFA analysis, comparing pre-startup plots, post-startup control plots, and post-startup amended plots (those receiving water, air, and nutrients) is presented in Figure 3. As can

TABLE 1. Sample analyses and sample frequency for the Kwajalein bioremediation demonstration.

Medium	Analysis	Sample Points (Total)	Frequency
Groundwater	Total chemical hydrocarbons Chemical oxygen demand pH Conductivity Nitrate Phosphate	Each of the monitoring wells (~23 total wells)	Before startup and every ~4 weeks thereafter
Groundwater[a]	Coliform	Designated monitoring wells	As necessary
Soil[a]	Total chemical hydrocarbons pH Hydrocarbons Moisture Microbes	Each of the in situ and ex situ plots (18 total plots)	Before startup and every ~4 weeks thereafter
Soil[b]	Phospholipid fatty acid metals	Designated in situ plots	Before startup and as necessary thereafter
Soil gas[a]	Oxygen Carbon dioxide Hydrocarbons	Each of the vapor implants (24 total implants)	Periodic
Liquid feed[a]	pH Conductivity Nitrate Phosphate	Feed streams to plots	Periodic

(a) On-site analyses.
(b) Off-site analyses.

be seen, there was a substantial increase in the CFU between pre- and post-startup soil samples, as well as between post-startup controls and post-startup amended soils (Ringelberg et al. 1994, Walker & Walker 1994). The increase was seen at both the 4- to 5-ft (1.22- to 1.52-m) and 5- to 6-ft (1.52- to 1.83-m) levels, which contained the greatest concentrations of hydrocarbon contamination. Results of the PLFA analyses also indicated (1) that there was a shift in the population from predominantly gram positive to a population of ~50% gram-negative bacteria; (2) that some of the bacterial populations included species of *Pseudomonas*, *Xanthomyces*, and *Actinomyces* that are known to degrade petroleum components (Andelin et al. 1991, Atlas 1981, Pettigrew et al. 1991); and (3) that microorganisms from the post-startup soil samples showed an increase in aerobic potential and/or

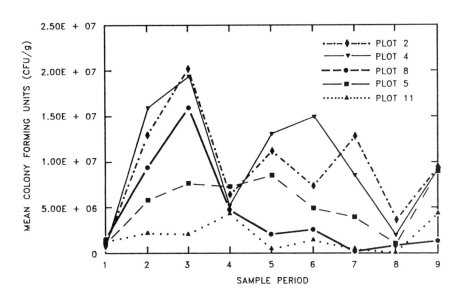

FIGURE 2. Plot of the mean CFU during the entire demonstration period for plots receiving water, air, and nutrients.

a decrease in the number of stationary-phase microorganisms as compared with pre-startup soils, where the bacteria appeared to be starved for essential nutrients and were not actively dividing (Ringelberg et al. 1994, Walker & Walker 1994). Because the petroleum hydrocarbons were the primary carbon source in subsurface areas sampled, it is probable that the shift in the bacterial community and the increase in cell population occurred as a result of the bacteria using the added

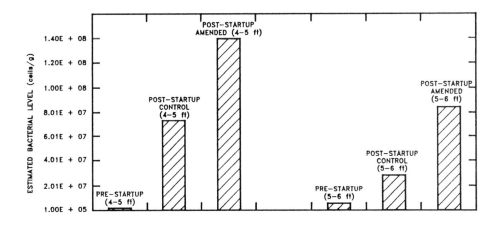

FIGURE 3. Mean estimated levels of bacterial cells by PLFA analysis in pre- and post-startup soil samples.

amendments (air, water, and nutrients) to degrade the petroleum hydrocarbons present.

Gas chromatograph analysis of soil samples indicated that the hydrocarbon contamination within the demonstration area at Kwajalein was primarily weathered diesel fuel. Data also showed that some of the hydrocarbons present within the demonstration area were not adsorbed onto the soil particles and were moving within the demonstration area due to tidal fluctuations, air sparging, etc., which complicated analysis of the data. Statistical analysis of the data indicated that reductions in the hydrocarbon concentration during the demonstration period occurred only in those plots receiving a combination of water, air, and nutrients Walker & Walker 1994). A bar graph showing hydrocarbon concentrations over time, as well as the rate of hydrocarbon reduction, for those plots is presented in Figure 4. The hydrocarbon reduction rate ranged from 6 to 12 $mg \cdot kg^{-1} \cdot d^{-1}$. If the average rate could be maintained, it would take ~3 years to remediate the demonstration site. However, it is probable that the degradation rate would slow because the lightest remaining hydrocarbons would probably be degraded first, leaving successively higher-molecular-weight hydrocarbons that would be more difficult to biodegrade.

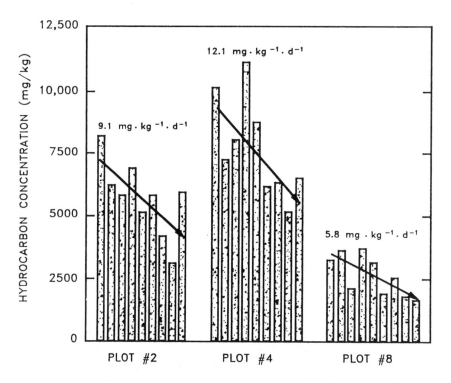

FIGURE 4. Concentration of hydrocarbons with time and rate of hydrocarbon reduction for those plots receiving water, air, and nutrients.

Although it cannot be shown definitively that the decrease in hydrocarbon concentration within the in situ plots is due to biological degradation, results of this study indicate that at least a portion of the decrease is due to this process. The following evidence supports this conclusion: (1) the hydrocarbons at the demonstration site consisted of weathered diesel; the remaining components were not easily volatilized; (2) PLFA analyses indicated that prior to the demonstration, bacteria present within the contaminated soils were not actively dividing; however, soil samples taken during the demonstration indicated that there had been a decrease in the number of stationary-phase bacteria and/or that the microorganisms showed an increase in aerobic potential; and (3) only plots receiving a combination of air, water, and nutrients — those components necessary for biodegradation — showed a decrease in hydrocarbons over the demonstration period (Walker & Walker 1994).

REFERENCES

Adler, H. I., R. L. Jolley, and T. L. Donaldson. 1992. *Bioremediation of Petroleum Contaminated Soil on Kwajalein Island: Microbial Characterization and Biotreatability Studies.* ORNL/TM-11925. Oak Ridge National Laboratory, Oak Ridge, TN.

Andelin, J., R. W. Niblock, and W. E. Westermeyer. 1991. *Bioremediation for Marine Oil Spills.* OTA-BP-0-70. Government Printing Office, Washington, DC.

Atlas, R. M. 1981. "Microbial Degradation of Petroleum Hydrocarbons: An Environmental Perspective." *Microbiol. Rev.* 45(1): 180-209.

Pettigrew, C. A., B. E. Haigler, and J. C. Spain. 1991. "Simultaneous Biodegradation of Chlorobenzene and Toluene by a Pseudomonas Strain." *Appl. Environ. Microbiol.* 57(1): 157-162.

Phelps, T. J., and R. L. Siegrist. 1993. *Bioremediation of Petroleum-Contaminated Soil on Kwajalein Island: Column Biotreatability Studies.* ORNL/TM-12273, DOE/HWP-131. Oak Ridge National Laboratory, Oak Ridge, TN.

Ringelberg, D. B., S. D. Sutton, and D. C. White. 1994. "Microbial Biomass, Community Structure, and Metabolic Status." Unpublished report, Center for Environmental Biotechnology, The University of Tennessee, Knoxville, TN.

Siegrist, R. L., N. E. Korte, D. A. Pickering, and T. J. Phelps. 1991. *Bioremediation Demonstration on Kwajalein Island: Site Characterization and On-site Biotreatability Studies.* ORNL/TM-11894. Oak Ridge National Laboratory, Oak Ridge, TN.

Walker, J. F., Jr., and A. B. Walker. 1994. *Bioremediation of Petroleum-Contaminated Soil on Kwajalein Island: On-Site Demonstration.* ORNL/TM-12871. Oak Ridge National Laboratory, Oak Ridge, TN.

Membrane Oxygen Dissolution at the Libby, Montana, Superfund Site

Charles J. Gantzer and David Cosgriff

ABSTRACT

The creosote- and pentachlorophenol-contaminated aquifer at the Libby Superfund Site is being bioremediated using naturally occurring aerobic microorganisms. Water is injected into the aquifer downgradient from the major contaminant source area. Between January 1991 and May 1993, the injection water was amended with hydrogen peroxide at a delivered concentration of approximately 100 mg/L. Theoretically, this hydrogen peroxide decomposed in the aquifer to produce approximately 50 mg/L of biologically available dissolved oxygen. The use of hydrogen peroxide was successful in making portions of the aquifer aerobic, which reduced water-phase contaminant concentrations. In May 1993, the hydrogen peroxide system was replaced by an oxygen generation/dissolution system that reduced the operating costs for oxygenating the aquifer by about $35,000 annually. Oxygen is now generated on site by a pressure-swing absorption oxygen generator and is dissolved by four membrane oxygen dissolution devices. The membrane oxygen dissolution system has operated at the Libby Superfund site for more than 26 months with no loss in performance due to membrane fouling or membrane fatigue.

INTRODUCTION

The Libby Superfund Site is located in northwestern Montana and is an active lumber-production facility. Wood-treating operations were conducted on the site from 1946 through 1969. Uncontrolled releases of creosote and pentachlorophenol (PCP) occurred in a waste pit. In addition to contaminating the soils adjacent to the source, the groundwater beneath the site is contaminated with polycyclic aromatic hydrocarbons (PAHs) and PCP. Remedial efforts have centered on the shallowest aquifer, because of its potential use as a domestic water supply. This aquifer is located at depths of 18 to 70 ft (5.5 to 21.3 m) below ground surface. The contaminant plume is nearly 1 mile (1.6 km) in length. To promote the aerobic in situ bioremediation of the shallowest aquifer, oxygenated water and nutrients are added to the aquifer at two locations: the intermediate injection wells 400 ft (122 m) downgradient of the source area and the boundary injection wells 1,200 ft (365 m) downgradient of the source area.

The water being added to the aquifer at the intermediate injection wells was amended with hydrogen peroxide at a delivered concentration of approximately 100 mg/L between January 1991 and May 1993. Theoretically, this hydrogen peroxide decomposed in the aquifer to produce approximately 50 mg/L of biologically available dissolved oxygen. The use of hydrogen peroxide was successful in making portions of the aquifer aerobic. Observations of elevated dissolved oxygen concentrations in the monitoring wells downgradient of the intermediate injection wells have typically correlated with reduced PAH and PCP concentrations. For example, oxygen breakthrough and contaminant reduction occurred in a well located about 150 ft (45 m) downgradient of the intermediate injection wells in November 1991. As the oxygen concentration approached 15 mg/L, the total PAH concentration dropped from 73 mg/L to less than 3 mg/L and the PCP concentration dropped from 420 mg/L to less than 3 mg/L (Piotrowski et al. 1994). No analyses were performed to determine the presence of oxidized PAH intermediates and lower-chlorinated phenols.

Despite the success of using hydrogen peroxide at the site, the decision was made to replace the hydrogen peroxide system with an oxygen generation/dissolution system for two reasons. First, hydrogen peroxide is expensive compared to oxygen. The chemical feed cost of adding 100 mg H_2O_2/L into a water flow of 100 gpm at Libby was $100.80 per day. In contrast, the cost of generating the same amount of oxygen (50 mg/L at 100 gpm) on site with a pressure-swing absorption oxygen generator was estimated to be about $1.80 per day assuming electricity costs of $0.055/kW·h. A second reason for switching to an oxygen-based system was the health hazard associated with handling hydrogen peroxide on a small scale, i.e., 55-gallon (208-L) drums, especially with regard to dermal contact.

The theory and the performance of the membrane oxygen dissolution system installed at the Libby site to replace the hydrogen peroxide system is the focus of this presentation.

BUBBLELESS OXYGEN DISSOLUTION USING MEMBRANES

Membran Corporation's gas-dissolution technology (U.S. Patent 5,034,164 with others pending) can generate elevated dissolved gas concentrations. The direct (bubbleless) dissolution of gases is accomplished in pipes ("modules") containing thousands of sealed, hollow, gas-permeable fibers that are filled with pure gases under pressure. A schematic diagram of a module is provided in Figure 1. The fibers measure 200 to 400 μ in diameter. The small diameter of the fibers means that a very large surface area of membrane can be installed in a module. The sealed ends of the fibers are not joined and are free to move independently in the turbulent water flow found inside the pipe. The gas diffuses across the fiber walls and dissolves directly into the water that flows over the

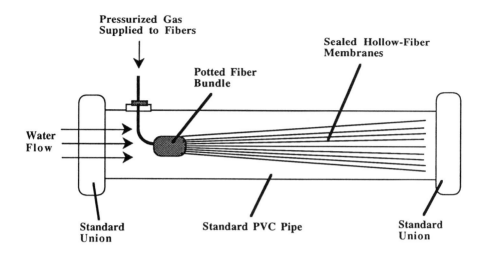

FIGURE 1. Schematic diagram of a bubbleless gas-dissolution device.

outer surface of the fiber membrane. For a given fiber packing density and fiber length, gas-dissolution performance is controlled by changing the water flowrate (influences water-boundary-layer thickness) and the gas pressure (alters driving force for gas dissolution).

The observed increase in dissolved gas concentration obtained with a single pass through a Membran gas-dissolution module can be described by the following equations:

$$\Delta C = C_{eff} - C_{inf} \tag{1}$$

$$C_{eff} = C^* - (C^* - C_{inf}) \exp\left(\frac{-K\,a\,L}{u}\right) \tag{2}$$

in which ΔC is the observed increase in dissolved gas concentration (mg/L), C_{eff} is the dissolved gas concentration in the module effluent (mg/L), C_{inf} is the dissolved gas concentration in the module influent (mg/L), C^* is the water-phase gas concentration that would be in equilibrium with the pressurized gas inside the fibers (mg/L), K is the overall mass transfer rate coefficient (cm/h), a is the specific surface area over which gas dissolution occurs (cm^2/cm^3), L is the effective fiber length (cm), and u is the velocity of the water flowing past the fibers inside the module (cm/h).

The value of C^* used in equation (2) is a function of the length-averaged gas pressure existing inside the hollow-fiber membranes and the Henry's law constant for the gas being dissolved by the module.

$$C^* = f\left(\frac{P_m}{H}\right) \tag{3}$$

in which P_m is the length-averaged gas pressure inside the fibers (psig), and H is the Henry's law constant (atm/mole fraction).

The membrane technology offers several operational advantages compared to other oxygen dissolution technologies. First, the membrane technology can dissolve oxygen without generating bubbles. No bubble generation means no oxygen wastage and reduced VOC and odor emissions from bioreactors. Second, the technology offers relatively high-energy efficiencies (i.e., lb O_2/HP·h), because pressurized water is not a requirement for high performance. Third, high dissolved gas concentrations can be generated by operating the membrane modules in series. Performance is almost additive. For example, if one membrane can increase the oxygen concentration by about 20 mg/L, then two modules in series will increase the oxygen concentration by about 39 mg/L, and three modules in series will increase the oxygen concentration by about 57 mg/L.

MEMBRANE OXYGEN DISSOLUTION AT LIBBY SITE

The hydrogen peroxide system was replaced with an oxygen generation/dissolution system that consisted of an AirSep AS-80 oxygen generator, a 5-HP air compressor, and four Membran BMA-75-1 oxygen-dissolution membrane modules operated in series. A schematic diagram of the oxygen generation/dissolution system is provided in Figure 2. Each 3-in.-diameter (7.6-cm-diameter) membrane module holds about 7,500 hollow-fiber composite membranes that have with an outside diameter of about 300 μ and an effective length of about 42 in. (106 cm). The predicted ability of four membrane modules to increase dissolved oxygen concentrations as a function of water temperature is provided in Figure 3, based on the performance of the modules in Minneapolis tap water.

The bubble-free dissolved oxygen concentrations generated by the four membrane modules ranged from 32 to 49 mg/L during the first 75 weeks of operation at the intermediate injection wells. During this time, the water temperatures ranged from 1 to 19°C, water flowrates ranged from 85 to 95 gpm, oxygen pressures applied to the hollow-fiber membranes ranged from 40 to 70 psig, and influent oxygen concentrations ranged from 7.4 to 12.6 mg/L. As illustrated in Figure 4, the four membrane modules performed equal to or better than the level predicted by laboratory-derived correlations. The only time the correlations grossly overpredicted performance was for the week 13 reading, when the influent oxygen concentration was not measured and was assumed equal to the saturation value at 12°C. The ability of the four membrane modules to perform at or above the predicted level suggests that there was no loss of performance due to any type of membrane fouling during the 75 weeks of operation at the intermediate injection wells.

During the 75 weeks of operation at the intermediate injection wells, there have been two operational problems with the oxygen generation/dissolution system. The first problem was a failure of the pressure-swing absorption oxygen

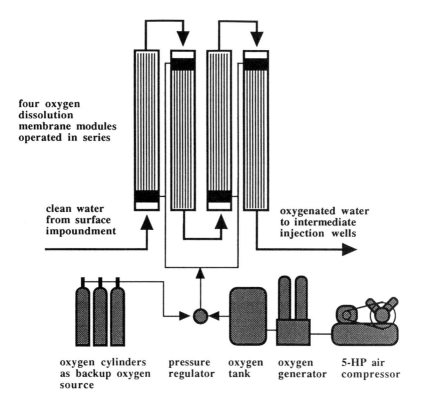

FIGURE 2. Schematic diagram of the oxygen generation/dissolution system installed at the Libby Superfund site, which replaced an existing hydrogen peroxide injection system.

generator to produce oxygen-enriched air due to the apparent compaction of the absorbent. The absorbent was replaced. The second problem was the excessive growth of algae in the membrane modules. The modules were installed next to a window, and nutrients were injected upstream of the modules. The problem was solved by covering the clear PVC shells of the modules to prevent light penetration and by moving the nutrient injection downstream of the modules.

Prior to replacing the hydrogen peroxide system at the intermediate injection wells in May 1993, the four oxygen dissolution modules had operated for 7 months at the boundary injection wells for evaluation purposes. Two problems were encountered during startup. First, PVC pipe shavings or fillings created by sawing PVC pipe during installation were not adequately flushed from the plumbing prior to startup. The shavings were responsible for some fiber tangling in the modules and some oxygen bubble generation. The second problem was caused by the improper operation of a check valve, which caused a rapid surge of water to flow backwards through the modules during startup when the pumps

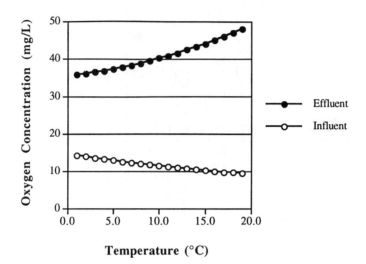

FIGURE 3. Predicted effluent dissolved oxygen concentrations generated by the four membrane modules as a function of temperature, assuming a water flowrate of 90 gpm, an oxygen pressure of 65 psig applied to the hollow-fiber membranes, an influent water stream having an oxygen concentration in equilibrium with the atmosphere at the plotted temperature, and sufficient hydrostatic pressures inside the modules to keep the high oxygen concentrations in solution.

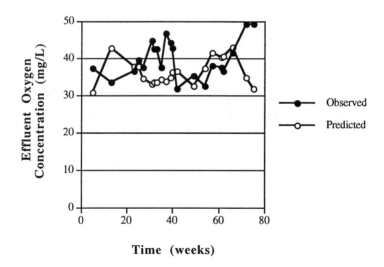

FIGURE 4. Comparison of observed and predicted effluent dissolved oxygen concentrations generated by the four membrane oxygen-dissolution modules during operation at the intermediate injection wells.

were periodically turned on and off for testing purposes. The backwards water flow caused the 7,500 42-in.-long (102-cm-long) fibers in the first module to become a tangled mat. The tangled mat eventually created gas leaks in the membrane fibers. This module was replaced.

SUMMARY

A membrane oxygen dissolution system has operated continuously at the Libby Superfund site for 26 months (7 months at the boundary injection wells, followed by 19 months at the intermediate injection wells) with no apparent loss in performance due to membrane fouling or membrane fatigue. The four membrane modules generated dissolved oxygen concentrations ranging from 32 to 49 mg/L in a water flowing at 90 gpm. Variations in generated oxygen concentrations were due to variations in water temperature, influent dissolved oxygen concentrations, and oxygen pressures applied to the fibers. Replacement of the hydrogen peroxide injection system with the oxygen generation/dissolution system has reduced annual operating costs from about $40,000 to less than $5,000 with no appreciable change in the rate of aquifer bioremediation.

REFERENCE

Piotrowski, M. R., J. R. Doyle, D. Cosgriff, and M. C. Parsons. 1994. "Bioremedial Progress at Libby, Montana, Superfund Site." In R. E. Hinchee, D. B. Anderson, F. B. Metting, Jr., and G. D. Sayles (Eds.), *Applied Biotechnology for Site Remediation*, pp. 240-255. CRC Press, Inc., Boca Raton, FL.

Oxygen-Enhanced In Situ Bioremediation in a Sand and Gravel Aquifer

Sean R. Carter and James E. Clark

ABSTRACT

In situ bioremediation was chosen to remediate shallow oxygen-limited groundwater contaminated with volatile and semivolatile aromatic hydrocarbons from a fuel release. The remediation system included groundwater recovery at rates up to 100 L/min and treatment with a packed-tower air stripper to remove volatiles and increase dissolved oxygen levels. Dissolved oxygen was further increased using a pressure-swing adsorption (PSA) oxygen generator and hollow-fiber oxygen dissolution membranes. This oxygenated water was injected back to the subsurface through two horizontal injection galleries. Prior to start-up of the remediation system, groundwater in contaminated wells was oxygen-limited, with levels from 0 to less than 1 mg/L. After several months of groundwater injection, dissolved oxygen levels began to increase in contaminated wells by 1 to 2 mg/L. A significant decrease in dissolved-phase hydrocarbons was observed in a well nearest an injection gallery once dissolved oxygen was increased to background levels (>5 mg/L). A decrease in nitrogen was also observed, suggesting that aerobic biodegradation was a significant factor in the hydrocarbon decrease.

INTRODUCTION

In situ bioremediation can be an efficient, cost-effective means of degrading volatile and semivolatile organic compounds in groundwater (Brubaker and Stroo 1992 and Anid et al. 1993). Sufficient oxygen and nutrient levels must be established for indigenous microorganisms to be effective in this process (Madsen 1991). However, aquifers contaminated with these compounds will generally exhibit anoxic conditions within the plume, inhibiting the degradation process. The described adaptation of enhancing dissolved oxygen levels in the affected area of the aquifer was used to promote bioremediation at this site. This method of remediation is becoming a widely used technique for removing petroleum hydrocarbons from groundwater (Nelson et al. 1994 and Norris et al. 1994).

Site Description

The project site is an active petroleum bulk storage facility located in a residential area of a small rural hamlet of upstate New York. It is located over a shallow glacial valley-fill aquifer, which is used as the potable water supply for the area. The site is characterized by soils consisting of sands and gravels and little silt deposited during glacial outwash activity (Cadwell 1986). The depth to groundwater varies seasonally at the site from 1 to 2 m below grade, with a southwest gradient of 0.001. The aquifer thickness is estimated at 10 m, with relatively high transmissivity, estimated at approximately 13,500 m^2/day (Miller 1982).

Numerous releases of gasoline and distillates totaling in excess of 11,400 L (3,000 gal) had been documented at this site between 1977 and 1991. A plume of contaminated groundwater was delineated while conducting remedial investigations. The impacted area covered approximately 4,000 m^2, consisting of the facility property and an area under an adjoining road and two neighboring residential properties (Figure 1). All of the subject properties have private water supply wells, but no wells have been impacted by the release.

REMEDIAL APPROACH

Feasibility analyses were performed for several remedial technologies at this site. Pump-and-treat methods to influence the aquifer for plume containment were not selected since the contaminant plume was mature, well defined, and not impacting potential sensitive receptors. Due to the high transmissivity of the aquifer, pumping rates to achieve a suitable radius of influence would be in excess of 1,000 L/min, making this a cost-prohibitive option. However, groundwater was pumped to provide a vector for injecting dissolved oxygen and treatment prior to injection was required.

Air sparging in conjunction with vapor extraction was considered as an option, but had several drawbacks. Semivolatiles present in the contaminant plume would not be prone to volatilization and removal in the airstream. These compounds would need to be biologically degraded using dissolved oxygen provided by the sparging system. The volatile compounds present would react well to air sparging, but vapor extraction would not be effective to contain the off-gas in the narrow unsaturated zone exhibited at this site. In addition, a structural concrete containment dike for the petroleum storage tanks was recently constructed in the area where the releases occurred, rendering access to the most highly impacted soils impossible.

Based on these conditions, in situ bioremediation was considered as a means of remediating the aquifer. Analysis of groundwater samples taken from across the site indicated that the area of the aquifer impacted by the plume was oxygen deficient, yet contained nitrate-nitrite nitrogen levels ranging from 8.5 to 55 mg/L and ammonia-nitrogen levels ranging from 0.7 to 1.5 mg/L. Groundwater analyses from two monitoring wells (MW1 and MW9) located upgradient of the

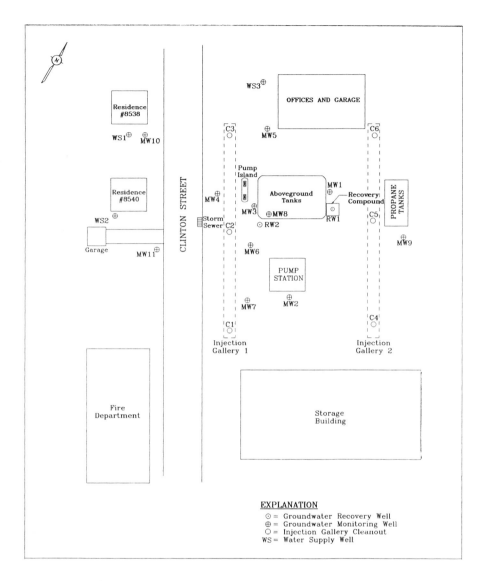

FIGURE 1. Site map.

impacted area historically have shown dissolved oxygen levels ranging from 5 to 9 mg/L, indicating aerobic conditions in the aquifer. Groundwater analyses from two monitoring wells (MW10 and MW11) downgradient of the plume have shown low impactant levels (<50 µg/L) and dissolved oxygen levels 1 to 3 mg/L higher than in impacted wells. The dissolved oxygen profile is illustrated in Figure 2 for three selected monitoring wells. Based on these results, it was determined that if dissolved oxygen levels could be enhanced in the area of the plume, in situ bioremediation could be a viable alternative.

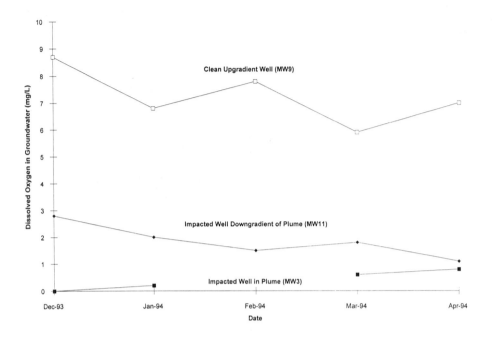

FIGURE 2. Groundwater dissolved oxygen levels in upgradient, contaminated, and downgradient monitoring wells.

Remedial System Description

Groundwater was pumped from recovery well RW2 to a packed-tower air stripper (Delta Cooling Tower, Fairfield, New Jersey) using a GRS (Groundwater Recovery Systems, Inc., Exton, Pennsylvania) dual-pump system. Treated water was pumped from the air stripper at a rate up to 114 L/min (30 gal/min) to a series of 4 Membran (Membran Corporation, Minneapolis, Minnesota) bubbleless membrane aerators (BMAs) encased in 5-cm (2-in.) polyvinyl chloride (PVC) pipe. A detailed description of the BMA system and process is provided elsewhere (Semmens and Gantzer, 1993). Oxygen was supplied to each BMA module with an AirSep (AirSep Corporation, Buffalo, New York) AS-20 pressure-swing adsorption (PSA) oxygen generator. The PSA unit is an air separation process which uses two packed beds of molecular sieve to adsorb nitrogen from air. The unit is supplied by an air compressor and produces oxygen at 90 to 95% purity. The total oxygen supply rate is approximately 1 L/min at a delivery pressure to the BMA modules of 4.2 kg/cm^2 (60 lb/in.^{2}). A process flow diagram is shown in Figure 3.

Following oxygenation, the water was reintroduced to the subsurface via two injection galleries 49 m in length and consisting of perforated 10-cm (4-in.) PVC pipe set in pea stone at a depth of 1 m below grade. The galleries were sealed with plastic sheeting and had access/cleanout ports at both ends and in the middle. The remediation system operated continuously at an average daily flowrate

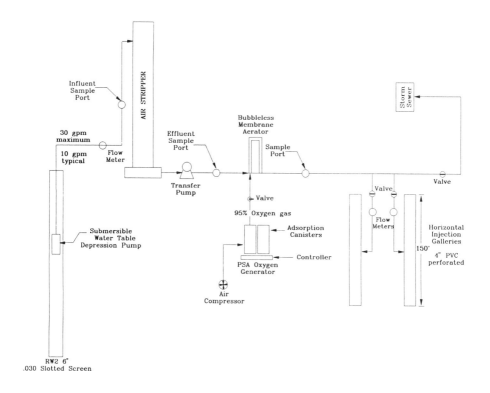

FIGURE 3. Remediation system process flow diagram.

of 86,000 L/day. Injected water was equally distributed to the two galleries, except during high water conditions when all or most of the flow was diverted to a storm sewer. Injected groundwater typically contained 8 to 12 mg/L of dissolved oxygen, much lower than the design level of 30 mg/L.

The poor oxygen transfer efficiency was due to high levels of iron and manganese which accumulated on the membranes. Only immediately following acid treatment of the membranes to remove precipitated iron had dissolved oxygen exceeded 15 mg/L.

RESULTS AND DISCUSSION

The remediation system began full-scale operation in the 4th quarter of 1993. During the first two months of operation, little effect was observed on groundwater dissolved oxygen, with increases in several monitoring wells of less than 1 mg/L. However, during the third month of operation, dissolved oxygen began to substantially increase in all site monitoring wells, with the highest increase in wells nearest the injection galleries. This indicated that the oxygen increase was most likely due to the remediation system. Monitoring well MW4, located directly downgradient of injection gallery 1, as shown in Figure 1, showed a stepwise increase in dissolved oxygen during months 2 through 6, from 0.1 mg/L to 1.3, 3.4, 5.8, and 7.8 mg/L, respectively.

Dissolved oxygen and hydrocarbon concentrations from groundwater from MW4 are shown in Figure 4. Dissolved oxygen results are only shown for the dates corresponding to the quarterly hydrocarbon analysis. The results show a clear decrease in hydrocarbon levels and an increase in dissolved oxygen levels from the 4th quarter 1993 sample, which was taken prior to system startup. The remediation system was not in operation for three weeks prior to the 3rd quarter 1994 sample while system repairs were being made. A slight increase in hydrocarbon levels was observed at this time, and dissolved oxygen decreased to about 1 mg/L from as high as 7.8 mg/L when the system was operating. These results were expected since MW4 is located near injection gallery 1 and is likely diluted by the injection water when the system is operating. However, the hydrocarbon concentration measured was nearly three times lower than the initial reading prior to system startup. It can be concluded that biodegradation, not dilution, contributed significantly to the hydrocarbon depletion.

Dissolved oxygen and hydrocarbon results are shown in Figure 5 for monitoring well MW2, located between the injection galleries. Although no change in hydrocarbon levels have been observed from this well, groundwater is no longer oxygen limited. It is anticipated that this change from oxygen- to hydrocarbon-limited conditions should result in a decrease in dissolved-phase hydrocarbons over the next several quarters, as observed in MW4. However, the level of dissolved oxygen needed to stimulate microbial activity was undetermined due to

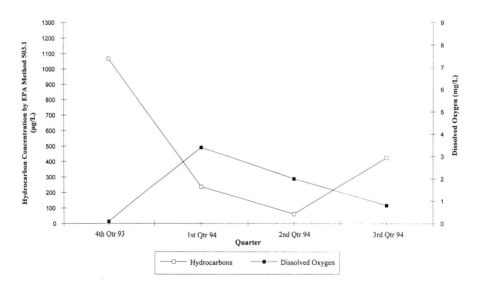

FIGURE 4. Dissolved-phase hydrocarbon and oxygen levels in monitoring well MW4.

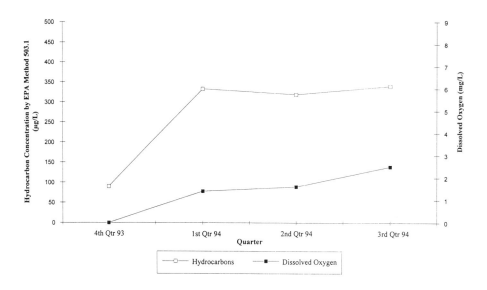

FIGURE 5. Dissolved-phase hydrocarbon and oxygen levels in monitoring
well MW2.

a lack of data. There were also nonbiological processes occurring which consumed oxygen (i.e., iron oxidation) and contributed to dissolved-phase hydrocarbon levels (i.e., desorption, solubilization from free-phase hydrocarbons).
Therefore, a mass balance on substrates and electron acceptors was not possible
with the data.

Results obtained during the first year of operation indicate that using oxygen
enhancement has changed groundwater conditions from oxygen limited to hydrocarbon limited in areas of the site directly influenced by groundwater injection.
Groundwater dissolved oxygen levels in the area of the plume have increased
from nondetectable levels up to 1 to 3 mg/L. One well nearest an injection gallery has shown dissolved oxygen increases up to the level of clean upgradient
wells and a greater than two-fold decrease in hydrocarbon levels. Nitrogen depletion was also observed in monitoring wells located directly in the plume and
downgradient. Decreased hydrocarbon and nitrogen levels following an increase
in dissolved oxygen indicate that aerobic biodegradation played a significant
role in remediation.

ACKNOWLEDGMENTS

The authors recognize the contributions of Donald R. Seymour, Alan Setchell,
and Patrick Bliek of Matrix Environmental Technologies Inc., Charles Gantzer
of Membran Corporation, and Angelo Barberic of AirSep Corporation. This work
is dedicated to the memory of Mr. David W. Graeper.

REFERENCES

Anid, P. J., P.J.J. Alvarez, and T. M. Vogel. 1993. "Biodegradation of Monoaromatic Hydro-carbons in Aquifer Columns Amended with Hydrogen Peroxide and Nitrate." *Water Research* 27(4): 685-691.

Brubaker, G. R., and H. F. Stroo. 1992. "In Situ Bioremediation of Aquifers Containing Poly-aromatic Hydrocarbons." *Journal of Hazardous Materials* 32: 163-177.

Cadwell, D. H. 1986. *Surficial Geologic Map of New York, Finger Lakes Sheet.* Scale 1:250,000. New York State Museum — Geological Survey, Map and Chart Series #40, University of the State of New York, State Education Department.

Madsen, E. L. 1991. "Determining In Situ Biodegradation, Facts and Challenges." *Environmental Science and Technology* 25(10): 1663-1673.

Miller, T. S. 1982. *Geohydrology of the Valley-Fill Aquifer in the Corning Area, Steuben County, New York.* Scale 1:24,000. U.S. Geological Survey, U.S. Department of the Interior, Washington, DC.

Nelson, C. H., R. J. Hicks, and S. D. Andrews. 1994. "In Situ Bioremediation: An Integrated System Approach." In R. E. Hinchee, B. C. Alleman, R. E. Hoeppel, and R. N. Miller (Eds.), *Hydrocarbon Bioremediation*, pp. 125-132. CRC Press, Boca Raton, FL.

Norris, R. D., K. Dowd, and C. Maudlin. 1994. "The Use of Multiple Oxygen Sources and Nutrient Delivery Systems to Effect In Situ Bioremediation of Saturated and Unsaturated Soils." In R. E. Hinchee, B. C. Alleman, R. E. Hoeppel, and R. N. Miller (Eds.), *Hydrocarbon Bioremediation*, pp. 405-410. CRC Press, Boca Raton, FL.

Semmens, M. J., and C. J. Gantzer. 1993. "Gas Transfer Using Hollow Fiber Membranes." Paper presented at Proceedings of the 66th Annual Water Environment Federation Confer-ence and Exposition, October 3-7, 1993, Anaheim, CA.

H₂O₂ Enhancement of Microbial Removal of Ethylene Glycol Contamination

Paul E. Flathman, Mary L. Laski, John H. Carson, Jr.,
Kathleen S. Leis, Douglas E. Jerger, and Paul R. Lear

ABSTRACT

The objectives of the laboratory study were (1) to evaluate the benefit of hydrogen peroxide (H_2O_2) as a source of molecular oxygen for enhanced biological treatment of ethylene glycol in a simulated groundwater environment, (2) to assess the tolerance of the ethylene glycol-adapted indigenous microflora to H_2O_2, and (3) to determine the magnitude of the nonenzymatic decomposition of H_2O_2 in the subsurface soil used for the study. Test (n = 3) and control (n = 3) upflow soil columns containing sandy soil from a site previously contaminated with ethylene glycol were used for the study. This soil exhibited extremely low activity in nonenzymatically catalyzing the breakdown of H_2O_2. Test and control columns received an influent ethylene glycol concentration of 2,000 mg/L in Dworkin-Foster medium. Influent H_2O_2 concentration in the test columns was incrementally increased to 5,400 mg/L. With greater than an 80% reduction in influent total organic carbon (TOC) in the test columns in excess of the control, the benefit of H_2O_2 addition was demonstrated. At an influent H_2O_2 concentration of 5,400 mg/L, a toxic effect for treatment of the influent TOC was not demonstrated, and a significant increase in bacterial population density in the test columns over the controls was observed.

INTRODUCTION

The use of hydrogen peroxide (H_2O_2) as a source of molecular oxygen for in situ bioremediation of available organics is well documented (Brown & Norris 1994, Lu 1994, Pardieck et al. 1992, Aggarwal et al. 1991, and Huling et al. 1990). One of the best studied sites involving the use of H_2O_2 was a recently completed U.S. Environmental Protection Agency and U.S. Coast Guard joint full-scale evaluation of in situ biological treatment of petroleum hydrocarbons following spillage of aviation gasoline at a Coast Guard Air Station in Traverse City,

Michigan (Wilson et al. 1994 and Huling et al. 1990). In that study, the benefit of H_2O_2 addition for the biodegradation of benzene, toluene, ethylbenzene, and xylenes (BTEX) was demonstrated. Since the predominant contaminants in soil and groundwater are petroleum hydrocarbons (PHCs), most of the laboratory- and full-scale projects involving the evaluation and/or use of H_2O_2 have centered on this group of compounds. Leaking underground storage tanks have been the most common source of these contaminants.

Ethylene glycol was selected as the test compound for this study because it (1) is a common environmental contaminant, (2) is not oxidized by H_2O_2, (3) is infinitely soluble in water, (4) is not inhibitory to bacterial growth at high concentrations, (5) is readily biodegraded by acclimated microflora, and (6) under test conditions a dose/response determination is easily made. The objectives of this laboratory study were to (1) evaluate the benefit of H_2O_2 as a source of molecular oxygen for enhanced biological treatment of ethylene glycol, a readily available organic, in a simulated groundwater environment; (2) assess the tolerance of the ethylene glycol-adapted indigenous microflora to increasing concentrations of H_2O_2; and (3) determine the magnitude of the nonenzymatic decomposition of H_2O_2 in the subsurface soil used for the study.

The bacterial metabolism of ethylene glycol under both aerobic and anaerobic conditions is well documented. A brief review of that literature has been presented by Flathman and Bottomley (1994). In summary, ethylene glycol had been shown to support microbial growth under aerobic conditions. The aerobic metabolism of ethylene glycol is relatively common, and the pathways of its metabolism are known. The most likely pathway of ethylene glycol catabolism by a bacterial isolate that had been studied was sequential oxidation to glycolate and glyoxylate. By reaction with acetyl-CoA, glyoxylate would form malate, a TCA cycle intermediate. Anaerobic metabolism of ethylene glycol has also been reported. Using a sewage sludge inoculum under methanogenic conditions, ethylene glycol was converted to ethanol, acetate, and methane. The ethanol produced was further oxidized to acetate with methane as the final end product. *Clostridium glycolicum* fermentation of ethylene glycol has been shown to yield equimolar amounts of acetate and ethanol. The metabolism of ethylene glycol by a *Flavobacterium* sp. under microaerophilic conditions followed the sequence acetyl-CoA, acetyl-phosphate, and acetate. Thus, ethylene glycol mineralization can occur in both aerobic and anaerobic environments, and metabolic intermediates can accumulate under conditions that are not aerobic.

MATERIALS AND METHODS

The experimental design and laboratory apparatus were similar to that utilized by Flathman et al. (1991) and the Texas Research Institute (Britton & TRI 1985). Six 2-piece upflow, 40-mm × 600-mm columns (Corning 38460-40) were utilized (Figure 1). Three of the columns were used as test columns (i.e., columns 1, 2, and 3) and received increasing concentrations of H_2O_2. The remaining three columns (i.e., columns 4, 5, and 6) were used as a control to evaluate

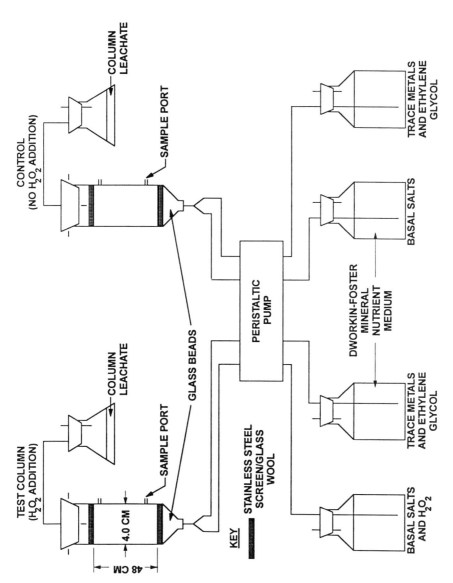

FIGURE 1. Laboratory apparatus for test and control upflow soil columns.

the benefit of H_2O_2 addition for biological treatment of the ethylene glycol. The H_2O_2, i.e., TYSUL WW 50 (Du Pont Chemicals, Wilmington, Delaware), was used as received and was standardized by iodometric titration. The ethylene glycol was filter sterilized (0.22 µ) prior to use. The 4-L feed reservoirs were constantly mixed using a magnetic stirrer during the study to ensure the complete mixing of all reagents, and the stability of the H_2O_2 in those reservoirs was confirmed.

Sandy soil from a site previously contaminated with ethylene glycol was used for the study (Flathman & Bottomley 1994). Dworkin-Foster medium (Dworkin & Foster 1958) was used to supply the mineral nutrients required for enhanced microbial growth on ethylene glycol and any incomplete oxidation products that might accumulate. The medium was prepared using procedures adapted by the Texas Research Institute (Harding 1988). In addition to supporting growth on the available organics, Dworkin-Foster medium was selected because it had been shown to appreciably reduce the nonenzymatic breakdown of H_2O_2, particularly in the presence of ferric ions (Britton & TRI 1985). The columns received an influent ethylene glycol concentration of 2,000 mg/L in Dworkin-Foster medium. The influent H_2O_2 concentration in the test columns was incrementally increased to 5,400 mg/L.

An Ismatec multichannel peristaltic pump (Cole-Parmer Instrument Company, Chicago, Illinois) was used to move the reagents through the soil columns. Flowrate in each column was 0.20 mL/min. Tygon™ tubing having a 1.30 mm i.d. was used through the pump. A void volume of 28.9 ± 1.56% (x ± s, n = 2) for the soil in the columns was determined by volume displacement, and based on that determination, hydraulic residence time in the columns was calculated to be 0.61 day.

Because incomplete oxidation products (i.e., ethanol and acetate) have been shown to accumulate under microaerophilic, fermentative, and methanogenic conditions, reduction in the influent soluble total organic carbon (TOC) concentration in the soil columns was used as the test parameter. TOC was determined according to U.S. Environmental Protection Agency (U.S. EPA) Method 9060 (USEPA 1986). When flow through the upflow columns was terminated at the end of 260 days, soil in each column was sectioned by depth from the top [i.e., 0 to 16 cm (Section C), 16 to 32 cm (Section B), and 32 to 48 cm (Section A) from the top] and replicate samples were collected. The aerobic heterotrophic bacterial population density was quantified immediately in each of the replicate pairs. The bacterial population density was determined according to Standard Methods' procedures (APHA, AWWA, WPCF 1989) using R2A Agar, Difco 1826 (Difco Laboratories, Detroit, Michigan). Incubation was at 22°C for 7 days.

Using procedures described by Lawes (1991), the soil used for the study exhibited extremely low activity in nonenzymatically catalyzing the breakdown of H_2O_2. In a period of six hours, Lawes demonstrated that at a 0.1% H_2O_2 concentration in a 7.5:1 liquid-to-soil mixture only 3% of the H_2O_2 decomposed (Lawes 1989). At the lower liquid-to-soil ratio of 1:3, approximately 47% of the H_2O_2 was decomposed after 6 hours compared to 100% decomposition of the H_2O_2 in an active topsoil within 6 min.

The theoretical oxygen demand (ThOD) for aerobic mineralization of ethylene glycol was calculated from the following relationship:

$$2(CH_2OH)_2 + 5O_2 = 4CO_2 + 6H_2O \tag{1}$$

ThOD is 1.29 mg O_2 per mg of ethylene glycol. With an influent ethylene glycol concentration of 2,000 mg/L, 2,580 mg/L O_2 would be required for complete oxidation. Based on the following relationship for the decomposition of H_2O_2, 5,480 mg/L of H_2O_2 would be required for complete oxidation of the influent ethylene glycol.

$$2H_2O_2 = 2H_2O + O_2 \tag{2}$$

RESULTS AND DISCUSSION

The percent reduction of soluble TOC for the study is presented in Figure 2. The data display considerable fluctuation with time. Some of this fluctuation was due to common causes, such as changes in temperature and barometric pressure, which can be seen in the behavior of test and control columns alike. An increase in barometric pressure, for example, will result in an increase in the influent

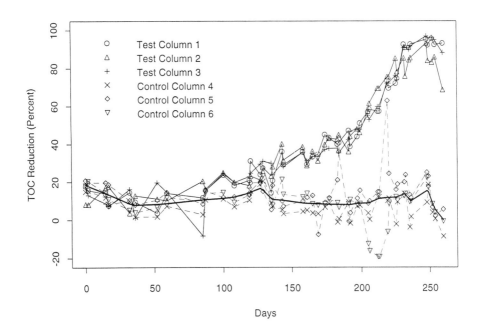

FIGURE 2. **TOC reduction in test and control columns versus time. The heavy line presented in the control is a pooled "moving average" estimate for TOC reduction.**

dissolved oxygen concentration to the columns. Some of the fluctuation was undoubtedly due to special conditions, such as a change in flow, for example, which would not affect all columns. Some of the fluctuation was due to measurement error. Estimated percent reductions that are negative can be attributed to measurement error or to transient special conditions.

These special conditions also include the evolution of each soil/bacterial system as an independent dynamic system. This independent evolution is evident from population density measurements taken at the beginning and at the end of the study and is predicted by the theory of random processes. With reference to the theory of stochastic processes (Karlin & Taylor 1975), the microbial population as a function of time in each column may be viewed as an independent realization of a nonstationary birth and death process. Each column has slightly different initial conditions, and, in addition to the designed changes in H_2O_2 concentration, the coefficients of the respective generating equations vary slightly from column to column and in time.

To adjust the response variable for uncontrolled common causes of variation, a pooled "moving average" estimate of the reduction attributable to the control columns was constructed. The smoothed "moving average" is a weighted super-smoother fit computed using the S-PLUS™ procedure "supsmu" (Statistical Sciences, Inc. 1994 and Chambers and Hastie 1992). S-PLUS™ was used to provide all of the statistical computations and graphics presented in further analyzing test and control column data. To robustify this estimate against the effects of the obvious outliers in the control data set (Figure 2), robust weights were obtained from a robust linear regression fit to the control column data. Since the data for individual controls appear to be mean stationary (irregular) time series, weights from a robust location estimator could have been used. To provide some protection against an undetected trend, a robust linear regression was chosen instead. This model was computed using the procedure "rreg." This dynamic control was then subtracted from the reduction estimated for each of the test columns to obtain a relative reduction in excess of control (RREC). Since flowrates and concentrations varied slightly from column to column and from time to time and since the control columns evolved dynamically, it was appropriate to work with RREC (Figure 3).

A generalized linear interactive model (GLIM) was fit to the RREC data (Dobson 1983). The GLIM model, which was finally selected, modeled the expected value of RREC as a linear function of the predictors with constant residual variance and a symmetric, but not necessarily Gaussian, model for the errors. The response variable is a difference of two ratios, each of which has quantities derived from sample measurements in both the numerator and denominator. This fact makes a Gaussian error distribution an untenable assumption. The fitting algorithm that was used, i.e., M-estimation (Hoaglin et al. 1983), is highly efficient for Gaussian errors, is robust against "outliers," and is superefficient for a wide range of symmetric error distributions that have heavier tails than the Gaussian. Normal quantile plots of the studentized model residuals confirm that protection against symmetric, heavy-tailed alternatives to the normal is a wise choice.

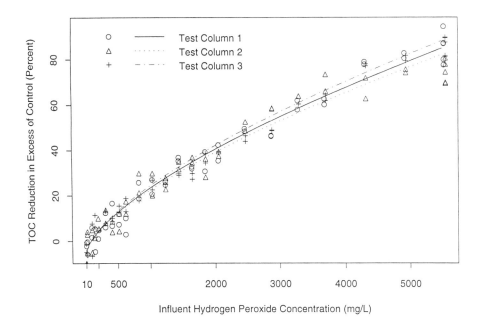

FIGURE 3. TOC reduction in test columns in excess of control versus influent H_2O_2 concentration.

H_2O_2 concentration, quantified as mg/L, raised to the $2/3$ power (denoted as H) was found to be an extremely significant predictor (Tables 1 and 2). Although the model generating the data is nonlinear (Figure 3), the model can be linearized by a power transformation of the H_2O_2 concentration (Figure 4). When linearization of a nonlinear model can be attained through the simple transformation of a predictor, the linearized form of the model is preferred. The intercept term was significant. This may be due to lack of complete linearization. Although no theoretical justification based on underlying kinetics was presented, this power transformation of the predictor was highly effective in linearizing the model (Figure 4). The estimated model is:

$$\% \, RREC = 0.29 \, * \, C_{H_2O_2}^{2/3} \, - \, 5.5$$

Slight but significant differences were found between test columns in the estimated coefficient for the predictor H. This was expected since the columns may be viewed as random samples from an "infinite" population of possible soil columns which could have been prepared from the previously contaminated site. These differences were statistically significant at the 0.01 level (Table 2). A components of variance model (using the method of maximum likelihood) was used to explore the contributions of random differences between columns to the overall experimental error. The ratio of the standard deviation of the random slope component of the model to the residual standard deviation, for example, was less

TABLE 1. Estimated model coefficients.

Term	Estimate	Standard Error	t-Value
Constant	−5.50	0.65	−8.42
H[a]	0.290	0.0039	74.0
H:(Test Col. 1)[b]	−0.00440	0.0028	−1.58
H:(Test Col. 2)[b]	0.00495	0.0016	3.08

(a) [Influent H_2O_2 concentration (mg/L)]$^{2/3}$.
(b) Interaction term between column and predictor H (i.e., individual components of the slope for each column).

than 0.15%. Although the random slope component was statistically significant under experimental conditions, it had no practical significance. Under conditions of full-scale in situ biological treatment; however, the random variability of the soil may become an important source of variability in treatment effect.

As presented in Figures 3 and 4, treatment of influent TOC in test columns was an increasing function of influent H_2O_2 concentration. The slope of the curve presented in Figure 3 decreased as influent H_2O_2 concentration increased but did not approach an asymptotic level for the range of H_2O_2 tested. This indicated that an appreciable toxic effect was not observed at the highest influent H_2O_2 concentration tested. At that H_2O_2 concentration, dissolved oxygen was detected in the test reactor effluent (CHEMetrics Inc., Calverton, Virginia). Although H_2O_2 toxicity to bacteria has been reported at much lower concentrations, it seems likely the gradual increase in H_2O_2 concentration over a period of months allowed the microflora in the test columns to acclimate. In a soil column study performed by Britton and the Texas Research Institute (1985), the highest concentration of H_2O_2 initially tolerated by a mixed biofilm culture was 500 mg/L. Tolerance levels were increased to 2,000 mg/L by incrementally increasing the influent H_2O_2 concentration to the test columns over time. As presented by Pardieck et al. (1992), a possible explanation for the apparent acclimation was the growth

TABLE 2. Analysis of deviance for the fitted model.

Terms	Degrees of Freedom	Deviance	Residual Degrees of Freedom	Residual Deviance	F-Statistic	p-Value
Null			146	12.23861		
H[a]	1	11.87901	145	0.35960	5,839.850	~0
H:Column[b]	2	0.02463	143	0.33497	6.053	0.003

(a) [Influent H_2O_2 concentration (mg/L)]$^{2/3}$.
(b) Interaction term between column and predictor H (i.e., individual components of the slope for each column).

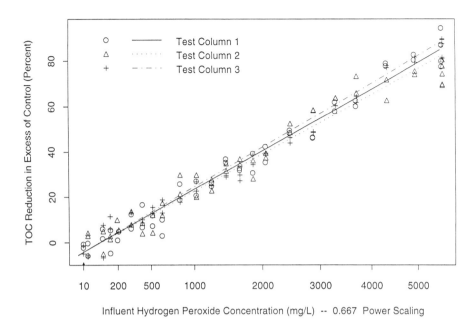

FIGURE 4. TOC reduction in test columns in excess of control versus H_2O_2 concentration raised to the ⅔ power.

in the numbers of catalase-positive bacteria in the biofilm. Bacteria are also able to tolerate higher concentrations of H_2O_2 at higher cell densities than they are at lower cell densities. With more catalase-positive bacteria present in a more dense population, the bacteria are exposed to H_2O_2 for shorter periods of time. The result is higher catalase activity of the population which results in more rapid decomposition of the H_2O_2.

Four samples of the soil used for the columns were collected after mixing but before the soil was allocated to the columns. Replicate (n = 2) analyses were performed to quantify the indigenous bacterial population density in the soil. The geometric mean of those analyses was 5.2×10^6 colony-forming units (cfu)/g dry-weight. The arithmetic mean and variance for those analyses was 7.4×10^6 and 3.1×10^{13} cfu/g dry-weight, respectively. The results of those analyses demonstrated some heterogeneity in the soil.

At the end of the study, the columns were sacrificed and sectioned into three equal portions, designated as layers A, B and C, where A was the influent end. Replicate (n = 2) samples were collected from each section and analyzed for bacterial population density (Figure 5). A higher bacterial population density was evident in the test columns compared to the controls. There also appeared to be real differences between test columns. Bacterial population densities in test and control columns at the end of the study are presented in Table 3.

Based on probability theory, bacterial population density measurements can be viewed as being proportional to Poisson random variables where the multipliers

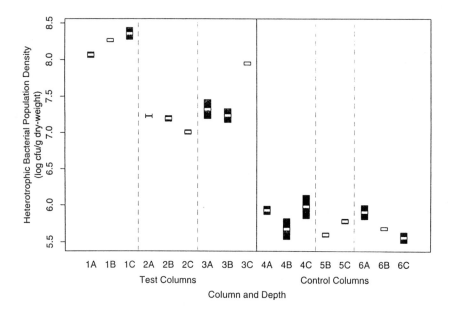

FIGURE 5. Heterotrophic bacterial population density versus depth in test and control columns. Influent end of each soil column is identified as "A."

are determined by the mass of dry soil and the dilution factor used for the analysis. Under this model, the variance of repeated measurements would be proportional to their mean. Because this also holds true for the gamma distribution, the population density data were modeled using a GLIM with gamma errors and a log link function.

The experimental design for the population density data was a 3-stage nested design with replication. Treatment was the fixed-effect factor of interest. Column was a random effect nested within treatment, and layer was an additional random effect nested within column. Treatment was an extremely significant predictor (p-value ~ 0). The random column effect nested within treatment was very significant (p-value ~ 10^{-10}), and the random layer effect nested with column was also fairly significant (p-value ~ 10^{-4}). Because these effects are additive in the log scale, they are multiplicative in the original scale.

TABLE 3. Comparison of final bacterial population densities in test and control columns.

	Geometric Mean	Arithmetic Mean	Variance
Control Columns	5.84×10^5	6.35×10^5	8.13×10^{10}
Test Columns	4.23×10^7	7.86×10^7	6.87×10^{15}

The studentized model residuals (log scale) for layer C (effluent end) had significantly greater variance than those of the other layers. At the end of the study, channelling in all test columns was visually evident. Channeling was most pronounced in layer C and provided a clear physical explanation of the observed variance heterogeneity. Because bacterial population density data for layer A of column 5 were not obtained and because of variance heterogeneity associated with layer C, inference from this model is only approximate. Although these results are only approximate, the p-values for the treatment effect and for the random column effect are so small that they are quite convincing.

The data in Table 3 indicate roughly a 100-fold increase in bacterial population density in the test columns over the controls. A naive analysis of the raw data in the original scale is skewed by the extreme effect of column 1 and by the extreme increase in variance for the test columns due to the combined effects of column 1 and of the generally increased bacterial population densities. The estimate from the GLIM model is that an approximate 8-fold increase in bacterial population density may be attributed to the treatment. Of the log scale variance not explained by treatment, approximately 79% and 15% are accounted by the random column and layer effects, respectively.

CONCLUSIONS

The benefit of H_2O_2 addition for biological treatment of available organics was demonstrated. At an influent H_2O_2 concentration of 5,400 mg/L, greater than 90% of the available TOC was mineralized, and a toxic effect to the indigenous microflora was not observed. H_2O_2 addition would be particularly advantageous for the biological treatment of hazardous organics in the sludges of surface impoundments and other similar environments where aeration by conventional methods would result in the liberation of objectionable odors.

ACKNOWLEDGMENTS

For preparation of this paper, the authors would like to thank Carol D. Litchfield, George Mason University, Fairfax, Virginia, for her suggestions in the design of this study; Bernard C. Lawes, E.I. Du Pont de Nemours & Company, Wilmington, Delaware, for his invaluable suggestions and assistance throughout the study; and Laura L. Duhigg-Wolsiffer, OHM Remediation Services Corporation, Findlay, Ohio, for her valuable assistance in preparing this paper.

REFERENCES

Aggarwal, P. K., J. L. Means, D. C. Downey, and R. E. Hinchee. 1991. "Use of Hydrogen Peroxide as an Oxygen Source for In Situ Biodegradation. Part II. Laboratory Studies." *Journal of Hazardous Materials*, 27: 301-314.

American Public Health Association, American Water Works Association, and Water Pollution Control Federation. 1989. *Standard Methods for the Examination of Water and Wastewater*, 17th ed. American Public Health Association, Washington, DC.

Britton, L. N., and Texas Research Institute (TRI). 1985. "Feasibility Studies on the Use of Hydrogen Peroxide to Enhance Microbial Degradation of Gasoline." Publication No. 4389. American Petroleum Institute, Washington, DC.

Brown, R. A., and R. D. Norris. 1994. "The Evolution of a Technology: Hydrogen Peroxide in In Situ Bioremediation." In R. E. Hinchee, B. C. Alleman, R. E. Hoeppel, and R. N. Miller (Eds.), *Hydrocarbon Bioremediation*, pp. 148-162. Lewis Publishers, Boca Raton, FL.

Chambers, J. M., and T. J. Hastie (Eds.). 1992. Statistical Methods in S. Wadsworth & Brooks/Cole Advanced Books & Software, Pacific Grove, CA.

Dobson, A. J. 1983. *Introduction to Statistical Modeling*. Chapman and Hall, New York, NY.

Dworkin, M., and J. W. Foster. 1958. "Experiments with Some Microorganisms which Utilize Ethane and Hydrogen." *Journal of Bacteriology*, 75: 592-603.

Flathman, P. E., and L. S. Bottomley. 1994. "Bioremediation of Ethylene Glycol-Contaminated Groundwater at the Naval Air Warfare Center in Lakehurst, New Jersey." In P. E. Flathman, D. E. Jerger, and J. H. Exner (Eds.), *Bioremediation: Field Experience*, pp. 491-503. Lewis Publishers, Boca Raton, FL.

Flathman, P. E., J. H. Carson, Jr., S. J. Whitehead, K. A. Khan, D. M. Barnes, and J. S. Evans. 1991. "Laboratory Evaluation of the Utilization of Hydrogen Peroxide for Enhanced Biological Treatment of Petroleum Hydrocarbon Contaminants in Soil." In R. E. Hinchee and R. F. Olfenbuttel (Eds.), *In Situ Bioreclamation*, pp. 125-142. Butterworth-Heinemann, Stoneham, MA.

Harding, G. L. 1988. Texas Research Institute, Austin, TX, personal communication, January 14.

Hoaglin, D. C., F. Mosteller, and J. W. Tukey. 1983. *Understanding Robust and Exploratory Data Analysis*. John Wiley & Sons, Inc., New York, NY.

Huling, S. G., B. E. Bledsoe, and M. V. White. 1990. *Enhanced Bioremediation Utilizing Hydrogen Peroxide as a Supplemental Source of Oxygen: A Laboratory and Field Study*. EPA/600/2-90/006.

Karlin, S., and H. M. Taylor. 1975. *A First Course in Stochastic Processes*, 2nd ed. Academic Press, Inc., San Diego, CA.

Lawes, B. C. 1989. Dupont, Wilmington, DE, personal communication, April 7.

Lawes, B. C. 1991. "Soil-Induced Decomposition of Hydrogen Peroxide." In R. E. Hinchee and R. F. Olfenbuttel (Eds.), *In Situ Bioreclamation*, pp. 140-147. Butterworth-Heinemann, Stoneham, MA.

Lu, C. J. 1994. "Effects of Hydrogen Peroxide on the In Situ Biodegradation of Organic Chemicals in a Simulated Groundwater System." In R. E. Hinchee, B. C. Alleman, R. E. Hoeppel, and R. N. Miller (Eds.), *Hydrocarbon Bioremediation*, pp. 148-162. Lewis Publishers, Boca Raton, FL.

Pardieck, D. L., E. J. Bouwer, and A. T. Stone. 1992. "Hydrogen Peroxide Use to Increase Oxidant Capacity for In Situ Bioremediation of Contaminated Soils and Aquifers: A Review." *Journal of Contaminant Hydrology*, 9(3) pp. 221-242.

Statistical Sciences, Inc. 1994. *S-PLUS for Windows, Version 3.2, Supplement*. Statsci: a Division of MathSoft, Inc., Seattle, WA.

U.S. Environmental Protection Agency. 1986. *Test Methods for Evaluating Solid Waste, Physical/Chemical Methods*, 3rd ed. SW-846. Office of Solid Waste and Emergency Response, Washington, DC.

Wilson, J. T., J. M. Armstrong, and H. S. Rafai. 1994. "A Full-Scale Field Demonstration on the Use of Hydrogen Peroxide for In Situ Bioremediation of an Aviation Gasoline-Contaminated Aquifer." In P. E. Flathman, D. E. Jerger, and J. H. Exner (Eds.), *Bioremediation: Field Experience*, pp. 333-359. Lewis Publishers, Boca Raton, FL.

In Situ Bioremediation Strategies for Organic Wood Preservatives

James G. Mueller, Michael D. Tischuk,
Mitchell D. Brourman, and Garet E. Van De Steeg

ABSTRACT

Laboratory biotreatability studies evaluated the use of bioventing and biosparging plus groundwater circulation (UVB technology) for their potential ability to treat soil and groundwater containing creosote and pentachlorophenol. Soils from two former wood-treatment facilities were used in these studies. These studies provided useful, site-specific data demonstrating enhanced biodegradation of all monitored organic constituents. The results suggest that the introduction and delivery of co-reagents (i.e., oxygen and nitrogen) essential to in situ biodegradation of organic wood preservatives represents an important component of effective in situ bioremediation. Full-scale implementation strategies are being considered based on the findings of these studies.

INTRODUCTION

In 1992 in situ bioremediation was recommended for 4% of the U.S. Environmental Protection Agency's (U.S. EPA) Superfund sites (20/498 sites) (U.S. EPA 1992). As of June 1993, this number increased to 26 applications, with 16 systems in the design phase, 9 systems in the installation/operational phases, and 1 application completed (U.S. EPA 1994). In situ installation at non-Superfund sites has been even more popular. This growing trend of implementing in situ bioremediation technologies is expected to continue, especially with recent field documentation of natural attenuation and intrinsic biodegradation occurring in situ with little or no augmentation (Wilson et al. 1994).

Historically, in situ bioremediation has focused on the treatment of materials containing refined petroleum products, and only a few efforts have targeted organic wood preservatives, such as pentachlorophenol (PCP) and polycyclic aromatic hydrocarbons (PAHs). This is because conventional in situ bioremediation technologies address most effectively factors such as adding electron acceptors (e.g., oxygen) and inorganic nutrients (e.g., nitrogen), but they typically are limited in their ability to overcome other physicochemical factors known to inhibit the biodegradation of PAHs (e.g., bioavailability) (Mueller et al. 1993; Sims et al. 1994).

The purpose of these studies was to test the effectiveness of in situ bioremediation for PAHs/PCP in vadose zone soil by bioventing, and in saturated zone soil by groundwater circulation/air sparging using soils collected from two field sites: (1) the Feather River Superfund Site, Oroville, California; and (2) the former Moss-American Creosote Site, Sauget, Illinois.

EXPERIMENTAL PROCEDURES AND MATERIALS

Kopper's Company, Inc. Superfund Site, Feather River Plant, Oroville, California (FR)

Three intact soil cores (ca. 7.6 cm diameter × 61 cm length) were obtained from a single boring of the saturated zone (10 to 32 m deep) near a former creosote pond in northern California. Intact soil cores were loaded into laboratory columns (see below) to assess the effect of in situ groundwater circulation combined with air biosparging and nutriation on the rate of PAH/PCP biodegradation by indigenous microflora over an 8-week period. Three in situ microcosms (soil columns) were established as follows:

| | Column Number | | |
Parameter/Treatment	1	2	3
Aeration	none	dissolved oxygen	dissolved oxygen
Circulating Liquid	buffered water	buffered nutrients	buffered nutrients
Sample Core Depth	30.8 to 31.4 m	10.7 to 11.3 m	10.1 to 10.4 m
Column Duration	8 weeks	4 weeks	8 weeks

Former Moss-American Wood Treating Site, Sauget, Illinois (MA)

Vadose zone soil (non-creosote saturated, but with creosote impact) was excavated from six locations on site, all within 5 m of ground surface, and soil was composited on site. Columns were packed in the laboratory with homogenized soil to assess the effect of in situ bioventing (air) combined with nutriation through aqueous (urea, phosphorus) or gaseous (anhydrous ammonia) amendments on the rate of PAH biodegradation by indigenous microflora over a 16-week period. The effects were tested in replicate (4) in situ microcosms as follows:

| Column | Treatment | | | |
Number	Air Addition	Aqueous Nutrients	Water Circulation	Gaseous Nitrogen
1, 2, 3, 4	—	—	—	—
5, 6, 7, 8	+	—	+	—
9, 10, 11, 12	+	—	+	+
13, 14, 15, 16	+	+	+	—

Column Design and Operation

For columns designed to model biosparging/groundwater circulation (FR soils), humidified air was introduced at the top of the water column at a rate of 200 mL/min, and oxygenated water was circulated throughout the columns from the bottom upward at a flow rate of ca. 7 mL/min. Nutrients (urea, mono- and di-basic potassium phosphate) were made to the aqueous solutions of appropriate columns at the time of startup to yield a C(PAH):N:P ratio of 50:3:1. Soil in the control column was kept under saturated, non-oxygenated conditions by circulating buffered, distilled water. Columns designed to model bioventing (MA soils) were operated in a similar manner. However, humidified air was introduced to the aerated column not receiving aqueous additions (which kept the soils at >80% of field capacity).

Gaseous anhydrous ammonia additions were made at predetermined intervals by pulsing optimized amounts through the soil column (saturated with distilled water) with the permeating airstream (data not shown). All four columns of this treatment received an initial pulse of anhydrous ammonia upon startup (16 pulses of 10 minute 50 second duration at 30 minute cycles). After 72 days of column operation, the two remaining columns (columns 11 and 12) received another pulsing administered in the same manner. Using this strategy, ammonia-N was shown to migrate slowly up the soil column similar to a plug-flow model. Within 7 days of initial exposure, soil pH and nitrogen concentrations were shown to equilibrate within the soil columns (data not shown). Thus, sequential pulsing with anhydrous ammonia was shown to be a practical means to add nitrogen in situ in response to increased nitrogen demands associated with effective bioremediation.

Sampling and Analysis

The sampling plan common to both studies is summarized in Table 1. It should be noted, however, that the study with the MA soils was more detailed, including mass balance of an added radiotracer (9-^{14}C-phenanthrene), Toxicity Characteristic Leaching Procedure analyses, etc. For FR soils, samples from cores at time zero were composited from core shavings necessary to make the core fit the inner diameter of the columns. Intermittent liquid samples for weekly

TABLE 1. Summary of analytical methods, sample requirements, and sample preservation guidelines common to both studies.

Parameter Measured	Method	Sample Size	Preservative
Critical Parameters (triplicate analyses at 4-week intervals)			
PAH/PCP chemistry	SW-846 8270	100 g	pH < 2
Bacterial counts	SBP/ASTM 9215	10 g	4°C
Noncritical Parameters (individual analyses at 4-week intervals)			
Total Kjeldahl nitrogen	EPA 351.2	50 g	4°C
Ammonia nitrogen	EPA 350.2	25 g	4°C
Nitrate nitrogen	EPA 353.2	25 g	4°C
Total phosphorus	EPA 365.1	25 g	4°C
Available phosphorus	ASA II Chap. 24	25 g	4°C
Bulk density	ASA I Chap. 13	25 g	4°C
Particle density	ASA I Chap. 14	25 g	4°C
USDA soil texture	ASTM D2487	25 g	4°C
Weekly Monitoring Parameters (individual analyses)			
pH	EPA 150.1	10 g	4°C
Dissolved oxygen	probe	10 mL	NA
Daily Monitoring Parameters (individual analyses)			
Temperature, airflow rates, liquid circulation (where appropriate)			

ASA Methods: *Methods of Soil Analysis; Parts I and II*, American Society of Agronomy, Madison, WI (1986).
ASTM Standard Methods for the Examination of Water and Wastewater, 18th ed., 1992.
EPA Methods: *Methods for Chemical Analysis of Water and Wastes*, EPA 600/4-79/020, March 1983.
SW-846 Methods: *Test Methods for Evaluating Solid Wastes*, 3rd ed., November 1986.

monitoring were taken from the bottom of each column. Air leaving all columns was filtered through a series of three activated carbon filters. These filters were extracted upon the termination of each column to aid in mass balance determinations of organic constituents of interest (COI); namely PAH and PCP. Entire columns of each treatment were sacrificed at 4-week intervals to obtain replicate soil samples. All COI analyses were performed in triplicate with Level III or IV analysis protocol to provide the minimum data required for accurate statistics in accordance with the *Guide for Conducting Treatability Studies Under CERCLA* (U.S. EPA 1991).

RESULTS AND DISCUSSIONS

Changes in Noncritical Parameters

For both soils, physicochemical data at the time of sampling showed relatively low amounts of inorganic nutrients prior to additions (data not shown). Thus, a lack of essential inorganic nutrients, namely N, was presumably a factor limiting intrinsic in situ COI biodegradation. Changes in the amount of inorganic nutrients in soil during the column microcosm study showed that added nutrients were rapidly consumed in the actively treated, oxygenated columns. Presumably, nutrients were consumed for catabolism of resident soil COI. This was evidenced by a correlation between an increased number of catabolically relevant bacteria (data not shown) and COI biodegradation (see below).

Changes in Critical Parameters

Organic COIs were considered as the critical parameters in both studies. Potentially carcinogenic PAHs (pcPAHs) were identified as the following six compounds: benz[a]anthracene, benzo[a]pyrene, benzo[b]fluoranthene, benzo[k]-fluoranthene, chrysene, and indeno[1,2,3-cd]pyrene. In addition, dibenz[a,h]-anthracene was identified at the MA Site. Mass balance chemical analyses of COI included measurement of COI in soil, column leachate (if any), off-gas, and column residue (if any).

Feather River Biosparging/Groundwater Circulation Studies. At the initiation of the FR column studies, soil cores in Columns 1, 2, and 3 contained an average amount of total PAHs (tPAH) of 153, 98, and 99 mg tPAH/kg soil d.w., respectively (Table 2). PCP in initial soil extracts was below the detection limit (detection limit 0.1 mg/kg soil d.w.). During in situ bioremediation evaluations, biodegradation of COI was demonstrated for both active columns 2 and 3. These changes were beyond those observed in control column 1 (Table 2). After 8 weeks of in situ biotreatment, essentially no semivolatiles were detected in the column water, but the liquid did contain PCP at 1.1 mg/L. The presence of PCP in column water was attributed to low amounts of soil PCP leaching into the column water. No other COI were detected in column water (data not shown). Analysis of activated carbon showed a maximum total of 0.212 mg tPAH recovered per column, with a majority being naphthalene (0.148 mg). Thus, losses of COI observed over the course of these studies were due to biological activity.

Mathematical interpretation of total PAH biodegradation data suggested that the active in situ biosparging treatment had greater rates and extent of COI biodegradation than the control column (Table 2). The average of the two treated columns offered a biodegradation rate (k) of 12 mg tPAH/kg soil/week. Using first-order kinetics, this yields a tPAH in situ soil half-life of 11.6 weeks (average of the 2 columns, with individual values of 4.6 and 18.5 weeks). Similar results were observed with cumulative pcPAH biodegradation kinetics where first-order mathematical models determined that the active in situ biosparging treatment

TABLE 2. Total PAH and pcPAH biodegradation kinetics based on analytical data acquired during the 8-week laboratory biosparging study: Feather River soils.

Treatment Average	Starting PAH Concentration (mg/kg soil d.w.)	Ending PAH Concentration (mg/kg soil d.w.)	PAH Biodegraded (%)	Biodegradation Rate (k) (mg PAH/kg soil/wk)	PAH Half-Life in Soil ($T_{1/2}$) (weeks)
Total PAHs					
Control Column 1	153	163	0	0	ND
Active Bioventing Column 2	98	23	77	19	4.6
Active Bioventing Column 3	99	60	40	5	18.5
pcPAHs					
Control Column 1	12	14	0	0	ND
Active Bioventing Column 2	5	3	40	0.5	13.9
Active Bioventing Column 3	7	5	29	0.3	27.7

Calculations:

PAH half-life in soil ($T_{1/2}$) based on first-order PAH biodegradation kinetics according to the following models:

$$\ln C = a + K_1 t \qquad \text{and} \qquad T_{1/2} = 0.693/K_1$$

where C = PAH concentration (mg/kg soil dry weight) at time (t), a = Y-axis intercept, and K_1 is the slope of the first-order regression line.

Biodegradation rates (k) based on the slope of the zero-order regression line.

ND = not determined.

effectively reduced the pcPAH soil half-life to about 21 weeks (Table 2). In both cases it is important to recognize that differences in the starting COI concentrations for the control and active columns are due to variations in the source concentrations (soil cores taken from different depths as described above), and are not necessarily associated with large error in sampling and analysis.

In general, we view first-order modeling as more accurate to biodegradation studies with creosote. This is because the multi-phasic (different creosote constituents are biodegraded at different rates [Pritchard et al. 1995; Sims et al. 1994]) and asymptotic (rates slowing down with time due to bioavailability limitations) natures of common creosote biodegradation patterns are not well integrated into zero-order mathematical equations. This is most evident with creosote bioremediation processes especially as they encounter lower substrate concentrations. Thus, soil half-life factors ($T_{1/2}$) are used here as more useful points of treatment comparison.

Former Moss-American Site Bioventing Studies. The MA soils had a much higher starting concentration of COI (7,130 mg tPAH/kg soil on a normalized basis) than the FR soils. Despite this significant difference, mathematical modeling of total PAH (tPAH) biodegradation kinetics calculated over the course of the 16-week in situ bioventing study showed that the columns which received liquid nutrients had the highest biodegradation rate (k) and the shortest tPAH half-life ($T_{1/2}$) of all the treatments tested (Table 3). When air bioventing was coupled with the addition of liquid nutrients, first-order linear regression analysis ($r^2 = 0.84$) determined the in situ $T_{1/2}$ to be 33.8 weeks. Columns that received air only exhibited kinetic values ($r^2 = 0.97$) just slightly lower (k = 193.9 mg tPAH/kg soil d.w./week; $T_{1/2}$ = 40.8 weeks) than those observed with the addition of liquid nutrients. But these were better than those observed with the columns that received anhydrous ammonia additions (k = 129.2 mg tPAH/kg soil d.w./week; $T_{1/2}$ = 69.3 weeks), recognizing a lower correlation coefficient for the modeling of this treatment ($r^2 = 0.59$). All treatments tested were more effective in removing COI than the control columns, where a $T_{1/2}$ of > 100 weeks was simply estimated for comparative purposes.

In the columns treated with anhydrous ammonia, there was a notably large decrease in the concentration of total PAHs between the week 12 and week 16 sampling points, which was associated with the stimulation of PAH-degraders (specifically, phenanthrene-degraders) upon a second pulsing of anhydrous ammonia that occurred after 72 days of incubation (data not shown). Efforts are in progress to better characterize this process and to identify a protocol for acclimating indigenous microbial populations for more effective use of anhydrous ammonia during in situ bioventing applications.

CONCLUSIONS

The combination of chemical and microbiological analytical data from studies with soils from Feather River (biosparging) and Moss American site (bioventing/

TABLE 3. Total PAH and pcPAH biodegradation kinetics based on normalized analytical data acquired during the 16-week incubation period: Moss American bioventing study.

Treatment Average	Starting PAH Concentration (mg/kg soil d.w.)	PAH After 16 Weeks (mg/kg soil d.w.)	PAH Biodegraded (%)	Biodegradation Rate (k) (mg PAH/kg soil/wk)	PAH Half-Life in Soil ($T_{1/2}$) (weeks)
Total PAH					
Control	7,130	5,754	19.3	8.45	>100
Air Only	7,130	2,921	59.0	193.9	40.8
Air + Ammonia Gas	7,130	3,791	46.8	129.2	69.3
Air + Liquid Nutrients	7,130	2,713	62.0	217.4	33.8
pcPAHs					
Control	707	823	0	0	>500
Air Only	707	747	0	0	>500
Air + Ammonia Gas	707	804	0	0	>500
Air + Liquid Nutrients	707	635	10.2	1.4	554

See Table 2 for calculations.

groundwater circulation) suggested that biodegradation of organic COI could be stimulated by adding oxygen and nitrogen to the indigenous microflora. Over the relatively short time frame of these studies, however, biodegradation of pcPAHs was limited which is in accordance with much of the existing scientific literature. But on a site-specific basis, appropriately designed in situ bioremediation systems may represent effective strategies for treating organic COI typically present at wood treating sites. The continuing development of effective implement tools promises to provide even better means of delivering essential co-reagents, such as oxygen and nitrogen, to affect situ biodegradation of organic wood preservatives.

REFERENCES

Mueller, J. G., J.-E. Lin, S. E. Lantz, and P. H. Pritchard. 1993. "Recent Developments in Cleanup Technologies: Implementing Innovative Bioremediation Technologies." *Remediation* (Summer).

Pritchard, P. H., J. G. Mueller, S. E. Lantz, and D. L. Santavy. 1995. "The Potential Importance of Biodiversity in Environmental Biotechnology Applications: Bioremediation of PAH-Contaminated Soils and Sediments." In D. Allsop et al. (Eds.), *Microbial Diversity and Ecosystem Function.* Chapter 9, pp. 161-182. CAB International Publishers, London.

Sims, R. C., J. L. Sims, D. L. Sorensen, D. K. Stevens, S. G. Huling, B. E. Bledsoe, J. E. Matthews, and D. Pope. 1994. "Performance Evaluation of Full-Scale *In Situ* and *Ex Situ* Bioremediation of Creosote Wastes in Groundwater and Soils." *Proceedings of the Symposium on Bioremediation of Hazardous Wastes: Research, Development and Field Evaluations.* EPA/600/R-94/075. pp. 35-39.

U.S. EPA. 1991. *Guide for Conducting Treatability Studies Under CERCLA.* EPA/540/2-91/013A.

U.S. EPA. 1992. *Innovative Treatment Technologies: Semi-Annual Status Report.* EPA/542/R-92/011.

U.S. EPA. 1994. *Tech Trends.* February. EPA/542/N-94/001.

Wilson, J. T., J. W. Weaver, and D. H. Kampbell. 1994. "Intrinsic Bioremediation of TCE in Groundwater at an NPL Site in St. Joseph, Michigan." *Proceedings of the Symposium on Bioremediation of Hazardous Wastes: Research, Development and Field Evaluations.* EPA/600/R-94/075. pp. 3-10.

In Situ Bioventing at a Natural Gas Dehydrator Site: Field Demonstration

Alonzo W. Lawrence, Daniel L. Miller, Jeffrey A. Miller,
Robin L. Weightman, Richard M. Raetz, and Thomas D. Hayes

ABSTRACT

This paper describes a bioventing/biosparging field demonstration that was conducted over a 10-month period at a former glycol dehydrator site located near Traverse City, Michigan. The goal of the project was to determine the feasibility of this technology for dehydrator site remediation and to develop engineering design concepts for applying bioventing/biosparging at similar sites. The chemicals of interest are benzene, toluene, ethylbenzene, and xylenes (BTEX) and alkanes (C_4 through C_{10}). Soil sampling indicated that the capillary fringe and saturated zones were heavily contaminated, but that the unsaturated zone was relatively free of the contaminants. A pump-and-treat system has operated since 1991 to treat the groundwater BTEX plume. Bioventing/biosparging was installed in September 1993 to treat the contaminant source area. Three different air sparging operating modes (pulse, continuous, and vapor recycle) were tested to determine an optimal process configuration for site remediation. These operational modes were compared through in situ respirometry studies. Respirometry measurements were used to estimate biodegradation rates. Dissolved oxygen and carbon dioxide were monitored in the groundwater. A hydrocarbon mass balance based on soil and groundwater sampling was compared to the estimate of hydrocarbons biologically degraded based on the respiration studies. Gaseous-phase nutrients, nitrous oxide, and triethyl phosphate (TEP) were added to stimulate the rates of biodegradation. The results of the study suggest that bioventing/biosparging is a feasible technology for in situ remediation of soil and groundwater at gas industry glycol dehydrator sites.

INTRODUCTION

This Gas Research Institute (GRI) field experiment at a member company's site was performed to investigate the feasibility of using bioventing/biosparging for cost-effective remediation of natural gas glycol dehydrator site contamination. Daily field activities began on September 1, 1993, and ended July 4, 1994. Post-demonstration groundwater and soil sampling was conducted in October 1994, and a postdemonstration respirometry study was conducted in November 1994. A final sampling event is scheduled for the end of the 3rd quarter 1995 to document the long-term performance of bioventing/biosparging.

A series of air sparge wells and multilevel monitor points were installed in the location of the former glycol dehydrator, which was the source of a 1900-ft (580-m) BTEX groundwater plume. Figure 1 is a site plan for this field experiment.

A number of process equipment configurations and process operational programs were field-tested to determine which approach resulted in maximum biodegradation rates. Groundwater, soil, and soil gas samples were collected and analyzed to determine the effectiveness of the system. Realtime soil gas and groundwater field measurements were taken to monitor performance. Gaseous-phase nutrients were added when biokinetic rates determined from the respiration studies declined sufficiently to suggest that nutrients had become rate limiting. When nutrients were added, the field-measured biokinetic rates increased.

EXPERIMENTAL DESIGN

Experimental Plan

The bioventing/biosparging system consists of two linked process operations, i.e., a biosparging process and a bioventing process. The biosparging process is

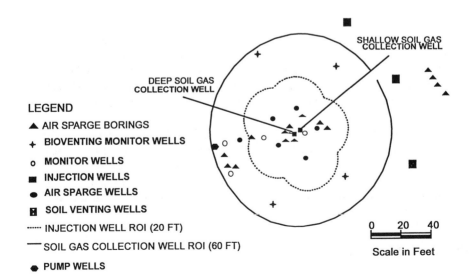

FIGURE 1. Site plan.

designed to inject air into the saturated zone, and the bioventing process is designed to collect soil gas to control and monitor subsurface airflow.

The experimental plan consisted of a mechanical system design, an analytical sampling plan, a field monitoring plan, and an operating plan. The following equation was used to estimate the mass biodegraded as determined by soil, groundwater, and vapor analytical sampling:

$$IMASS - TMASS - PTMASS - SVEMASS = BDMASS_{ANALYTICAL} \qquad (1)$$

where: IMASS = hydrocarbon mass initially in treatment zone
   TMASS = hydrocarbon mass at time (t) in treatment zone
   PTMASS = hydrocarbon mass leaving treatment zone from pump-and-treat system
   SVEMASS = hydrocarbon mass extracted with soil vapor extraction system
   $BDMASS_{ANALYTICAL}$ = hydrocarbon mass biologically degraded

Zero-order biodegradation rates for the unsaturated zone were estimated by measuring oxygen depletion in monitor points screened in the unsaturated zone following periodic cessation of the air sparging. The saturated zone biodegradation rates were estimated by measuring dissolved oxygen utilization in the groundwater in the monitor points screened in the saturated zone. The average biodegradation rates for both the saturated and unsaturated zones were then used to estimate the mass biologically degraded based on the following equation:

$$UMASS + SMASS = BDMASS_{RESPIROMETRY} \qquad (2)$$

where: UMASS = hydrocarbon mass removed from the unsaturated zone
   SMASS = hydrocarbon mass removed from the saturated zone
   $BDMASS_{RESPIROMETRY}$ = hydrocarbon mass biologically degraded

Finally, the two calculated biologically degraded masses were compared for agreement,

$$\frac{BDMASS_{ANALYTICAL}}{BDMASS_{RESPIROMETRY}} \approx 1 \qquad (3)$$

Facility Design

An air sparging blower, six air sparge wells, and soil gas monitor points had been installed prior to initiation of the field experiment. Figure 1 is a site plan and Figure 2 is a process and instrument diagram for the biosparging system. Mathematical modeling confirmed the need for a soil vapor collection blower (bioventing) to control subsurface airflow. Flowmeters, nutrients, nutrient delivery equipment, and a soil vapor collection blower (bioventing) were added to the existing biosparging system. The bioventing blower was added to the

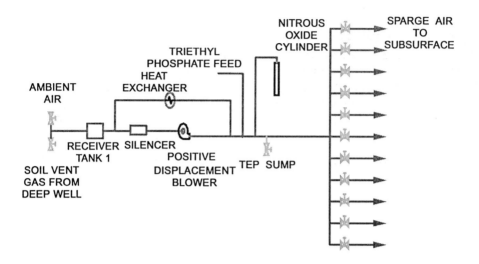

FIGURE 2. Biosparging process and instrument diagram.

treatment system to control subsurface airflows so that soil gases sparged into the unsaturated zone by biosparging were collected and the hydrocarbon concentration was measured prior to release to the atmosphere. Vapor-phase nutrients, nitrous oxide and triethyl phosphate, at approximately 100:10:2 C:N:P ratios, were selected for this demonstration based on reported experience at the Savannah River Site (Hazen et al. 1993). Nitrous oxide is a vapor at ambient conditions and was easily introduced into the biosparge flow. Triethyl phosphate is a liquid at ambient conditions but has a high vapor pressure. Thus, processing equipment was required to volatilize the triethyl phosphate in the biosparge flow. A chemical feed pump and injection nozzle were used to accurately measure the triethyl phosphate feed and improve volatilization. A trap was also added to the biosparge piping to collect and measure the triethyl phosphate that did not volatilize.

FIELD OPERATIONS AND RESULTS

Operations Monitoring

Phase I operations, a pulsed biosparging mode, began on September 29, 1993. Table 1 summarizes the operation dates for the four phases of the field experiment. Phase II, a stepped continuous airflow mode, began on October 25, 1993, and continued through February 4, 1994. Gaseous nutrient addition began November 18, 1993. Nutrients were added to both the saturated and unsaturated zones. However, mechanical problems developed with the triethyl phosphate nutrient feed pump and injection system, and material compatibility problems were also experienced. The mechanical problems and material incompatibilities

TABLE 1. List of system operational dates and respiration rates.

	System Operational Dates		Cumulative Number of Days	Respiration Rates	
	Dates	Number of Days		Unsaturated Zone Soil mg/kg-day	Saturated Zone Soil mg/kg-day
Background	09/27/93 to 09/28/93	-2	—		
Phase I Cycle I					
Operation	09/29/93 to 10/04/93	6	6		
Respirometry	10/05/93 to 10/12/93	8	14	3.65	0.0695
Phase I Cycle II					
Operation	10/13/93 to 10/17/93	5	19		
Respirometry	10/18/93 to 10/24/93	7	26	0.65	0.0071
Phase II Cycle I					
Operation	10/25/93 to 12/12/93	49	75		
Respirometry	12/13/93 to 12/19/93	7	82		
No Operation	12/20/93 to 01/10/94	22	104	0.21	0.0319
Phase II Cycle II					
Operation	01/11/94 to 01/28/94	18	122		
Respirometry	01/29/94 to 02/4/94	7	129	5.92	0.4327
No Operation — System Modified for Mode III Soil Gas Recycle	02/5/94 to 03/7/94	31	160		

TABLE 1. (Continued).

	System Operational Dates			Respiration Rates	
	Dates	Number of Days	Cumulative Number of Days	Unsaturated Zone Soil mg/kg-day	Saturated Zone Soil mg/kg-day
Phase III Cycle I					
Mechanical Shake Down	03/08/94 to 03/17/94	10	170		
Operation	03/18/94 to 03/28/94	11	181		
Operation w/increase in flow	03/29/94 to 04/17/94	20	201		
Respirometry	04/18/94 to 4/26/94	9	210	1.22	0.0195
Phase IV Cycle I					
Operation	4/27/94 to 6/19/94	54	264		
Respirometry	6/27/94 to 7/4/94	15	279	0.28	0.0118
Continued Operations	7/5/94-Present				
Bacterial Seed Added	August-September 1994				
Respiration	November 1994			4.28	0.42

were resolved, and Phase II was restarted January 11, 1994. The second Phase II respirometry study (fourth respiration) was performed beginning January 29, 1994, and suggested that the addition of nutrients had improved the biodegradation rates. A controlled laboratory study showed that dissolved triethyl phosphate was not air stripped from water. This confirmed that triethyl phosphate could not easily enter the unsaturated zone through biosparging from the saturated zone and, thus, nutrients were added to the unsaturated and saturated zones.

In Phase III, a soil gas recycle mode, a continuous reading lower explosive limit (LEL) meter was installed to monitor and shut down the system if the measured hydrocarbon vapor concentration was above 25% of the LEL. The respirometry study conducted during this phase indicated no significant improvement in biodegradation rates compared to those observed in Phases I and II. Additionally, the hydrocarbon concentrations of the off-gas were higher than for the other two operating modes.

The field experiment ended July 4, 1994 (279 cumulative days). Site remediation is continuing under the direction of the site owner's consultant. While several modifications have been made to the equipment configuration and operations since July 1994, one respirometry study was performed in November 1994 to document the ongoing remediation progress (Lawrence et al. 1994).

Mass Balances of Source Area Hydrocarbons

Table 2 summarizes the hydrocarbon mass balance for the source area soil and groundwater samples. Soil BTEX concentrations ranged from nondetect (ND) to 1,815 mg/kg, and total petroleum hydrocarbons (TPH) ranged from ND to 12 mg/kg. Groundwater BTEX ranged from ND to 60.8 mg/L, and TPH ranged from ND to 24 mg/L. As shown in Table 2, the estimated initial mass of hydrocarbons was less than the mass estimated from event two. This can be explained because the sampling intervals were changed as a result of the first event samples. The average of events one and two is assumed to be the best estimate of the initial hydrocarbon mass. An average of the hydrocarbon mass from events three and four was 1,262 lb (574 kg), which was the remaining mass. Using equation (1), the hydrocarbon mass biologically degraded was estimated to be 4,985 lb (2266 kg) (see Table 2).

Biokinetic Rates of Hydrocarbon Degradation Determined by Field Respirometry Measurements

Seven respirometry studies were performed. Oxygen depletion as percent oxygen in the soil gas and dissolved oxygen in the groundwater were measured over time during periods when the bioventing blower and the biosparging blower were turned off.

Table 1 shows calculated zero-order biodegradation rates for each of the seven respirometry studies. Based on these respirometry-determined biodegradation rates, the estimated contaminant mass biologically degraded during

TABLE 2. Hydrocarbon mass balance.

Media	Event One September 1993 lb (kg) Hydrocarbon	Event Two December 1993 lb (kg) Hydrocarbon	Event Three June 1994 lb (kg) Hydrocarbon	Event Four October 1994 lb (kg) Hydrocarbon
Groundwater	24 (11)	340 (155)	24 (11)	24 (11)
Unsaturated Soil	2,363 (1,074)	3,952 (1,796)	619 (281)	662 (301)
Saturated Soil	2,864 (1,302)	4,715 (2,143)	567 (258)	628 (285)
Total	**5,251 (2,387)**	**9,007 (4,094)**	**1,210 (550)**	**1,314 (597)**

Biodegraded Mass Balance

	lb (kg)
Average Hydrocarbon Mass Events One and Two	7,129 (3,240)
Average Hydrocarbon Mass Events Three and Four	1,262 (574)
Mass Removed from Pump-and-Treat System	342 (155)
Mass Volatilized	540 (245)
Biodegraded Mass	4,985 (2,266)

the study period is 1,970 lb (895 kg). Four of the seven respiration-measured biodegradation rates from this field experiment compare well with published biodegradation rates from other projects (1 to 21 mg/kg/day) (Hinchee et al. 1992). It should be noted that the high rate measured in the seventh respiration is most probably a result of the injection of bacterial seed into the capillary fringe and groundwater approximately 1 month prior to the seventh respiration event. Thus, it is probably not representative of the preceding bioactivity at the site.

ENGINEERING EVALUATION

According to the National Research Council (Committee 1993) recommended criteria for evaluating the efficiency of in situ bioremediation, this study showed that:

- Hydrocarbon contaminant concentrations declined in the ground-water and soils;
- Indigenous microorganisms in site soil and groundwater samples were shown to have the potential to transform the contaminants as shown by the microbial counts (see Figure 3), and;
- Biodegradation was realized as shown by the increase in carbon dioxide in the soil gas, and the soil gas oxygen utilization observed in the respirometry studies (see Figure 4).

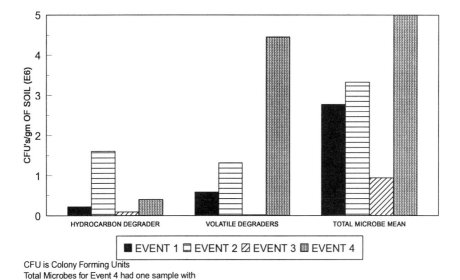

CFU is Colony Forming Units
Total Microbes for Event 4 had one sample with
5 E7 CFUs/gm of soil

FIGURE 3. Soil microbial counts.

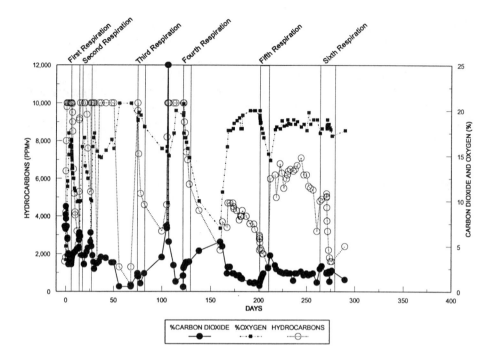

FIGURE 4. Trend plot of soil gas concentrations at the centrally located subsurface soil gas monitoring location for the duration of the field demonstration.

According to equation 3, the result of the biodegraded hydrocarbon mass balance based on analytical sampling over the respirometry-based biodegraded hydrocarbon mass would equal unity. The calculated ratio was 2.5. Variability was observed in the soil hydrocarbon concentrations between sampling events most probably due to the difficulty of obtaining truly representative samples of the contaminant distribution in the subsurface and the use of relatively few samples to characterize relatively large soil masses. The mass balance technique appears to be highly sample specific and thus is a relatively insensitive tool for evaluating the effectiveness of the bioventing process. The only way to overcome this difficulty would be to significantly increase the number of soil and groundwater samples used to compute the mass balances, which would entail considerably greater expense in terms of both field sample collection and analytical expense.

Conversely, the in situ respirometry technique of evaluating the rate of oxygen depletion both in the soil vapor and groundwater following periodic cessation of biosparging appears to be a more useful tool both for monitoring the progress of in situ bioremediation and estimating the total mass of hydrocarbons which are biologically degraded and physically removed from the subsurface.

Respiratory studies performed at the site suggested that biological oxidation of the hydrocarbon contaminants became nutrient (nitrogen and/or phosphorus) limited. Introduction of nutrients into the saturated and unsaturated subsurface zones appears to be a critical element in increasing the effectiveness of the bioventing/biosparging and achieving remediation at this site. The site soils were predominantly sand and gravel with total organic carbon concentrations consistently below laboratory detection limits. The nutrient limitation hypothesis is supported by nutrient concentrations in both soil and groundwater that were consistently below laboratory detection limits and the increase in the biodegradation rates following successful injection of nutrients into the subsurface. It does not appear that oxygen concentration was a limiting factor in the rate of biodegradation. A dissolved oxygen (DO) level of 1 mg/L would be sufficient to support aerobic biological activity and was supported by field measurement of DO concentrations above 1.0 mg/L at the groundwater wells. Figure 3 is a graph showing the change in microbial populations measured as colony-forming units/gram of soil from the baseline soil sampling event and for the three additional soil sampling events. This graph shows an increase in biological activity. Figure 4 is a trend plot for hydrocarbon, oxygen, and carbon dioxide concentrations for the monitor location screened in the capillary fringe which is located in the center of the treatment zone. The hydrocarbon and oxygen concentrations declined, whereas carbon dioxide concentrations increased during the respiration studies.

Biosparging System Operational Analysis

The four bioventing/biosparging operating modes evaluated in this study appear to be successful. Controlled laboratory studies have indicated that pulsed airflow operations may produce better biodegradation rates while minimizing volatilization. (Dupont & Lakshmiprasad 1993) Based on stoichiometry, atmospheric air containing approximately 21% oxygen by volume can supply sufficient oxygen to biodegrade a maximum of 20 mg of hexane equivalent/kg of soil utilizing all available oxygen. Thus, during continuous operations, any hydrocarbons volatilized above this concentration would be vented. Stated another way, the maximum vapor-phase concentration that can be biologically degraded is 2.5% hexane by volume; any concentration above 2.5% would be vented to the atmosphere. Pulsed operations would minimize volatilization. This hypothesis was not positively confirmed in this field experiment. Based on the field results, recycling the hydrocarbons (Phase III) does not appear to improve remediation. The off-gas hydrocarbon concentrations during the Phase III recycle mode were higher than those observed during the other operating modes. Also, the recycle system is more capital expensive than the nonrecycle system. A generalized engineering evaluation, in terms of implementability, performance, and cost, indicates that biosparging using continuous flow through operations or the pulsed airflow mode of operations may be more cost effective than recycling the soil gases.

CONCLUSIONS AND RECOMMENDATIONS

This project has demonstrated that bioventing/biosparging at natural gas dehydration sites is a feasible remediation alternative. The objective of identifying and quantifying engineering design parameters has been partially achieved. However, to fully understand and apply the technology across the board at natural gas dehydrator sites, it will be necessary to study the technology at additional dehydrator sites with different soil and groundwater characteristics.

Soils from this site have been archived and may be used in controlled laboratory studies to more fully evaluate the kinetics of the bioventing/biosparging process. These laboratory results could be used in conjunction with the field results obtained in this field experiment to develop a design hypothesis for remediation of natural gas industry glycol dehydrator sites by bioventing/biosparging. The design hypothesis will be refined in the projected additional field experiments of in situ bioremediation of natural gas industry glycol dehydrator sites.

ACKNOWLEDGMENTS

This field demonstration was performed for GRI by Remediation Technologies, Inc., under GRI Contract No. 5091-253-2215 entitled "Technical Assessments of Environmental Control Strategies in the Natural Gas Production Industry," and by Global Remediation Technologies, Inc., of Traverse City, Michigan, under subcontract to Remediation Technologies, Inc. The ongoing support and encouragement of the GRI staff are greatly appreciated.

Global Remediation Technologies, Inc., of Traverse City, Michigan, performed the majority of the fieldwork and assisted with data collection and reduction. The field activities could not have been performed without their assistance.

REFERENCES

Committee on In Situ Bioremediation Water Science and Technology Board, Commission on Engineering and Technical Systems, and National Research Council. 1993. *In Situ Bioremediation — When Does It Work?*, National Academy Press, Washington, DC.

Dupont, R. R., and T. Lakshmiprasad. 1993. "Assessment of Operating Mode and Nutrient Amendment on Performance of a Pilot Scale Bioventing System." Presented at IGT Biotechnology Symposium, Colorado Springs, CO.

Hazen, T. C., C. B. Fliermans, M. Enzien, J. M. Dougherty, and K. Lombar. 1993. *In Situ Methanotrophic Bioremediation Using Horizontal Well Technology.* Savannah River Project-U.S. Department of Energy, Westinghouse Environmental Corporation.

Hinchee, R. E., S. K. Ong, R. N. Miller, D. C. Downey, and R. Frandt. 1992. *Test Plan And Technical Protocol For A Field Treatability Test For Bioventing*, for U.S. Air Force Center for Environmental Excellence, Brooks Air Force Base, TX.

Lawrence, A. Wm., D. L. Miller, J. A. Miller, R. M. Raetz, and T. D. Hayes. 1994. "In Situ Bioventing for Environmental Remediation of a Natural Gas Dehydrator Site: A Field Demonstration." SPE Paper 28351 presented at the 1994 SPE Annual Technical Conference and Exhibition, New Orleans, LA.

AUTHOR LIST

Abriola, Linda M.
University of Michigan
Dept. of Civil & Environ. Engrg.
Room 116 EWRE
Ann Arbor, MI 48109-2125 USA

Acomb, Lawrence J.
Geosphere, Inc.
3055 Seawind Drive
Anchorage, AK 99516 USA

Aelion, C. Marjorie
University of South Carolina
Dept. of Env. Health Sci.
Health Sci. Bldg., Room 311
Columbia, SC 29208 USA

Alleman, Bruce C.
Battelle Columbus
505 King Avenue
Columbus, OH 43201-2693 USA

Alphenaar, P. Arne
TAUW Infra Consult b.v.
    Environment
Handelskade 11
P.O. Box 133
7400 AC Deventer
THE NETHERLANDS

Archabal, Steven R.
Parsons Engineering Science, Inc.
1700 Broadway, Suite 900
Denver, CO 80439 USA

Armstrong, James E.
Komex International, Ltd.
#100 4500 16th Ave. NW
Calgary, Alberta T3B 0M6
CANADA

Baker, Ralph S.
ENSR Consulting & Engineering
35 Nagog Park
Acton, MA 01720 USA

Barker, Jim
University of Waterloo
Waterloo Centre for Groundwater
    Research
200 University Avenue, West
Waterloo, Ontario N2L 3G1
CANADA

Barry, William L.
U.S. Air Force
15 CES/CEVR
75 H Street
Hickam AFB, HI 96853-5233 USA

Bass, David H.
Groundwater Technology, Inc.
100 River Ridge Drive
Norwood, MA 02062 USA

Bell, Pamela E.
Growth Environmental Srvcs., Inc.
2340 Commonwealth Dr., Suite 202
Charlottesville, VA 22901 USA

Benediktsson, Catharine V.
Federal Aviation Administration
Airway Facilities Division
AAL-460H
222 West 7th Avenue #14
Anchorage, AK 99513-7587 USA

Berglund, Scott T.
Federal Aviation Administration
Airway Facilities Division
AAL-460H
222 West 7th Avenue #14
Anchorage, AK 99513-7587 USA

Billings, Bradford G.
Billings & Assoc., Inc.
3816 Academy Parkway N-NE
Albuquerque, NM 87109 USA

Billings, Jeffery F.
Billings & Associates, Inc.
3816 Academy Pkwy N-NE
Albuquerque, NM 87109 USA

Blaske, Allan R.
ETG Environmental, Inc.
7707 Rickle Road
Lansing, MI 48917 USA

Blystone, Paul G.
Purus Inc.
2713 North First Street
San Jose, CA 95134 USA

Boersma, Paul M.
CH2M Hill Inc.
411 E. Wisconsin Ave., Suite 1600
Milwaukee, WI 53202 USA

Bouillard, Jacques X.
Argonne National Laboratory
9700 S. Cass Ave. ES/200
Argonne, IL 60439-4831 USA

Bowling, Leon
U.S. Marine Corps
Natl. Resources/Env. Affairs Div.
P.O. Box 188110, Bldg. 1451
MCAGCC
Twentynine Palms, CA 92278-5000
USA

Bracco, Angelo A.
GE Corporate R&D Center
1 River Road, K1-5B33
P.O. Box 8
Schenectady, NY 12301 USA

Breedveld, Gijs D.
Norwegian Geotechnical Institute
P.O. Box 3930 Ullevaal Hageby
N-0806 Oslo
NORWAY

Brenner, Richard C.
U.S. Environ. Protection Agency
Natl. Risk Mgmt. Research Lab
26 W. Martin Luther King Drive
Cincinnati, OH 45268 USA

Briseid, Tormod
SINTEF Oslo
P.O. Box 124 Blindern
N-0314 Oslo
NORWAY

Brourman, Mitchell D.
Beazer East
436 7th Avenue
Pittsburgh, PA 15219-1822 USA

Brown, Richard A.
Groundwater Technology, Inc.
310 Horizon Center Drive
Trenton, NJ 08691 USA

Bruell, Clifford J.
University of Massachusetts
Civil Engineering Dept.
One University Avenue
Lowell, MA 01854 USA

Burke, George K.
Hayward Baker Environmental, Inc.
1130 Annapolis Road
Odenton, MD 21113 USA

Carothers, Gar
CH2M Hill Inc.
2550 Denali Street, 8th Floor
Anchorage, AK 99503 USA

Carson, Jr., John H.
OHM Remediation Srvcs. Corp.
16406 U.S. Route 224 E
Findlay, OH 45840 USA

Carter, Sean R.
Matrix Environmental Technologies
8461 Old Ridge Road
P.O. Box 408
Alton, NY 14413-0408 USA

Caskey, K. Kyle
Parsons Engineering Science, Inc.
1357 Kapiolani Blvd., Suite 1120
Honolulu, HI 96814 USA

Chao, Keh-Ping
Polytechnic University
Dept. of Civil & Environ. Engrg.
333 Jay Street
Brooklyn, NY 11201 USA

Chapdelaine, Marie-Claude
Biogénie, inc.
350 rue Franquet entrée 10
Sainte-Foy, Québec G1P 4P3
CANADA

Ciampa, John D.
General Electric Environmental and
    Facility Progams
100 Woodlawn Avenue
Pittsfield, MA 01201 USA

Clark, David
The Atchison, Topeka and Santa Fe
    Railway Company
920 S.E. Quincy
Topeka, KS 66612-1116 USA

Clark, James E.
Agway, Inc.
P.O. Box 4933
Syracuse, NY 13221-4933 USA

Clayton, Wilson S.
Groundwater Technology, Inc.
6436 S. Racine Circle, Suite 200
Englewood, CO 80111 USA

Collver, Bryan F.
ARCO Alaska Inc.
PRV P.O. Box 100360
Anchorage, AK 99510-0360 USA

Cosgriff, David
Champion International Corp.
P.O. Box 1590, Highway 2 South
Libby, MT 59923 USA

Currier, Paul
Army Corps of Engineers
Cold Regions Research &
    Engineering Laboratory
72 Lyme Road
Hanover, NH 03755 USA

Cuypers, Chiel
Wageningen Agricultural Univ.
Dept. of Environmental Technology
Bomenweg 2, P.O. Box 8129
6700 EV Wageningen
THE NETHERLANDS

Cyr, Benoit
Biogénie, inc.
350 rue Franquet entrée 10
Sainte-Foy, Québec G1P 4P3
CANADA

Darnall, Andrew W.
Integrated Science & Tech., Inc.
1349 Old Highway 41, Suite 225
Marietta, GA 30060-1000 USA

de Wit, Johannes C.M.
TAUW Milieu b.v.
Handelskade 11
P.O. Box 133
7400 AC Deventer
THE NETHERLANDS

DiGiulio, Dominic C.
U.S. Environ. Protection Agency
R.S. Kerr Environ. Research Lab
919 Kerr Research Drive
P.O. Box 1198
Ada, OK 74820 USA

Dijkhuis, Edwin J.
Bioclear Environ. Biotechnology
P.O. Box 2262
NL-9704 CG Groningen
THE NETHERLANDS

Dillon, Jr., Thomas
IT Corporation
2790 Mosside Blvd.
Monroeville, PA 15146 USA

Dortch, Ira J.
Shell Development Co.
P.O. Box 1380
Houston, TX 77251-1380 USA

Downey, Douglas C.
Parsons Engineering Science, Inc.
1700 Broadway, Suite 900
Denver, CO 80439 USA

Eberle, Michael F.
Dames & Moore
2325 Maryland Road
Willow Grove, PA 19090 USA

Elder, Robert
ARCO Alaska, Inc.
PRV, P.O. Box 100360
Anchorage, AK 99510 USA

Enzien, Michael V.
Argonne National Laboratory
9700 S. Cass Ave. ES/362
Argonne, IL 60439-4815 USA

Flathman, Paul E.
OHM Remediation Srvcs. Corp.
16406 U.S. Route 224 E
Findlay, OH 45839-0551 USA

Foor, Dean C.
Battelle Columbus
505 King Avenue
Columbus, OH 43201-2693 USA

Frank, James R.
Argonne National Laboratory
9700 S. Cass Ave. ES/362
Argonne, IL 60439 USA

Frisbie, Seth H.
ENSR Consulting & Engineering
35 Nagog Park
Acton, MA 01720 USA

Frishmuth, Russell A.
Parsons Engineering Science, Inc.
1700 Broadway, Suite 900
Denver, CO 80439 USA

Gantzer, Charles J.
Membran Corporation
1037 10th Avenue SE
Minneapolis, MN 55414 USA

Gentry, Jeff L.
CH2M Hill Inc.
825 N.E. Multnomah, Suite 1300
Portland, OR 97232-2146 USA

Gómez-Lahoz, César
Universidad de Málaga
Departmento de Ingeniería Química
Facultad De Ciencias
29071 Málaga
SPAIN

Goodwin, Steve
University of Massachusetts
Department of Microbiology
Morrill Science Center
Amherst, MA 01003 USA

Göschl, Reinhard
Innovative Umwelttechnik GmbH
Schiltern 100
A-2824 Seebenstein
AUSTRIA

Graves, Duane
IT Corporation
312 Directors Drive
Knoxville, TN 37923-4799 USA

Griswold, James E.
Billings & Assoc., Inc.
3816 Academy Parkway N-NE
Albuquerque, NM 87109 USA

Grotenhuis, Tim
Wageningen Agricultural Univ.
Dept. of Environmental Technology
Bomenweg 2, P.O. Box 8129
6700 EV Wageningen
THE NETHERLANDS

Gudehus, Gerd
University of Karlsrühe
Inst. of Soil and Rock Mechanics
Kaiserstrasse 12, P.O. Box 6980
76128 Karlsrühe
GERMANY

Hague, Keith
IT Corporation
312 Directors Drive
Knoxville, TN 37923 USA

Hansen, Erik E.
Shell Development Co.
P.O. Box 1380
Houston, TX 77251-1380 USA

Hardisty, Paul E.
Komex International, Ltd.
#100-4500 16th Ave., N.W.
Calgary, Alberta T3B 0M6
CANADA

Harkness, Mark R.
GE Corporate R&D Center
1 River Road, K1-5B10
P.O. Box 8
Schenectady, NY 12301-0008 USA

Hauge, Audun
Norwegian Geotechnical Institute
P.O. Box 3930, Ullevaal Hageby
N-0806 Oslo
NORWAY

Hayes, Michael E.
Univ. of Massachusetts, Amherst
Dept. of Civil Engrg., Marston Hall
Amherst, MA 01003 USA

Hayes, Thomas D.
Gas Research Institute
8600 West Bryn Mawr Avenue
Chicago, IL 60631 USA

Headington, Gregory L.
Battelle Columbus
505 King Avenue
Columbus, OH 43201-2693 USA

Heijs, Sander K.
Bioclear Environ. Biotechnology
P.O. Box 2262
NL-9704 CG Groningen
THE NETHERLANDS

Henssen, Maurice J.C.
Bioclear Environ. Biotechnology
P.O. Box 2262
NL-9704 CG Groningen
THE NETHERLANDS

Heuckeroth, Deborah M.
Dames & Moore
2325 Maryland Road
Willow Grove, PA 19090 USA

Hill, Joe
Growth Environmental Srvcs., Inc.
5217 Linbar Road, Suite 306
Nashville, TN 37211 USA

Hinchee, Robert E.
Battelle Columbus
505 King Avenue
Columbus, OH 43201-2693 USA

Hoeppel, Ronald E.
U.S. Navy
Naval Facilities Engrg. Srvc. Center
ERD Code ESC414KD
560 Center Drive
Port Hueneme, CA 93043-4328 USA

Hoffman, Gregory D.
Environ. Science & Engrg., Inc.
3208 Spring Forest Road
Raleigh, NC 27604 USA

Hoffman, Roderick W.
ARCO Alaska Inc.
PRV P.O. Box 100360
Anchorage, AK 99510-0360 USA

Holman, Hoi-Ying
Lawrence Berkeley Laboratory
Earth Sciences Division
1 Cyclotron Road
Berkeley, CA 94720 USA

Hopkins, Harley H.
American Petroleum Institute
1220 L Street NW
Washington, DC 20005 USA

Huber, J. Scott
Amoco Corporation
38705 Seven Mile Road, Suite 360
Livonia, MI 48152 USA

Hullman, Aaron S.
Integrated Science & Tech., Inc.
1349 Old Highway 41, Suite 225
Marietta, GA 30060-1000 USA

Javanmardian, Minoo
Amoco Corporation
150 W. Warrenville Road MC H-7
Naperville, IL 60563-8460 USA

Jerger, Douglas E.
OHM Remediation Services Corp.
16406 U.S. Route 224 E
Findlay, OH 45840 USA

Johnson, Paul C.
Arizona State University
Department of Civil Engineering
Tempe, AZ 85287-5306 USA

Johnson, Richard L.
Oregon Graduate Institute
Dept. of Environ. Science & Engrg.
19600 NW von Neumann Drive
Beaverton, OR 97006-1999 USA

Keuning, Sytze
Bioclear Environ. Biotechnology
P.O. Box 2262
NL-9704 CG Groningen
THE NETHERLANDS

Klein, Jerry
IT Corporation
2790 Mosside Blvd.
Monroeville, PA 15146 USA

Kremesec, Jr., Victor J.
Amoco Corporation
150 W. Warrenville Road MC H-7
Naperville, IL 60563-8460 USA

Kuhn, Edward M.
Environ. Science & Engrg., Inc.
3208 Spring Forest Road
Raleigh, NC 27604 USA

Kumar, Priti
Battelle Columbus
505 King Avenue
Columbus, OH 43201-2693 USA

Kyburg, Christopher
U.S. Navy
NAVFAC Engineering Command
SW Division Code 1822
1220 Pacific Highway
San Diego, CA 92132 USA

Lang, John R.
University of Michigan
Dept. of Civil and Environ. Engrg.
Room 116, EWRE
Ann Arbor, MI 48109-2125 USA

Laski, Mary L.
OHM Remediation Srvcs. Corp.
16406 U.S. Route 224 E
Findlay, OH 45840 USA

Lawrence, Alonzo W.
Remediation Technologies, Inc.
3040 William Pitt Way
Pittsburgh, PA 15238 USA

Leahy, Maureen C.
Groundwater Technology Inc.
431 F. Hayden Station Road
Windsor, CT 06095 USA

Lear, Paul R.
OHM Corporation
Remediation Services
16406 U.S. Route 224 E
Findlay, OH 45840 USA

Leeson, Andrea
Battelle Columbus
505 King Avenue
Columbus, OH 43201-2693 USA

Lei, Jiyu
Biogénie, inc.
350 rue Franquet entrée 10
Sainte-Foy, Québec G1P 4P3
CANADA

Leis, Kathleen S.
OHM Remediation Srvcs. Corp.
16406 U.S. Route 224 E
Findlay, OH 45840 USA

Leonard, Wendy C.
Groundwater Technology, Inc.
3110 Cherry Palm Drive, Suite 390
Tampa, FL 33619 USA

Linck, Joyce
Delta Environ. Consultants, Inc.
2775 S. Moorland Road, Suite 300
Milwaukee, WI 53151 USA

Linkenheil, Ronald
Remediation Technologies, Inc.
23 Old Town Square, Suite 250
Fort Collins, CO 80524 USA

Longe, Timothy A.
Virginia Dept. of Environ. Quality
329 East Main Street
Richmond, VA 23219 USA

Lord, Denis
Biogénie, inc.
350 rue Franquet entrée 10
Sainte-Foy, Québec G1P 4P3
CANADA

Lund, Nils Christian
University of Karlsrühe
Inst. of Soil and Rock Mechanics
Kaiserstrasse 12, P.O. Box 6980
76128 Karlsrühe
GERMANY

Lundegard, Paul D.
Unocal Corporation
Environmental Technology Group
376 S. Valencia Avenue
Brea, CA 92621 USA

Malina, Grzegorz
Technical Univ. of Czestochowa
Hydrology & Water Supply Dept.
Dabrowskiego 69
42-200 Czestochowa
POLAND

Manz, Chris
Delta Environ. Consultants, Inc.
2775 S. Moorland Road, Suite 300
Milwaukee, WI 53151 USA

Marley, Michael C.
Envirogen, Inc.
480 Neponset Street
Canton, MA 02021 USA

Marshall, Timothy R.
Woodward-Clyde Consultants
2020 E. First St., Suite 400
Santa Ana, CA 92705 USA

Martinson, Michael M.
Delta Environ. Consultants, Inc.
3900 Northwoods Dr., Suite 200
St. Paul, MN 55112 USA

Masin, Carol A.
Amoco Corporation
150 W. Warrenville Rd. MS H-7
Naperville, IL 60563-8460 USA

McCauley, Paul T.
U.S. Environ. Protection Agency
26 W. Martin Luther King Jr. Drive
Natl. Risk Mgmt. Research Lab
Cincinnati, OH 45268 USA

McCaulou, Douglas R.
Hydro Geo Chem, Inc.
1430 N. Sixth Avenue
Tucson, AZ 85705 USA

McKay, Daniel
U.S. Army Corps of Engineers
Cold Regions Research Engrg. Lab
72 Lyme Road
Hanover, NH 03755 USA

McLaughlin, John
IT Corporation
2790 Mosside Blvd.
Monroeville, PA 15146 USA

Michelsen, Donald L.
VA Polytechnic Inst. & State Univ.
Dept. of Chemical Engineering
133 Randolph Hall
Blacksburg, VA 24061-0211 USA

Miller, Daniel L.
Remediation Technologies, Inc.
3040 William Pitt Way
Pittsburgh, PA 15238 USA

Miller, Jeffrey A.
Remediation Technologies, Inc.
3040 William Pitt Way
Pittsburgh, PA 15238 USA

Miller, Ross N.
U.S. Air Force
8001 Arnold Drive, Bldg 642
Brooks AFB, TX 78235-5357 USA

Montney, Paul A.
Georgia-Pacific Corporation
290 Ferry Street
Newark, NJ 07105 USA

Moore, Brent J.
Komex International Ltd.
#100-4500 16th Ave. NW
Calgary, Alberta T3B 0M6
CANADA

Mountain, Stewart A.
Integrated Science & Tech., Inc.
1349 Old Highway 41, Suite 225
Marietta, GA 30060-1000 USA

Moyer, Ellen E.
ENSR Consulting & Engineering
35 Nagog Park
Acton, MA 01720 USA

Mueller, James G.
SBP Technologies Inc.
One Sabine Island Drive
Gulf Breeze, FL 32561-3999 USA

Neaville, Chris
Shell Development Company
P.O. Box 1380
Houston, TX 77251-1380 USA

Newman, Pixie A.B.
CH2M Hill Inc.
8501 W. Higgins, Suite 300
Chicago, IL 60631-2801 USA

Olson, Carl B.
Amoco Oil Co.
One Prudential Plaza
130 E. Randolph Drive
M/C P064102
Chicago, IL 60601 USA

Olson, Gus
U.S. Army Corps of Engineers
Fairbanks Residence Office
P.O. Box 35066/Bldg. 2104
Ft. Wainwright, AK 99703 USA

Olstad, Gunnar
University of Oslo
Department of Geology
P.O. Box 1047 Blindern
N-0316 Oslo
NORWAY

Ong, Say Kee
Iowa State University
Dept. of Civil & Const. Engrg.
497 Town Engineering Bldg.
Ames, IA 50011 USA

Ostendorf, David W.
University of Massachusetts
Civil Engineering Dept.
Marston Hall
Amherst, MA 01003 USA

Payne, Frederick C.
ETG Environmental, Inc.
7707 Rickle Road
Lansing, MI 48917 USA

Pennington, Leslie H.
Wasatch Environment, Inc.
2251 W. California Ave., Suite B
Salt Lake City, UT 84104 USA

Peters, Robert W.
Argonne National Laboratory
9700 S. Cass Ave. ES/362
Argonne, IL 60439 USA

Petrak, Debra
Growth Environmental Srvcs., Inc.
2340 Commonwealth Dr., Suite 202
Charlottesville, VA 22901 USA

Petrofske, Tim
Delta Environ. Consultants, Inc.
2775 S. Moorland Road, Suite 300
Milwaukee, WI 53151 USA

Phelps, Michael B.
Parsons Engineering Science, Inc.
1301 Marina Vllage Pkwy.
Suite 200
Alameda, CA 94501 USA

Pierson, Greg D.
Parsons Engineering Science, Inc.
1357 Kapiolani Blvd., Suite 1120
Honolulu, HI 96814 USA

Piontek, Keith R.
CH2M Hill Inc.
10 S. Broadway, Suite 450
St. Louis, MO 63102-1761 USA

Pluhar, Christopher J.
Parsons Engineering Science, Inc.
199 S. Los Robles Avenue
Pasadena, CA 91109 USA

Pritchard, David
Remediation Technologies, Inc.
23 Old Town Square, Suite 250
Fort Collins, CO 80524 USA

Raetz, Richard M.
Global Remediation Tech., Inc.
1235 Woodmere
Traverse City, MI 49682 USA

Rathfelder, Klaus M.
University of Michigan
Dept. of Civil & Environ. Engrg.
Room 116 EWRE
Ann Arbor, MI 48109-2125 USA

Ratz, John W.
Parsons Engineering Science, Inc.
1700 Broadway, Suite 900
Denver, CO 80290 USA

Ray, Richard P.
University of South Carolina
Department of Civil Engineering
Columbia, SC 29208 USA

Reeves, Howard W.
Northwestern University
Department of Civil Engineering
Evanston, IL 60208-3109 USA

Reisinger, H. James
Integrated Science & Tech., Inc.
1349 Old Highway 41, Suite 225
Marietta, GA 30060-1000 USA

Rhodes, Derek K.
Hayward Baker Environmental, Inc.
1130 Annapolis Road
Odenton, MD 21113 USA

Richards, Robin J.
University of Massachusetts
Department of Microbiology
Morrill Science Center
Amherst, MA 01003 USA

Rodríguez-Maroto, José Míguel
Universidad de Málaga
Departmento Ingeniería Química
Facultad de Ciencias
29071 Málaga
SPAIN

Rulkens, Wim H.
Wageningen Agricultural Univ.
Department Milieutechnologie
Bomenweg 2, P.O. Box 8129
6700 EV Wageningen
THE NETHERLANDS

Rykaczewski, Michael J.
Dames & Moore
2325 Maryland Road
Willow Grove, PA 19090 USA

Sansregret, Jean-Luc
Biogénie, inc.
350 rue Franquet entrée 10
Sainte-Foy, Québec G1P 4P3
CANADA

Sayles, Gregory D.
U.S. Environ. Protection Agency
26 W. Martin Luther King Drive
Cincinnati, OH 45268 USA

Scharff, Davis L.
Union Pacific Resources Company
801 Cherry Street
Fort Worth, TX 76101-0007 USA

Schrauf, Todd W.
Wasatch Environmental, Inc.
2251 W. California Ave., Suite B
Salt Lake City, UT 84104 USA

Schwartz, Ward P.
Amoco Corporation
150 W. Warrenville Rd. MS H-7
Naperville, IL 60563-8460 USA

Seep, David
Burlington Northern Railroad
9401 Indian Creek Pkwy., 14th Fl.
Shawnee Mission, KS 66210-2007
USA

Shanke, Craig A.
Remediation Technologies, Inc.
2670 Mutchler
Madison, WI 53719 USA

Shaw, J. Nikki
University of South Carolina
Dept. of Environ. Health Sciences
Columbia, SC 29208 USA

Sherhart, Thomas V.
Federal Aviation Administration
Airway Facilities Div., AAL-460H
222 West 7th Avenue #14
Anchorage, AK 99513-7587 USA

Simpkin, Thomas J.
CH2M Hill Inc.
100 Inverness Terrace
Englewood, CO 80112 USA

Sitler, Jeffrey A.
Growth Environmental Srvcs., Inc.
2340 Commonwealth Dr., Suite 202
Charlottesville, VA 22901 USA

Smith, Nancy
Hayward Baker Environmental, Inc.
1130 Annapolis Road
Odenton, MD 21113 USA

Stamm, Juergen
University of Karlsrühe
Institute of Hydromechanics
Kaiserstrasse 12
D-76128 Karlsrühe
GERMANY

Stanin, Frederick T.
Parsons Engineering Science, Inc.
1301 Marina Village Pkwy.
Suite 200
Alameda, CA 94501 USA

Stearns, Steve M.
Shell Development Co.
P.O. Box 1380
Houston, TX 77251-1380 USA

Symons, Brian D.
Remediation Technologies, Inc.
23 Old Town Sq., Suite 250
Fort Collins, CO 80524 USA

Tischuk, Michael D.
Beazer East
436 Seventh Avenue
Pittsburgh, PA 15219-1822 USA

Tsang, Yvonne W.
Lawrence Berkeley Laboratory
Earth Sciences Division
1 Cyclotron Road
Berkeley, CA 94720 USA

Urlings, Leon G.C.M.
TAUW Milieu b.v.
Handelskade 11
P.O. Box 133
7400 AC Deventer
THE NETHERLANDS

van der Waarde, Jaap J.
Bioclear Environ. Biotechnology
P.O. Box 2262
NL-9704 CG Groningen
THE NETHERLANDS

Van De Steeg, Garet E.
Kerr McGee Corporation
P.O. Box 25861
2312 NW 113 Place
Oklahoma City, OK 73125-0861
USA

VanHouten, Gregory A.
ETG Environmental Inc.
7707 Rickle Road
Lansing, MI 48917 USA

Vogel, Catherine M.
U.S. Air Force
Environics Directorate
AL/EQW-OL
139 Barnes Dr., Suite 2
Tyndall AFB, FL 32403-5319 USA

Walker, Angela B.
Oak Ridge National Laboratory
P.O. Box 2008
Oak Ridge, TN 37831 USA

Walker, Jr., Joseph F.
Oak Ridge National Laboratory
P.O. Box 2008
Oak Ridge, TN 37831-6044 USA

Walter, Gary R.
Hydro Geo Chem, Inc.
1430 N. Sixth Avenue
Tucson, AZ 85705 USA

Weightman, Robin L.
Remediation Technologies, Inc.
3040 William Pitt Way
Pittsburgh, PA 15238 USA

Weinig, Walter T.
Hydro Geo Chem, Inc.
1430 N. 6th Avenue
Tucson, AZ 85705 USA

Weymann, David F.
Environ. Science & Engrg. Inc.
3208 Spring Forest Road
Raleigh, NC 27604 USA

Widdowson, Mark A.
VA Polytechnic Inst. & State Univ.
Dept. of Civil Engineering
Blacksburg, VA 24061-0105 USA

Williams, Allison D.
Growth Environmental Srvcs., Inc.
7421 Whitepine Road
Richmond, VA 23237 USA

Wilson, Bill
IT Corporation
312 Directors Drive
Knoxville, TN 37923 USA

Wilson, David J.
Vanderbilt University
Dept. of Chemistry
Box 1822, Station B
Nashville, TN 37235 USA

Würdemann, Hilke
Karlsrühe University
Inst. for Soil and Rock Mechanics
Richard-Willstratter-Allee
Postbox 6980
76128 Karlsrühe
GERMANY

Zwick, Thomas C.
Battelle Columbus
505 King Avenue
Columbus, OH 43201-2693 USA

INDEX